INTEGRAL AND FUNCTIONAL ANALYSIS

INTEGRAL AND FUNCTIONAL ANALYSIS

JIE XIAO

Nova Science Publishers, Inc.
New York

For permission to use material from this book please contact us:
Telephone 631-231-7269; Fax 631-231-8175
Web Site: http://www.novapublishers.com

Library of Congress Cataloging-in-Publication Data

Xiao, Jie, 1963-
Integral and functional analysis / Jie Xiao.
p. cm.
Includes bibliographical references and index.
ISBN-13: 978-1-60021-784-5 (hardcover : alk. paper)
ISBN-10: 1-60021-784-2 (hardcover : alk. paper)
1. Integral equations. 2. Metric spaces. 3. Functional analysis. I. Title.
QA431.X53 2007
515'.45--dc22

2007026127

Published by Nova Science Publishers, Inc. ✣ New York

To My Family

Contents

Preface

This book *Integral And Functional Analysis* is based on two closely-related courses: (a) Integration and Metric Spaces; (b) Functional Analysis, which I have offered over the past four years at Memorial University. Though the contents of Functional Analysis have been used for both an undergraduate course and an introductory graduate course, this text is designed primarily for the undergraduate students. The prerequisites of this book are deliberately modest, and it is assumed that the students have some familiarity with Introductory Calculus and Linear Algebra plus the basic (direct, indirect) proof methods.

I have striven to give an exposition which is at the same time introductory and modern in spirit, yet which addresses itself to the classical concerns of these two courses in mathematics. This approach leads to my aim in writing this book: I must present in a natural sequence the basic ideas and results of this area. On the other hand, enough material is covered to provide a firm base on which to build for later studies in Advanced Analysis and Partial Differential Equations.

The book comprises two parts, with results from the first part being used to partially motivate problems discussed in the second part, which could be used as a text of two courses treating metric spaces and their continuous maps as a joint portion, say, (i) Integration Theory; (ii) Functional Analysis, and be covered from beginning to end in two semesters:

The first part (Chapters 1, 2, 3, 4) – Integral Analysis – a mathematical theory that defines the reasonable integrals for functions of different kinds. The *integral* of an individual function is a generalization of area, mass, volume, sum, and total. There are several possible definitions of integration with different technical underpinnings. In this part, we start with the basic arithmetic and topological properties of the real number system. Then we discuss Riemann integration including some essential properties and the fundamental theorem of calculus, and use it as a model to handle both Riemann-Stieltjes integration via bounded variation and Lebesgue–Radon–Stieltjes integration covering three convergence theorems and Fubini–Tonelli's theorem.

The second part (Chapters 5, 6, 7, 8, 9) – Functional Analysis – a mathematical theory that is concerned with function spaces and their functionals and operators. It has its historical roots in the investigation of transformations such as the Fourier transform and in the study of differential and integral equations. The word *functional* goes back to the calculus of variations, implying a function whose argument is a function. In this part, motivated by the first part, we first work with more abstract metric spaces and their continuous mappings, and next introduce elements of functional analysis including Banach spaces, and Hilbert spaces whose norms arise from inner products. Of course, we also discuss major and foundational results of this theory such as the Hahn–Banach theorem extending functionals from a subspace to the full space in a norm-preserving fashion, the uniform boundedness principle, the open mapping theorem, the closed graph theorem, and the approximation theorem for compact operators.

In the process of learning these two courses, the students are strongly suggested to follow an important principle; that is, the best way to learn mathematics is to do mathematics. Moreover, the students are urged to acquire the habit of studying with paper and pencil in hand – in this way mathematics will become increasingly meaningful to them. Each chapter is followed by a series of exercises dealing with the material presented in that chapter. Although complete solutions or brief hints for these exercises are included, the students are recommended to at least do most of the exercises before checking their solutions or hints. A list of references is provided – those books make an effectual supplement to this text since some of their contents were selectively adapted during my preparing for the courses. Last but not least, an index is attached.

To close this preface, I wish to acknowledge my colleagues (in alphabetical order): Hermann Brunner, Herb Gaskill, Philip Heath, Jongjin Kim, Charles Lee, Marco Merkli, Mike Parmenter, Paul Peng, Bruce Watson and Xiaoqiang Zhao, who assisted directly or indirectly with the writing of the original text and subsequent revisions. Next, I am grateful to the students and markers of the Department of Mathematics and Statistics at Memorial University, who actively participated in the two courses and gave some helpful comments on the text. Finally, I would like to thank both Paul Gauthier (for his constructive criticism on the entire manuscript) and Toka Diagana (for his suggesting to add a part on answers to problems) – who made the book publishable by Nova Science Publishers.

St. John's, NL, Canada
Fall Semesters, 2002-2006

Xiao Jie
jxiao@math.mun.ca

Chapter 1

Preliminaries

The objective of this chapter of two sections is to set up an appropriate ground for developing the integral and functional analysis. The first section establishes some conventions concerning sets, relations, functions, and cardinal and ordinal numbers. The second section is devoted to collecting the basic properties (as axioms) of the real numbers including their arithmetic, order and least upper bound, as well as limit rules.

1.1 Sets, Relations, Functions, Cardinals and Ordinals

A set is a group or collection of objects, considered as an entity onto itself. Usually, sets are symbolized by boldface, capital, italicized, uppercase letters such as $\mathbf{A}$, B, C, $\mathcal{D}$. Each object in a set is called an element or a member or a point of the set. If x is an element of the set X, then we write $x \in X$, and hence we denote by $x \notin X$ whenever x is not an element of X. Sets may be expressed either by explicitly listing their members – for example, $\{a, b, c\}$ is the set having a, b, and c as elements, or by giving the property that every element of the set possesses but also the property that is possessed by no element not in the set – for instance, $\{x : x \text{ is a car}\}$ is the set of all cars, or the set of all points x such that each x is a car. Below are the basic sets that will be denoted by boldface letters and used throughout this text:

$$\begin{aligned}
\mathbf{N} &= \text{the set of natural numbers} = \{1, 2, 3, \dots, n, \dots\};\\
\mathbf{Z} &= \text{the set of integers} = \{0, 1, -1, 2, -2, 3, -3, \dots, n, -n, \dots\};\\
\mathbf{Q} &= \text{the set of rational numbers} = \left\{\frac{m}{n} : m \text{ and } n \text{ are integers with } n \neq 0\right\};\\
\mathbf{R} &= \text{the set of real numbers};\\
\mathbf{C} &= \text{the set of complex numbers.}
\end{aligned}$$

Remark 1.1.

(i) In $\mathbf{Q}$ we identify $\frac{m}{n}$ and $\frac{k}{l}$ if $lm = kn$.

(ii) $\mathbf{C} = \mathbf{R} + i\mathbf{R} = \{z = x + iy : x, y \in \mathbf{R}\}$, where $i = \sqrt{-1}$ is the imaginary unit; $x = \Re z$ and $y = \Im z$ are called the real and imaginary parts of $z = x + iy$ respectively.

Definition 1.2. Given two sets X and Y. We say that:

(i) X is a subset of Y, written $X \subseteq Y$, provided $x \in X$ implies $x \in Y$ – clearly $X \not\subseteq Y$ denotes that X is not a subset of Y;

(ii) X and Y are equal, denoted $X = Y$, provided $X \subseteq Y$ and $Y \subseteq X$ – clearly, $X \neq Y$ means that X is not equal to Y;

(iii) X is a proper subset of Y, written $X \subset Y$, provided $X \subseteq Y$ but $X \neq Y$;

(iv) $X \cup Y$, $X \cap Y$, and $X \setminus Y$ are the union of X and Y, i.e., the set $\{x : x \in X \text{ or } x \in Y\}$, the intersection of X and Y, i.e., the set $\{x : x \in X \text{ and } x \in Y\}$, and the complement of Y in X, i.e., the set $\{x : x \in X \text{ and } x \notin Y\}$;

(v) $\emptyset$ is the empty set, i.e., the set which contains no elements – moreover, X and Y are disjoint whenever $X \cap Y = \emptyset$.

As the two most basic set operations, union and intersection can be used for any family of sets. More precisely, if $\{X_j\}_{j\in I}$ is any family of sets indexed by some set I which may be considered simply as a set of labels for distinguishing the various members of the family of sets, then

$$\cup_{j\in I} X_j = \{x : x \in X_j \text{ for some } j \in I\}$$

and

$$\cap_{j\in I} X_j = \{x : x \in X_j \text{ for all } j \in I\}$$

stand for the union and intersection of $\{X_j\}_{j\in I}$ respectively. Acting with the complement operation, the union and intersection satisfy the DeMorgan law for an arbitrary family of sets as follows.

Proposition 1.3. *Given a set X, let $\{X_j\}_{j\in I}$ be a family of sets indexed by I. Then*

$$\cup_{j\in I}(X \setminus X_j) = X \setminus \cap_{j\in I} X_j \quad \textit{and} \quad \cap_{j\in I}(X \setminus X_j) = X \setminus \cup_{j\in I} X_j.$$

Proof. It suffices to verify the left-hand equality since the right-hand one can be proved similarly. First, suppose $x \in \cup_{j\in I}(X \setminus X_j)$. Then $x \in X \setminus X_j$ for some $j \in I$ and hence $x \notin X_j$, implying $x \notin \cap_{j\in I} X_j$. Consequently, $x \in X \setminus \cap_{j\in I} X_j$, namely,

$$\cup_{j\in I}(X \setminus X_j) \subseteq X \setminus \cap_{j\in I} X_j.$$

On the other hand, if $x \in X \setminus \cap_{j\in I} X_j$ then $x \in X$ but $x \notin \cap_{j\in I} X_j$. Accordingly, there exists some $j \in I$ such that $x \in X \setminus X_j$. Then $x \in \cup_{j\in I} X \setminus X_j$. Consequently,

$$X \setminus \cap_{j\in I} X_j \subseteq \cup_{j\in I}(X \setminus X_j).$$

According to Definition 1.2 (ii), we derive the desired equality. □

Next, we introduce the Cartesian product and relation, and equivalence relation.

Definition 1.4. Given two sets X and Y.

(i) The Cartesian product $X \times Y$ of X and Y is defined to be the set of all ordered pairs (x, y) such that $x \in X$ and $y \in Y$ – here the ordered pair (x, y) is the set whose elements are $\{x\}$, $\{x, y\}$, in symbols $(x, y) = \{\{x\}, \{x, y\}\}$.

(ii) A subset R of $X \times Y$ is called a relation between X and Y – in particular a subset of $X \times X$ is said to be a relation on X – in this case, $(x, y) \in R$ may also be denoted by xRy or x being R-related to y.

(iii) A relation R on X is an equivalence relation provided it has the following properties for all $x, y, z \in X$:
(a) xRx (reflexivity);
(b) xRy implies yRx (symmetry);
(c) xRy and yRz yield xRz (transitivity).

Here, for simplicity we have chosen (x, y) as the notation of an ordered pair, but hope that this symbolic choice will not make any trouble whenever the same notation is used later on to stand for an open interval in $\mathbf{R}$.

Of course, the equality "=" on any set X is an equivalence relation. To better understand this definition, we prove the following proposition.

Proposition 1.5. *Let* $(x, y), (x', y') \in X \times Y$. *Then* $(x, y) = (x', y')$ *if and only if* $x = x'$ *and* $y = y'$.

Proof. Clearly, $x = x'$ and $y = y'$ imply

$$(x, y) = \{\{x\}, \{x, y\}\} = \{\{x'\}, \{x', y'\}\} = (x', y').$$

Conversely, suppose $(x, y) = (x', y')$. To prove $x = y$ and $x' = y'$, we consider two cases.

Case 1: $x = y$. Then $\{x\} = \{x, y\}$ and hence $(x', y') = (x, y) = \{\{x\}\}$. This means that $\{\{x'\}, \{x', y'\}\}$ has only one element $\{\{x\}\}$ and so that $\{x', y'\} = \{x'\} = \{x\} = \{y\}$. Accordingly, $x' = y'$.

Case 2: $x \neq y$. Then the argument for *Case 1* yields $x' \neq y'$. Since $(x, y) = (x', y')$, we conclude $\{x\} \in \{\{x'\}, \{x', y'\}\}$ and so either $\{x\} = \{x'\}$ or $\{x\} = \{x', y'\}$. This in turns implies $x' \in \{x\}$ and then $x = x'$. Similarly, $\{x, y\} \in \{\{x'\}, \{x', y'\}\}$ yields either $\{x, y\} = \{x'\}$ or $\{x, y\} = \{x', y'\}$. But since $x \neq y$, we must have $\{x, y\} = \{x', y'\}$. Now $x = x'$, $x \neq y$ and $y \in \{x', y'\}$, it follows that $y = y'$, as desired. □

As a special relation, we have the notion of a function.

Definition 1.6. Given two sets X and Y.

(i) A function f between X and Y is a nonempty relation $f \subseteq X \times Y$ such that if $(x, y), (x, y') \in f$ then $y = y'$. The following sets

$$D(f) = \{x \in X : \text{ there is a } y \in Y \text{ such that } (x, y) \in f\}$$

and

$$R(f) = \{y \in Y : \text{ there is an } x \in X \text{ such that } (x, y) \in f\}$$

are called the domain and the range of f respectively. In the case of $D(f) = X$, f is called a function from X into Y, denoted $f : X \to Y$, with

$$f(A) = \{f(x) : x \in A\}\} \quad \text{and} \quad f^{-1}(B) = \{x \in X : y = f(x) \in B\}$$

as the image of $A \subseteq X$ and the pre-image of $B \subseteq Y$, respectively.

(ii) A function $f : X \to Y$ is called onto or surjective provided $f(X) = Y$.

(iii) A function $f : X \to Y$ is called one-to-one or injective provided that $f(x) = f(x')$ for any $x, x' \in X$ implies $x = x'$.

(iv) A surjection is an onto function, while an injection is a one-to-one function. Furthermore, a function which is both onto and one-to-one is said to be bijective or a bijection.

Proposition 1.7. *Given two sets X and Y, let $f : X \to Y$ be a function.*

(i) *Suppose $A, B \subseteq X$. Then $f(A \cup B) = f(A) \cup f(B)$. Furthermore $f(A \cap B) = f(A) \cap f(B)$ whenever f is injective.*

(ii) *Suppose $A \subseteq X$ and $B \subseteq Y$. Then $f^{-1}(f(A)) = A$ respectively $f(f^{-1}(B)) = B$ provided f is injective respectively surjective.*

Proof. (i) If $y \in f(A \cup B)$, then by definition there is an $x \in A \cup B$ such that $y = f(x)$. Now $x \in A$ or $x \in B$, consequently $f(x) \in f(A)$ or $f(x) \in f(B)$. In either case, $y \in f(A) \cup f(B)$. This proves $f(A \cup B) \subseteq f(A) \cup f(B)$. On the other hand, if $y \in f(A) \cup f(B)$ then $y \in f(A)$ or $y \in f(B)$ and hence there exists $x \in A \cup B$ such that $y = f(x)$, namely, $y \in f(A \cup B)$. Thus, $f(A) \cup f(B) \subseteq f(A \cup B)$. Accordingly, $f(A \cup B) = f(A) \cup f(B)$.

Clearly, $f(A \cap B) \subseteq f(A) \cap f(B)$. Now if f is injective, then for any $y \in f(A) \cap f(B)$ there exist $x \in A$ and $x' \in B$ such that $y = f(x) = f(x')$ and hence $x = x' \in A \cap B$. Accordingly, $y \in f(A \cap B)$, i.e., $f(A) \cap f(B) \subseteq f(A \cap B)$, whence giving $f(A \cap B) = f(A) \cap f(B)$.

(ii) This follows immediately from Definition 1.6 (i). □

Remark 1.8. We make two comments on Proposition 1.7 (ii).

(i) The symbol $f^{-1}(B)$ is not to be thought of as an inverse function applied to points in B. But, if $f^{-1}(y) = \{x \in X : f(x) = y\}$ (for each $y \in Y$) contains precisely one member in X, then f^{-1} defines a function from Y into X. In fact, this amounts to $f : X \to Y$ being bijective. To see this, if f is a bijection then for any $y \in Y$ there exists one (surjective) and only one (injective) element $x \in X$ such that $y = f(x)$, and hence $f^{-1}(y) = x$ is uniquely defined for each $y \in Y$. Consequently, f^{-1} is a function from Y into X. Conversely, if $f^{-1} : Y \to X$ is a function, then for each $y \in Y$, $f^{-1}(y) = x$ is a unique member of X. In other words, f is injective. Moreover, $f^{-1}(y) = x$ produces $f(x) = y$ and so that f is surjective. Therefore, f is bijective.

(ii) The symbols $f^{-1}(f(A))$ and $f(f^{-1}(B))$ induce the notion of composition of functions. For functions $f : X \to Y$ and $g : Y \to Z$, we say that $g \circ f$, the composition of g with f, is a function from X into Z determined by $(g \circ f)(x) = g(f(x))$ for each $x \in X$. In order to make this meaningful, we naturally require $f(X) \subseteq Y$. It is evident to see that if $f : X \to Y$ is bijective then $f^{-1} : Y \to X$ is bijective and $f^{-1} \circ f = i_X$ and $f \circ f^{-1} = i_Y$ where $i_X : X \to X$ and $i_Y : Y \to Y$ stand for the identity functions:

$$i_X(x) = x \quad \text{for } x \in X \quad \text{and} \quad i_Y(y) = y \quad \text{for } y \in Y.$$

We now introduce the cardinality of a set, which is a property describing the size of the set by describing it using a cardinal number. This is actually equivalent to comparing two sets, and so leads to the following concept.

Definition 1.9. Two sets X and Y are called equivalent, or said to have the same cardinality, denoted $X \sim Y$, if there exists a bijection between X and Y. In particular, any set that has the same cardinality $\aleph_0$ as the set of all natural numbers $\mathbf{N}$ is said to be an infinite countable set, and if a set is $\emptyset$ or there is a bijection between this set and $\{1, 2, \ldots, n\}$ for some $n \in \mathbf{N}$ of then it is said to be finite; otherwise, the set is said to be uncountable.

Example 1.10.

(i) If $X = \{a, b, c\}$ and $Y = \{\text{monitor, radio, telephone}\}$, then they both have three elements.

(ii) The set $2\mathbf{N} = \{2, 4, 6, \ldots, 2n, \ldots\}$ has the same cardinality as $\mathbf{N}$ since the function $f(n) = 2n$, is a bijection between $\mathbf{N}$ and $2\mathbf{N}$.

(iii) $\mathbf{Z}$ has the cardinality $\aleph_0$. In fact, if

$$\mathbf{Z}_+ = \mathbf{N} \quad \text{and} \quad \mathbf{Z}_- = \{-1, -2, -3, \ldots, -n, \ldots\}$$

and

$$f(x) = \begin{cases} 2x\,, & x \in \mathbf{Z}_+, \\ 1\,, & x = 0, \\ (-1)(2x) + 1\,, & x \in \mathbf{Z}_-, \end{cases}$$

then $\mathbf{Z} = \mathbf{Z}_+ \cup \{0\} \cup \mathbf{Z}_-$ and f is a bijection between $\mathbf{N}$ and $\mathbf{Z}$.

Proposition 1.11.

(i) *Any subset of a finite set is finite.*

(ii) *Any subset of any countable set is countable.*

(iii) *The union of any countable collection of countable sets is countable.*

(iv) *The Cartesian product of any two countable sets is countable.*

Proof. (i) Suppose X is finite and $A \subseteq X$. Then either X is $\emptyset$ or there exists a bijection $f : X \to \{1, 2, 3, \ldots, n\}$ for some $n \in \mathbf{N}$. If $A = \emptyset$ then it is finite. If $A \neq \emptyset$ then the assumption $A \subseteq X$ yields

$$f(A) \subseteq \{1, 2, 3, \ldots, n\}$$

and hence we may assume

$$f(A) = \{j_1, j_2, j_3, \ldots, j_m\}.$$

Consequently, defining

$$g : A \to \{1, 2, 3, \ldots, m\} \text{ by } g(x) = k \text{ where } f(x) = j_k \text{ for } x \in A,$$

we see that A is finite.

(ii) Assume X is countable and $S \subseteq X$. Then $X = \{x_j\}_{j=1}^{\infty}$. If $S = \emptyset$ then it is countable. If $S \neq \emptyset$ then it contains at least one element, say s. For each $j \in \mathbf{N}$, set $y_j = x_j$ or $y_j = s$ when $x_j \in S$ or $x_j \notin S$. Then this establishes a bijection between S and $\{y_j\}_{j=1}^{\infty}$ and hence S is countable.

(iii) Suppose $\{A_j\}_{j=1}^{\infty}$ is a countable collection of countable sets $A_j = \{a_{jk}\}_{k=1}^{\infty}$. Define $f(a_{jk}) = 2^j 3^k$. Then f is a bijection between $\cup_{j=1}^{\infty} A_j$ and a subset of $\mathbf{N}$, and hence $\cup_{j=1}^{\infty} A_j$ is countable due to (ii).

(iv) Assume $X = \{x_j\}_{j=1}^{\infty}$ and $Y = \{y_j\}_{j=1}^{\infty}$. Then each member of $X \times Y$ has the form (x_j, y_k) for $j, k \in \mathbf{N}$. Define $f : X \times Y \to \mathbf{N}$ by $f(x_j, y_k) = 2^j 3^k$. Then f is one-to-one and hence $X \times Y$ is countable. □

Example 1.12.

(i) $\mathbf{Q}$ is countable. In fact, associating $\frac{m}{n}$, $n \neq 0$, m and n relatively prime, we see that $\mathbf{Q}$ has the same cardinality as a subset of $\mathbf{Z} \times \mathbf{Z}$ which is a countable set by Proposition 1.11 (iv).

(ii) $\mathbf{R}$ is uncountable. To verify this, let X be the set of unending decimals between 0 and 1 and that contain only 0 and 1 as digits. If f is an arbitrary function from $\mathbf{N}$ into X, then f cannot be onto and hence X is uncountable. In fact, we form a member $d = 0.x_1x_2x_3x_4\ldots$ of X in the following way. If the first digit of $f(1)$ is 0 or 1, then x_1 is taken to be 1 or 0, and consequently, d differs from $f(1)$ in the first digit. We choose x_2 to be either 0 or 1, but different from the second digit of $f(2)$. Continuing this process, we find that d is not $f(n)$ for any n since d differs from $f(n)$ for any n at least in the nth digit. Consequently, $d \notin f(\mathbf{N})$, and so f is not surjective. Note that X is a subset of $\mathbf{R}$. So if $\mathbf{R}$ were countable then X would also be countable by Proposition 1.11 (ii). This contradiction proves that $\mathbf{R}$ is uncountable.

The preceding discussion on the cardinals of sets reveals

$$X = \{1, 2, 3, \ldots\} \sim Y = \{\ldots, 3, 2, 1\}.$$

However, if X is ordered by the usual relation $\leq$ and Y ordered by $\geq$ then X has a first but not a last element, and Y has a last but not a first, and hence this gives a way to distinguish both sets. So, we are finally led to a brief consideration of the ordinals of sets.

Definition 1.13. Let $\preceq$ be a relation on the given set X.

(i) $\preceq$ is said to be a partial order on X provided the following three properties hold for $x, y, z \in X$:

(a) $x \preceq x$ (reflexivity);
(b) $x \preceq y$ and $y \preceq x$ imply $x = y$ (antisymmetry);
(c) $x \preceq y$ and $y \preceq z$ yield $x \preceq z$ (transitivity).

In this case, $(X, \preceq)$ stands for a partially ordered set in which not all pairs of elements are mutually comparable.

(ii) $\preceq$ is said to be a total/linear order provided the following three properties hold for $x, y, z \in X$:

(a) $x \preceq y$ or $y \preceq x$ (totalness);
(b) $x \preceq y$ and $y \preceq x$ imply $x = y$ (antisymmetry);
(c) $x \preceq y$ and $y \preceq z$ yield $x \preceq z$ (transitivity).

In this case, $(X, \preceq)$ is stands for a totally/linearly ordered set, or a chain. The totalness property can be stated as that any pair of elements in the chain are mutually comparable.

Notice that the totalness condition implies reflexivity. Thus a total order is also a partial order; that is, a binary relation which is reflexive, antisymmetric and transitive. It follows that a total order can also be defined as a partial order that is total.

Example 1.14.

(i) Given a set X, let $\mathbf{P}(X)$ be the collection of all subsets of X. Then $\big(\mathbf{P}(X), \subseteq\big)$ is a partially ordered set, but usually it is not totally ordered.

(ii) $(\mathbf{Z}, \leq)$ is totally ordered.

Definition 1.15. Let $(X, \preceq)$ be a partially ordered set and $A \subseteq X$.

(i) An element u of X is an upper bound of A, provided $a \preceq u$ for all elements $a \in A$ – in this case, A is called bounded from above. Using $u \preceq a$ instead of $a \preceq u$ leads to the definition of a lower bound of A, i.e., A being bounded from below.

(ii) A least upper bound (a greatest lower bound) or a supremum (an infimum) of A is such an element $u \in X$ that u is an upper bound (a lower bound) of A and $u \preceq v$ ($u \succeq v$) holds for any upper bound (any lower bound) v of A – clearly, if A has a supremum (an infimum), then the supremum (the infimum) is unique, and hence denoted by $\sup A$ ($\inf A$).

(iii) An element m of A is a maximal (minimal) element of A if $m \preceq a$ ($m \succeq a$) for some $a \in A$ implies $m = a$.

Generally speaking, a subset of a partially ordered set may fail to have any upper bound. For instance, the subset of $\mathbf{N}$ whose members are greater than a given natural number has no upper bound. On the other hand, a set may have many several upper and lower bounds, and hence we are usually interested in picking out specific elements from the sets of upper or lower bounds.

What is important to note about maximal elements is that they are in general not the greatest elements of a subset S. Indeed, consider $\mathbf{P}(\mathbf{N})$ – the set of all subsets of the natural numbers ordered by subset inclusion. The subset S of all one-element sets of $\mathbf{N}$ consists only of maximal elements, but has no greatest element. This example also shows that maximal elements are usually not unique and that it is well possible for an element to be both maximal and minimal at the same time. In addition, if a subset contains a greatest element, then this is the unique maximal element. Nevertheless, in a totally ordered set, the terms maximal (minimal) element and greatest (least) element are the same, which is why both terms are used interchangeably in fields like analysis where only total orders are considered.

With the previous concepts, we may state the celebrated Zorn's lemma, also known as the Kazimierz Kuratowski–Max Zorn lemma, as follows.

Zorn's Lemma. *Every partially ordered set in which every totally ordered subset has an upper bound contains at least one maximal element.*

We offer no proof for this lemma because it is equivalent to the following axiom of choice in the sense that either one is sufficient to prove the other:

The Axiom of Choice. *Given an arbitrary collection* $\{A_j\}_{j\in I} = \{A_j : j \in I\}$ *of nonempty sets indexed by the nonempty set* I*, there is a function*

$$f : I \to \cup_{j\in I} A_j,$$

called a choice or selection function, such that $f(j) \in A_j$ *when* $j \in I$*.*

Here, it is worth pointing out that Zorn's Lemma, as the most useful of all equivalents of the axiom of choice, occurs in the proofs of several theorems of crucial importance – for example, the Hans Hahn - Stefan Banach theorem in functional analysis, the theorem that every vector space has a basis, the Andrey Nikolayevich Tychonoff theorem in topology saying that every product of compact spaces is compact, and those theorems in abstract algebra that each ring has a maximal ideal and that each field has an algebraic closure.

1.2 Reals, Some Basic Theorems and Sequence Limits

In this section we will list the basic properties of the reals rather than to construct the reals, and then use them to derive some foundational theorems. Furthermore, we consider sequences of reals and their most important limit theorems including the Augustin Louis Cauchy criterion for the convergence of a sequence.

The properties used to define $\mathbf{R}$ (along with an ordered pair of functions from $\mathbf{R} \times \mathbf{R}$ into $\mathbf{R}$) are usually regarded as axioms and classified into three different groupings.

Field Axioms. *There are two functions* $+$ *and* $\cdot$ *on* $\mathbf{R}$ *such that* $\mathbf{R}$ *becomes a field:*

F1. $x + y = y + x$ *and* $x \cdot y = y \cdot x$ *for every* $x, y \in \mathbf{R}$ *(commutativity);*
F2. $(x + y) + z = x + (y + z)$ *and* $(x \cdot y) \cdot z = x \cdot (y \cdot z)$ *for every* $x, y, z \in \mathbf{R}$ *(associativity);*

F3. *$x \cdot (y+z) = x \cdot y + x \cdot z$ for every $x, y, z \in \mathbf{R}$ (distributivity);*
F4. *There are distinct elements 0 and 1 in $\mathbf{R}$ such that $x + 0 = x$ and $x \cdot 1 = x$ for every $x \in \mathbf{R}$ (existence of neutral elements);*
F5. *For every $x \in \mathbf{R}$ there is an element of $\mathbf{R}$, denoted $-x$, such that $x + (-x) = 0$, and for every nonzero $x \in \mathbf{R}$ there is an element of $\mathbf{R}$, denoted $x^{-1} = 1/x$, such that $x \cdot x^{-1} = 1$ (existence of additive and multiplicative inverses).*

Here and elsewhere we will employ the common notational conventions when no confusion is possible. For example, we often write xy and $x-y$ for $x \cdot y$ and $x+(-y)$ respectively. Most of the rules of elementary algebra can be justified by these five axioms. For instance, for any $a, b \in \mathbf{R}$ the equation $x + a = b$ has one and only one solution $x = b - a$.

The next group of axioms is:

Order Axioms. *There is an order relation $<$ defined on $\mathbf{R}$ satisfying:*
O1. *If $x, y \in \mathbf{R}$ then one and only one of: $x < y$, $x = y$, $y < x$ holds (trichotomy);*
O2. *If $x < y$ and $y < z$ for $x, y, z \in \mathbf{R}$ then $x < z$ (transitivity);*
O3. *If $x < y$ and $x, y, z \in \mathbf{R}$ then $x + z < y + z$;*
O4. *If $x < y$, $x, y, z \in \mathbf{R}$ and $0 < z$ then $xz < yz$.*

We also write $y > x$ for $x < y$ and define $x \leq y$ (i.e., $y \geq x$) for either $x < y$ or $x = y$. Consequently, if $x > 0$ or $x < 0$ then we say that x is positive or negative, and according to Definition 1.13 (ii), $(\mathbf{R}, \leq)$ is a totally ordered set. Naturally, the inequality $0 < 1$ follows from these axioms. Furthermore, let

$$|x| = \begin{cases} x\,, & x > 0, \\ 0\,, & x = 0, \\ -x\,, & x < 0. \end{cases}$$

Then the axioms of field and order can be used to derive that the triangle inequality and its reverse counterpart:

$$|x+y| \leq |x| + |y| \quad \text{and} \quad \big||x| - |y|\big| \leq |x - y|$$

hold for every $x, y \in \mathbf{R}$.

The last axiom for $\mathbf{R}$ is the following, which gives a further condition on the ordering of $\mathbf{R}$.

Axiom of Least Upper Bound (LUB). *If a subset S of $\mathbf{R}$ is nonempty and bounded from above, then it has a least upper bound.*

Under this axiom and Definition 1.15 (ii), we can write $\sup S$ for the least upper bound of S, but also prove that any nonempty subset S of $\mathbf{R}$ having a lower bound in $\mathbf{R}$ must have a greatest lower bound. In fact, a set $S \subseteq \mathbf{R}$ is bounded from below when and only when the set $T = \{x \in \mathbf{R} : \; -x \in S\}$ is bounded from above, and if $S \neq \emptyset$ is bounded from below then $-\sup T$ is the greatest lower bound $\inf S$ of S.

To better understand the above axioms, we proceed to show that the axiom of completeness is not valid for the rationals, but the reals are not very far from the rationals in the sense that any real number may be approximated by a rational number as closely as we wish. More precisely, we have the following result.

Theorem 1.16.

(i) *If* $S = \{r \in \mathbf{Q} : r > 0$ *and* $r^2 < 2\}$ *then* S *has an upper bound in* $\mathbf{Q}$ *but does not have a least upper bound in* $\mathbf{Q}$.

(ii) $\mathbf{Q}$ *is dense in* $\mathbf{R}$ *in the sense that for* $x, \epsilon \in \mathbf{R}$ *with* $\epsilon > 0$ *there exists an* $r \in \mathbf{Q}$ *such that* $|x - r| < \epsilon$.

Proof. (i) Clearly, 2 is an upper bound of S. Suppose S has a rational supremum s. Then by definition, for any rational ϵ: $0 < \epsilon < s$, there is a rational $r \in S$ such that $0 < s - \epsilon < r$. Consequently, $(s - r)^2 < r^2 < 2$. Note that $s + \epsilon$ is a rational greater than s. So $s + \epsilon \notin S$. This yields $(s + \epsilon)^2 \geq 2$ and then

$$(s - \epsilon)^2 < 2 \leq (s + \epsilon)^2.$$

Now

$$(s - \epsilon)^2 < s^2 \leq (s + \epsilon)^2.$$

Thus

$$|s^2 - 2| < (s + \epsilon)^2 - (s - \epsilon)^2 = 4s\epsilon.$$

This is valid for $0 < \epsilon < s$, and therefore certainly for those rational numbers $\epsilon \geq s$. Accordingly, $s^2 = 2$. Since s is rational, it can be written as m/n where $n \neq 0$, and $m, n \in \mathbf{Z}$ have no common factor. From this it follows that $m^2 = 2n^2$ and so that m^2 is even $2k$. Consequently, $n^2 = 2k^2$ which implies that n is even. We have seen that m and n have 2 as a common factor, contradicting that m and n have no common factor. This argument actually shows that S has no rational supremum, as desired.

(ii) Given $x, \epsilon \in \mathbf{R}$ and $\epsilon > 0$, to get a rational r obeying $|x - r| < \epsilon$, we first verify three intermediate step results.

Step 1. There is an $n \in \mathbf{Z}$ such that $n > x$. To see this, assume $n \leq x$ for all $n \in \mathbf{Z}$. Then $\mathbf{Z}$ has an upper bound x and hence it has a least upper bound in $\mathbf{R}$, say z, by the axiom of LUB. But $n \in \mathbf{Z}$ implies $n + 1 \in \mathbf{Z}$. So $n + 1 \leq z$, i.e., $n \leq z - 1$, thus showing that $z - 1$ is also an upper bound of $\mathbf{Z}$, contradicting that z is the least.

Step 2. There is an $n \in \mathbf{Z}$ such that $n \leq x < n + 1$. By *Step 1*, we choose a natural number $N > |x|$, so that $-N < x < N$. Now we take n to be the greatest element of the finite set

$$\{-N, -N + 1, \ldots, -1, 0, 1, \ldots, N - 1, N\}$$

which is less than or equal to x.

Step 3. There is an $n \in \mathbf{N}$ such that $1/n < \epsilon$. By *Step 1*, we take an integer $n > 1/\epsilon > 0$, hence proving $1/n < \epsilon$ thanks to O4 above.

Now, for the above-given x, ϵ, we use *Step 3* to find a natural number N such that $1/N < \epsilon$, then apply *Step 2* to Nx to get an $n \in \mathbf{Z}$ such that $n \leq Nx < n + 1$, and hence derive $0 \leq x - n/N < 1/N < \epsilon$, as desired. $\square$

As important consequences of the axiom of LUB of $\mathbf{R}$, we will prove three theorems – the nested interval theorem; the Bernard Bolzano–Karl Theodor Wilhelm Weierstrass theorem; the Eduard Heine–Félix Édouard Justin Émile Borel theorem – which will serve as useful tools in the subsequent chapters.

First of all, we use the following conventions: For $a, b \in \mathbf{R}$ with $a < b$ let

$$(a, b) = \{x \in \mathbf{R} : \ a < x < b\} \quad \text{and} \quad [a, b] = \{x \in \mathbf{R} : \ a \leq x \leq b\},$$

which are called open and closed intervals with endpoints a and b, respectively, and let

$$(a, b] = \{x \in \mathbf{R} : \ a < x \leq b\} \quad \text{and} \quad [a, b) = \{x \in \mathbf{R} : \ a \leq x < b\}$$

which are called open-closed and closed-open intervals with endpoints a and b, respectively. In all cases, the length of an interval I is defined by $|I| = b - a$.

We next introduce three concepts required respectively by the above-mentioned theorems.

Definition 1.17.

(i) $(I_n)_{n=1}^{\infty}$ is called a sequence of intervals provided it is a function that assigns an interval I_n to each $n \in \mathbf{N}$. If $I_{n+1} \subseteq I_n$ (respectively $I_n \subseteq I_{n+1}$) for all $n \in \mathbf{N}$, then $(I_n)_{n=1}^{\infty}$ is called a nested downward (respectively upward) sequence of intervals.

(ii) Given $S \subseteq \mathbf{R}$ and $x \in \mathbf{R}$, x is called a cluster point of S provided

$$(x - \epsilon, x + \epsilon) \cap \big(S \setminus \{x\}\big) \neq \emptyset$$

for each $\epsilon > 0$.

(iii) A set $S \subseteq \mathbf{R}$ is said to be a closed set provided each cluster point in S is an element of S.

Theorem 1.18.

(i) *Nested interval property: If $(I_n)_{n=1}^{\infty}$ is a nested downward sequence of closed intervals in $\mathbf{R}$, then $\cap_{n=1}^{\infty} I_n$ is a nonempty set.*

(ii) *Bolzano-Weierstrass property: If a subset S of $\mathbf{R}$ is infinite and bounded from below and above, then S has at least one cluster point in $\mathbf{R}$.*

(iii) *Heine-Borel property: Let $\mathcal{F}$ be a family of open intervals covering a closed interval I in $\mathbf{R}$. Then $\mathcal{F}$ contains a finite subcovering; that is, there are finitely many open intervals from $\mathcal{F}$ such that their union covers I.*

Proof. (i) Let $I_n = [a_n, b_n]$ be nested. Then $I_n \subseteq I_1$ and hence $a_n \leq b_1$ for all $n \in \mathbf{N}$. This just says that $\{a_n\}_{n=1}^{\infty}$ is bounded from above. By the axiom of LUB, the supremum $x = \sup\{a_n\}_{n=1}^{\infty}$ of $\{a_n\}_{n=1}^{\infty}$ exists in $\mathbf{R}$. Of course, $a_n \leq x$ for all $n \in \mathbf{N}$. Note that $\cdots \subseteq I_3 \subseteq I_2 \subseteq I_1$. So it follows that

$$a_1 \leq a_2 \leq a_3 \leq \cdots \leq a_n \leq \cdots \quad \text{and} \quad b_1 \geq b_2 \geq b_3 \geq \cdots \geq b_n \geq \cdots$$

and consequently $a_m \leq a_n < b_n$ when $m \leq n$ as well as $a_m < b_m \leq b_n$ when $m \geq n$. In both case we always have $a_m \leq b_n$, thus finding that b_n is an upper bound of $\{a_n\}_{n=1}^{\infty}$ and so $x \leq b_n$. Therefore, $x \in \cap_{n=1}^{\infty} I_n$.

(ii) By hypothesis, S is a subset of some closed interval $I_1 = [a_1, b_1]$. Now, subdivide I_1 into two equal intervals: $[a_1, \frac{a_1+b_1}{2}]$ and $[\frac{a_1+b_1}{2}, b_1]$. Note that S is infinite. So one of the last two intervals, denoted I_2, must contain an infinite number of points in S. Continuing this argument we obtain a nested sequence of closed intervals I_n containing an infinite number of points of S. According to (i), there is a point $x \in \cap_{n=1}^{\infty} I_n$. This fact clearly tells us that for any $\epsilon > 0$ there is an $n_0 \in \mathbf{N}$ such that $|I_n| = 2^{1-n}(b_1 - a_1) < \epsilon$ as $n > n_0$. Since I_n contains x, it must be the case that $I_n \subseteq (x - \epsilon, x + \epsilon)$ when $n > n_0$. In particular,

$$I_{n_0+1} \subseteq (x - \epsilon, x + \epsilon) \quad \text{and so} \quad (S \setminus \{x\}) \cap (x - \epsilon, x + \epsilon) \neq \emptyset.$$

In other words, x is a cluster point of S.

(iii) Suppose that the conclusion is false; that is, $\mathcal{F}$ has no finite subcovering for I. As in (ii), let $I_1 = I = [a_1, b_1]$. By bisecting I_1 we obtain two intervals

$$\left[a_1, \frac{a_1 + b_1}{2}\right] \quad \text{and} \quad \left[\frac{a_1 + b_1}{2}, b_1\right].$$

Since I_1 can not be covered by finitely many intervals in $\mathcal{F}$, at least one of the last two subintervals, labeled I_2, can not be covered by finitely many intervals in $\mathcal{F}$. Repeating this process we find a nested sequence of closed intervals I_n which fail to be covered by any finite number of intervals in $\mathcal{F}$. An application of (i) yields a point $x \in \cap_{n=1}^{\infty} I_n$. Furthermore, $x \in I_1$ produces an open interval (a, b) in $\mathcal{F}$ such that $a < x < b$. Now if δ is the smaller of $x - a$ and $b - x$, then there is an $n_0 \in \mathbf{N}$ such that $n > n_0$ implies $|I_n| < \delta$. Since $x \in I_n$, it follows that $I_n \subseteq (a, b)$ as $n > n_0$. But, this contradicts the choice of I_n. Therefore, $\mathcal{F}$ contains a finite subcover of I. □

Remark 1.19. We will see Theorem 1.18 in Chapter 5 from an equivalent perspective. Yet, the following simple comments can help us get a better understanding of Theorem 1.18.

(i) The requirement "closed" in the nested interval property can not be replaced by "open" or "open-closed" or "closed-open". For example, if $I_n = (0, n^{-1})$ or $(0, n^{-1}]$ or $[-n^{-1}, 0)$ then $\cap_{n=1}^{\infty} I_n = \emptyset$.

(ii) Any finite set has no cluster point. Of course, an infinite set may fail to have cluster points – for example, $\mathbf{N}$. Nevertheless, according to the Bolzano-Weierstrass theorem, any bounded (from above and below) infinite subset of $\mathbf{R}$ must have at least one cluster point.

(iii) Although $(0, 1) \subseteq \cup_{n=1}^{\infty}(n^{-1}, 1 - n^{-1})$, the open interval $(0, 1)$ cannot be covered by any finitely many intervals from $\{(n^{-1}, 1 - n^{-1})\}_{n=1}^{\infty}$. However, this does not vilolate the Heine-Borel property which is valid for all finite closed intervals.

We close this section by discussing sequences of reals and their limits.

Definition 1.20.

(i) A sequence $(s_n)_{n=1}^{\infty}$ in $\mathbf{R}$ is a function from $\mathbf{N}$ into $\mathbf{R}$. We use $\{s_n\}_{n=1}^{\infty} = \{s_n : n \in \mathbf{N}\}$ as the range of the sequence.

(ii) A sequence $(s_n)_{n=1}^{\infty}$ is called bounded provided its range is bounded; that is, there exists a $B > 0$ such that $\sup\{|s_n|\}_{n=1}^{\infty} \leq B$.

(iii) For $s \in \mathbf{R}$ and a sequence $(s_n)_{n=1}^{\infty}$, we say that $(s_n)_{n=1}^{\infty}$ converges (or is convergent) to s, denoted $\lim_{n\to\infty} s_n = s$ or $s_n \to s$, if and only if for any $\epsilon > 0$ there exists an $n_0 \in \mathbf{N}$ such that $n > n_0$ implies $|s_n - s| < \epsilon$. A sequence that is not convergent is called divergent.

It is easy to see that a convergent sequence has only one limit, but also is bounded. Moreover, if $\lim_{n\to\infty} s_n = s \neq 0$, then for $\epsilon = |s|/2$ there is an $n_0 \in \mathbf{N}$ such that $|s_n - s| < \epsilon$ as $n > n_0$, and hence $|s_n| \geq |s| - \epsilon = |s|/2$. Using these facts and the triangle inequality, we can establish the following limit theorem.

Theorem 1.21. *For $s, t \in \mathbf{R}$ and sequences $(s_n)_{n=1}^{\infty}$ and $(t_n)_{n=1}^{\infty}$ in $\mathbf{R}$, let $\lim_{n\to\infty} s_n = s$ and $\lim_{n\to\infty} t_n = t$. Then:*

(i) $\lim_{n\to\infty}(s_n + t_n) = s + t$;

(ii) $\lim_{n\to\infty}(s_n t_n) = st$;

(iii) $\lim_{n\to\infty}(cs_n) = cs$ for any $c \in \mathbf{R}$;

(iv) $\lim_{n\to\infty}(s_n/t_n) = s/t$ provided $t \neq 0$ and $t_n \neq 0$ for each $n \in \mathbf{N}$.

(v) $s \leq t$ provided $s_n \leq t_n$ for each $n \in \mathbf{N}$.

Proof. We leave the demonstration as an exercise. □

Definition 1.22.

(i) A function f from $\mathbf{N}$ into $\mathbf{N}$ is called increasing provided $f(m) \leq f(n)$ for $m, n \in \mathbf{N}$ with $m < n$. Moreover, a sequence $(x_n)_{n=1}^{\infty}$ in $\mathbf{R}$ is called a subsequence of a given sequence $(s_n)_{n=1}^{\infty}$ in $\mathbf{R}$ when there is an increasing function $f : \mathbf{N} \to \mathbf{N}$ such that $x_n = s_{f(n)}$ for each $n \in \mathbf{N}$.

(ii) A sequence $(s_n)_{n=1}^{\infty}$ in $\mathbf{R}$ is called increasing (respectively, strictly increasing) if $s_n \leq s_{n+1}$ (respectively, $s_n < s_{n+1}$) for any $n \in \mathbf{N}$. Meanwhile, a sequence $(s_n)_{n=1}^{\infty}$ in $\mathbf{R}$ is called decreasing (respectively, strictly decreasing) if $s_n \geq s_{n+1}$ (respectively, $s_n > s_{n+1}$) for each $n \in \mathbf{N}$. Furthermore, a sequence is called monotonic provided it is either increasing or decreasing.

The following result, in which (i) characterizes the convergence of a sequence by its subsequences and (ii) is the monotone convergence theorem, is natural, important and useful.

Theorem 1.23. *Let $(s_n)_{n=1}^{\infty}$ be a sequence in $\mathbf{R}$ and $s \in \mathbf{R}$. Then:*

(i) $(s_n)_{n=1}^{\infty}$ is convergent to s when and only when each subsequence of $(s_n)_{n=1}^{\infty}$ is convergent to s;

(ii) $(s_n)_{n=1}^{\infty}$ is convergent whenever it is monotonic and bounded.

Proof. (i) Suppose $s_n \to s$ and $(s_{n_k})_{k=1}^{\infty}$ is a subsequence of $(s_n)_{n=1}^{\infty}$. Then for $\epsilon > 0$ there is an $n_0 \in \mathbf{N}$ such that $n > n_0$ implies $|s_n - s| < \epsilon$, and consequently, if $k > n_0$ then $n_k \geq k > n_0$ and hence $|s_{n_k} - s| < \epsilon$; that is, $s_{n_k} \to s$. Conversely, suppose every subsequence of $(s_n)_{n=1}^{\infty}$ is convergent to s. If $(s_n)_{n=1}^{\infty}$ is not convergent to $s \in \mathbf{R}$, then by negation of the limit definition, there is $\epsilon_0 > 0$ such that for any $k \in \mathbf{N}$ one can always find s_{n_k} from $(s_n)_{n=1}^{\infty}$ such that $|s_{n_k} - s| \geq \epsilon_0$. This actually means that $(s_{n_k})_{k=1}^{\infty}$ does not converge to s, a contradiction.

(ii) It suffices to consider the case that $(s_n)_{n=1}^{\infty}$ is increasing and bounded since the other case can be handled similarly. To this end, we see from the axiom of LUB that $a = \sup\{s_n\}_{n=1}^{\infty}$ is a finite element of $\mathbf{R}$. Also, by definition, for every $\epsilon > 0$ there is an $n_0 \in \mathbf{N}$ such that $a - \epsilon < s_{n_0}$. Hence $a - \epsilon < s_{n_0} \leq s_n \leq a$ as $n > n_0$. Consequently, $s_n \to a$. □

Without using subsequences we can also characterize the convergence of a sequence. To see this, we introduce the notion of Cauchy's sequence.

Definition 1.24. A sequence $(s_n)_{n=1}^{\infty}$ in $\mathbf{R}$ is called a Cauchy sequence provided for every $\epsilon > 0$ there exists an $n_0 \in \mathbf{N}$ such that $|s_m - s_n| < \epsilon$ for $m, n > n_0$.

The next property of $\mathbf{R}$ is the so-called completeness of the reals which plays an extremely important role in analysis.

Theorem 1.25. *A sequence in* $\mathbf{R}$ *is convergent if and only if it is a Cauchy sequence.*

Proof. Suppose the sequence $(s_n)_{n=1}^{\infty}$ in $\mathbf{R}$ is convergent to s. Then for any $\epsilon > 0$ there is an $n_0 \in \mathbf{N}$ such that $n > n_0$ implies $|s_n - s| < \epsilon/2$ and consequently, if $m, n > n_0$ then by the triangle inequality,

$$|s_m - s_n| \leq |s_m - s| + |s_n - s| < \epsilon,$$

namely, $(s_n)_{n=1}^{\infty}$ is a Cauchy sequence.

Conversely, if $(s_n)_{n=1}^{\infty}$ is a Cauchy sequence, then there is an $n_0 \in \mathbf{N}$ such that $|s_{n+1} - s_{n_0+1}| < 1$ and thus $|s_{n+1}| < 1 + |s_{n_0+1}|$ whenever $n > n_0$. Accordingly, $\{s_n\}_{n=1}^{\infty}$ is bounded. Let us consider two cases as follows.

Case 1: $\{s_n\}_{n=1}^{\infty}$ is finite. This case yields that some member, say s, in this sequence must be repeated infinitely. Thus, there exists a subsequence $(s_{n_k})_{k=1}^{\infty}$ such that $|s_{n_k} - s| = 0$ for all $k \in \mathbf{N}$.

Case 2: $\{s_n\}_{n=1}^{\infty}$ is infinite. Then using the Bolzano-Weierstrass property, we can also get a subsequence $(s_{n_k})_{k=1}^{\infty}$ that is convergent to some $s \in \mathbf{R}$. Consequently, for any $\epsilon > 0$ there are $k_1, k_2 \in \mathbf{N}$ such that $|s_{n_k} - s| < \epsilon/2$ as $k > k_1$ and $|s_m - s_n| < \epsilon/2$ for $m, n > k_2$. Finally, if $n > k_3 = \sup\{k_1, k_2\}$ then by taking $k \geq k_3$ we derive

$$|s_n - s| \leq |s_n - s_{n_k}| + |s_{n_k} - s| < \epsilon/2 + \epsilon/2 = \epsilon,$$

thus proving $s_n \to s$. □

Remark 1.26.

(i) The argument for Theorem 1.25 yields the Bolzano-Weierstrass property for sequences: A bounded sequence in $\mathbf{R}$ has a convergent subsequence.

(ii) Also, Theorem 1.25 produces another way to look at the difference between $\mathbf{R}$ and $\mathbf{Q}$. To be more specific, let $(s_n)_{n=1}^{\infty}$ be a sequence of rationals with $s_n \to \sqrt{2}$ (by the density of $\mathbf{Q}$ in $\mathbf{R}$). Then this sequence is a Cauchy sequence in $\mathbf{Q}$ but its limit $\sqrt{2}$ is in $\mathbf{R} \setminus \mathbf{Q}$. In other words, $\mathbf{Q}$ is not complete, but $\mathbf{R}$ is.

Problems

1.1. The symmetric difference of two given sets X and Y is defined as $(X \cup Y) \setminus (X \cap Y)$. Prove $(X \cup Y) \setminus (X \cap Y) = (X \setminus Y) \cup (Y \setminus X)$.

1.2. For $j \in \mathbf{N}$ let $X_j = [0, j^{-1}]$. Find $\cup_{j=1}^{\infty} X_j$ and $\cap_{j=1}^{\infty} X_j$.

1.3. Given a set X, let $\{X_j\}_{j \in I}$ be a family of sets indexed by I. Prove

$$X \cap \big(\cup_{j \in I} X_j\big) = \cup_{j \in I}(X \cap X_j) \quad \text{and} \quad X \cup \big(\cap_{j \in I} X_j\big) = \cap_{j \in I}(X \cup X_j).$$

1.4. Prove that if X, Y and Z are sets then $X \times (Y \cup Z) = (X \times Y) \cup (X \times Z)$.

1.5. Let (a, b) be an open interval of $\mathbf{R}$. Find a bijection from $(0, 1)$ onto (a, b) and then onto $(0, \infty)$.

1.6. Prove that if $f : X \to Y$ and $g : Y \to Z$ are two functions and C is a subset of Z then $(g \circ f)^{-1}(C) = f^{-1}\big(g^{-1}(C)\big)$.

1.7. Prove that if X is an infinite set and $x \in X$ then $X \sim X \setminus \{x\}$.

1.8. Suppose f is a one-to-one function from X into Y with Y countable. Show that X is countable.

1.9. Prove that if X is the set of all functions $f : [0, 1] \to \mathbf{R}$ then there is no function from $[0, 1]$ onto X.

1.10. Use the field axioms to show the following properties:
(i) If $a, b \in \mathbf{R}$ with $a \neq 0$ then the equation $ax = b$ has one and only one solution;
(ii) If $a \in \mathbf{R}$ is nonzero then $(a^{-1})^{-1} = a$;
(iii) If $a, b \in \mathbf{R}$ are nonzero then $(ab)^{-1} = a^{-1}b^{-1}$.

1.11. Use the mathematical induction to prove that

$$|a_1 + a_2 + \cdots + a_n| \leq |a_1| + |a_2| + \cdots + |a_n|$$

is valid for $a_1, a_2, \ldots, a_n \in \mathbf{R}$.

1.12. Let $a, b \geq 0$. Prove that $a \leq b$ if and only if $a^3 \leq b^3$.

1.13. For two nonempty subsets X and Y of $\mathbf{R}$ let

$$X+Y=\{x+y:\ x\in X \quad \text{and} \quad y\in Y\}.$$

Prove

$$\sup(X+Y)=\sup X+\sup Y \quad \text{and} \quad \inf(X+Y)=\inf X+\inf Y.$$

1.14. In the notation of Theorem 1.18 and its proof, prove the following three facts:
(i) $a=\lim_{n\to\infty}a_n$ and $b=\lim_{n\to\infty}b_n$ are in $\cap_{n=1}^{\infty}I_n$;
(ii) $[a,b]=\cap_{n=1}^{\infty}I_n$;
(iii) $\cap_{n=1}^{\infty}I_n$ is a single point provided $\lim_{n\to\infty}(b_n-a_n)=0$.

1.15. Prove Theorem 1.21.

1.16. A sequence $(s_n)_{n=1}^{\infty}$ is said to diverge to ∞ respectively $-\infty$, denoted $\lim_{n\to\infty}s_n=\infty$ respectively $\lim_{n\to\infty}s_n=-\infty$, provided for any $M\in\mathbf{R}$ there is an $n_0\in\mathbf{N}$ such that $n>n_0$ implies $s_n>M$ respectively $s_n<M$. Prove that if $(s_n)_{n=1}^{\infty}$ is a sequence of positive numbers in $\mathbf{R}$ then $\lim_{n\to\infty}s_n=\infty$ if and only if $\lim_{n\to\infty}(1/s_n)=0$.

1.17. For $n\in\mathbf{N}$ let $s_n=1+2^{-1}+\cdots+n^{-1}$. Prove:
(i) $(s_n)_{n=1}^{\infty}$ is increasing but divergent;
(ii) $(s_n)_{n=1}^{\infty}$ is not a Cauchy sequence although $\lim_{n\to\infty}|x_{n+1}-x_n|=0$.

1.18. Let $(s_n)_{n=1}^{\infty}$ be a bounded sequence in $\mathbf{R}$. A subsequential limit of $(s_n)_{n=1}^{\infty}$ is a real number that is the limit of some subsequence of $(s_n)_{n=1}^{\infty}$. If S is the set of all subsequential limits of $(s_n)_{n=1}^{\infty}$, then we define the limit superior/upper limit and the limit inferior/lower limit of $(s_n)_{n=1}^{\infty}$ to be

$$\limsup s_n=\sup S \quad \text{and} \quad \liminf s_n=\inf S.$$

Prove the following two facts:
(i)

$$\limsup s_n=\lim_{m\to\infty}\sup\{s_n:\ n>m\} \text{ and } \liminf s_n=\lim_{m\to\infty}\inf\{s_n:\ n>m\};$$

(ii) $(s_n)_{n=1}^{\infty}$ is convergent if and only if $\limsup s_n=\liminf s_n$.

Chapter 2

Riemann Integrals

The Riemann integral – the first rigorous definition of the integral of a function on an interval, created by Bernhard Riemann, is the integral normally encountered in real analysis and used by physicists and engineers.

In this chapter, we discuss the definition and basic properties of the Riemann integral for real-valued functions of one real variable. Here we are concerned with the simplest results, up to Riemann sums, the integrability of a continuous function and the fundamental theorem of calculus. Moreover, we consider the improper integral as the limit of Riemann's integral on an interval, when an endpoint, or both endpoints, of the interval approaches either a specified real number or infinity.

2.1 Definitions, Examples, and Basic Properties

In what follows, we denote the implication "if A then B" by $A \Rightarrow B$. Without a special remark, $[a, b]$ always stands for a finite closed interval in $\mathbf{R}$. Let f be a real-valued function on the interval $[a, b]$. A partition P of $[a, b]$ is a set $\{x_k\}_{k=0}^n$ satisfying $a = x_0 < x_1 < \cdots < x_n = b$, $n \in \mathbf{N}$. The length of the subinterval $[x_{k-1}, x_k]$ is written as $\Delta x_k = x_k - x_{k-1}$, and the norm $\|P\|$ of the partition P is defined by

$$\|P\| = \max\{\Delta x_k : k = 1, 2, \ldots, n\}.$$

Thus P determines n subintervals of $[a, b]$ of which the largest has length $\|P\|$, and the subinterval $[x_{k-1}, x_k]$ is called the kth subinterval associated with P. In each of the n subintervals, choose a number $\xi_k \in [x_{k-1}, x_k]$, and form the following sum

$$S(f, P, \xi) = S(f, P, \{\xi_k\}_{k=1}^n) = \sum_{k=1}^{n} f(\xi_k)\Delta x_k.$$

This last sum is called a Riemann sum for the function f on $[a, b]$. With some familiarity with integral calculus, we can immediately recognize that if f is nonnegative then $S(f, P, \xi)$ gives an approximation to the area of the region between the graph of f and the horizontal axis. Needless to say, if f is not continuous on $[a, b]$, it is not easy to think of the graph of f as serving as a boundary for any such region.

Another analytic interpretation which has the advantage of being free of geometrical dependence, is that $S(f,P,\xi)$ represents a certain average value of f on $[a,b]$. This aspect can be seen as follows:

$$\frac{S(f,P,\xi)}{b-a}=\sum_{k=1}^{n} f(\xi_k)\frac{\Delta x_k}{b-a}.$$

In the last sum, $f(\xi_k)$ is multiplied by $\Delta x_k/(b-a)$ that gives the fractional part of $[a,b]$ from which ξ_k is chosen. Thus the sum is a weighted average of the n values $\{f(\xi_k)\}_{k=1}^{n}$. Multiplying this weighted average by the length $b-a$ of $[a,b]$, we get $S(f,P,\xi)$. Consequently, it is very natural to expect that $S(f,P,\xi)/(b-a)$ gives an average of the values of f over $[a,b]$. Such an average is a better indicator of the behavior of f when P determines only small subintervals. From this perspective we see that the behavior of $S(f,P,\xi)$ as $\|P\|\to 0$ can be well examined.

Definition 2.1. The function f is called Riemann integrable on $[a,b]$ provided $\lim_{\|P\|\to 0} S(f,P,\xi)$ exists. In this case the limit value, denoted $\int_a^b f(x)dx$, is said to be the Riemann integral of f on $[a,b]$. The set of all Riemann integrable functions on $[a,b]$ is written as $R[a,b]$.

Remark 2.2. We must acknowledge that the limit $\lim_{\|P\|\to 0} S(f,P,\xi)$ in Definition 2.1 is neither a sequential limit nor a function limit (because $S(f,P,\xi)$ is not a function of $\|P\|$). In order to fully appreciate the latter assertion, we consider the fact that for a given value of $\|P\|$, there could be many partitions of $[a,b]$ whose largest subinterval has length $\|P\|$. For example, $[-1,1]$ may be partitioned by

$$\begin{aligned} P_1 &= \Big\{-1,-\frac{2}{3},-\frac{1}{3},0,\frac{1}{3},\frac{2}{3},1\Big\};\\ P_2 &= \Big\{-1,-\frac{3}{4},-\frac{1}{2},-\frac{1}{3},0,\frac{1}{3},\frac{1}{2},\frac{3}{4},1\Big\};\\ P_3 &= \Big\{-1,-\frac{2}{3},-\frac{1}{2},-\frac{2}{5},-\frac{1}{5},0,\frac{1}{5},\frac{2}{5},\frac{1}{2},\frac{2}{3},1\Big\}, \end{aligned}$$

and then $\|P_1\|=\|P_3\|=\|P_3\|=\frac{1}{3}$. Moreover, for each partition of $[a,b]$ having the given norm $\|P\|$, there are many ways of choosing $\{\xi_k\}_{k=1}^{n}$ from the n subintervals. Thus the value of $\|P\|$ does not determine $S(f,P,\xi)$. So, it is necessary to give a complete description of the limit concept introduced in Definition 2.1.

Definition 2.3. That $\lim_{\|P\|\to 0} S(f,P,\xi)=I\in\mathbf{R}$ exists means that if $\epsilon>0$ then there exists a $\delta>0$ such that for every partition P of $[a,b]$ with $\|P\|<\delta$ and any choice of the points $\{\xi_k\in[x_{k-1},x_k]\}_{k=1}^{n}$, the inequality $|S(f,P,\xi)-I|<\epsilon$ holds.

Usually, a direct argument for the existence of $\lim_{\|P\|\to 0} S(f,P,\xi)$ is too complicated to handle, but Definition 2.3 for $\int_a^b f(x)dx$ has certain advantages for developing the theory. In the forthcoming section we prove an equivalent formulation of the limit which is easier to use in proving the integrability of particular functions. Meanwhile, however, we deal first with several examples.

Example 2.4. If f is a constant κ on $[a,b]$, then $f \in R[a,b]$ and $\int_a^b f(x)dx = \kappa(b-a)$. In fact, for any partition P of $[a,b]$, we have

$$S(f,P,\xi) = \kappa \sum_{k=1}^{n} \Delta x_k = \kappa(x_n - x_0) = \kappa(b-a).$$

Thus, for a given $\epsilon > 0$, the inequality $|S(f,P,\xi) - \kappa(b-a)| = 0 < \epsilon$ is satisfied trivially. Hence $\int_a^b f(x)dx = \lim_{\|P\|\to 0} S(f,P,\xi) = \kappa(b-a)$.

Example 2.5. Fix a point $c \in [a,b]$ and let

$$f(x) = \begin{cases} 1, & x = c, \\ 0, & x \neq c, \end{cases}$$

then $f \in R[a,b]$ and $\int_a^b f(x)dx = 0$. Actually, for any $S(f,P,\xi)$ corresponding to a partition P of $[a,b]$ we have $|S(f,P,\xi)| \leq 2\|P\|$, where 2 appears since c may be one of the partition points x_k and we may in this case have both ξ_k and ξ_{k+1} equal to c. So $\int_a^b f(x)dx = 0$.

Example 2.6. Let $[\alpha,\beta] \subset [a,b]$ and

$$f(x) = \begin{cases} 1, & x \in (\alpha,\beta), \\ 0, & x \in [a,b] \setminus (\alpha,\beta), \end{cases}$$

then $f \in R[a,b]$ and $\int_a^b f(x)dx = \beta - \alpha$. To verify this, suppose that $P = \{x_0, x_1, \ldots, x_n\}$ is a partition of $[a,b]$ obeying $\|P\| < \delta$, and $S(f,P,\xi)$ corresponds to this P. Note that $f(\xi_k) = 1$ or $f(\xi_k) = 0$ according as $\xi_k \in (\alpha,\beta)$ or $\xi_k \notin (\alpha,\beta)$. So we have

$$S(f,P,\xi) = \sum_{\xi_k \in (\alpha,\beta)} \Delta x_k.$$

Now choose p, q from $\{1,2,\ldots,n\}$ such that

$$x_{p-1} \leq \alpha < x_p, \quad x_{q-1} \leq \beta < x_q.$$

Then $\xi_k \in (\alpha,\beta)$ whenever $k \in [p+1, q-1]$, as well as, $\xi_k \notin (\alpha,\beta)$ whenever $k \notin [p+1, q-1]$. Therefore

$$\sum_{p+1 \leq k \leq q-1} \Delta x_k \leq S(f,P,\xi) \leq \sum_{p \leq k \leq q} \Delta x_k.$$

By the choice of p and q, we see

$$\beta - \alpha \leq x_q - x_{p-1} < (q-p+1)\|P\|,$$

so that if δ is sufficiently small then $p+1 \leq q-1$ must be true, and hence

$$x_{q-1} - x_p \leq S(f,P,\xi) \leq x_q - x_{p-1}.$$

Hence

$$(x_{q-1}-\beta)-(x_p-\alpha)\le S(f,P,\xi)-(\beta-\alpha)\le(x_q-\beta)-(x_{p-1}-\alpha).$$

Note that $x_{q-1}-\beta$, $x_p-\alpha$, $x_q-\beta$ and $x_{p-1}-\alpha$ are of absolute values less than $\|P\|$. So

$$|S(f,P,\xi)-(\beta-\alpha)|<2\delta.$$

This implies that $\int_a^b f(x)dx=\beta-\alpha$.

Example 2.7. If

$$f(x)=\begin{cases}1\,, & x\in\mathbf{Q}\,,\\ 0\,, & x\notin\mathbf{Q}\,,\end{cases}$$

then $f\notin R[a,b]$ for any interval $[a,b]$. To prove the result, we take $\epsilon=(b-a)/2$ and use Theorem 1.16 (ii) – the density of the rational numbers in $\mathbf{R}$, equivalently, the density of the irrational numbers in $\mathbf{R}$. For any partition P of $[a,b]$, no matter how small $\|P\|$ may be, each subinterval associated with P must contain both rational numbers and irrational numbers, say, $\xi_k'\in[x_{k-1},x_k]\cap\mathbf{Q}$ and $\xi_k''\in[x_{k-1},x_k]\cap(\mathbf{R}\setminus\mathbf{Q})$. Then

$$S(f,P,\xi')=\sum_{k=1}^{n}f(\xi_k')\Delta x_k=b-a$$

and

$$S(f,P,\xi'')=\sum_{k=1}^{n}f(\xi_k'')\Delta x_k=0.$$

Since these two numbers are $b-a$ units apart, there is no such number I that can be within ϵ of both sums. Hence, $\lim_{\|P\|\to 0}S(f,P,\xi)$ does not exist, so f is not in $R[a,b]$.

Because of working on an entirely new limit concept, we must begin by proving such basic results as the uniqueness of the limit.

Theorem 2.8. *If $f\in R[a,b]$, then $\int_a^b f(x)dx$ is unique and f is bounded.*

Proof. Suppose $\lim_{\|P\|\to 0}S(f,P,\xi)=I$, let $J\ne I$ and take $\epsilon=|I-J|/2$. Since ϵ is half of the distance between I and J, it follows that $(I-\epsilon,I+\epsilon)$ and $(J-\epsilon,J+\epsilon)$ do not intersect. When P is a partition of $[a,b]$ with $\|P\|$ being sufficiently small, $S(f,P,\xi)$ is in $(I-\epsilon,I+\epsilon)$ for any choice of $\{\xi_k\}_{k=1}^n$. Then $S(f,P,\xi)$ is not in $(J-\epsilon,J+\epsilon)$, so $|S(f,P,\xi)-J|\ge\epsilon$. Hence $\lim_{\|P\|\to 0}S(f,P,\xi)$ cannot equal J.

Let us next prove the boundedness of f on $[a,b]$. If f is not bounded on $[a,b]$, then for any partition P of $[a,b]$, f must be unbounded on at least one of the subintervals associated with P, say, $[x_{m-1},x_m]$. For $k\ne m$, choose $\{\xi_k\}_{k=1}^n$ satisfying $x_{k-1}\le\xi_k\le x_k$. Thus for any fixed number I we have determined the number $|I|+\sum_{k\ne m}|f(\xi_k)|\Delta x_k$. Now we use the unboundedness of f on $[x_{m-1},x_m]$ to choose ξ_m so that

$$|f(\xi_m)(x_m-x_{m-1})|>1+|I|+\sum_{k\ne m}|f(\xi_k)|\Delta x_k.$$

Thus the mth term dominates $S(f,P,\xi)$, and we have $|S(f,P,\xi)|>1+|I|$. Hence $\lim_{\|P\|\to 0}S(f,P,\xi)$ cannot exist, so f does not belong to $R[a,b]$, a contradiction. □

The next theorem shows that an integral can be evaluated on two adjacent intervals, and the resulting values are added.

Theorem 2.9. *If $f \in R[a,b]$ and $f \in R[b,c]$, then $f \in R[a,c]$ and $\int_a^c f(x)dx = \int_a^b f(x)dx + \int_a^c f(x)dx$.*

Proof. Any partition P of $[a,c]$ determines partitions P_1 and P_2 on $[a,b]$ and $[b,c]$, respectively, since if b is not one of the partition points of P then it can be inserted between x_{j-1} and x_j where j is the least integer such that $b \le x_j$. The number ξ_j in the sum $S(f,P,\xi)$ is selected from the subinterval $[x_{j-1},x_j]$, and we may have either $\xi_j \in [x_{j-1},b]$ or $\xi_j \in [b,x_j]$. In the former case, we can write

$$\begin{aligned} S(f,P,\xi) &= \sum_{k=1}^{j-1} f(\xi_k)\Delta x_k + f(\xi_j)(b-x_{j-1}) \\ &- f(b)(x_j-b) + f(\xi_j)(x_j-b) \\ &+ f(b)(x_j-b) + \sum_{k=j+1}^{n} f(\xi_k)\Delta x_k \\ &= S(f,P_1,\xi') + \big(f(\xi_j)-f(b)\big)(x_j-b) + S(f,P_2,\xi''), \end{aligned}$$

where $\xi' = \{\xi_k\}_{k=1}^{j}$ and $\xi'' = \{b\} \cup \{\xi_k\}_{k=j+1}^{n}$. Similarly, if $\xi_j \in [b,x_j]$, then we can write

$$S(f,P,\xi) = S(f,P_1,\xi') + \big(f(\xi_j)-f(b)\big)(b-x_{j-1}) + S(f,P_2,\xi''),$$

where $\xi' = \{\xi_k\}_{k=1}^{j-1} \cup \{b\}$ and $\xi'' = \{\xi_k\}_{k=j}^{n}$. By the boundedness of f on $[a,c]$, we have a constant $\kappa > 0$ such that $|f(x)| < \kappa$ on $[a,c]$ and then

$$|S(f,P,\xi) - S(f,P_1,\xi') - S(f,P_2,\xi'')| \le 2\kappa\|P\|,$$

because

$$b - x_{j-1} \le x_j - x_{j-1} \le \|P\| \quad \text{and} \quad x_j - b \le x_j - x_{j-1} \le \|P\|.$$

If $\epsilon > 0$, then $f \in R[a,b] \cap R[b,c]$ allows us to choose a $\delta > 0$ so that $\max\{\|P_1\|, \|P_2\|\} < \delta$ implies

$$\left|S(f,P_1,\xi') - \int_a^b f(x)dx\right| < \epsilon/3 \quad \text{and} \quad \left|S(f,P_2,\xi'') - \int_b^c f(x)dx\right| < \epsilon/3.$$

We can also choose δ even smaller, if necessary, so that $\delta < \epsilon/(6\kappa)$. Now since $\max\{\|P_1\|, \|P_2\|\} \le \|P\|$, we conclude that $\|P\| < \delta$ implies

$$\begin{aligned} &\left|S(f,P,\xi) - \left(\int_a^b f(x)dx + \int_b^c f(x)dx\right)\right| \\ &\le \left|S(f,P,\xi) - S(f,P_1,\xi') - S(f,P_2,\xi'')\right| \\ &+ \left|S(f,P_1,\xi') - \int_a^b f(x)dx\right| + \left|S(f,P_2,\xi'') - \int_b^c f(x)dx\right| \\ &< 2\kappa\|P\| + \epsilon/3 + \epsilon/3 < \epsilon. \end{aligned}$$

Hence

$$\int_a^c f(x)dx = \int_a^b f(x)dx + \int_b^c f(x)dx. \qquad \square$$

From Theorem 2.9 it follows that we should set

$$\int_a^a f(x)dx = 0 \text{ and } \int_a^b f(x)dx = -\int_b^a f(x)dx.$$

Motivated by the argument of Theorem 2.9, we find that in averaging a large set of numbers, it is possible to change a few values without altering the average very much. This is true for $S(f, P, \xi)$ and the resulting integral value.

Theorem 2.10. *If $f \in R[a, b]$ and $g = f$ for all but a finite number of points in $[a, b]$, then $g \in R[a, b]$ and $\int_a^b g(x)dx = \int_a^b f(x)dx$.*

Proof. It suffices to prove that the assertion in which g differs from f at exactly one point in $[a, b]$, because we can produce finite changes in f by changing the value at one point and repeating the procedure finitely many times. So we may assume that $g(x) = f(x)$ for all $x \in [a, b] \setminus \{c\}$. For any partition P, the point c can be in at most two of the subintervals in that c may be a partition point, say, $[x_{m-1}, x_m]$ and $[x_m, x_{m+1}]$. Then

$$\begin{aligned}
&\left|S(g, P, \xi) - \int_a^b f(x)dx\right| \\
&\le \left|\sum_{k=1}^{n} (g(\xi_k) - f(\xi_k))\Delta x_k\right| + \left|S(f, P, \xi) - \int_a^b f(x)dx\right| \\
&\le |g(c) - f(c)|(x_m - x_{m-1}) + |g(c) - f(c)|(x_{m+1} - x_m) \\
&+ \left|S(f, P, \xi) - \int_a^b f(x)dx\right| \\
&\le |g(c) - f(c)|(2\|P\|) + \left|S(f, P, \xi) - \int_a^b f(x)dx\right|.
\end{aligned}$$

Given $\epsilon > 0$, let $\delta \le \epsilon/(4|g(c) - f(c)|)$. So, for any partition P of $[a, b]$ we have that $\|P\| < \delta$ implies $|S(f, P, \xi) - \int_a^b f(x)dx| < \epsilon/2$. Substituting this into

$$|g(c) - f(c)|(2\|P\|) + \left|S(f, P, \xi) - \int_a^b f(x)dx\right|,$$

we see that $\|P\| < \delta$ implies

$$\left|S(g, P, \xi) - \int_a^b f(x)dx\right| < |g(c) - f(c)|(2\delta) + \epsilon/2 < \epsilon. \qquad \square$$

Here it is worthwhile pointing out that the finiteness in Theorem 2.10 is important; see Example 2.7.

2.2 Algebraic Operations and the Darboux Criterion

Theorem 2.11. *If $f_1, f_2 \in R[a,b]$ and $c_1, c_2 \in \mathbf{R}$, then $c_1 f_1 + c_2 f_2 \in R[a,b]$.*

Proof. It suffices to prove $f_1 + f_2 \in R[a,b]$. Assume $\epsilon > 0$ and choose such $\delta_1 > 0$ and $\delta_2 > 0$ that

$$\|P\| < \delta_1 \Rightarrow \left| S(f_1, P, \xi) - \int_a^b f_1(x)dx \right| < \epsilon/2$$

and

$$\|P\| < \delta_2 \Rightarrow \left| S(f_2, P, \xi) - \int_a^b f_2(x)dx \right| < \epsilon/2.$$

Now define $\delta = \min\{\delta_1, \delta_2\}$. This guarantees that if $\|P\| < \delta$ then

$$\begin{aligned} &\left| S(f_1 + f_2, P, \xi) - \Big(\int_a^b f_1(x)dx + \int_a^b f_2(x)dx \Big) \right| \\ &\le \left| S(f_1, P, \xi) - \int_a^b f_1(x)dx \right| + \left| S(f_2, P, \xi) - \int_a^b f_2(x)dx \right| < \epsilon. \end{aligned}$$

Hence $f_1 + f_2 \in R[a,b]$ and

$$\int_a^b \big(f_1(x) + f_2(x)\big)dx = \int_a^b f_1(x)dx + \int_a^b f_2(x)dx. \qquad \square$$

When evaluating a limit of some expression that is bounded above or below, we may use the same bound to control the limit value.

Corollary 2.12. *If $f_1, f_2 \in R[a,b]$ with $f_1(x) \le f_2(x)$ for every $x \in [a,b]$, then $\int_a^b f_1(x)dx \le \int_a^b f_2(x)dx$.*

Proof. Consider the case in which f_1 is identically 0. Then $f_2 \ge 0$ on $[a,b]$, so $S(f_2, P, \xi) \ge 0$. If $I = \int_a^b f_2(x)dx < 0$ and $\epsilon = -I$, then it is impossible to have $|S(f_2, P, \xi) - I| < \epsilon$ because the distance between $S(f_2, P, \xi)$ and I is at least equal to $|I|$.

Now for the general case: $f_1 \le f_2$ on $[a,b]$. Define $f = f_2 - f_1$. Clearly, $f \ge 0$, and, by Theorem 2.11, $f \in R[a,b]$. So the first case of this proof ensures that

$$0 \le \int_a^b f(x)dx = \int_a^b f_2(x)dx - \int_a^b f_1(x)dx. \qquad \square$$

In order to prove that multiplication is closed in $R[a,b]$, we need to develop a characterization of $R[a,b]$ (the so-called Jean Gaston Darboux criterion for integrability) that does not rely on predicting the value of the limit $\lim_{\|P\|\to 0} S(f, P, \xi)$. In this sense, it is analogous to Cauchy's criterion for sequential convergence.

Let f be a bounded function on $[a,b]$ and P be a partition of $[a,b]$. Due to the boundedness of f on each $[x_{k-1}, x_k]$, we may define

$$m_k = \inf\{f(x) : x \in [x_{k-1}, x_k]\}; \quad M_k = \sup\{f(x) : x \in [x_{k-1}, x_k]\},$$

and form the lower sum and upper sum for f with respect to P:

$$L(f,P)=\sum_{k=1}^{n} m_k\Delta x_k;\quad U(f,P)=\sum_{k=1}^{n} M_k\Delta x_k.$$

Clearly, we have

$$L(f,P)\le S(f,P,\xi)\le U(f,P)$$

although the lower and upper sums need not be Riemann sums since m_k and M_k may not be in the range of f.

Let P and P' be partitions of $[a,b]$. If $P\subseteq P'$ then P' is called a refinement of P. Thus, one can produce a refinement of P by inserting additional partition points between those in P. It is obvious that if P' is a refinement of P then $\|P'\|\le\|P\|$. Also, if P and P^* are partitions of $[a,b]$, then they have a common refinement; for example, $P\cup P^*$ is a refinement of both P and P^* because it contains both sets of partition points.

Lemma 2.13. *Let P and P^* be partitions of $[a,b]$. Then $L(f,P)\le U(f,P^*)$.*

Proof. Note first that whenever partition points are added to a partition P, the lower sums increase and the upper sums decrease. For if $L(f,P)=\sum_{k=1}^{n} m_k\Delta x_k$ and we add a point $z\in(x_{j-1},x_j)$ to form $P'=P\cup\{z\}$ then

$$L(f,P')=\sum_{k\neq j}^{n} m_k\Delta x_k+m'(z-x_{j-1})+m''(x_j-z),$$

where m' and m'' are the greatest lower bounds of f on $[x_{j-1},z]$ and $[z,x_j]$, respectively. Thus $m'\ge m_j$ and $m''\ge m_j$, so

$$m'(z-x_{j-1})+m''(x_j-z)\ge m_j(z-x_{j-1})+m_j(x_j-z)=m_j(x_j-x_{j-1}).$$

Hence $L(f,P')\ge L(f,P)$. Similarly, $U(f,P')\le U(f,P)$.

Suppose now P and P^* are any two partitions of $[a,b]$, and let $P'=P\cup P^*$. Since P' is a refinement of both P and P^*, the preceding observation gives us

$$L(f,P)\le L(f,P')\le U(f,P')\le U(f,P^*),$$

as desired. □

In the light of the foregoing lemma, we may define

$$\lambda(f)=\sup_P L(f,P);\quad \Lambda(f)=\inf_P U(f,P),$$

where both the supremum and the infimum are taken over all partitions P of $[a,b]$. From Lemma 2.13 it follows that $\lambda(f)\le\Lambda(f)$. Moreover, the forthcoming lemma gives the necessary connection between the limit concept as $\|P\|$ tends to 0 and the supremum and infimum concepts.

Lemma 2.14. *If f is a bounded function on $[a,b]$, then*

$$\lim_{\|P\|\to 0} L(f,P) = \lambda(f); \quad \lim_{\|P\|\to 0} U(f,P) = \Lambda(f).$$

Proof. It suffices to prove that $\lim_{\|P\|\to 0} U(f,P) = \Lambda(f)$. Suppose $|f(x)| < \kappa$ for all $x \in [a,b]$ where $\kappa > 0$ is a constant. By the definition of $\Lambda(f)$, for any $\epsilon > 0$ there exists a partition $P^* = \{z_i\}_{i=0}^{q}$ of $[a,b]$ such that

$$U(f,P^*) < \Lambda(f) + \epsilon/2.$$

Defining $\delta = \epsilon/(4q\kappa)$, we show that if $\|P\| < \delta$ for any partition P of $[a,b]$ then $U(f,P) < \Lambda(f) + \epsilon$. To do so, let $P' = P \cup P^* = \{x_k\}_{k=0}^{n}$. Then some of the partition points of P are z_i's from P^*, and some are not. Consequently,

$$U(f,P') = \sum_{[x_{k-1},x_k]\cap P^*=\emptyset} M_k \Delta x_k + \sum_{[x_{k-1},x_k]\cap P^*\neq\emptyset} M_k \Delta x_k.$$

Since the terms of the first sum on the right-hand side of the last representation are also terms of $U(f,P)$, it follows that $U(f,P) - U(f,P')$ consists of at most $2q$ terms (one for each of z_0 and z_q, and two for each of $z_1, \ldots, z_{q-1}$), each of which does not exceed

$$\kappa\|P'\| \leq \kappa\|P\| < \kappa\delta = (\kappa\epsilon)/(4q\kappa) = \epsilon/(4q).$$

Therefore

$$U(f,P) - U(f,P') < (2q)\big(\epsilon/(4q)\big) < \epsilon/2.$$

Accordingly, we have

$$\Lambda(f) \leq U(f,P) < U(f,P') + \epsilon/2 \leq U(f,P^*) + \epsilon/2 < \Lambda(f) + \epsilon,$$

whence completing the proof. □

Because the Riemann sums lie between the upper and lower sums, it is natural to ask what happens if $\lambda(f) = \Lambda(f)$. One would expect that this forces the Riemann sums to converge, with their limit being equal to the common value of $\lambda(f)$ and $\Lambda(f)$. That is precisely what does happen, and it provides the following Darboux characterization of integrability.

Theorem 2.15. *Let $f : [a,b] \to \mathbf{R}$ be bounded. The following statements are equivalent:*

(i) $f \in R[a,b]$;

(ii) $\lambda(f) = \Lambda(f)$;

(iii) *For any $\epsilon > 0$ there is a $\delta > 0$ such that $U(f,P) - L(f,P) < \epsilon$ as $\|P\| < \delta$.*

Proof. (ii)$\Rightarrow$(iii)$\Rightarrow$(i). Assume $\lambda(f) = \Lambda(f) = I$, and suppose $\epsilon > 0$. Using Lemma 2.14, we can choose $\delta > 0$ so that $\|P\| < \delta$ implies

$$L(f,P) > I - \epsilon/2; \quad U(f,P) < I + \epsilon/2.$$

Then for any choice of $\{\xi_k\}_{k=1}^n$ associated with a partition $P = \{x_k\}_{k=0}^n$ of $[a, b]$, we have

$$I - \epsilon/2 < L(f, P) \le S(f, P, \xi) \le U(f, P) < I + \epsilon/2.$$

Thus, $\|P\| < \delta$ implies $U(f, P) - L(f, P) < \epsilon$, and so $|S(f, P, \xi) - I| < \epsilon$ which yields $f \in R[a, b]$ and $\int_a^b f(x)dx = I$.

(i)$\Rightarrow$(iii)$\Rightarrow$(ii). If $f \in R[a, b]$ and $\int_a^b f(x)dx = I$, then for any $\epsilon > 0$ we can find $\delta > 0$ such that $\|P\| < \delta$ implies $|S(f, P, \xi) - I| < \epsilon/4$. By the definitions of M_k and m_k, there exist points $\xi_k', \xi_k'' \in [x_{k-1}, x_k]$ satisfying

$$f(\xi_k') > M_k - \frac{\epsilon}{4(b-a)}; \quad f(\xi_k'') < m_k + \frac{\epsilon}{4(b-a)}.$$

Then

$$\begin{aligned} U(f, P) &= \sum_{k=1}^n M_k \Delta x_k \\ &< \sum_{k=1}^n \Big(f(\xi_k') + \frac{\epsilon}{4(b-a)}\Big)\Delta x_k \\ &= S(f, P, \xi') + \frac{\epsilon}{4(b-a)} \sum_{k=1}^n \Delta x_k \\ &< I + \frac{\epsilon}{2}. \end{aligned}$$

Similarly, $L(f, P) > I - \epsilon/2$. Hence $U(f, P) - L(f, P) < \epsilon$ which infers

$$0 \le \Lambda(f) - \lambda(f) \le U(f, P) - L(f, P) < \epsilon.$$

This, along with Lemma 2.14, implies $\lambda(f) = \Lambda(f)$. So, the proof is complete. □

Remark 2.16. It is worth remarking that $\int_a^b f(x)dx = \lambda(f) = \Lambda(f)$ holds for $f \in R[a, b]$.

We have known that $R[a, b]$ is closed under addition and constant multiplication. To completely establish the algebraic closure of $R[a, b]$, we now use Theorem 2.15 to prove the result for the product of two general functions in $R[a, b]$.

Theorem 2.17. *If $f_1, f_2 \in R[a, b]$, then $f_1 f_2 \in R[a, b]$.*

Proof. For convenience, let $f = f_1$ and $g = f_2$. We first prove the assertion for the special case: $f, g \ge 0$. Suppose that P is any partition of $[a, b]$, and let $M_{f,k}$, $M_{g,k}$ and $M_{fg,k}$ denote the least upper bounds of f, g, and fg, respectively, on the kth subinterval $[x_{k-1}, x_k]$. It is not hard to see that $M_{fg,k} \le M_{f,k}M_{g,k}$. Similarly, if $m_{f,k}, m_{g,k}$, and $m_{fg,k}$ are the corresponding greatest lower bounds on $[x_{k-1}, x_k]$, then $m_{fg,k} \ge m_{f,k}m_{g,k}$. Thus

$$M_{fg,k} - m_{fg,k} \le M_{f,k}M_{g,k} - m_{f,k}m_{g,k}.$$

Now let $M_f = \sup_{x\in[a,b]} f(x)$ and $M_g = \sup_{x\in[a,b]} g(x)$ and rewrite the last inequality as

$$\begin{aligned} M_{fg,k} - m_{fg,k} &\le M_{f,k}M_{g,k} - m_{f,k}M_{g,k} + m_{f,k}M_{g,k} - m_{f,k}m_{g,k} \\ &\le (M_{f,k} - m_{f,k})M_g + (M_{g,k} - m_{g,k})M_f. \end{aligned}$$

Accordingly, we have

$$\begin{aligned} U(fg,P) - L(fg,P) &= \sum_{k=1}^{n}(M_{fg,k} - m_{fg,k})\Delta x_k \\ &\le M_g \sum_{k=1}^{n}(M_{f,k} - m_{f,k})\Delta x_k + M_f \sum_{k=1}^{n}(M_{g,k} - m_{g,k})\Delta x_k \\ &= M_g\big(U(f,P) - L(f,P)\big) + M_f\big(U(g,P) - L(g,P)\big). \end{aligned}$$

By Theorem 2.15, we have that if $\epsilon > 0$ then $f, g \in R[a,b]$ allows us to choose P so that

$$U(f,P) - L(f,P) < \frac{\epsilon}{2(1+M_g)}; \quad U(g,P) - L(g,P) < \frac{\epsilon}{2(1+M_f)}.$$

This gives $U(fg,P) - L(fg,P) < \epsilon$ and so $fg \in R[a,b]$.

To prove the general case in which f and g need not be nonnegative, we use Theorem 2.8 which assures us that f and g are bounded from below, say, by constants δ and η respectively. Then $f-\delta, g-\eta \ge 0$ on $[a,b]$ and $f-\delta, g-\eta \in R[a,b]$, so the case just proved can be applied to conclude that $(f-\delta)(g-\eta) \in R[a,b]$. Note that

$$fg = (f-\delta)(g-\eta) + \delta g + \eta f - \delta\eta$$

for which each term of the right-hand member is in $R[a,b]$. Thus it follows from the above special case, as well as Theorem 2.11, that $fg \in R[a,b]$. □

It may be observed that something is missing: No explicit formula is valid for $\int_a^b f_1(x)f_2(x)dx$. But, there is an inequality to connect it with $\int_a^b f_1^2(x)dx$ and $\int_a^b f_2^2(x)dx$. This is just the Cauchy–Schwarz inequality or the Cauchy–Bunyakovski-Schwarz inequality, named after Augustin Louis Cauchy, Hermann Amandus Schwarz and Viktor Yakovlevich Bunyakovsky.

Theorem 2.18. *If $f_1, f_2 \in R[a,b]$, then*

$$\Big|\int_a^b f_1(x)f_2(x)dx\Big| \le \Big(\int_a^b f_1^2(x)dx\Big)^{1/2}\Big(\int_a^b f_2^2(x)dx\Big)^{1/2}.$$

Proof. It is clear that $f_1f_2, f_1^2, f_2^2 \in R[a,b]$ and $\int_a^b f_1^2(x)dx, \int_a^b f_2^2(x)dx \ge 0$. Define

$$A = \int_a^b f_1^2(x)dx, \quad B = 2\int_a^b f_1(x)f_2(x)dx, \quad C = \int_a^b f_2^2(x)dx.$$

And, let $f(t) = At^2 + Bt + C$. Then $f(t) = \int_a^b \big(tf_1(x) + f_2(x)\big)^2 dx \geq 0$. From elementary algebra we recall that $f(t) = 0$ has two roots in $\mathbf{R}$ if and only if $B^2 - 4AC > 0$. Since $f(t)$ is never negative, the quadratic equation $f(t) = 0$ can not have two real roots, which means that $B^2 - 4AC \leq 0$. But this says that

$$\Big(\int_a^b f_1(x)f_2(x)dx\Big)^2 - \Big(\int_a^b f_1^2(x)dx\Big)\Big(\int_a^b f_2^2(x)dx\Big) \leq 0. \qquad \square$$

2.3 Fundamental Theorem of Calculus

This section is devoted to proving the fundamental theorem of calculus via an investigation of the integrability of continuous functions.

The ordinary definition of continuity is actually pointwise continuity and allows us to choose δ (in terms of the $\epsilon - \delta$ language) in a point-by-point manner, using different choices of δ for different points in the domain of f. But sometimes, say, $f(x) = x^2$, $x \in [-5, 5]$, or $f(x) = 1/x$, $x \in [1, \infty)$, we are able to choose one δ that works uniformly well at any point in the domain of f. This provides both the motivation and the name of the next concept.

Definition 2.19. Given a set $D \subseteq \mathbf{R}$ and a function $f : D \to \mathbf{R}$, we say that:

(i) f has a limit $L \in \mathbf{R}$ at $c \in D$, written $\lim_{x\to c} f(x) = L$, provided that for any $\epsilon > 0$ there is a $\delta > 0$ such that

$$x \in D \text{ and } 0 < |x - c| < \delta \Rightarrow |f(x) - L| < \epsilon;$$

(ii) f is continuous on D provided that it is continuous at any point $c \in D$, i.e., for any $\epsilon > 0$ there is a $\delta > 0$ such that

$$x \in D \text{ and } |x - c| < \delta \Rightarrow |f(x) - f(c)| < \epsilon;$$

(iii) f is uniformly continuous on D provided that for any $\epsilon > 0$ there exists a $\delta > 0$ (depending only on ϵ and D) such that

$$x_1, x_2 \in D \text{ and } |x_1 - x_2| < \delta \Rightarrow |f(x_1) - f(x_2)| < \epsilon.$$

It is plain that the linear function $f(x) = ax + b$, $a \neq 0$, is uniformly continuous on $\mathbf{R}$: For $\epsilon > 0$, take $\delta = \epsilon/|a|$. However, the sign function $f(x) = |x|/x$ is not uniformly continuous on $\mathbf{R} \setminus \{0\}$ although it is so on $(-\infty, 0)$ and $(0, \infty)$. Also, it is easy to see that if f is uniformly continuous on D, then f is continuous on D. Though its converse is not true in general, there are situations in which continuity at every point of D does imply uniform continuity on D.

Unless a special remark is made, the symbol $C[a, b]$ will be employed to represent the set of all real-valued continuous functions on $[a, b]$. The following are some important properties of $C[a, b]$ which are frequently used from now on.

Theorem 2.20. *Let* $f \in C[a, b]$. *Then*

(i) f *is bounded; that is,* $\sup\{|f(x)| : x \in [a, b]\} < \infty$.

(ii) f *has a minimum and a maximum – there exist* $x_1, x_2 \in [a,b]$ *such that* $f(x_1) = \sup\{f(x) : x \in [a,b]\}$ *and* $f(x_2) = \inf\{f(x) : x \in [a,b]\}$.

(iii) *Intermediate value theorem – for any* y *between* $f(a)$ *and* $f(b)$ *there is* $x \in [a,b]$ *such that* $f(x) = y$.

(iv) f *is uniformly continuous on* $[a,b]$.

Proof. (i) If not, then for any $n \in \mathbf{N}$ there is an $x_n \in [a,b]$ such that $|f(x_n)| \geq n$. By the Bolzano-Weierstrass property – see also Theorem 1.18 (ii), there exist $x \in [a,b]$ and a subsequence $(x_{n_k})_{k\in\mathbf{N}}$ of $(x_n)_{n\in\mathbf{N}}$ such that $x_{n_k} \to x$. Hence, $f \in C[a,b]$ yields $\lim_{k\to\infty} f(x_{n_k}) = f(x)$ and so $\big(f(x_{n_k})\big)_{k\in\mathbf{N}}$ is bounded. This is a contradiction since $|f(x_{n_k})| \geq n_k \geq k$ for any $k \in \mathbf{N}$. Therefore, f must be bounded on $[a,b]$.

(ii) By (i), $M = \sup\{f(x) : x \in [a,b]\}$ exists in $\mathbf{R}$. This produces a sequence $x_n \in [a,b]$ with $M - n^{-1} < f(x_n) \leq M$ for any $n \in \mathbf{N}$. Again by the Bolzano-Weierstrass property, there is a subsequence $(x_{n_k})_{k=1}^{\infty}$ of $(x_n)_{n=1}^{\infty}$ such that $x_{n_k} \to x \in [a,b]$. Accordingly, by $f \in C[a,b]$ and Theorem 1.21,

$$f(x_{n_k}) \to f(x) \quad \text{and} \quad f(x_{n_k}) \to M \quad \text{and hence} \quad M = f(x).$$

The argument for a minimum is similar.

(iii) It suffices to consider the case $f(a) \neq f(b)$. Of course, we may assume $f(a) < y < f(b)$ and $S = \{x' \in [a,b] : f(x') < y\}$. Since $a \in S$, $S \neq \emptyset$ and it has an upper bound b. The axiom of LUB for $\mathbf{R}$ implies that $x = \sup S$ exists. The definition of S gives $a < x < b$. Next, we prove $f(x) = y$. To do so, we consider two cases below.

Case 1: $f(x) < y$. Since $f \in C[a,b]$, there is a $\delta > 0$ such that

$$|x_1 - x| < \delta \text{ and } x_1 \in [a,b] \Rightarrow f(x_1) < y.$$

Consequently, there is an $x_2 \in [a,b]$ with $x_2 > x$ and $f(x_2) < y$, contradicting the definition of x.

Case 2: $f(x) > y$. Like *Case 1*, we can find a $\delta > 0$ such that

$$x - \delta < x_3 < x \text{ and } x_3 \in [a,b] \Rightarrow f(x_3) > y,$$

which is against the choice of x.

Therefore, we must have $f(x) = y$.

(iv) Let $c \in [a,b]$. Since $f \in C[a,b]$, for any $\epsilon > 0$ there is a $\delta_c > 0$ such that

$$|x - c| < \delta_c \Rightarrow |f(x) - f(c)| < \frac{\epsilon}{2}.$$

Now consider the collection of open intervals:

$$\mathcal{O} = \{(c - \delta_c/2, c + \delta_c/2) : c \in [a,b]\}.$$

For each $c \in [a,b]$, there is an interval in $\mathcal{O}$ centered at c, so $\mathcal{O}$ is obviously an open cover of $[a,b]$. By the Heine-Borel property – see also Theorem 1.18 (iii), there exists a finite subcollection of $\mathcal{O}$ that covers $[a,b]$, say,

$$[a,b] \subset \bigcup_{j=1}^{n} \left(c_j - \frac{\delta_{c_j}}{2}, c_j + \frac{\delta_{c_j}}{2}\right).$$

Define $\delta = \min_{1\le j\le n} \delta_{c_j}/2$. Now if $|x_1 - x_2| < \delta$ for $x_1, x_2 \in [a,b]$, then x_1 is in one of the n intervals in the above finite covering, so $|x_1 - c_j| < \delta$ holds for some c_j. Consequently,

$$|x_2 - c_j| \le |x_2 - x_1| + |x_1 - c_j| < \delta + \delta_{c_j}/2 \le \delta_{c_j}.$$

Thus, by the choice of δ_{c_j},

$$|f(x_1) - f(c_j)| < \epsilon/2; \quad |f(x_2) - f(c_j)| < \epsilon/2,$$

which yields

$$|f(x_1) - f(x_2)| \le |f(x_1) - f(c_j)| + |f(x_2) - f(c_j)| < \epsilon.$$

We are done. □

Example 2.21. To handle the integrability of continuous functions, we consider the integrability of the following function

$$f(x) = \begin{cases} 1/q\,, & x = p/q \in \mathbf{Q} \cap (0,1] \text{ and p/q in lowest terms,} \\ 0\,, & x \in \{0\} \cup \Big((0,1] \cap (\mathbf{R} \setminus \mathbf{Q})\Big). \end{cases}$$

Recall that this function f is continuous at each irrational number and discontinuous at each rational number in $(0,1)$: in fact, if $c \in (0,1)$ is rational, then we take irrational points $s_k \in (0,1)$ converging to c and hence $\lim_{k\to\infty} f(s_k) = 0 \ne f(c)$; to see that f is continuous at any irrational $d \in (0,1)$, let $\epsilon > 0$ and note that there are only a finite number of irreducible fractions p/q in $(0,1)$ such that $1/q \ge \epsilon$. Therefore there is a $\delta > 0$ such that those fractions do not belong to $(d-\delta, d+\delta)$. This means that for all x satisfying $|x - d| < \delta$, we have $0 \le f(x) < \epsilon$. It is worth mentioning that f is continuous from the right at 0 and discontinuous from the left at 1. We now assert that $f \in R[0,1]$ with $\int_0^1 f(x)dx = 0$. As a matter of fact, the density of $\mathbf{R} \setminus \mathbf{Q}$ in $\mathbf{R}$ ensures that $L(f,P) = 0$ for every partition P of $[0,1]$. Thus, for any $\epsilon > 0$, we seek a partition P such that $U(f,P) < \epsilon$. In $[0,1]$ there are just finitely many points p/q such that $1/q > \epsilon/2$. Let m be the number of such points in $[0,1]$ and let P be a partition such that $\|P\| < \epsilon/(4m)$. In $U(f,P) = \sum_{k=1}^{n} M_k \Delta x_k$ there are at most $2m$ terms where $M_k > \epsilon/2$; for each of these terms we have $M_k \Delta x_k \le 1 \cdot \|P\| < \epsilon/(4m)$. Therefore the total of these terms is less than $(2m)\big(\epsilon/(4m)\big) = \epsilon/2$. In each of the remaining terms, $M_k \le \epsilon/2$, so their total is less than $(\epsilon/2)\sum_{k=1}^{n} \Delta x_k = \epsilon/2$. Hence $U(f,P) < \epsilon$, so the Darboux's integrability criterion implies that $f \in R[0,1]$ and $\int_0^1 f(x)dx = 0$.

Up to this point, we have seen very few examples that we could verify as being integrable functions. But, the next two theorems provide us with a very large set of such examples.

Theorem 2.22. *If $f \in C[a,b]$, then $f \in R[a,b]$.*

Proof. By Theorem 2.20 (iv), f is uniformly continuous on $[a,b]$, and so for any $\epsilon > 0$ there is a $\delta > 0$ such that

$$x', x'' \in [a,b] \text{ and } |x' - x''| < \delta \Rightarrow |f(x') - f(x'')| < \epsilon/(b-a).$$

Now choose a partition P such that $\|P\| < \delta$, and consider the kth subinterval $[x_{k-1}, x_k]$. There are $\xi'_k, \xi''_k \in [x_{k-1}, x_k]$ such that $f(\xi'_k) = M_k, f(\xi''_k) = m_k$ thanks to Theorem 2.20 (ii). Note that $|\xi'_k - \xi''_k| \leq \Delta x_k \leq \|P\| < \delta$. So it follows that $M_k - m_k < \epsilon/(b-a)$. Thus

$$U(f,P) - L(f,P) = \sum_{k=1}^{n} (M_k - m_k)\Delta x_k < \epsilon;$$

and hence $f \in R[a,b]$ by Theorem 2.15. □

As a consequence of Theorem 2.22, we can establish the mean value theorem for integrals.

Theorem 2.23. *If $f \in C[a,b]$, then there is a number $\xi \in [a,b]$ such that $f(\xi)(b-a) = \int_a^b f(x)dx$.*

Proof. By Theorem 2.22, we have $f \in R[a,b]$. Let

$$m = \min_{x \in [a,b]} f(x) \quad \text{and} \quad M = \max_{x \in [a,b]} f(x).$$

Then

$$m(b-a) \leq \int_a^b f(x)dx \leq M(b-a);$$

that is, $\int_a^b f(x)dx/(b-a)$ lies between m and M. Since $f \in C[a,b]$, f assumes any value between m and M and so there is a $\xi \in [a,b]$ such that $f(\xi)$ is equal to $\int_a^b f(x)dx/(b-a)$. □

The idea involved in the argument of Theorem 2.23 also leads to the following result.

Theorem 2.24. *If f is monotonic on $[a,b]$; that is, f is increasing:*

$$x_1 \leq x_2 \textit{ and } x_1, x_2 \in [a,b] \Rightarrow f(x_1) \leq f(x_2)$$

or decreasing:

$$x_1 \leq x_2 \textit{ and } x_1, x_2 \in [a,b] \Rightarrow f(x_1) \geq f(x_2),$$

then $f \in R[a,b]$.

Proof. Without loss of generality, we may assume that f is increasing and nonconstant (otherwise, there is nothing to argue). Then for any subinterval $[x_{k-1}, x_k]$ of $[a, b]$, M_k occurs at the right endpoint: $M_k = f(x_k)$. Similarly, $m_k = f(x_{k-1})$. Therefore, if P is any partition of $[a, b]$ then

$$\begin{aligned} U(f,P) - L(f,P) &= \sum_{k=1}^{n} (M_k - m_k)\Delta x_k \\ &\leq \|P\| \sum_{k=1}^{n} \big(f(x_k) - f(x_{k-1})\big) \\ &= \|P\| |f(b) - f(a)|. \end{aligned}$$

Now if $\epsilon > 0$, then we simply select a partition P such that

$$\|P\| < \epsilon/\big(f(b) - f(a) + 1\big) \quad \text{and hence} \quad U(f,P) - L(f,P) < \epsilon.$$

This infers that $f \in R[a, b]$ by Theorem 2.15. □

To get the fundamental theorem of calculus linking an integral to a derivative, we recall the notion of differentiation and the corresponding mean value theorem.

Definition 2.25. For an interval $I \subseteq \mathbf{R}$ containing an element c, we say that the function $f : I \to \mathbf{R}$ is differentiable at c or has a derivative at c provided the limit

$$f'(c) = \lim_{x \to c} \frac{f(x) - f(c)}{x - c}$$

exists; that is, for any $\epsilon > 0$ there exists a $\delta > 0$ such that

$$x, c \in I \text{ and } 0 < |x - c| < \delta \Rightarrow \left| f'(c) - \frac{f(x) - f(c)}{x - c} \right| < \epsilon.$$

If f is differentiable at every element of the set $D \subseteq I$, then f is called differentiable on D, and the function $f' : D \to \mathbf{R}$ is called the derivative of f on D.

Obviously, we can read off that if f is differentiable at c then it is continuous but not conversely. At the same time, we can take the derivative of the sum, product, quotient and composition of two differentiable functions. Moreover we can establish the generalized mean value theorem for derivatives as follows.

Theorem 2.26. *Let $f, g \in C[a, b]$ be differentiable on (a, b). Then there exists a point $c \in (a, b)$ such that $\big(f(b) - f(a)\big)g'(c) = \big(g(b) - g(a)\big)f'(c)$.*

Proof. Define the function $h : [a, b] \to \mathbf{R}$ by

$$h(x) = \big(f(b) - f(a)\big)g(x) - \big(g(b) - g(a)\big)f(x).$$

Then $h \in C[a, b]$ and is differentiable on (a, b) with $h(a) = h(b)$. An application of Theorem 2.20 (ii) produces two points $x_1, x_2 \in [a, b]$ such that

$$\inf\{h(x) : x \in [a, b]\} = h(x_1) \quad \text{and} \quad \sup\{h(x) : x \in [a, b]\} = h(x_2).$$

If x_1 and x_2 are both endpoints of $[a, b]$ then $h(x) = h(a) = h(b)$ for any $x \in [a, b]$ and hence f is a constant, giving $h'(x) = 0$ for all $x \in (a, b)$. Otherwise, we may assume $x_2 \in (a, b)$. Now let $s_n = x_2 - n^{-1}$ be a sequence converging to x_2 such that $a < s_n < x_2$ for sufficiently large $n \in \mathbf{N}$. Since h is differentiable at x_2, we have

$$0 \le \frac{h(s_n) - h(x_2)}{s_n - x_2} \to h'(x_2) \quad \text{as} \quad n \to \infty,$$

whence $h'(x_2) \ge 0$. Similarly, if $x_2 < t_n = x_2 + n^{-1} < b$ then

$$0 \ge \frac{h(t_n) - h(x_2)}{t_n - x_2} \to h'(x_2) \quad \text{as} \quad n \to \infty,$$

and hence $h'(x_2) \le 0$. Therefore, we have $h'(x_2) = 0$, whence

$$\big(f(b) - f(a)\big)g'(x_2) = \big(g(b) - g(a)\big)f'(x_2).$$

We are done. □

Below is the fundamental theorem of calculus whose importance can hardly be overstated.

Theorem 2.27. *If $f \in R[a, b]$ and $F'(x) = f(x)$ for $x \in [a, b]$, then $\int_a^b f(x)dx = F(b) - F(a)$. Conversely, if $f \in C[a, b]$ and $F(x) = \int_a^x f(t)dt$ for $x \in [a, b]$, then $F'(x) = f(x)$ for $x \in [a, b]$.*

Proof. Let P be a partition of $[a, b]$, and consider the collapsing sum

$$F(b) - F(a) = \sum_{k=1}^{n} \big(F(x_k) - F(x_{k-1})\big).$$

Since F is differentiable on $[x_{k-1}, x_k]$, we can apply the special case (where $g(x) = x$) of Theorem 2.26 to get a number $\xi_k \in [x_{k-1}, x_k]$ such that

$$F(x_k) - F(x_{k-1}) = F'(\xi_k)\Delta x_k = f(\xi_k)\Delta x_k.$$

Substituting the right-hand member of this equation into the collapsing sum, we get $F(b) - F(a) = S(f, P, \xi)$, a Riemann sum for f with respect to P. Thus we have shown that for any partition P, the points $\{\xi_k\}_{k=1}^n$ can be chosen so that $S(f, P, \xi)$ is $F(b) - F(a)$. Therefore $F(b) - F(a)$ is the only possible value of $\lim_{\|P\| \to 0} S(f, P, \xi)$. Since $f \in R[a, b]$, this limit must exist and its value is denoted by $\int_a^b f(x)dx$. Hence $\int_a^b f(x)dx = F(b) - F(a)$.

To prove the converse, let $c \in [a, b]$ and consider the difference quotient

$$Q_c(h) = \frac{F(c + h) - F(c)}{h} = \frac{1}{h} \int_c^{c+h} f(t)dt.$$

By Theorem 2.23, there is a ξ between c and $c + h$ such that

$$\int_c^{c+h} f(t)dt = f(\xi)h.$$

Substituting this into the expression for $Q_c(h)$, we obtain $Q_c(h) = f(\xi)$. As $h \to 0$, it follows that $\xi \to c$; therefore

$$F'(c) = \lim_{h \to 0} Q_c(h) = \lim_{\xi \to c} f(\xi) = f(c),$$

thanks to the continuity of f at c. □

Theorem 2.27 is a powerful tool for the computation of integrals. For example, if $n \in \mathbf{N}$ then $x^{n+1}/(n+1)$ has the continuous derivative x^n, so that

$$\int_a^b x^n dx = \frac{b^{n+1} - a^{n+1}}{n+1}.$$

Additionally, we should notice that the condition $F' = f$ in the first part of Theorem 2.27 cannot guarantee $f \in R[a, b]$; for instance, if

$$F(x) = \begin{cases} x^2 \sin \frac{1}{x^2}, & x \neq 0, \\ 0, & x = 0, \end{cases}$$

then

$$F'(x) = \begin{cases} 2x \sin \frac{1}{x^2} - \frac{2}{x} \cos \frac{1}{x^2}, & x \neq 0, \\ 0, & x = 0, \end{cases}$$

and hence $f = F' \notin R[-1, 1]$ due to the fact that f is unbounded on $[-1, 1]$.

As a consequence of Theorem 2.27, we can establish the following formula of change of variable for Riemann integrals.

Corollary 2.28. *Let U and V be open intervals in $\mathbf{R}$, $\phi : U \to V$ a differentiable function with continuous derivative, and $f : V \to \mathbf{R}$ a continuous function. Then for any $a, b \in U$*

$$\int_{\phi(a)}^{\phi(b)} f(v)dv = \int_a^b f(\phi(u))\phi'(u)du.$$

Proof. Let $F : V \to \mathbf{R}$ be the function defined by $F(y) = \int_{\phi(a)}^{y} f(v)dv$ for all $y \in V$. Then F is differentiable and $F' = f$ by Theorem 2.27. The function $G : U \to \mathbf{R}$ defined by $G(x) = \int_{\phi(a)}^{\phi(x)} f(v)dv$ is actually the composition $G = F \circ \phi$ of two differentiable functions, hence is itself differentiable. By the chain rule we have

$$G'(x) = F'(\phi(x))\phi'(x) = f(\phi(x))\phi'(x)$$

for all $x \in U$. Hence

$$G(x) = \int_a^x f(\phi(u))\phi'(u)du + C$$

for some constant $C \in \mathbf{R}$. Setting $x = a$ we get $C = 0$, so that

$$G(x) = \int_a^x f(\phi(u))\phi'(u)du.$$

This last equation holds for all $x \in U$. Setting $x = b$ gives us the desired formula. □

2.4 Improper Integrals

Since there are many useful, commonly encountered functions whose domains are unbounded or whose graphs have vertical asymptotes, in this section we extend Riemann integrals to cover two new types of integrals for some of these functions. As one of their applications, we prove the Weierstrass approximation theorem via the convolution of two functions on **R**.

We start by defining a notion of integration on unbounded intervals.

Definition 2.29.

(i) Let $a \in \mathbf{R}$ and $f \in R[a,t]$ for every $t \geq a$. Then the improper integral of f on $[a,\infty)$ is defined by

$$\int_a^\infty f(x)dx = \lim_{t\to\infty} \int_a^t f(x)dx.$$

If the limit exists; that is, for any $\epsilon > 0$ there is a $T > 0$ such that

$$t > T \Rightarrow \left| \int_a^t f(x)dx - \int_a^\infty f(x)dx \right| < \epsilon,$$

then the improper integral is said to be convergent; otherwise, the improper integral is divergent.

(ii) The improper integral of a function f on $(-\infty, b]$ is defined similarly:

$$\int_{-\infty}^b f(x)dx = \lim_{t\to-\infty} \int_t^b f(x)dx.$$

(iii) If $f \in R[-t,t]$ for any $t > 0$, then the improper integral of f on $(-\infty,\infty)$ is defined by

$$\int_{-\infty}^\infty f(x)dx = \lim_{t\to-\infty} \int_t^c f(x)dx + \lim_{t\to\infty} \int_c^t f(x)dx \quad \text{for all } c \in \mathbf{R}.$$

If $\int_{-\infty}^c f(x)dx$ and $\int_c^\infty f(x)dx$ are convergent, then

$$\int_{-\infty}^\infty f(x)dx = \int_{-\infty}^c f(x)dx + \int_c^\infty f(x)dx.$$

The following example shows how to evaluate these improper integrals.

Example 2.30.

(i)

$$\int_1^\infty \frac{1}{x^2}dx = \lim_{t\to\infty} \int_1^t \frac{1}{x^2}dx = \lim_{t\to\infty}\left(1 - \frac{1}{t}\right) = 1,$$

so the improper integral is convergent.

(ii)

$$\int_{-\infty}^0 \cos x dx = \lim_{t\to-\infty} \int_t^0 \cos x dx = \lim_{t\to-\infty} (-\sin t),$$

so the improper integral is divergent.

(iii)

$$\int_{-\infty}^{\infty} \frac{1}{1+x^2}dx = \int_{-\infty}^{0} \frac{1}{1+x^2}dx + \int_{0}^{\infty} \frac{1}{1+x^2}dx$$
$$= \lim_{t\to-\infty} \arctan x|_t^0 + \lim_{t\to\infty} \arctan x|_0^t = \pi,$$

so the improper integral is convergent.

(iv)

$$\int_{-\infty}^{\infty} \frac{1}{e^x}dx = \int_{-\infty}^{0} \frac{1}{e^x}dx + \int_{0}^{\infty} \frac{1}{e^x}dx$$
$$= \lim_{t\to-\infty} (-e^x)|_t^0 + \lim_{t\to\infty} (-e^x)|_0^t = \infty,$$

so the improper integral is divergent.

Here is a basic result on the improper integrals of which (iii) is called Cauchy's convergence criterion.

Theorem 2.31. *Let* $\int_a^\infty f_1(x)dx$ *and* $\int_a^\infty f_2(x)dx$ *exist. Then*

(i) $\int_a^\infty (c_1 f_1(x) + c_2 f_2(x))dx = c_1 \int_a^\infty f_1(x)dx + c_2 \int_a^\infty f_2(x)dx$ *for any constants* $c_1, c_2 \in \mathbf{R}$.

(ii) $\int_a^\infty f_1(x)dx \le \int_a^\infty f_2(x)dx$ *provided* $f_1 \le f_2$ *on* $[a,\infty)$.

(iii) $\int_a^\infty f(x)dx$ *exists if and only if for any* $\epsilon > 0$ *there is a* $T > 0$ *such that* $b_2 > b_1 > T$ *implies* $\left|\int_{b_1}^{b_2} f(x)dx\right| < \epsilon$.

Proof. As an exercise, the argument for (i) and (ii) is left for the students. Now we verify (iii). If $\int_a^\infty f(x)dx$ exists, then for any $\epsilon > 0$ there is a $T > 0$ such that

$$t > T \Rightarrow \left|\int_a^t f(x)dx - \int_a^\infty f(x)dx\right| < \epsilon/2.$$

Thus the desired inequality follows from taking $b_2 > b_1 > T$.

On the other hand, if for any $\epsilon > 0$ there is a $T > 0$ such that $b_2 > b_1 > T$ implies $\left|\int_{b_1}^{b_2} f(x)dx\right| < \epsilon$, then the sequence $\left(\int_a^{a+n} f(x)dx\right)_{n=1}^\infty$ is a Cauchy sequence, and hence converges to a finite number L. This gives that for $\epsilon > 0$ there exists a $T > 0$ such that

$$a + n \ge T \Rightarrow \left|\int_a^{a+n} f(x)dx - L\right| < \epsilon.$$

Then if $N \in \mathbf{N}$ satisfies $N > T - a$, then $t > a + N$ yields

$$\left|\int_a^t f(x)dx - L\right| = \left|\int_a^{a+N} f(x)dx - L + \int_{a+N}^t f(x)dx\right| < 2\epsilon,$$

as required. □

Defining the improper integral in terms of the definite Riemann integral has both advantages and disadvantages. On the positive side, there is no need to develop a separate limit theory for the new type of integral. But, on the other hand, we are required to evaluate $\int_a^t f(x)dx$ as a function of t in order to determine whether $\int_a^\infty f(x)dx$ is convergent, and the difficulty of finding the primitive of a given function is well known to the students. Since it is frequently sufficient to determine convergence of $\int_a^\infty f(x)dx$ without finding its value, it will be very helpful to have a test that says that under some appropriate conditions the convergence of a simple integral implies that of a complicated one. Such a result is called a comparison test. That is the nature of the next theorem.

Theorem 2.32. *Let $f_1, f_2 \in R[a,t]$ and $0 \le f_1(t) \le f_2(t)$ for every $a \le t < \infty$. If $\int_a^\infty f_2(x)dx$ is convergent, then $\int_a^\infty f_1(x)dx$ is convergent too.*

Proof. Let $f = f_1$ and $g = f_2$. First, we verify that if there is a number $B > 0$ such that $F(t) = \int_a^t f(x)dx \le B$ for every $t \ge a$, then $\int_a^\infty f(x)dx$ is convergent. In fact, since $F(t+h) - F(t) = \int_t^{t+h} f(x)dx$, it follows that F is increasing on $[a, \infty)$. Therefore $F(t) \le B$ ensures that

$$\lim_{t\to\infty} F(t) = \sup_{t\ge a} F(t) < \infty, \quad \text{i.e.,} \quad \lim_{t\to\infty} \int_a^t f(x)dx \quad \text{exists.}$$

Secondly, define $h(x) = g(x) - f(x)$ for $x \ge a$. Then $h \in R[a,t]$ and $h(t) \ge 0$ for every $t \ge a$, and

$$\int_a^t h(x)dx \le \int_a^t g(x)dx \le \int_a^\infty g(x)dx.$$

Thus $\int_a^\infty g(x)dx$ is an upper bound for $\int_a^t h(x)dx$ for $t \ge a$, so by the first paragraph, $\int_a^\infty h(x)dx$ is convergent. Now

$$\lim_{t\to\infty} \int_a^t f(x)dx = \lim_{t\to\infty} \int_a^t g(x)dx - \lim_{t\to\infty} \int_a^t h(x)dx,$$

and the last two limits exist because both $\int_a^\infty g(x)dx$ and $\int_a^\infty h(x)dx$ are convergent. □

The utility of this result is illustrated in the convergence of the improper integral

$$\int_1^\infty (1+x^3)^{-1}dx \quad \text{since} \quad (1+x^3)^{-1} \le x^{-2} \quad \text{holds for} \quad x \ge 1.$$

Regarding the integrals of unbounded functions, we have the following definition.

Definition 2.33.

(i) Let $f \in R[c,d]$ for every $[c,d] \subset [a,b)$. Then the improper integral of f on $[a,b]$ is defined by

$$\int_a^{b^-} f(x)dx = \lim_{t\to b^-} \int_a^t f(x)dx.$$

If the limit exists; that is, for any $\epsilon > 0$ there is a $\delta > 0$ such that

$$0 < b - t < \delta \Rightarrow \Big| \int_a^{b^-} f(x)dx - \int_a^t f(x)dx \Big| < \epsilon,$$

then the improper integral is said to be convergent; otherwise, the improper integral is divergent.

(ii) Similarly, we define the analogous improper integral:

$$\int_{a^+}^b f(x)dx = \lim_{t \to a^+} \int_t^b f(x)dx.$$

(iii) If f is unbounded at a and b, then for any $c \in (a, b)$, the improper integral $\int_{a^+}^{b^-} f(x)dx$ is defined by $\lim_{t \to a^+} \int_t^c f(x)dx + \lim_{t \to b^-} \int_c^t f(x)dx$. It is convergent if both $\int_{a^+}^c f(x)dx$ and $\int_c^{b^-} f(x)dx$ are convergent, and in that case

$$\int_{a^+}^{b^-} f(x)dx = \int_{a^+}^c f(x)dx + \int_c^{b^-} f(x)dx.$$

Example 2.34.

(i)

$$\int_0^1 (x^2 - 1)^{-1} dx, \quad \int_{-1}^0 (x^2 - 1)^{-1} dx, \text{ and } \int_{-1}^1 (x^2 - 1)^{-1} dx$$

are improper integrals satisfying the foregoing definition.

(ii) Plainly, the preceding types of improper integrals can be used in combination to form the improper integral of any function with a graph that has at most a finite number of asymptotes. For instance, if $f(x) = \big((x - a)(x - b)\big)^{-1}$, where $a < b$, then we choose an arbitrary number $c \in (a, b)$ and write

$$\begin{aligned} \int_{-\infty}^{\infty} f(x)dx &= \int_{-\infty}^{a-1} f(x)dx + \int_{a-1}^{a^-} f(x)dx + \int_{a^+}^{c} f(x)dx \\ &+ \int_c^{b^-} f(x)dx + \int_{b^+}^{b+1} f(x) + \int_{b+1}^{\infty} f(x)dx. \end{aligned}$$

Though the calculation of such an integral may be cumbrous – we have just decomposed one improper integral into six limits – the major achievement here is that we do not need a separate theory for each situation. There are just two basic types of improper integrals, and finite combinations of these two types suffice for most functions.

Naturally, there is a comparison test for the improper integrals of unbounded functions. It is analogous to Theorem 2.32 and its proof can be achieved similarly.

Theorem 2.35. *Let $f_1, f_2 \in R[a, t]$ and $f_1(t) \le f_2(t)$ for every $a \le t < b$. If $\int_a^{b^-} f_2(x)dx$ is convergent, then $\int_a^{b^-} f_1(x)dx$ is convergent too.*

This theorem has an obvious dual for $\int_{a+}^{b} f(x)dx$, which we illustrate by $\int_{0+}^{1}(x(x+1))^{-1}dx$ being divergent – since $(x(x+1))^{-1} \geq (2x)^{-1}$ for $x \in (0,1]$.

As a good application of the improper integrals, we consider the Gamma function.

Example 2.36. For each $x > 0$, let

$$\Gamma(x) = \int_{0+}^{\infty} e^{-t}t^{x-1}dt$$

be the Gamma function. Then

(i) $\Gamma(x)$ is convergent;

(ii) $\Gamma(x+1) = x\Gamma(x)$ – in particular, $\Gamma(n+1) = n!$ for any $n \in \mathbf{N}$;

(iii) $\lim_{x\to 0^+} \Gamma(x) = \infty$.

For (i), we write

$$\int_{0+}^{\infty} e^{-t}t^{x-1}dt = \int_{0+}^{1} e^{-t}t^{x-1}dt + \int_{1}^{\infty} e^{-t}t^{x-1}dt.$$

The first term is finite since $e^{-t}t^{x-1} \leq t^{x-1}$ for $t \in (0,1)$ and $\int_{0+}^{1} t^{x-1}dt = x^{-1}$ for $x > 0$. The second term is finite too due to the fact that $\lim_{t\to\infty} e^{-t}t^{n} = 0$ for $n \in \mathbf{N}$, that $\int_{1}^{\infty} t^{-2}dt < \infty$, and that

$$e^{-t}t^{x-1} \leq e^{-t}t^{x+1}t^{-2} < t^{-2} \quad \text{for} \quad n \geq x+1.$$

For (ii), let $\epsilon, b > 0$. Using integration by parts, we have

$$\int_{\epsilon}^{1} e^{-t}t^{x-1}dt = -e^{-\epsilon}\epsilon^{x}x^{-1} + e^{-1}x^{-1} + x^{-1}\int_{\epsilon}^{1} e^{-t}t^{x}dt.$$

Letting $\epsilon \to 0$, we get

$$\int_{0+}^{1} e^{-t}t^{x-1}dt = e^{-1}x^{-1} + x^{-1}\int_{0+}^{1} e^{-t}t^{x}dt.$$

Similarly,

$$\int_{1}^{b} e^{-t}t^{x-1}dt = e^{-b}b^{x}x^{-1} - e^{-1}x^{-1} + x^{-1}\int_{1}^{b} e^{-t}t^{x}dt$$

and letting $b \to \infty$, we obtain

$$\int_{1}^{\infty} e^{-t}t^{x-1}dt = -e^{-1}x^{-1} + x^{-1}\int_{1}^{\infty} e^{-t}t^{x}dt,$$

reaching $\Gamma(x) = x^{-1}\Gamma(x+1)$. This and $\Gamma(1) = 0!$ deduce $\Gamma(n+1) = n!$ via induction.
For (iii), let $x > 0$. Then

$$\Gamma(x) > \int_{0+}^{1} e^{-t}t^{x-1}dt \geq e^{-1}x^{-1} \to \infty \quad \text{as} \quad x \to 0^{+}.$$

As an interesting and deep application of some of the previous results, we introduce an important "product" – the so-called convolution of two functions, and use it to prove the polynomial approximation theorem on an interval.

Definition 2.37. Let $f_1, f_2 : \mathbf{R} \to \mathbf{R}$. The convolution $f_1 * f_2$ of f_1 and f_2 is defined by

$$f_1 * f_2(x) = \int_{-\infty}^{\infty} f_1(x-y) f_2(y) dy,$$

provided the improper integral exists.

It is an easy exercise to prove that $f_1 * f_2 = f_2 * f_1$. Also, it can be shown that the convolution exists for a large class of functions; however, we shall restrict our discussion to the class of continuous functions.

Definition 2.38. A sequence $\phi_n : \mathbf{R} \to \mathbf{R}$ is a Dirac sequence or a delta sequence or an approximate identity provided:

(i) $\phi_n(t) \geq 0$ for all $t \in \mathbf{R}$;

(ii) ϕ_n is continuous and integrable over $\mathbf{R}$ with $\int_{-\infty}^{\infty} \phi_n(t) dt = 1$;

(iii) Given any $\delta > 0$, $\lim_{n\to\infty} \left(\int_{-\infty}^{-\delta} \phi_n(t) dt + \int_{\delta}^{\infty} \phi_n(t) dt \right) = 0$.

Example 2.39. $\phi_n(t) = 1/\big(\pi(nt^2 + 1/n)\big)$ is the Siméon-Denis Poisson kernel. For our purpose, let us consider the Edmund Georg Hermann Landau kernel:

$$\phi_n(t) = \begin{cases} (1-t^2)^n / c_n, & |t| < 1, \\ 0, & |t| \geq 1, \end{cases}$$

where $c_n = \int_{-1}^{1} (1-t^2)^n dt$. It is obvious that this function satisfies (i) and (ii) of Definition 2.38. For (iii), note that

$$c_n = 2 \int_0^1 (1-t^2)^n dt \geq 2 \int_0^1 (1-t)^n dt = 1/(n+1).$$

Thus, if $\delta \in (0,1)$ is fixed, then

$$\int_\delta^1 \phi_n(t) dt = \frac{1}{c_n} \int_\delta^1 (1-t^2)^n dt \leq 2^{-1}(n+1)(1-\delta^2)^n (1-\delta) \to 0 \text{ as } n \to \infty.$$

By symmetry, $\int_{-1}^{-\delta} \phi_n(t) dt = \int_\delta^1 \phi_n(t) dt$, and (iii) follows.

Theorem 2.40. *Let ϕ_n be a Dirac sequence, and $f : \mathbf{R} \to \mathbf{R}$ be bounded and continuous. Then $\lim_{n\to\infty} \sup_{x \in [a,b]} |f * \phi_n(x) - f(x)| = 0$ for any finite closed interval $[a,b]$ of $\mathbf{R}$.*

Proof. The existence of $f * \phi_n$ is established by the following estimate that for any finite interval $[a,b]$,

$$\int_a^b |f(x-t)\phi_n(t)| dt \leq \sup_{x \in \mathbf{R}} |f(x)| \int_{-\infty}^{\infty} |\phi_n(t)| dt.$$

Using the continuity of f, we have that given a finite interval $[a,b]$ and for arbitrary $\epsilon > 0$ there is a $\delta > 0$ such that $|f(x-t)-f(x)| < \epsilon/2$ for $x \in [a,b]$ and $|t| \leq \delta$. Since f is bounded, $M = \sup_{x\in\mathbf{R}} |f(x)| + 1$ is finite. Consequently, there is an $N \in \mathbf{N}$ such that

$$n \geq N \Rightarrow \int_{-\infty}^{-\delta} \phi_n(t)dt + \int_{\delta}^{\infty} \phi_n(t)dt < \frac{\epsilon}{4M}.$$

Thus, for $x \in K$ and $n \geq N$ we get

$$\begin{aligned}
|f * \phi_n(x) - f(x)| &= \Big|\int_{-\infty}^{\infty} (f(x-t) - f(x))\phi_n(t)dt\Big| \\
&\leq \Big(\int_{-\infty}^{-\delta} + \int_{-\delta}^{\delta} + \int_{\delta}^{\infty}\Big)|f(x-t) - f(x)|\phi_n(t)dt \\
&\leq 2M\int_{-\infty}^{-\delta} \phi_n(t)dt + \frac{\epsilon}{2}\int_{-\delta}^{\delta} \phi_n(t)dt + 2M\int_{\delta}^{\infty} \phi_n(t)dt \\
&\leq 2M\Big(\frac{\epsilon}{4M}\Big) + \frac{\epsilon}{2}\int_{-\infty}^{\infty} \phi_n(t)dt = \epsilon.
\end{aligned}$$

□

By choosing the Landau kernel, we obtain the classical Weierstrass approximation theorem for continuous functions on bounded and closed intervals on $\mathbf{R}$ as follows.

Theorem 2.41. *Let $f \in C[a,b]$. Then for each $\epsilon > 0$ there is a polynomial p such that $|f(x) - p(x)| < \epsilon$ for all $x \in [a,b]$.*

Proof. We first simplify the problem by making some changes of variables. Let $u = (x-a)/(b-a)$. Then $x = (b-a)u+a$ and $u \in [0,1]$. Set $g(u) = f((b-a)u+a) = f(x)$. If we can find a polynomial p such that $|p(u) - g(u)| < \epsilon$ for all $u \in [0,1]$, then

$$\Big|p\Big(\frac{x-a}{b-a}\Big) - f(x)\Big| < \epsilon$$

for all $x \in [a,b]$, and the function defined by $p\big((x-a)/(b-a)\big)$ is a polynomial. So, we may assume that $[a,b] = [0,1]$.

Next, let $h(x) = f(x) - f(0) - \big(f(1) - f(0)\big)x$. If we can approximate h uniformly by a polynomial on $[0,1]$, then f can be uniformly approximately by a polynomial on $[0,1]$. Since $h(0) = h(1) = 0$, we may assume that $f(0) = f(1) = 0$.

Assuming this, we extend f continuously to $\mathbf{R}$ by setting $f(x) = 0$ for $x \notin [0,1]$. Then the extension, which we still denote by f, is bounded and continuous on $\mathbf{R}$. Suppose ϕ_n is the Landau kernel. It is not hard to see that $\phi_n(x-t) = (1-(x-t)^2)^n/c_n$ is a polynomial in x and t; so

$$\int_{-\infty}^{\infty} \phi_n(x-t)f(t)dt = \phi_n * f(x) = f * \phi_n(x)$$

is a polynomial in x. The result now follows from Theorem 2.40. □

Problems

2.1. Verify following four results:
(i) $f \in R[0,1]$ and $\int_0^1 f(x)dx = 0$ for

$$f(x) = \begin{cases} 1\,, & x = 1/2, \\ 0\,, & x \neq 1/2; \end{cases}$$

(ii) $f \in R[0,1]$ and $\int_0^1 f(x)dx = 0$ for

$$f(x) = \begin{cases} 1\,, & x = 1, 1/2, 1/3, \dots, \\ 0\,, & \text{otherwise}; \end{cases}$$

(iii) $f \in R[0,2]$ and $\int_0^2 f(x)dx = -1$ for

$$f(x) = \begin{cases} 1\,, & x \in [0,1], \\ -2\,, & x \in (1,2]; \end{cases}$$

(iv) $f \in R[0,2]$ and $\int_0^2 f(x)dx = 3$ for

$$f(x) = \begin{cases} 2\,, & x \in [0,1), \\ 5\,, & x = 1, \\ 1\,, & x \in (1,2]. \end{cases}$$

2.2. Prove that if $f \in R[0,1]$ then

$$\lim_{n\to\infty} \frac{1}{n} \sum_{k=1}^{n} f\left(\frac{k}{n}\right) = \int_0^1 f(x)dx.$$

What about $f(x) = \sqrt{1-x^2}$?

2.3. Determine whether or not the function

$$f(x) = \begin{cases} 2\,, & x \le 0, \\ \frac{1}{x}\,, & x > 0, \end{cases}$$

is Riemann integrable on $[0,1]$, $[-1,0]$, and $[-1,1]$.

2.4. Prove that if $f \in R[a,b]$ and $m \le f(x) \le M$ for all $x \in [a,b]$, then $m(b-a) \le \int_a^b f(x)dx \le M(b-a)$.

2.5. Given $f(x) = x$ and $P_n = \{k/n\}_{k=0}^{n}$, find $L(f, P_n)$ and $U(f, P_n)$. Then, show $f \in R[0,1]$. Finally, evaluate $\int_0^1 f(x)dx$.

2.6. Prove that if $f \in R[a,b]$ then $|f| \in R[a,b]$ with $\left|\int_a^b f(x)dx\right| \le \int_a^b |f(x)|dx$, but not conversely.

2.7. Let f be bounded on $[a,b]$. Prove that $f \in R[a,b]$ if and only if $f \in R[c,d]$ for all $[c,d] \subset (a,b)$ if and only if $f \in R[a,c]$ and $f \in R[c,b]$ for some $c \in (a,b)$.

2.8. Prove $\int_0^\pi \sqrt{x\sin x}dx \le \pi$.

2.9. Let $f, g \in R[a,b]$. Prove the Minkowski inequality:

$$\left(\int_a^b (f(x)+g(x))^2 dx\right)^{1/2} \le \left(\int_a^b f^2(x)dx\right)^{1/2} + \left(\int_a^b g^2(x)dx\right)^{1/2}.$$

2.10. Show that if $f \in R[a,b]$ and there is a constant $\delta > 0$ such that $f(x) \ge \delta > 0$ for all $x \in [a,b]$, then $1/f \in R[a,b]$.

2.11. Prove that $f(x) = \sqrt{x}$ is uniformly continuous on $[0,\infty)$ by choosing $\delta = \epsilon^2/4$.

2.12. Prove that if f is uniformly continuous on (a,b) then f is bounded there.

2.13. Prove that $f(x) = \cos(1/x)$ is not uniformly continuous on $(0,1]$.

2.14. Prove that if $f(x)$ is the linear function $a_n x + b_n$ on $[n-1,n)$ for $n = 1,2,\ldots,k$ then $f \in R[0, k-1/2]$.

2.15. Let

$$f(x) = \begin{cases} \frac{\sin x}{x}, & x \ne 0, \\ 3, & x = 0. \end{cases}$$

Prove $f \in R[0,5]$.

2.16. Prove that if $f \in R[a,b]$ and $F(x) = \int_a^x f(t)dt$ then $F \in C[a,b]$.

2.17. Prove that if $f \in C[a,b]$ with $f > 0$ and $F(x) = \int_a^x f(t)dt$ then F is strictly increasing on $[a,b]$; that is, $x_1 < x_2 \Rightarrow F(x_1) < F(x_2)$.

2.18. Let

$$f(x) = \begin{cases} \sin\frac{1}{x}, & x \ne 0, \\ 0, & x = 0. \end{cases}$$

Is f continuous on $[0, 1/\pi]$? Is f in $R[0,1/\pi]$? Explain your answers.

2.19. For what values of p is $\int_1^\infty x^p dx$ or $\int_{0+}^1 x^p dx$ convergent?

2.20. In the sequel, determine whether the improper integral is convergent:

(i) $\int_1^\infty \frac{1}{x\sqrt{x+1}}dx$;

(ii) $\int_{-\infty}^\infty xe^{-x^2}dx$;

(iii) $\int_0^{\frac{\pi}{2}-} \tan x dx$;

(iv) $\int_{1+}^\infty \frac{1}{x(\ln x)^2}dx$.

2.21. Prove that $\int_{-1}^1 \frac{dx}{x}$ and $\int_{-\infty}^\infty \frac{2xdx}{x^2+1}$ are divergent, but their Cauchy principal values are finite:

$$\lim_{a\to 0^+}\left(\int_{-1}^{-a}\frac{dx}{x} + \int_a^1 \frac{dx}{x}\right) = 0 \quad \text{and} \quad \lim_{a\to\infty}\int_{-a}^a \frac{2xdx}{x^2+1} = 0.$$

2.22. For $a, b > 0$ let $f(x) = e^{-a|x|}$ and $g(x) = e^{-b|x|}$. Evaluate $f * g$.

2.23. Let $f \in C[0,1]$ and $\int_0^1 f(x)x^n dx = 0$ for $n = 0, 1, 2, \ldots$. Prove $f = 0$.

2.24. Evaluate $\int_{0+}^{1-} \left(\ln \frac{1}{u}\right)^{-1/2} du$.

2.25. Prove $\Gamma(n + 1/2) = (2n)!\sqrt{\pi}(4^n n!)^{-1}$ for any nonnegative integer n.

2.26. If the domain of f includes $[0, \infty)$, then the Pierre-Simon Laplace transform of f is defined by

$$L(f)(x) = \int_{0+}^{\infty} e^{-xt} f(t)dt.$$

Note that if $f(t)$ is bounded as $t \to 0^+$, then $L(f)(x)$ is the improper integral of $e^{-xt}f(t)$ on $[0, \infty)$, and if $f(t)$ is unbounded as $t \to 0^+$, then we write

$$L(f)(x) = \int_{0+}^{b} e^{-xt} f(t)dt + \int_{b}^{\infty} e^{-xt} f(t)dt.$$

Prove the following results for $a, b \in \mathbf{R}$:

(i) $L(e^{-x}) = (x + 1)^{-1}$ for $x > -1$ and $L(x) = x^{-2}$ for $x > 0$;

(ii) $L(af + bg) = aL(f) + bL(g)$;

(iii) If $L(f)(x)$ is defined for $x > b$, then $L\big(e^{ax}f(x)\big) = L(f)(x - a)$ for $x > a + b$;

(iv) If f has a continuous derivative on $[0, \infty)$ and if $\lim_{t\to\infty} e^{-xt}f(t) = 0$ and $L(f)(x)$ exists when $x > a$, then $L(f')(x) = xL(f)(x) - f(0)$ for $x > a$;

(v) $L(xe^{ax}) = (x - a)^{-2}$ and $L(e^{ax} + axe^{ax}) = x(x - a)^{-2}$ for $x > a$.

Chapter 3

Riemann–Stieltjes Integrals

In this chapter, we work with the so-called Riemann–Stieltjes integration. This integration is Thomas Joannes Stieltjes' generalization of the Riemann integration which is very useful in applied analysis. A particularly convenient feature of the Riemann–Stieltjes integrals is that they can be employed to represent discrete sums.

3.1 Functions of Bounded Variation

Recall that a partition P of a closed interval $[a, b]$ of $\mathbf{R}$ is such a set $\{x_k\}_{k=0}^n$ that $a = x_0 < x_1 < \cdots < x_n = b$. Let f be a function on $[a, b]$ and consider the sum

$$S(f, P) = \sum_{k=1}^{n} |f(x_k) - f(x_{k-1})|.$$

We wish to handle the set of all values of $S(f, P)$, where P ranges over all partitions of $[a, b]$. This set of values may be bounded above or unbounded above, and we write the supremum of this set of values as $\sup_P S(f, P)$.

Definition 3.1. The function f is said to have bounded variation on $[a, b]$ provided $\sup_P S(f, P)$ is finite. In this case, $V_a^b f$ is used as $\sup_P S(f, P)$, the variation of f on $[a, b]$. Moreover, the collection of all functions having bounded variation on $[a, b]$ is denoted by $BV[a, b]$.

Example 3.2. If f is a monotonic function on $[a, b]$, then $S(f, P) = |f(b) - f(a)|$ for any partition P of $[a, b]$. Moreover, if

$$f(x) = \begin{cases} 0\,, & x \leq 1, \\ 1\,, & x > 1 \end{cases}$$

and

$$g(x) = \begin{cases} 0\,, & x \neq 1, \\ 1\,, & x = 1, \end{cases}$$

then $V_0^2 f = 1$ and $V_0^2 g = 2$.

The first theorem on this topic is a simple, sufficient condition to ensure that a function has bounded variation.

Theorem 3.3. *If f has bounded derivative on $[a,b]$, then $f \in BV[a,b]$. Conversely, if $f \in BV[a,b]$, then f is bounded on $[a,b]$.*

Proof. First, let $f \in BV[a,b]$ and $P = \{x_k\}_{k=0}^n$ any partition of $[a,b]$. Then f is differentiable on the kth subinterval $[x_{k-1}, x_k]$, and hence by the mean value theorem for derivatives there exists a number $\xi_k \in [x_{k-1}, x_k]$ such that

$$f'(\xi_k) = \frac{f(x_k) - f(x_{k-1})}{\Delta x_k}.$$

Using this, we get

$$S(f,P) = \sum_{k=1}^{n} |f'(\xi_k)| \Delta x_k \le \sup_{x \in [a,b]} |f'(x)|(b-a).$$

Hence $V_a^b f \le \sup_{x \in [a,b]} |f'(x)|(b-a)$.

Conversely, suppose $f \in BV[a,b]$. If $x \in [a,b]$, let P be the simple partition $\{a, x, b\}$. Then

$$S(f,P) = |f(x) - f(a)| + |f(b) - f(x)| \le V_a^b f.$$

Therefore, $|f(x)| \le |f(a)| + V_a^b f$, i.e., f is bounded on $[a,b]$. □

Of course, the finiteness of $V_a^b f$ does not imply that f has bounded derivative. Next we see that differentiability does not imply bounded variation.

Example 3.4. Let

$$f(x) = \begin{cases} x^2 \sin \frac{\pi}{2x^2}, & x \ne 0, \\ 0, & x = 0. \end{cases}$$

Then $f \notin BV[0,1]$ although f is differentiable on $[0,1]$. To see $V_0^1 f = \infty$, we may choose a partition $P = \{x_j\}_{j=0}^n$ where $n \in \mathbf{N}$ and

$$x_0 = 0,\ x_1 = \frac{1}{\sqrt{2n-1}},\ \cdots,\ x_k = \frac{1}{\sqrt{2(n-k)+1}},\ \cdots,\ x_{n-1} = \frac{1}{\sqrt{3}},\ x_n = 1.$$

This choice gives

$$|f(x_{n-k}) - f(x_{n-k+1})| = \frac{1}{2k+1} + \frac{1}{2k-1} > \frac{2}{2k+1}.$$

Note that the series $\sum_{k=1}^{\infty} 1/(2k+1)$ is divergent. So it follows that by letting n be large enough, there will be enough terms in $S(f,P)$ so that the corresponding partial sum exceeds any given big number. To establish the differentiability of f, it suffices to consider this at $x = 0$. But

$$f'(0) = \lim_{x \to 0} x \sin \frac{\pi}{2x^2} = 0 \quad \text{since} \quad \left| x \sin \frac{\pi}{2x^2} \right| \le |x|.$$

Remark 3.5. Suppose $f \in BV[a,b]$ and $x \in [a,b]$. It is easy to show that $f \in BV[a,x]$ since any partition P of $[a,x]$ can be extended to a partition P^* of $[a,b]$ by adjoining the one additional point $x_{n+1} = b$. Then clearly $S(f,P) \le S(f,P^*) \le V_a^b f$. Thus we can define the variation function v_f by $v_f(x) = V_a^x f$ for $x \in [a,b]$.

Lemma 3.6. *Let $f \in BV[a,b]$. Then:*

(i) $V_a^y f = V_a^x f + V_x^y f$ *for any* $a \le x < y \le b$*;*

(ii) v_f *and* $v_f - f$ *are increasing on* $[a,b]$*.*

Proof. (i) Let $a \le x < y \le b$. We first show $V_a^y f \ge V_a^x f + V_x^y f$. In fact, if P_1 and P_2 are any partitions of $[a,x]$ and $[x,y]$, respectively, then $P_1 \cup P_2$ is a partition of $[a,y]$, and

$$\begin{aligned} S(f,P_1) + S(f,P_2) &= \sum_{x_k \le x} |f(x_k) - f(x_{k-1})| + \sum_{x_k > x} |f(x_k) - f(x_{k-1})| \\ &= \sum_{x_k \in P_1 \cup P_2} |f(x_k) - f(x_{k-1})| \\ &= S(f, P_1 \cup P_2) \\ &\le \sup\{S(f,P) : \text{all partitions } P \text{ of } [a,y]\}. \end{aligned}$$

Accordingly,

$$\sup_{P_1} S(f,P_1) + \sup_{P_2} S(f,P_2) \le V_a^y f;$$

that is, $V_a^x f + V_x^y f \le V_a^y f$.

Secondly, we prove the inverse inequality. To this end, let P be a partition of $[a,y]$ and P' the partition obtained by adding the point x to P. Let P_1 and P_2 be the partitions of $[a,x]$ and $[x,y]$, respectively, induced by P'. Then

$$S(f,P) \le S(f,P') = S(f,P_1) + S(f,P_2) \le V_a^x f + V_x^y f.$$

Taking the supremum over all partitions P yields $V_a^x f + V_x^y f \ge V_a^y f$. So, (i) follows.

(ii) That v_f is increasing on $[a,b]$ is clear from (i). Next, we prove that $v_f - f$ is increasing there. If $a \le x \le y \le b$, then we have by (i)

$$V_a^y f - f(y) - \big(V_a^x f - f(x)\big) = V_x^y f - \big(f(y) - f(x)\big) \ge 0.$$

The reason why the right-hand number is nonnegative is that $|f(y) - f(x)|$ is precisely $S(f,P)$ when P is the trivial partition $\{x,y\}$. So, we conclude $v_f(x) - f(x) \le v_f(y) - f(y)$, which completes the proof. □

Theorem 3.7. $f \in BV[a,b]$ *if and only if there exist increasing functions* f_1 *and* f_2 *such that* $f = f_1 - f_2$ *on* $[a,b]$*.*

Proof. Suppose $f = f_1 - f_2$ on $[a,b]$, where f_1 and f_2 are increasing. Then $f_1, f_2 \in BV[a,b]$, so $f_1 - f_2 \in BV[a,b]$.

Conversely, if $f \in BV[a,b]$, then Lemma 3.6 shows that v_f and $v_f - f$ are increasing functions on $[a,b]$, and it is obvious that $f = v_f - (v_f - f)$. □

It is also the case that if f is a continuous function of bounded variation, then f can be written as the difference of two increasing continuous functions. From the proof of Theorem 3.7, this statement would follow immediately if the variation function v_f were continuous when f is continuous. This is precisely the content of the next theorem.

Theorem 3.8. *Let $f \in BV[a,b]$. If f is continuous at $x_0 \in [a,b]$, then v_f is continuous at x_0.*

Proof. Let $\epsilon > 0$ and $x_0 < b$. There is a partition P of $[x_0, b]$ such that

$$V_{x_0}^b f < S(f,P) + \epsilon/2.$$

Since f is continuous at x_0, we may add a point x_1 to P to obtain a partition $P' = \{x_0, x_1, \ldots, x_n\}$ of $[x_0, b]$ such that $|f(x_1) - f(x_0)| < \epsilon/2$. Then

$$S(f,P') = |f(x_1) - f(x_0)| + \sum_{j=2}^{n} |f(x_j) - f(x_{j-1})| < \epsilon/2 + V_{x_1}^b f$$

implies

$$V_{x_0}^b f < S(f,P) + \epsilon/2 \leq S(f,P') + \epsilon/2 < \epsilon + V_{x_1}^b f.$$

Accordingly, $0 \leq v_f(x_1) - v_f(x_0) < \epsilon$ holds due to Lemma 3.6 (ii). Since Lemma 3.6 (ii) indicates also that v_f is increasing, the limit $\lim_{x \to x_0^+} v_f(x)$ exists and by the last inequality, must equal $v_f(x_0)$.

Similarly, if $a < x_0$, then $\lim_{x \to x_0^-} v_f(x) = v_f(x_0)$, and hence v_f is continuous at x_0. □

3.2 Definition and Basic Properties

We start by defining the Riemann–Stieltjes integral on a finite interval.

Definition 3.9. Suppose f and g are functions defined and bounded on $[a,b]$. Let $P = \{x_k\}_{k=0}^n$ be a partition of $[a,b]$ and let $\{\xi_k\}_{k=1}^n$ be such that each ξ_k is in the kth subinterval associated with P; that is, $x_{k-1} \leq \xi_k \leq x_k$. Then:

(i)

$$\sum_{k=1}^{n} f(\xi_k)\big(g(x_k) - g(x_{k-1})\big)$$

is called a Riemann–Stieltjes sum for f with respect to g;

(ii) f is called Riemann–Stieltjes integrable with respect to g on $[a,b]$ provided there is a number J such that if $\epsilon > 0$ then there is a $\delta > 0$ such that

$$\|P\| < \delta \Rightarrow \Big| J - \sum_{k=1}^{n} f(\xi_k)\big(g(x_k) - g(x_{k-1})\big)\Big| < \epsilon$$

regardless of the choice of $\xi_k \in [x_{k-1}, x_k]$. In this case, J is called the Riemann–Stieltjes integral of f with respect to g, and denoted by $\int_a^b f(x)dg(x)$. Also, f is called the integrand and g is called the integrator. The class of all functions Riemann–Stieltjes integrable on $[a,b]$ with respect to g is written as $RS_g[a,b]$.

Note that if $g(x) = x$ for $x \in [a, b]$ then the above definition goes back to the Riemann setting. However, the Riemann–Stieltjes integrals are different from the Riemann integrals.

Example 3.10. Suppose $f \in C[a, b]$ and

$$g(x) = \begin{cases} 0\,, & x \in [a, t], \\ 1\,, & x \in (t, b]. \end{cases}$$

Given $P = \{x_k\}_{k=0}^{n}$, the point of discontinuity t is in either one or two subintervals: either $x_{m-1} < t < x_m$, or else $t = x_m$, which gives $[x_{m-1}, t]$ and $[t, x_{m+1}]$ as subintervals corresponding to P. All the terms of the Riemann–Stieltjes sum that do not involve these subintervals are 0, so in the first case the sum reduces to $f(\xi_m)$ and in the second case the sum reduces to $f(\xi_m) \cdot 0 + f(\xi_{m+1}) = f(\xi_{m+1})$. As $\|P\| \to 0$, both ξ_m and ξ_{m+1} approach t; therefore the continuity of f implies that the limit of the Riemann–Stieltjes sums exists and equals $f(t)$. Hence $\int_a^b f(x)dg(x) = f(t)$.

The forthcoming theorem gives the connection between the Riemann–Stieltjes integrals and the Riemann integrals suggested by the use of the differential notation dg:

Theorem 3.11. *Let $f \in R[a, b]$ and $g' \in C[a, b]$. Then $f \in RS_g[a, b]$ and $\int_a^b f(x)dg(x) = \int_a^b f(x)g'(x)dx$.*

Proof. Given any partition $P = \{x_k\}_{k=0}^{n}$ of $[a, b]$, g is differentiable on the kth subinterval $[x_{k-1}, x_k]$, so by the mean value theorem for derivatives there exists a number $c_k \in [x_{k-1}, x_k]$ such that $g'(c_k) = \big(g(x_k) - g(x_{k-1})\big)/\Delta x_k$. Using this, we get

$$\begin{aligned} \sum_{k=1}^{n} f(\xi_k)\big(g(x_k) - g(x_{k-1})\big) &= \sum_{k=1}^{n} f(\xi_k)g'(c_k)\Delta x_k \\ &= \sum_{k=1}^{n} f(\xi_k)g'(\xi_k)\Delta x_k \\ &+ \sum_{k=1}^{n} f(\xi_k)\big(g'(c_k) - g'(\xi_k)\big)\Delta x_k. \end{aligned}$$

The third sum in the last equation is a Riemann sum for $fg' \in R[a, b]$. Then, as $\|P\| \to 0$ this sum approaches $\int_a^b f(x)g'(x)dx$. Hence we can complete our proof by showing that the second sum of the last equation approaches 0 as $\|P\| \to 0$. To achieve this goal we may assume $M = \sup_{x\in[a,b]} |f(x)| \neq 0$ and refer to the uniform continuity of g' – for $\epsilon > 0$ choose $\delta > 0$ so that

$$|\xi - c| < \delta \Rightarrow |g'(c) - g'(\xi)| < \frac{\epsilon}{(b-a)M}.$$

Now $\|P\| < \delta$ yields that $|c_k - \xi_k| < \delta$, and consequently, the second sum is less than or equal to

$$\sum_{k=1}^{n} |f(\xi_k)||\big(g'(c_k) - g'(\xi_k)\big)|\Delta x_k < \Big(\frac{\max_{1\le k\le n} |f(\xi_k)|\epsilon}{(b-a)M}\Big) \sum_{k=1}^{n} \Delta x_k \le \epsilon.$$

Thus, as $\|P\| \to 0$, the Riemann–Stieltjes sums approach $\int_a^b f(x)g'(x)dx$. □

The algebraic closure of the Riemann–Stieltjes integrals is included in the formulas (i) and (ii) below.

Theorem 3.12. *Let $f_1, f_2 \in RS_{g_1}[a,b] \cap RS_{g_2}[a,b]$ and $c_1, c_2 \in \mathbf{R}$. Then:*

(i)

$$\int_a^b \big(c_1 f_1(x) + c_2 f_2(x)\big) dg_1(x) = c_1 \int_a^b f_1(x) dg_1(x) + c_2 \int_a^b f_2 dg_1(x);$$

(ii)

$$\int_a^b f_1(x) d\big(c_1 g_1(x) + c_2 g_2(x)\big) = c_1 \int_a^b f_1(x) dg_1(x) + c_2 \int_a^b f_1(x) dg_2(x);$$

(iii) *When $f_1 \le f_2$ and g is increasing on $[a,b]$,*

$$\int_a^b f_1(x) dg(x) \le \int_a^b f_2(x) dg(x).$$

Proof. This is left as an exercise. □

The foregoing result is based on the condition: $a \le b$. In order to consider an integral such as $\int_b^a f(x)dg(x)$, where $a < b$, we adopt the familiar convention: $\int_b^a f(x)dg(x) = -\int_a^b f(x)dg(x)$.

Theorem 3.13. *Let $f \in RS_g[a,b] \cap RS_g[b,c] \cap RS_g[a,c]$. Then*

$$\int_a^c f(x)dg(x) = \int_a^b f(x)dg(x) + \int_b^c f(x)dg(x).$$

Proof. It suffices to prove that the formula holds under the assumption $a < b < c$. Given $\epsilon > 0$, choose $\delta > 0$ so that if P is a partition of $[a,b]$ or $[b,c]$ or $[a,c]$ satisfying $\|P\| < \delta$, then any choice of ξ_k's in those subintervals induced by P yields a Riemann–Stieltjes sum, written as $\sum_a^b$ or $\sum_b^c$ or $\sum_a^c$ which is within $\epsilon/3$ of the Riemann–Stieltjes integral, denoted by $\int_a^b$ or $\int_b^c$ or $\int_a^c$. So,

$$\Big|\int_a^b - \sum_a^b\Big| < \frac{\epsilon}{3}, \quad \Big|\int_b^c - \sum_b^c\Big| < \frac{\epsilon}{3}, \quad \Big|\int_a^c - \sum_a^c\Big| < \frac{\epsilon}{3}$$

whenever $\|P\| < \delta$. Since $a < b < c$, the sum $\sum_a^b + \sum_b^c$ becomes the Riemann–Stieltjes sum $\sum_a^c$ for $[a,c]$. Thus we can write

$$\begin{aligned}
\Big|\int_a^c - \Big(\int_a^b + \int_b^c\Big)\Big| &= \Big|\Big(\int_a^c - \sum_a^c\Big) - \Big(\int_a^b - \sum_a^b\Big) - \Big(\int_b^c - \sum_b^c\Big)\Big| \\
&\le \Big|\int_a^c - \sum_a^c\Big| + \Big|\int_a^b - \sum_a^b\Big| + \Big|\int_b^c - \sum_b^c\Big| \\
&< \frac{\epsilon}{3} + \frac{\epsilon}{3} + \frac{\epsilon}{3} = \epsilon.
\end{aligned}$$

Namely,

$$\Big|\int_a^c f(x)dg(x) - \Big(\int_a^b f(x)dg(x) + \int_b^c f(x)dg(x)\Big)\Big| < \epsilon.$$

Consequently, the desired formula follows. □

It is worth pointing out that in the above theorem we assume that all three integrals exist and then conclude that the formula holds. In the Riemann integral analogue, it was sufficient to assume only the existence of $\int_a^b$ and $\int_b^c$ which implies the existence of $\int_a^c$. That implication is not valid for the Riemann–Stieltjes integral, as we see in the following example:

Example 3.14. If

$$f(x) = \begin{cases} 0\,, & x \in [0,1], \\ 1\,, & x \in (1,2] \end{cases}$$

and

$$g(x) = \begin{cases} 0\,, & x \in [0,1), \\ 1\,, & x \in [1,2], \end{cases}$$

then $\int_0^1 f(x)dg(x) = 0$ and $\int_1^2 f(x)dg(x) = 0$. But $\int_0^2 f(x)dg(x)$ does not exist since f and g are discontinuous at 1; see the forthcoming Theorem 3.16.

3.3 Nonexistence and Existence for Integrals

We now proceed to establish some results on the nonexistence and existence of Riemann–Stieltjes integrals for special functions such as discontinuous functions, step functions and continuous functions.

First of all, let us have a look at the following example.

Example 3.15. If

$$f(x) = g(x) = \begin{cases} 0\,, & x \in [0,1], \\ 1\,, & x \in (1,2], \end{cases}$$

then $f \notin RS_g[0,2]$: For if P is a partition of $[0,2]$ containing 1 and having an arbitrarily small norm, then setting $x_{m-1} = 1$ yields

$$g(x_m) - g(x_{m-1}) = 1,$$

and consequently, choosing either $\xi_m = 1$ or $\xi_m > 1$ gives either

$$\sum_{k=1}^{n} f(\xi_k)\big(g(x_k) - g(x_{k-1})\big) = f(\xi_m)\big(g(x_m) - g(x_{m-1})\big) = 0,$$

or

$$\sum_{k=1}^{n} f(\xi_k)\big(g(x_k) - g(x_{k-1})\big) = 1.$$

Examples 3.14 and 3.15 illustrate a general non-existence result as follows.

Theorem 3.16. *If $f, g : [a, b] \to \mathbf{R}$ are both discontinuous at $c \in [a, b]$, then $f \notin RS_g[a, b]$.*

Proof. Two cases will be taken into account. First suppose that $\lim_{x\to c} g(x)$ does not exist. Then there is an $\epsilon_g > 0$ such that for any $\delta > 0$ we can choose $x_{m-1}, x_m \in [a, b]$ that satisfy

$$x_{m-1} < c < x_m; \quad x_m - x_{m-1} < \delta; \quad |g(x_m) - g(x_{m-1})| \geq \epsilon_g.$$

Now let P be a partition of $[a, b]$ with $\|P\| < \delta$ whose mth subinterval is $[x_{m-1}, x_m]$. The discontinuity of f at c implies the existence of an $\epsilon_f > 0$ and $\xi'_m, \xi''_m \in [x_{m-1}, x_m]$ such that

$$|f(\xi'_m) - f(\xi''_m)| \geq \epsilon_f.$$

If we choose $\xi'_k = \xi''_k$ for $k \neq m$, then the corresponding Riemann–Stieltjes sums differ by at least $\epsilon_f \epsilon_g$. Since $\|P\|$ is arbitrarily small, this shows that the Riemann–Stieltjes sums cannot approach a limit as $\|P\| \to 0$.

Next, we consider the case in which $\lim_{x\to c} g(x)$ exists but does not equal $g(c)$, say,

$$|g(c) - \lim_{x\to c} g(x)| = \epsilon_g > 0.$$

For a given $\delta > 0$, choose a partition P of $[a, b]$ such that $\|P\| < \delta$, $x_m = c$, and either

$$|g(c) - g(x_{m+1})| \geq \epsilon_g/2 \quad \text{or} \quad |g(c) - g(x_{m-1})| \geq \epsilon_g/2.$$

The discontinuity of f at c implies the existence of an $\epsilon_f > 0$ such that either $[x_{m-1}, x_m]$ or $[x_m, x_{m+1}]$ contains points ξ'_m and ξ''_m such that

$$|f(\xi'_m) - f(\xi''_m)| \geq \epsilon_f.$$

As above, this produces two Riemann–Stieltjes sums for P that differ by at least $\epsilon_f \epsilon_g/2$, so the sums do not approach a limit as $\|P\| \to 0$. □

Motivated by Examples 3.14 and 3.15, we consider integrators as step functions. These are functions which are constant throughout an interval except for a finite number of jump discontinuities.

Definition 3.17. Let g be defined on $[a, b]$ in such a way that g is discontinuous at a finite number of points $\{c_k\}_{k=1}^p$, where $p \in \mathbf{N}$ and $a \leq c_1 < c_2 < \cdots < c_p \leq b$. If g is a constant λ_k on each subinterval I_k with endpoints c_{k-1} and c_k, then g is called a step function and the number $g(c_k^+) - g(c_k^-)$ is called the jump of g at c_k, and hence $g = \sum_{k=1}^p \lambda_k 1_{I_k}$ where

$$1_{I_k}(x) = \begin{cases} 1, & x \in I_k, \\ 0, & x \notin I_k. \end{cases}$$

If $c_1 = a$ and $c_n = b$, then the jumps of g at c_1 and c_n are $g(c_1^+) - g(c_1)$ and $g(c_n) - g(c_n^-)$ respectively. Here for each $k = 1, 2, \ldots, n$,

$$g(c_k^+) = \lim_{0<x-c_k\to 0} g(x) \quad \text{and} \quad g(c_k^-) = \lim_{0>x-c_k\to 0} g(x).$$

Step functions not only have bounded variation, but also they can be used to represent Riemann–Stieltjes integrals as finite sums.

Theorem 3.18. *Let g be a step function on $[a,b]$ with jumps d_k at c_k where $p \in \mathbf{N}$ and $a \le c_1 < c_2 < \cdots < c_p \le b$. If f is defined on $[a,b]$ and continuous at each c_k. Then $f \in RS_g[a,b]$ and*

$$\int_a^b f(x)dg(x) = \sum_{k=1}^{p} f(c_k)d_k.$$

Proof. Let $\delta = \min_{1\le k\le p}(c_k - c_{k-1})$. It is clear that for any partition $P = \{x_k\}_{k=0}^n$ satisfying $\|P\| < \delta$, each interval $I_k = [x_{k-1}, x_k]$ can contain at most one of the points $\{c_k\}_{k=1}^p$. If I_k contains no c_j then $g(x_k) - g(x_{k-1}) = 0$. If I_k contains the point c_j in its interior then $g(x_k) - g(x_{k-1}) = d_j$. Finally, if the point c_j is common to $[x_{k-1}, x_k]$ and $[x_k, x_{k+1}]$; that is, if $c_j = x_k$, then

$$g(x_k) - g(x_{k-1}) + g(x_{k+1}) - g(x_k) = d_j.$$

Let $I_{k_1}, I_{k_2}, \ldots, I_{k_l}$ $(k_1 < \cdots < k_l)$ denote those intervals which contain a c_j. Then

$$\sum_{k=1}^{n} f(\xi_k)\big(g(x_k) - g(x_{k-1})\big) = \sum_{m=1}^{l} f(\xi_{k_m})\big(g(x_{k_m}) - g(x_{k_{m-1}})\big).$$

If c_j is in the interior of I_{k_m}, then the continuity of f at c_j implies that

$$f(\xi_{k_m})\big(g(x_{k_m}) - g(x_{k_{m-1}})\big) \to f(c_j)d_j \quad \text{as} \quad \|P\| \to 0.$$

If c_j is common to I_{k_m} and $I_{k_{m+1}}$, then the continuity of f at c_j implies that

$$f(\xi_{k_m})\big(g(x_{k_m}) - g(x_{k_{m-1}})\big) + f(\xi_{k_{m+1}})\big(g(x_{k_{m+1}}) - g(x_{k_m})\big) \to f(c_j)d_j$$

as $\|P\| \to 0$. Hence

$$\begin{aligned}\lim_{\|P\|\to 0} \sum_{k=1}^{n} f(\xi_k)\big(g(x_k) - g(x_{k-1})\big) &= \lim_{\|P\|\to 0} \sum_{m=1}^{l} f(\xi_{k_m})\big(g(x_{k_m}) - g(x_{k_{m-1}})\big) \\ &= \sum_{k=1}^{p} f(c_k)d_k,\end{aligned}$$

establishing the desired formula. □

Remark 3.19. If in Theorem 3.18 one has $[a,b] = [1,n]$ for any $n-1 \in \mathbf{N}$ and $g(x) = [x]$ – the greatest integer which is less than or equal to x, then for any real numbers $a_1, a_2, \ldots, a_n$ one can choose a function $f \in C[1,n]$ such that $f(k) = a_k$ for each k and hence by Theorem 3.18,

$$\sum_{k=1}^{n} a_k = \sum_{k=1}^{n} f(k) = \int_0^n f(x)d[x].$$

Namely, a finite sum is written as a Riemann–Stieltjes integral.

Generally, we have the following existence theorem for Riemann–Stieltjes integrals regarding continuous functions.

Theorem 3.20. *Let $f \in C[a,b]$ and $g \in BV[a,b]$. Then $f \in RS_g[a,b]$.*

Proof. By Theorem 3.7, we know that $g = g_1 - g_2$, where g_1, g_2 are increasing. If we prove that $\int_a^b f(x)dg_1(x)$ exists for any increasing g_1, then $\int_a^b f(x)dg_2(x)$ exists also. This implies the existence of

$$\int_a^b f(x)d\big(g_1(x) - g_2(x)\big),$$

which is $\int_a^b f(x)dg(x)$. For the sake of simplifying notation, we write g in place of g_1.

For any partition $P = \{x_k\}_{k=0}^n$, let $I_k = [x_{k-1}, x_k]$ and again

$$m_k = \inf\{f(x) : x \in I_k\}, \quad M_k = \sup\{f(x) : x \in I_k\}.$$

We also define the upper and lower sums of f with respect to g by

$$U(f,P;g) = \sum_{k=1}^n M_k\big(g(x_k) - g(x_{k-1})\big)$$

and

$$L(f,P;g) = \sum_{k=1}^n m_k\big(g(x_k) - g(x_{k-1})\big).$$

If $\xi_k \in I_k$, then $m_k \le f(\xi_k) \le M_k$, and hence

$$L(f,P;g) \le \sum_{k=1}^n f(\xi_k)\big(g(x_k) - g(x_{k-1})\big) \le U(f,P;g).$$

If P and P^* are two partitions of $[a,b]$, then $P \cup P^*$ is a refinement of both. It is easy to verify that refining a partition increases its lower sums and decreases its upper sums, so it follows that

$$L(f,P;g) \le L(f,P\cup P^*;g) \le U(f,P\cup P^*;g) \le U(f,P^*;g);$$

therefore any lower sum is less than or equal to any upper sum. It follows that the least upper bound of the set of all lower sums cannot exceed the greatest lower bound of the set of all upper sums:

$$L(f;g) = \sup_P L(f,P;g) \le \inf_P U(f,P;g) = U(f;g).$$

We can prove that $\int_a^b f(x)dg(x)$ exists if and only if for any $\epsilon > 0$ there is a $\delta > 0$ such that $\|P\| < \delta$ implies $U(f,P;g) - L(f,P;g) < \epsilon$ (equivalently, for any $\epsilon > 0$ there exists a partition P of $[a,b]$ such that $U(f,P;g) - L(f,P;g) < \epsilon$). In fact, the proof is virtually identical to the proof of Theorem 2.15, but with $g(x_k) - g(x_{k-1})$ replacing $\Delta x_k = x_k - x_{k-1}$.

Because any Riemann–Stieltjes sum (using P) is between $L(f, P; g)$ and $U(f, P; g)$, and $L(f; g)$ is also between $L(f, P; g)$ and $U(f, P; g)$, it follows that any such Riemann–Stieltjes sum must also be within ϵ of $L(f; g)$. Thus we establish that the Riemann–Stieltjes sums converge to $L(f; g)$ as $\|P\| \to 0$. By the uniform continuity of f, we choose $\delta > 0$ so that for any $x, y \in [a, b]$,

$$|x - y| < \delta \Rightarrow |f(x) - f(y)| < \frac{\epsilon/2}{g(b) - g(a)}.$$

Here, we assume naturally $g(a) \neq g(b)$, for otherwise the monotonic function g would be a constant and the conclusion is trivial. If $\|P\| < \delta$, then for $k = 1, \ldots, n$,

$$M_k - m_k < \frac{\epsilon}{g(b) - g(a)}.$$

Therefore

$$\begin{aligned} U(f, P; g) - L(f, P; g) &= \sum_{k=1}^{n} (M_k - m_k)\big(g(x_k) - g(x_{k-1})\big) \\ &< \frac{\epsilon}{g(b) - g(a)} \sum_{k=1}^{n} \big(g(x_k) - g(x_{k-1})\big) < \epsilon. \end{aligned}$$

□

The foregoing theorem can be used to deal with compositions acting on Riemann-Stieltjes integrable functions.

Theorem 3.21. *Let g be increasing on $[a, b]$ and $f \in RS_g[a, b]$ with the range of f contained in the closed interval $[c, d]$. If $\psi \in C[c, d]$ then $\psi \circ f \in RS_g[a, b]$.*

Proof. Since $\psi \in C[c, d]$, $M = 1 + \sup_{x \in [c,d]} |\psi(x)| < \infty$ and ϕ is uniformly continuous on $[c, d]$, and consequently, for any $\epsilon > 0$ there is a $\delta \in \big(0, \frac{\epsilon}{g(b) - g(a) + 2M}\big)$ such that

$$y_1, y_2 \in [c, d] \text{ and } |y_1 - y_2| < \delta \Rightarrow |\psi(y_1) - \psi(y_2)| < \frac{\epsilon}{g(b) - g(a) + 2M}.$$

Because of $f \in RS_g[a, b]$ we can use the argument in Theorem 3.20 to obtain a partition $P = \{x_k\}_{k=0}^{n}$ of $[a, b]$ such that

$$U(f, P; g) - L(f, P; g) = \sum_{k=1}^{n} (M_k - m_k)\big(g(x_k) - g(x_{k-1})\big) \leq \delta^2.$$

If

$$M_k^* = \sup_{x \in [x_{k-1}, x_k]} \psi \circ f(x) \quad \text{and} \quad m_k^* = \inf_{x \in [x_{k-1}, x_k]} \psi \circ f(x),$$

then

$$\sum_{k=1}^{n} (M_k^* - m_k^*)\big(g(x_k) - g(x_{k-1})\big)$$

$$= \Big(\sum_{M_k - m_k < \delta} + \sum_{M_k - m_k \ge \delta} \Big)(\cdots)$$

$$\le \frac{\epsilon}{g(b) - g(a) + 2M} \sum_{k=1}^{n} \big(g(x_k) - g(x_{k-1})\big)$$

$$+2M \sum_{M_k - m_k \ge \delta} \big(g(x_k) - g(x_{k-1})\big)$$

$$\le \frac{\epsilon\big(g(b) - g(a)\big)}{g(b) - g(a) + 2M} + \frac{2M}{\delta} \sum_{M_k - m_k \ge \delta} \delta\big(g(x_k) - g(x_{k-1})\big)$$

$$\le \frac{\epsilon\big(g(b) - g(a)\big)}{g(b) - g(a) + 2M} + \frac{2M}{\delta} \sum_{k=1}^{n} (M_k - m_k)\big(g(x_k) - g(x_{k-1})\big)$$

$$\le \frac{\epsilon\big(g(b) - g(a)\big)}{g(b) - g(a) + 2M} + 2M\delta < \epsilon,$$

and hence $\psi \circ f \in RS_g[a, b]$. □

Corollary 3.22. *Let g be increasing on $[a, b]$. If $f_1, f_2 \in RS_g[a, b]$ then $f_1 f_2, |f_1|, |f_2|, \max\{f_1, f_2\}, \min\{f_1, f_2\} \in RS_g[a, b]$.*

Proof. Letting $\psi(y) = y^2$ and $\phi(y) = |y|$, as well as noticing three identities:

$$f_1 f_2 = \frac{(f_1 + f_2)^2 - (f_1 - f_2)^2}{4};$$

$$\max\{f_1, f_2\} = \frac{f_1 + f_2 + |f_1 - f_2|}{2}; \quad \min\{f_1, f_2\} = \frac{f_1 + f_2 - |f_1 - f_2|}{2},$$

we obtain the desired result. □

In what follows, we will see that in many cases the continuity is essential for the existence of a Riemann–Stieltjes integral.

Definition 3.23. Let $g : \mathbf{R} \to \mathbf{R}$ be increasing. A subset E of $\mathbf{R}$ is called a g-null set if, for any $\epsilon > 0$ there exists a sequence $\big((a_j, b_j)\big)_{j=1}^{\infty}$ of open intervals such that

$$E \subseteq \cup_{j=1}^{\infty} (a_j, b_j) \quad \text{and} \quad \sum_{j=1}^{\infty} \big(g(b_j^-) - g(a_j^+)\big) < \epsilon.$$

Remark 3.24. Needless to say, if $g : \mathbf{R} \to \mathbf{R}$ is increasing, then the empty set is g-null; a subset of a g-null set is itself a g-null set; and the singleton $\{x\} \subseteq \mathbf{R}$ is a g-null set when and only when g is continuous at x.

Theorem 3.25. *Let $g : \mathbf{R} \to \mathbf{R}$ be increasing continuous and $f : [a, b] \to \mathbf{R}$ bounded function. Then $f \in RS_g[a, b]$ when and only when the set of discontinuous points of f is a g-null set.*

Proof. Since f is bounded on $[a,b]$, we may always assume that $M = 1 + \sup_{x\in[a,b]}|f(x)| < \infty$ but also that $\mathcal{D}(f)$ is the set of discontinuity points of f in $[a,b]$. For any interval $J \subseteq \mathbf{R}$ let

$$\omega_f(J) = \sup\{f(x) : x \in J \cap [a,b]\} - \inf\{f(x) : x \in J \cap [a,b]\},$$

and for $x \in [a,b]$ set

$$\omega_f(x) = \inf\{\omega_f(J) : \text{ any open interval } J \text{ containing } x\}.$$

It is clear that f is continuous at x if and only if $\omega_f(x) = 0$. This result indicates

$$\mathcal{D}(f) = \cup_{k=1}^{\infty}\mathcal{D}_k(f) \quad \text{where} \quad \mathcal{D}_k(f) = \{x \in [a,b] : \omega_f(x) \geq 1/k\}.$$

Because g is continuous on $\mathbf{R}$, one has $g(c^-) = g(c) = g(c^+)$ for $c \in \mathbf{R}$ – this fact plays an important role in the sequel.

On the one hand, suppose that f belongs to $RS_g[a,b]$. We want to prove that $\mathcal{D}(f)$ is a g-null set. Observe that if each $D_k(f)$ is a g-null set then any $\epsilon > 0$ there is a sequence of open intervals $\big((a_{k,j}, b_{k,j})\big)_{j=1}^{\infty}$ such that

$$\mathcal{D}_k(f) \subseteq \cup_{j=1}^{\infty}(a_{k,j}, b_{k,j}) \quad \text{and} \quad \sum_{j=1}^{\infty}\big(g(b_{k,j}) - g(a_{k,j})\big) < \epsilon 2^{-k};$$

but then

$$\mathcal{D}(f) \subseteq \cup_{k=1}^{\infty}\cup_{j=1}^{\infty}(a_{k,j}, b_{k,j}) \quad \text{and} \quad \sum_{k=1}^{\infty}\sum_{j=1}^{\infty}\big(g(b_{k,j}) - g(a_{k,j})\big) < \epsilon,$$

and so $\mathcal{D}(f)$ is a g-null set. Therefore, it suffices to verify that each $\mathcal{D}_k(f)$ is a g-null set. Fix now $k \in \mathbf{N}$. Because of $f \in RS_g[a,b]$, for any $\epsilon > 0$ there are a partition $P = \{x_j\}_{j=0}^{n}$ of $[a,b]$ and the lower and upper Riemann–Stieltjes sums $L(f,P;g)$ and $U(f,P;g)$ (see also the argument for Theorem 3.20) such that $U(f,P;g) - L(f,P;g) < \frac{\epsilon}{k}$. Consequently,

$$\begin{aligned}\frac{\epsilon}{2k} &> \sum_{(x_{j-1},x_j)\cap\mathcal{D}_k(f)\neq\emptyset}(M_j - m_j)\big(g(x_j) - g(x_{j-1})\big)\\ &+ \sum_{(x_{j-1},x_j)\cap\mathcal{D}_k(f)=\emptyset}(M_j - m_j)\big(g(x_j) - g(x_{j-1})\big).\end{aligned}$$

Note that every point of $\mathcal{D}_k(f)$ belongs to P or satisfies $(x_{j-1}, x_j) \cap \mathcal{D}_k(f) \neq \emptyset$ for some $j \in \{1,\ldots,n\}$. Accordingly,

$$\begin{aligned}\frac{\epsilon}{2k} &> \sum_{(x_{j-1},x_j)\cap\mathcal{D}_k(f)\neq\emptyset}(M_j - m_j)\big(g(x_j) - g(x_{j-1})\big)\\ &\geq \frac{1}{k}\sum_{(x_{j-1},x_j)\cap\mathcal{D}_k(f)\neq\emptyset}\big(g(x_j) - g(x_{j-1})\big),\end{aligned}$$

which means

$$\sum_{(x_{j-1},x_j)\cap\mathcal{D}_k(f)\neq\emptyset}\big(g(x_j)-g(x_{j-1})\big)<\frac{\epsilon}{2}.$$

Since g is uniformly continuous on $[a-1,b+1]$, there exists a $\delta>0$ such that

$$\sup_{0\le j\le n}\big(g(x_j+\delta)-g(x_j-\delta)\big)<\frac{\epsilon}{2(1+n)}.$$

But then

$$\mathcal{D}_k(f)\subseteq\Big(\bigcup_{(x_{j-1},x_j)\cap\mathcal{D}_k(f)\neq\emptyset}(x_{j-1},x_j)\Big)\Big(\bigcup_{j=0}^{n}(x_j-\delta,x_j+\delta)\Big)$$

and

$$\sum_{(x_{j-1},x_j)\cap\mathcal{D}_k(f)\neq\emptyset}\big(g(x_j)-g(x_{j-1})\big)+\sum_{j=0}^{n}\big(g(x_j+\delta)-g(x_j-\delta)\big)<\epsilon.$$

In other words, $\mathcal{D}_k(f)$ is a g-null set.

On the other hand, suppose that $\mathcal{D}(f)$ is a g-null set. We are about to prove $f\in RS_g[a,b]$. Thanks to $\mathcal{D}_k(f)\subseteq\mathcal{D}(f)$ for each $k\in\mathbf{N}$, we can readily derive that each $\mathcal{D}_k(f)$ is a g-null set too. Consequently, we can find open intervals $\{(a_{k,j},b_{k,j})\}_{j=1}^{\infty}$ such that

$$\mathcal{D}_k(f)\subseteq\cup_{j=1}^{\infty}(a_{k,j},b_{k,j})\quad\text{and}\quad\sum_{j=1}^{\infty}\big(g(b_{k,j})-g(a_{k,j})\big)<\frac{\epsilon}{4M}.$$

Note that each $\mathcal{D}_k(f)$ is closed and bounded. So by the Heine-Borel property – see also Theorem 5.28 (ii), we get a finite subset $\{(a_{k,j_l},b_{k,j_l})\}_{l=1}^{N}$ of $\{(a_{k,j},b_{k,j})\}_{j=1}^{\infty}$ such that $\mathcal{D}_k(f)\subseteq\cup_{l=1}^{N}(a_{k,j_l},b_{k,j_l})$. Therefore $[a,b]\setminus\cup_{l=1}^{N}(a_{k,j_l},b_{k,j_l})$ is a disjoint union of finitely many intervals $\{[c_{k,l},d_{k,l}]\}_{l=1}^{L}$. Hence

$$[a,b]=\big(\cup_{l=1}^{L}[c_{k,l},d_{k,l}]\big)\cup\big(\cup_{l=1}^{N}(a_{k,j_l},b_{k,j_l})\big).$$

Since $\omega_f(x)\ge 1/k$ whenever $x\in\mathcal{D}_k(f)$, we find that $\omega_f(x)<1/k$ whenever $x\in\cup_{l=1}^{L}[c_{k,l},d_{k,l}]$.

Now the step functions G and H are defined by

$$G(x)=\begin{cases}\inf_{t\in[c_{k,l},d_{k,l}]}f(t)\,, & x\in[c_{k,l},d_{k,l}],\ l=1,\dots,L,\\ \inf_{t\in(a_{k,j_l},b_{k,j_l})}f(t)\,, & x\in(a_{k,j_l},b_{k,j_l}),\ l=1,\dots,N,\end{cases}$$

and

$$H(x)=\begin{cases}\sup_{t\in[c_{k,l},d_{k,l}]}f(t)\,, & x\in[c_{k,l},d_{k,l}],\ l=1,\dots,L,\\ \sup_{t\in(a_{k,j_l},b_{k,j_l})}f(t)\,, & x\in(a_{k,j_l},b_{k,j_l}),\ l=1,\dots,N.\end{cases}$$

Then, for any $\epsilon>0$ there is an $n_0\in\mathbf{N}$ such that $n>n_0$ implies

$$\int_a^b(H(x)-G(x))dg(x)$$

$$\leq \frac{1}{n}\sum_{l=1}^{L}\big(g(d_{k,l}) - g(c_{k,l})\big) + 2M\sum_{l=1}^{N}\big(g(b_{k,j_l}) - g(a_{k,j_l})\big)$$
$$\leq \frac{g(b) - g(a)}{n} + \frac{\epsilon}{2} < \epsilon.$$

Hence $f \in RS_g[a, b]$, due to the argument for Theorem 3.20. □

3.4 Evaluation of Integrals

With the help of the previous discussion on the nonexistence and existence of Riemann–Stieltjes integrals, we can introduce some methods and techniques to evaluate Riemann–Stieltjes integrals.

Firstly, we compute each Riemann–Stieltjes integral by parts.

Theorem 3.26. *If $f \in RS_g[a, b]$, then $g \in RS_f[a, b]$ and*

$$\int_a^b f(x)dg(x) + \int_a^b g(x)df(x) = f(b)g(b) - f(a)g(a).$$

Proof. Any Riemann–Stieltjes sum for g with respect to f can be expanded and rewritten in the following way:

$$\sum_{k=1}^{n} g(\xi_k)\big(f(x_k) - f(x_{k-1})\big)$$
$$= g(\xi_1)\big(f(x_1) - f(a)\big) + \cdots + g(\xi_n)\big(f(b) - f(x_{n-1})\big)$$
$$= -f(a)g(a) - \sum_{k=1}^{n-1} f(x_k)\big(g(\xi_{k+1}) - g(\xi_k)\big) + f(b)g(b),$$

where we have introduced $\xi_0 = a$ and $\xi_n = b$. Note that the last sum is a Riemann–Stieltjes sum for f with respect to g on the partition $\{\xi_k\}_{k=0}^{n}$ with x_k belonging to $[\xi_k, \xi_{k+1}]$. So this summation identity ensures that if the Riemann–Stieltjes sums for $\int_a^b f(x)dg(x)$ converge as $\|P\| \to 0$, then the Riemann–Stieltjes sums for $\int_a^b g(x)df(x)$ also converge, and their limit values are related by the desired equation. □

Example 3.27. Integrating by parts, we get

$$\int_{-1}^{2} x d|x| = x|x|\Big|_{-1}^{2} - \int_{-1}^{2} |x| dx = \frac{5}{2}.$$

Closely related to the integration by parts formula is the following assertion in which (i)/(ii) is called the first/second mean value theorem for Riemann–Stieltjes integrals.

Theorem 3.28.

(i) *If $f \in C[a,b]$ and g is increasing on $[a,b]$, then there exists a point $\xi \in [a,b]$ such that*

$$\int_a^b f(x)dg(x) = f(\xi)\big(g(b) - g(a)\big).$$

(ii) *If f is monotonic on $[a,b]$ and $g \in C[a,b]$, then there is a point $\xi \in [a,b]$ such that*

$$\int_a^b f(x)dg(x) = f(a)\int_a^\xi dg(x) + f(b)\int_\xi^b dg(x).$$

Proof. (i) Assuming

$$m_f = \min_{x\in[a,b]} f(x) \quad \text{and} \quad M_f = \max_{x\in[a,b]} f(x),$$

we get by Theorems 3.12 (iii) and 3.20

$$m_f \int_a^b dg(x) \le \int_a^b f(x)dg(x) \le M_f \int_a^b dg(x).$$

If

$$g(b) - g(a) = \int_a^b dg(x) = 0$$

then g must be constant on $[a,b]$, and hence

$$\int_a^b f(x)dg(x) = 0.$$

In this case, ξ may be chosen to be any number in $[a,b]$. On the other hand, if $g(b) - g(a) > 0$ then by the condition $f \in C[a,b]$ we can find a point $\xi \in [a,b]$ such that

$$f(\xi) = \frac{\int_a^b f(x)dg(x)}{g(b) - g(a)},$$

thanks to the intermediate value theorem. Thus, the desired result follows.

(ii) Without loss of generality, we may assume that f is increasing. By Theorem 3.26, we have

$$\int_a^b f(x)dg(x) = f(b)g(b) - f(a)g(a) - \int_a^b g(x)df(x).$$

An application of (i) to $\int_a^b g(x)df(x)$ produces a point $\xi \in [a,b]$ such that

$$\int_a^b g(x)df(x) = g(\xi)\big(f(b) - f(a)\big).$$

Consequently,

$$\begin{aligned} \int_a^b f(x)dg(x) &= f(a)\big(g(\xi) - g(a)\big) + f(b)\big(g(b) - g(\xi)\big) \\ &= f(a)\int_a^\xi dg(x) + f(b)\int_\xi^b dg(x), \end{aligned}$$

as desired. □

Corollary 3.29.

(i) *If f is monotonic on $[a,b]$ and $h \in C[a,b]$, then there exists a point $\xi \in [a,b]$ such that*

$$\int_a^b f(x)h(x)dx = f(a)\int_a^\xi h(x)dx + f(b)\int_\xi^b h(x)dx.$$

(ii) *If f is nonnegative and increasing on $[a,b]$ and $h \in C[a,b]$, then there exists a point $\xi \in [a,b]$ such that*

$$\int_a^b f(x)h(x)dx = f(b)\int_\xi^b h(x)dx.$$

(iii) *If f is nonnegative and decreasing on $[a,b]$ and $h \in C[a,b]$, then there exists a point $\xi \in [a,b]$ such that*

$$\int_a^b f(x)h(x)dx = f(a)\int_a^\xi h(x)dx.$$

Proof. (i) Applying Theorems 3.28 (ii) and 3.11 to $g(x) = \int_a^x h(t)dt$, we reach the desired assertion.

(ii) and (iii) These can be verified straightforwardly by changing $f(a)$ and $f(b)$ of (i) into 0 respectively. Of course, we have used the fact that this change does not affect the Riemann integral $\int_a^b f(x)h(x)dx$; see also Theorem 2.10. □

As well-known, Corollary 3.29 (ii) is Pierre Ossian Bonnet's form of the second mean value theorem for Riemann–Stieltjes integrals.

We conclude this section with a useful result on the evaluation of Riemann–Stieltjes integrals – the change of variable formula.

Theorem 3.30. *Let $\phi \in C[a,b]$ be monotonic. If $f \in RS_g[\phi(a),\phi(b)]$, then $f\circ\phi \in RS_{g\circ\phi}[a,b]$ and*

$$\int_a^b f\circ\phi(x)dg\circ\phi(x) = \int_{\phi(a)}^{\phi(b)} f(t)dg(t).$$

Proof. It is enough to handle the case that ϕ is increasing. Since $\phi \in C[a,b]$, ϕ maps $[a,b]$ onto $[\phi(a),\phi(b)]$. Let $P = \{x_k\}_{k=0}^n$ be an arbitrary partition of $[a,b]$ and choose $\tau_k \in [x_{k-1},x_k]$ for $1 \le k \le n$. Suppose $\phi(P) = \{\phi(x_k)\}_{k=0}^n$. Then $\phi(P)$ is a partition of $[\phi(a),\phi(b)]$ and

$$\phi(x_{k-1}) \le \phi(\tau_k) \le \phi(x_k), \quad 1 \le k \le n.$$

We have

$$\sum_{k=1}^n f\circ\phi(\tau_k)\big(g\circ\phi(x_k) - g\circ\phi(x_{k-1})\big) = \sum_{k=1}^n f\big(\phi(\tau_k)\big)\Big(g\big(\phi(x_k)\big) - g\big(\phi(x_{k-1})\big)\Big).$$

Note that $\phi \in C[a,b]$. So it is uniformly continuous on $[a,b]$. It follows that $\|\phi(P)\| \to 0$ as $\|P\| \to 0$. We conclude

$$\begin{aligned}\int_a^b f \circ \phi(x) dg \circ \phi(x) &= \lim_{\|P\| \to 0} \sum_{k=1}^{n} f \circ \phi(\tau_k)\big(g \circ \phi(x_k) - g \circ \phi(x_{k-1})\big) \\ &= \lim_{\|P\| \to 0} \sum_{k=1}^{n} f(\phi(\tau_k))\Big(g\big(\phi(x_k)\big) - g\big(\phi(x_{k-1})\big)\Big) \\ &= \int_{\phi(a)}^{\phi(b)} f(t) dg(t). \qquad \square\end{aligned}$$

3.5 Improper Cases

The previously-discussed Riemann–Stieltjes integration relies upon the restrictions that f and g are not only defined but also bounded on a finite interval $[a,b]$. In this section, we will briefly extend the scope of integration by relaxing these restrictions, as we did for the improper Riemann integration.

Definition 3.31.

(i) Let $f \in RS_g[a,b]$ for every $b \ge a$. Then $\int_a^\infty f(x)dg(x)$ is said to be convergent and equal to A provided $A = \lim_{b\to\infty} \int_a^b f(x)dg(x)$ is finite; otherwise, $\int_a^\infty f(x)dg(x)$ is said to diverge.

(ii) Let f be defined on $(a,b]$ and $f \in RS_g[c,b]$ for any $c \in (a,b]$. Then $\int_{a+}^b f(x)dg(x)$ is said to be convergent and equal to A provided that $A = \lim_{c\to a^+} \int_c^b f(x)dg(x)$ is finite; otherwise, $\int_{a+}^b f(x)dg(x)$ is said to diverge.

The improper Riemann–Stieltjes integrals share almost all the properties of the improper Riemann integrals; indeed, the proofs of most results concerning the former are basically identical to the proofs of the corresponding results about the latter, yet with $dg(x)$ replacing dx. Below are some instances.

Theorem 3.32.

(i) *Let g be increasing on $[a,\infty)$ and $f \in RS_g[a,b]$ for any $b \ge a$. If $f \ge 0$ on $[a,\infty)$, then $\int_a^\infty f(x)dg(x)$ converges if and only if there exists a constant $M > 0$ such that $\int_a^b f(x)dg(x) \le M$ for all $b \ge a$.*

(ii) *Let g be increasing on $(a,b]$ and $f \in RS_g[c,b]$ for any $c \in (a,b]$. If $f \ge 0$ on $(a,b]$, then $\int_{a+}^b f(x)dg(x)$ converges if and only if there exists a constant $M > 0$ such that $\int_c^b f(x)dg(x) \le M$ for all $c \ge a$.*

Proof. Suffice it to prove (i). Clearly $\int_a^b f(x)dg(x)$ is increasing with b and so

$$\lim_{b\to\infty} \int_a^b f(x)dg(x) = \sup_{b\in[a,\infty)} \int_a^b f(x)dg(x).$$

The assertion follows from the above limit formula and the following observation that $\int_a^\infty f(x)dg(x) \le M$ whenever the integral converges. $\square$

Theorem 3.33.

(i) *Let g be increasing on $[a,\infty)$ and $f \in RS_g[a,b]$ for any $b \geq a$. If $f_2 \geq f_1 \geq 0$ on $[a,\infty)$, then $\int_a^\infty f_1(x)dg(x)$ converges whenever $\int_a^\infty f_2(x)dg(x)$ converges, and hence*

$$\int_a^\infty f_1(x)dg(x) \leq \int_a^\infty f_2(x)dg(x).$$

(ii) *Let g be increasing on $(a,b]$ and $f \in RS_g[c,b]$ for any $c \in (a,b]$. If $f_2 \geq f_1 \geq 0$ on $(a,b]$, then $\int_{a+}^b f_1(x)dg(x)$ converges whenever $\int_{a+}^b f_2(x)dg(x)$ converges, and hence*

$$\int_{a+}^b f_1(x)dg(x) \leq \int_{a+}^b f_2(x)dg(x).$$

Proof. (i) follows from

$$\int_a^b f_1(x)dg(x) \leq \int_a^b f_2(x)dg(x) \leq \int_a^\infty f_2(x)dg(x).$$

Similarly, we can verify (ii). □

Theorem 3.34.

(i) *Let g be increasing on $[a,\infty)$, $f_1, f_2 \in RS_g[a,b]$ for any $b \geq a$ and $f_1, f_2 \geq 0$ on $[a,\infty)$. If $\lim_{x\to\infty} f_1(x)/f_2(x) = L \in (0,\infty)$, then $\int_a^\infty f_1(x)dg(x)$ and $\int_a^\infty f_2(x)dg(x)$ both converge or both diverge.*

(ii) *Let g be increasing on $(a,b]$, $f_1, f_2 \in RS_g[c,b]$ for any $c \in (a,b]$ and $f_1, f_2 \geq 0$ on $(a,b]$. If $\lim_{x\to a^+} f_1(x)/f_2(x) = L \in (0,\infty)$, then $\int_{a+}^b f_1(x)dg(x)$ and $\int_{a+}^b f_2(x)dg(x)$ both converge or both diverge.*

Proof. To prove (i), we note that there is an $N \in \mathbf{N}$ such that

$$L/2 \leq f_1(x)/f_2(x) \leq 3L/2 \quad \text{as} \quad x \geq N.$$

The conclusion follows by applying Theorem 3.32 (i). Of course, the argument for (ii) is similar. □

Theorem 3.35.

(i) *Let g be increasing on $[a,\infty)$. If $f \in RS_g[a,b]$ for any $b \geq a$ and $\int_a^\infty |f(x)|dg(x)$ converges, then $\int_a^\infty f(x)dg(x)$ also converges.*

(ii) *Let g be increasing on $(a,b]$. If $f \in RS_g[c,b]$ for any $c \in (a,b]$ and $\int_{a+}^b |f(x)|dg(x)$ converges, then $\int_{a+}^b f(x)dg(x)$ also converges.*

Proof. This follows from the inequality $0 \leq |f(x)| - f(x) \leq 2|f(x)|$. □

As in the case of infinite series, we distinguish between absolutely and conditionally convergent integrals.

Definition 3.36. Let g be increasing on $[a,\infty)$ and $f \in RS_g[a,b]$ for every $b \geq a$. Then $\int_a^\infty f(x)dg(x)$ is said to be absolutely convergent provided $\int_a^\infty |f(x)|dg(x)$ exists. Also, $\int_a^\infty f(x)dg(x)$ is said to be conditionally convergent provided that $\int_a^\infty |f(x)|dg(x)$ does not exist, but $\int_a^\infty f(x)dg(x)$ exists.

For instance, $\int_1^\infty x^{-p}\sin x dx$ is absolutely convergent for $p \in (1,\infty)$. Of course, there are examples of conditional convergence. To see this, we need the following Johann Peter Gustav Lejeune Dirichlet test which is an analog of the Dirichlet test for infinite series.

Theorem 3.37. *Let f be a nonnegative decreasing function on $[a,\infty)$ such that $\lim_{x\to\infty} f(x) = 0$. If g is bounded on $[a,\infty)$ and $f \in RS_g[a,b]$ for every $b \geq a$, then $\int_a^\infty f(x)dg(x)$ is convergent.*

Proof. Integrating by parts, we have

$$\int_a^b f(x)dg(x) = f(b)g(b) - f(a)g(a) + \int_a^b g(x)d\big(-f(x)\big).$$

Now since g is bounded, we find $\lim_{b\to\infty} f(b)g(b) = 0$. Therefore, to complete the argument it suffices to prove that $\int_a^\infty g(x)d\big(-f(x)\big)$ is convergent. To do so, we assume $\sup_{x\in[a,\infty)}|g(x)| = M < \infty$ and get that $\int_a^\infty Md\big(-f(x)\big)$ is convergent in that $\lim_{b\to\infty}\int_a^b Md\big(-f(x)\big) = Mf(a)$. Note that $-f$ is increasing. So Theorem 3.33 (i) yields that $\int_a^\infty |g(x)|d\big(-f(x)\big)$ is convergent. We are done. □

On the other hand, the following result provides a practical way to determine whether or not an improper integral is conditionally convergent.

Theorem 3.38. *Let f be continuous and ϕ decreasing on $[a,\infty)$. If $F(t)=\int_a^t f(x)dx$ is bounded on $[a,\infty)$ and $\lim_{x\to\infty}\phi(x) = 0$. Then $\int_a^\infty f(x)\phi(x)dx$ converges.*

Proof. This result can be verified by Theorem 3.37. Nevertheless, we give a different argument as follows. By assumption, F is bounded on $[a,\infty)$, i.e., $M = \sup_{x\in[a,\infty)}|F(x)| < \infty$. Thus

$$\Big|\int_{t_1}^{t_2} f(x)dx\Big| = \big|F(t_2) - F(t_1)\big| \leq 2M, \quad a \leq t_1 < t_2 < \infty.$$

By Corollary 3.29 (ii) – Bonnet's form of the second mean value theorem, we have

$$\int_{t_1}^{t_2} f(x)\phi(x)dx = \phi(t_1)\int_{t_1}^{\zeta} f(x)dx$$

for some $\zeta \in [t_1, t_2]$. Hence

$$\Big|\int_{t_1}^{t_2} f(x)\phi(x)dx\Big| \leq 2M\phi(t_1).$$

Note that $\lim_{x\to\infty}\phi(x) = 0$ means that for any $\epsilon > 0$ there is $t_0 > 0$ such that $t_1 \geq t_0$ implies $\phi(t_1) < \epsilon$. So, it follows that for any $\epsilon > 0$ there is $t_0 > 0$ such that $t_2 > t_1 \geq t_0$ implies

$$\left|\int_{t_1}^{t_2} f(x)\phi(x)dx\right| \leq 2M\epsilon.$$

We conclude from Theorem 2.31 (iii) – Cauchy's convergence criterion that $\int_a^\infty f(x)\phi(x)dx$ is convergent. □

We can obtain many examples of conditional convergence via the following consequence of Theorem 3.38.

Corollary 3.39. *Let ϕ be a decreasing function on $[a,\infty)$ with $\lim_{x\to\infty}\phi(x) = 0$. Then $\int_a^\infty \phi(x)\sin x dx$ and $\int_a^\infty \phi(x)\cos x dx$ converge. Moreover, the convergence is absolute or conditional depending on whether $\int_a^\infty \phi(x)dx < \infty$ or $\int_a^\infty \phi(x)dx = \infty$.*

Proof. It is enough to verify the sine-case. Firstly, we have

$$\left|\int_a^t \sin x dx\right| = |\cos a - \cos t| \leq 2.$$

It follows from Theorem 3.38 that $\int_a^\infty \phi(x)\sin x dx$ is convergent.

Secondly, suppose that $\int_a^\infty \phi(x)dx$ is finite. We have $|\phi(x)\sin x| \leq \phi(x)$ for $x \in [a,\infty)$. We conclude from the comparison test that $\int_a^\infty |\phi(x)\sin x|dx$ is convergent. It remains to prove that

$$\int_a^\infty \phi(x)dx = \infty \Rightarrow \int_a^\infty |\phi(x)\sin x|dx = \infty.$$

To check this, we show

$$\lim_{n\to\infty}\int_a^{n\pi} |\phi(x)\sin x|dx = \infty.$$

Let m be a fixed integer $\geq a/\pi$. For $a/\pi \leq m < n$, we have

$$\int_a^{n\pi} |\phi(x)\sin x|dx \geq \int_{m\pi}^{n\pi} |\phi(x)\sin x|dx = \sum_{k=m+1}^{n}\int_{(k-1)\pi}^{k\pi} |\phi(x)\sin x|dx.$$

Since ϕ is decreasing, we have that if $m+1 \leq k \leq n$ then

$$\int_{(k-1)\pi}^{k\pi} |\phi(x)\sin x|dx \geq \phi(k\pi)\int_{(k-1)\pi}^{k\pi} |\sin x|dx = 2\phi(k\pi)$$

and

$$\int_{k\pi}^{(k+1)\pi} \phi(x)dx \leq \phi(k\pi)\int_{k\pi}^{(k+1)\pi} dx = \pi\phi(k\pi).$$

These two estimates give

$$\int_{(k-1)\pi}^{k\pi} |\phi(x)\sin x|dx \geq \frac{2}{\pi}\int_{k\pi}^{(k+1)\pi} \phi(x)dx.$$

Consequently,

$$\int_a^{n\pi} |\phi(x)\sin x|dx \geq \frac{2}{\pi} \sum_{k=m+1}^{n} \int_{k\pi}^{(k+1)\pi} \phi(x)dx = \frac{2}{\pi} \int_{(m+1)\pi}^{(n+1)\pi} \phi(x)dx.$$

Letting $n \to \infty$ in the last estimate, we obtain the desired result:

$$\int_a^{\infty} |\phi(x)\sin x|dx = \infty. \qquad \square$$

Example 3.40. In particular, $p \in (0, 1]$ ensures that $\int_1^\infty x^{-p} \sin x dx$ is conditionally convergent since $p \in (0, 1]$ implies $\int_1^\infty x^{-p} dx = \infty$.

Problems

3.1. Find the variations of the following functions on the indicated intervals:

(i) $f(x) = \sin x \quad \text{on} \quad [0, 3\pi]$;

(ii) $f(x) = 2x^3 - 3x^2 \quad \text{on} \quad [-1, 2]$;

(iii) $(a_k)_{k=1}^\infty$ is an infinite sequence of real numbers and

$$f(x) = \begin{cases} a_k\,, & x = \frac{1}{k+1},\ k \in \mathbf{N}, \\ 0\,, & \text{otherwise} \end{cases}$$

on $[0, 1]$.

3.2. Find $v_f(x)$ for $f(x) = \sin x$ on $[0, 2\pi]$.

3.3. Suppose that $x = x(t)$ and $y = y(t)$, $t \in [a, b]$ represents a continuous arc Γ on the plane. To each partition $P = \{t_k\}_{k=0}^n$ of $[a, b]$ there corresponds a sequence of points $\{P_k = \big(x(t_k), y(t_k)\big)\}_{k=0}^n$. Let $L(P)$ be the sum of the lengths of segments: $\overline{P_0P_1}$, $\overline{P_1P_2}$, $\cdots$ and $\overline{P_{n-1}P_n}$. Prove that $L = \sup_P L(P) < \infty$ (i.e., Γ is rectifiable) if and only if $x(t)$ and $y(t)$ have bounded variation.

3.4. A function $f : [a, b] \to \mathbf{R}$ is called absolutely continuous provided that for any $\epsilon > 0$ there is a $\delta > 0$ such that $\sum_{k=1}^n |f(b_k) - f(a_k)| < \epsilon$ for every finite colletion of disjoint open intervals $\{(a_k, b_k)\}_{k=1}^n$ in $[a, b]$ of total length $\sum_{k=1}^n (b_k - a_k) < \delta$. Prove that every absolutely continuous function is continuous and has bounded variation.

3.5. Prove that $V_a^b(f_1) < \infty$ and $V_a^b(f_2) < \infty$ imply $V_a^b(f_1 f_2) < \infty$.

3.6. Prove that the following function

$$f(x) = \begin{cases} x\cos\frac{\pi}{2x}\,, & x \neq 0, \\ 0\,, & x = 0 \end{cases}$$

has no bounded variation on $[0, 1]$.

3.7. For each $k \in \mathbf{N}$ let $f_k \in BV[a,b]$ and $\lim_{k\to\infty} f_k(x) = f(x)$ where $|f(x)| < \infty$ for each $x \in [a,b]$. Prove that if $\sup_{k\in\mathbf{N}} V_a^b(f_k) < \infty$ then $f \in BV[a,b]$.

3.8. Evaluate the following Riemann–Stieltjes integrals:

(i) $\int_0^4 x^2 d([x])$, where $[x]$ denotes the greatest integer function;

(ii) $\int_0^1 x^3 d(x^2)$;

(iii) $\int_a^c f(x)dg(x)$, where f is continuous and

$$g(x) = \begin{cases} 0\,, & a \le x \le b, \\ 1\,, & b < x \le c. \end{cases}$$

3.9. Prove Theorem 3.12.

3.10. Evaluate $\int_0^{\pi/2} x d(\sin x)$.

3.11. Suppose $\int_a^b f(x)dg(x)$ exists, $f \in C[a,b]$, and we replace g by a new integrator function h, where $h(x) = g(x)$ if $x \ne c$ for some $c \in (a,b)$. Prove $\int_a^b f(x)dh(x) = \int_a^b f(x)dg(x)$.

3.12. Compare the class of Riemann integrable functions with the class of functions having bounded variation; that is, prove or disprove each of the following statemetns:

(i) If $f \in R[a,b]$, then $f \in BV[a,b]$;

(ii) If $f \in BV[a,b]$, then $f \in R[a,b]$.

3.13. Construct two functions f and g on $[a,b]$ such that

$$g \in BV[a,b] \quad \text{and} \quad \lim_{\epsilon\to 0+} \int_{a+\epsilon}^b f(x)dg(x) \ne \int_a^b f(x)dg(x).$$

3.14. Let $g \in BV[a,b]$, $f \in RS_g[a,b]$ and $v_g(x) = V_a^x g$ for each $x \in (a,b]$, prove the following three results:

(i)

$$\left| \int_a^b f(x)dg(x) \right| \le \int_a^b |f(x)| dv_g(x) \le \sup_{x\in[a,b]} |f(x)| v_g(b);$$

(ii) If $(f_n)_{n=1}^\infty$ is a sequence in $RS_g[a,b]$, then

$$\lim_{n\to\infty} \sup_{x\in[a,b]} |f_n(x) - f(x)| = 0 \Rightarrow \lim_{n\to\infty} \int_a^b f_n(x)dg(x) = \int_a^b f(x)dg(x);$$

(iii) If $(g_n)_{n=1}^\infty$ is a sequence in $BV[a,b]$ with $\lim_{n\to\infty} V_a^b(g_n - g) = 0$ then

$$f \in C[a,b] \Rightarrow \lim_{n\to\infty} \int_a^b f(x)dg_n(x) = \int_a^b f(x)dg(x).$$

3.15. Let g be increasing on $[a,b]$ and $f\in R_g[a,b]$. Define $F(x)=\int_a^x f(t)dg(t)$ for $x\in[a,b]$. Prove the following four results:

(i) $F\in BV[a,b]$;

(ii) Every point of continuity of g is also a point of continuity of F;

(iii) If g is increasing on $[a,b]$, then $F'(x)$ exists at each point $x\in(a,b)$ where $g'(x)$ exists and where f is continuous. For such x, one has $F'(x)=f(x)g'(x)$;

(iv) If $h\in C[a,b]$ then $h\in RS_F[a,b]$ and $\int_a^b h(x)dF(x)=\int_a^b h(x)f(x)dg(x)$.

3.16. If $g\in C[0,1]$ and $\int_a^b f(x)dg(x)=0$ for all increasing functions f on $[0,1]$, prove that g must be constant on $[0,1]$.

3.17. If $s\neq 1$, use the Riemann–Stieltjes integration to derive:

(i) $\sum_{k=1}^n k^{-s}=n^{1-s}+s\int_1^n [x]x^{-(1+s)}dx$;

(ii) $\sum_{k=1}^{2n}(-1)^k k^{-s}=s\int_1^{2n}\big(2[x/2]-[x]\big)x^{-(1+s)}dx$.

3.18. Suppose $f_1,f_2\in RS_g[a,b]$ and g is increasing on $[a,b]$. Prove:

(i) The Cauchy–Schwarz inequality

$$\Big|\int_a^b f_1(x)f_2(x)dg(x)\Big|\le\Big(\int_a^b f_1^2(x)dg(x)\Big)^{\frac{1}{2}}\Big(\int_a^b f_2^2(x)dg(x)\Big)^{\frac{1}{2}};$$

(ii)

$$\begin{aligned}&\frac{1}{2}\int_a^b\Big(\int_a^b\big(f_1(y)-f_1(x)\big)\big(f_2(y)-f_2(x)\big)dg(y)\Big)dg(x)\\&=\big(g(b)-g(a)\big)\int_a^b f_1(x)f_2(x)dg(x)-\Big(\int_a^b f_1(x)dg(x)\Big)\Big(\int_a^b f_2(x)dg(x)\Big);\end{aligned}$$

(iii)

$$\Big(\int_a^b f_1(x)dg(x)\Big)\Big(\int_a^b f_2(x)dg(x)\Big)\le\big(g(b)-g(a)\big)\int_a^b f_1(x)f_2(x)dg(x)$$

holds for both f_1 and f_2 increasing (or decreasing) on $[a,b]$.

(iv) The reverse inequality in (iii) is valid when f_1 and f_2 are increasing and decreasing on $[a,b]$ respectively.

3.19. Prove the following three results:

(i) $\int_1^\infty\big(x\sqrt{x+1}\big)^{-1}dx$ converges but $\int_0^\infty\big(x\sqrt{x+1}\big)^{-1}dx$ diverges;

(ii) $\int_{0+}^\infty e^{-x}\sin x^{-1}dx$ converges absolutely;

(iii) $\int_{0+}^1 x^{-1}\cos x^{-1}dx$ converges conditionally.

Chapter 4

Lebesgue–Radon–Stieltjes Integrals

While the Riemann–Stieltjes integrals are suitable for many theoretic and applied purposes, they have some technical deficiencies. For instance, the integrals no longer commute with the uniform limits of functions. This fact can be verified by noting that if

$$f_n(x) = \begin{cases} \frac{1}{n}, & x \in [0, n], \\ 0, & x \in \mathbf{R} \setminus (n, \infty) \end{cases}$$

for each $n \in \mathbf{N}$ then f_n converges uniformly to $f = 0$ on $\mathbf{R}$ – in other words –

$$\lim_{n \to \infty} \sup_{x \in \mathbf{R}} |f_n(x) - f(x)| = 0,$$

but

$$\int_{-\infty}^{\infty} f_n(x)dx = 1 \quad \text{and} \quad \int_{-\infty}^{\infty} f(x)dx = 0,$$

and so

$$\lim_{n \to \infty} \int_{-\infty}^{\infty} f_n(x)dx \neq \int_{-\infty}^{\infty} \lim_{n \to \infty} f_n(x)dx.$$

A better route is to abandon the Riemann–Stieltjes integrals for the Lebesgue–Radon–Stieltjes integrals, named for Henri Leon Lebesgue, Johann Radon and Thomas Joannes Stieltjes, to whom much of the theory of the present topic is due. The integration of Lebesgue–Radon–Stieltjes has common applications in probability and stochastic processes, and plays an important role in real analysis and in many other mathematical fields.

In this chapter, we try to circumvent the abstract measure-theoretic approach (viewed as the most common expository method) to the Lebesgue–Radon–Stieltjes integrals. Instead, starting with the so-called g-measure of simple sets (where g is increasing on $\mathbf{R}$) , we use the limit of step functions (for which the Lebesgue–Radon–Stieltjes integral exists) to obtain the integrals for more general functions. Subsequently, we show the basic results and techniques used in Lebesgue–Radon–Stieltjes' integration theory.

4.1 Foundational Material

Again, let us consider a typical function which is not Riemann integrable.

Example 4.1. Let

$$f(x) = \begin{cases} 1\,, & x \in \mathbf{Q} \cap (0,1), \\ 0\,, & x \notin \mathbf{Q} \cap (0,1). \end{cases}$$

Then $f \notin R[0,1]$, but there exists a sequence of step functions $(f_n)_{n=1}^{\infty}$ such that $\lim_{n\to\infty} f_n(x) = f(x)$ for any $x \in [0,1]$. Thus, the pointwise limit is not closed in $R[0,1]$. Indeed, since the rational numbers in $(0,1)$ can be listed as $r_1, r_2, r_3, \ldots$, we may suppose

$$h_k(x) = \begin{cases} 1\,, & x = r_k, \\ 0\,, & x \in [0,1] \setminus \{r_k\}. \end{cases}$$

It is clear that each h_k is a step function and hence $h_k \in R[0,1]$. If $f_n = \sum_{k=1}^{n} h_k$, then it is a step function too and hence belongs to $R[0,1]$. Note that if x is irrational in $(0,1)$, 0 or 1, then $f_n(x) = 0 = f(x)$; and if $x \in (0,1)$ equals some r_N, then $f_n(r_N) = 1 = f(r_N)$ when $n \geq N$. So $f_n \to f$ pointwise on $[0,1]$ as $n \to \infty$.

Example 4.1 motivates the definition of Lebesgue–Radon–Stieltjes integration. To be more precise, firstly, we need to introduce a way to measure intervals and even simple sets. To do so, let $\mathbf{R}^e$ be the extended real number system consisting of all real numbers, $-\infty$ and $+\infty = \infty$. Sometimes, $[-\infty, \infty]$ is written in place of $\mathbf{R}^e$. Then $\mathbf{R}^e$ enjoys the following properties:

(a) $(\pm\infty) + x = x + (\pm\infty) = \pm\infty$ for any $x \in \mathbf{R}$;
(b) $(\pm\infty) + (\pm\infty) = \pm\infty$;
(c) $(\pm\infty) \cdot x = x \cdot (\pm\infty) = \pm\infty$ or $\mp\infty$ for any $x > 0$ or $x < 0$;
(d) $(\pm\infty) \cdot (\pm\infty) = \infty$, $\infty \cdot (-\infty) = (-\infty) \cdot \infty = -\infty$;
(e) $\infty + (-\infty)$, $(-\infty) + \infty$, $0 \cdot (\pm\infty)$, and $(\pm\infty) \cdot 0$ are undefined.

In addition, by an interval with endpoints $a, b \in \mathbf{R}^e$, we mean that it is one of $[a,b]$, $[a,b)$, $(a,b]$ or (a,b). Note that $[a,a) = (a,a] = (a,a) = \emptyset$ and $[a,a] = \{a\}$. When $a, b \in \mathbf{R}$, the interval is said to be bounded or finite.

Definition 4.2. Suppose $g : \mathbf{R} \to \mathbf{R}$ is an increasing function. For any $c \in \mathbf{R}$ let $g(c^+) = \lim_{0<x-c\to 0} g(x)$ and $g(c^-) = \lim_{0<c-x\to 0} g(x)$.

(i) $m_g(I)$, called the g-measure of an interval I with endpoints $a, b \in \mathbf{R}$, is defined by

$$m_g(I) = \begin{cases} 0\,, & I = (a,b),\ a = b, \\ g(b^-) - g(a^+)\,, & I = (a,b),\ a < b, \\ g(b^+) - g(a^-)\,, & I = [a,b],\ a \leq b, \\ g(b^+) - g(a^+)\,, & I = (a,b],\ a \leq b, \\ g(b^-) - g(a^-)\,, & I = [a,b),\ a \leq b. \end{cases}$$

(ii) A set $S \subseteq \mathbf{R}$ is called simple provided $S = \cup_{k=1}^{n} I_k$, the union of a finitely many disjoint finite intervals $\{I_k\}_{k=1}^{n}$ in $\mathbf{R}$. In this case, the g-measure of S is defined by $m_g(S) = \sum_{k=1}^{n} m_g(I_k)$.

Remark 4.3. $m_g(S)$ stands for the length of S whenever $g(x) = x$ and S is simple. Furthermore, m_g enjoys three basic properties below:

(a) $m_g(S) \geq 0$ for any simple set S;

(b) $m_g(S_2 \setminus S_1) = m_g(S_2) - m_g(S_1)$ when S_1 and S_2 are simple, $S_1 \subseteq S_2$;

(c) $m_g\big(\cup_{j=1}^n S_j\big) = \sum_{j=1}^n m_g(S_j)$ whenever $S_1, S_2, \ldots, S_n$ are pairwise disjoint simple sets.

The following result on the countable additivity of m_g is of fundamental importance in the Lebesgue–Radon–Stieltjes integrals on $\mathbf{R}$.

Theorem 4.4. *Let $g : \mathbf{R} \to \mathbf{R}$ be an increasing function. If $\mathcal{R}$ is the collection of the empty set and all simple sets in $\mathbf{R}$, then m_g satisfies $m_g(\emptyset) = 0$ and $m_g(\cup_{j=1}^\infty S_j) = \sum_{j=1}^\infty m_g(S_j)$ for every sequence $(S_j)_{j=1}^\infty$ of disjoint sets in $\mathcal{R}$ for which $\cup_{j=1}^\infty S_j \in \mathcal{R}$.*

Proof. It suffices to check the second property. Suppose $S = \cup_{j=1}^\infty S_j \in \mathcal{R}$. Then

$$m_g(S) = m_g(S \setminus \cup_{j=1}^n S_j) + m_g(\cup_{j=1}^n S_j) = m_g(S \setminus \cup_{j=1}^n S_j) + \sum_{j=1}^n m_g(S_j)$$

thanks to the properties (b) and (c) in Remark 4.3. Let $R_n = S \setminus \cup_{j=1}^n S_j$. Then $R_{n+1} \subseteq R_n$ for each $n \in \mathbf{N}$ and $\cap_{n=1}^\infty R_n = \emptyset$. So the argument will be finished by proving $\lim_{n\to\infty} m_g(R_n) = 0$. To this end, assume on the contrary that the last limit result is not valid. Then there is a constant $\delta > 0$ such that $m_g(R_n) > \delta$ for each $n \in \mathbf{N}$. But, since g is increasing on $\mathbf{R}$, for each $n \in \mathbf{N}$ we can find a simple set I_n and a closed simple set J_n such that $I_n \subseteq J_n \subseteq R_n$ and $m_g(R_n \setminus I_n) < \frac{\delta}{2^{n+1}}$. Accordingly, it follows from the properties (a)-(b)-(c) in Remark 4.3 that

$$m_g(\cap_{j=1}^n I_j) = m_g\Big(\cap_{j=1}^n \big(R_j \setminus (R_j \setminus I_j)\big)\Big) \geq m_g(R_n) - \sum_{j=1}^n m_g(R_j \setminus I_j) > \frac{\delta}{2},$$

and consequently, $\big(\cap_{j=1}^n J_j\big)_{n=1}^\infty$ is a sequence of nonempty, bounded, closed and decreasing sets. Therefore, we use Remark 5.33 of the next chapter to obtain $\emptyset \neq \cap_{n=1}^\infty J_n \subseteq \cap_{n=1}^\infty R_n = \emptyset$, a contradiction. $\square$

Secondly, we modify the Riemann–Stieltjes sums to define summable functions and admissible sequences.

Definition 4.5. Given an increasing function $g : \mathbf{R} \to \mathbf{R}$.

(i) A function $s : \mathbf{R} \to \mathbf{R}$ is called a step function provided $\{x \in \mathbf{R} : s(x) \neq 0\}$ is a simple set; that is, there are $n \in \mathbf{N}$, $c_1, \ldots, c_n \in \mathbf{R}$ and disjoint finite intervals $\{I_k\}_{k=1}^n$ such that $s = \sum_{k=1}^n c_k 1_{I_k}$. In this case, we write

$$A_g(s) = \sum_{k=1}^n c_k m_g(I_k)$$

for the g-area of s.

(ii) A function sequence $(s_k)_{k=1}^{\infty}$ on $\mathbf{R}$ is called admissible for a nonnegative function $f : \mathbf{R} \to \mathbf{R}^e$ provided:

(a) Each s_k is a step function on $\mathbf{R}$;
(b) Each s_k is nonnegative;
(c) $0 \le f \le \sum_{k=1}^{\infty} s_k$.

In this case, we write

$$S_g(f) = \inf\left\{\sum_{k=1}^{\infty} A_g(s_k)\right\}$$

for the g-sum of f, where the infimum ranges over all admissible function sequences for f.

Remark 4.6. A_g is just the Euclidean area under the graph of s when g is the identity. Moreover, there always exists an admissible function sequence for any nonnegative $f : \mathbf{R} \to \mathbf{R}^e$. To this end, we take $I_k = (-k, k)$ and $s_k = 1_{I_k}$. Clearly, $(s_k)_{k=1}^{\infty}$ is admissible for f. This demonstration tells us that S_g always exists even if it may be ∞.

To better understand both A_g and S_g, we begin with their basic properties as follows.

Theorem 4.7. *Let $g : \mathbf{R} \to \mathbf{R}$ be an increasing function.*

(i) *$A_g(\cdot)$ has the following four properties:*

(a) *$A_g(0) = 0$ and $A_g(s) \ge 0$ whenever s is a nonnegative step function on $\mathbf{R}$;*

(b) *$A_g(s_1) \le A_g(s_2)$ whenever s_1 and s_2 are step functions satisfying $s_1 \le s_2$ on $\mathbf{R}$;*

(c) *If s is a step function on $\mathbf{R}$, so are $|s|$, $s^+ = \max\{s, 0\}$, and $s^- = \max\{-s, 0\}$ on $\mathbf{R}$ with*

$$A_g(s) = A_g(s^+) - A_g(s^-) \quad \text{and} \quad A_g(|s|) = A_g(s^+) + A_g(s^-);$$

(d) *If $(s_k)_{k=1}^{n}$ are step functions on $\mathbf{R}$ and $\{c_k\}_{k=1}^{n}$ are finite real numbers, then $s = \sum_{k=1}^{n} c_k s_k$ is a step function on $\mathbf{R}$ and $A_g(s) = \sum_{k=1}^{n} c_k A_g(s_k)$.*

(ii) *$S_g(\cdot)$ has the following four properties:*

(a) *For $f : \mathbf{R} \to \mathbf{R}^e$, $S_g(f^{\pm}) \le S_g(|f|)$ where $f^+ = \max\{f, 0\}$ and $f^- = \max\{-f, 0\}$;*

(b) *For $f : \mathbf{R} \to \mathbf{R}^e$ and $c \in \mathbf{R}$, $S_g(|cf|) = |c| S_g(|f|)$;*

(c) *For $f_1, f_2 : \mathbf{R} \to \mathbf{R}^e$ with $0 \le f_1 \le f_2$, $S_g(f_1) \le S_g(f_2)$;*

(d) *If $(f_k)_{k=1}^{\infty}$ is a sequence of functions from $\mathbf{R}$ to $\mathbf{R}^e$ and $\sum_{k=1}^{\infty} f_k(x)$ converges for any $x \in \mathbf{R}$, then*

$$S_g\Big(\Big|\sum_{k=1}^{\infty} f_k\Big|\Big) \le \sum_{k=1}^{\infty} S_g(|f_k|).$$

(iii) *$A_g(s) = S_g(s)$ holds for any nonnegative step function s on $\mathbf{R}$.*

Proof. It is straightforward to verify part (i). Next we prove part (ii).

(a) It follows from the definitions of S_g, f^+ and f^-.

(b) If $c = 0$ then the result is trivial. Suppose now $c \neq 0$. Then $(s_k)_{k=1}^{\infty}$ is an admissible sequence for $|f|$ if and only if $(|c|s_k)_{k=1}^{\infty}$ is an admissible sequence for $|cf|$. Moreover,

$$S_g(|cf|) = \inf\left\{\sum_{k=1}^{\infty} A_g(|c|s_k)\right\} = |c|\inf\left\{\sum_{k=1}^{\infty} A_g(s_k)\right\} = |c|S_g(f).$$

(c) This follows from that if $(s_k)_{k=1}^{\infty}$ is admissible for f_2 then it is also admissible for f_1.

(d) Without loss of generality, we may assume $\sum_{k=1}^{\infty} S_g(|f_k|) < \infty$: Otherwise, there is nothing to argue. Under this assumption, we have naturally $S_g(|f_k|) < \infty$ for each $k \in \mathbf{N}$. This, along with the definition of the infimum, implies that for any $\epsilon > 0$ there exists a function sequence $(s_{k,j})_{j=1}^{\infty}$ which is admissible for $|f_k|$ and satisfies

$$\sum_{j=1}^{\infty} A_g(s_{k,j}) \leq S_g(|f_k|) + 2^{-k}\epsilon.$$

Thus

$$\sum_{k,j=1}^{\infty} A_g(s_{k,j}) = \sum_{k=1}^{\infty}\Big(\sum_{j=1}^{\infty} A_g(s_{k,j})\Big) \leq \sum_{k=1}^{\infty} S_g(|f_k|) + \epsilon.$$

Note that

$$0 \leq \Big|\sum_{k=1}^{\infty} f_k\Big| \leq \sum_{k=1}^{\infty} |f_k| \leq \sum_{k=1}^{\infty}\Big(\sum_{j=1}^{\infty} s_{k,j}\Big) = \sum_{k,j=1}^{\infty} s_{k,j}.$$

So $(s_{k,j})_{k,j=1}^{\infty}$ is an admissible sequence for $|\sum_{k=1}^{\infty} f_k|$. Further, we get

$$S_g\Big(\Big|\sum_{k=1}^{\infty} f_k\Big|\Big) \leq \sum_{k,j=1}^{\infty} A_g(s_{k,j}) \leq \sum_{k=1}^{\infty} S_g(|f_k|) + \epsilon,$$

and consequently,

$$S_g\Big(\Big|\sum_{k=1}^{\infty} f_k\Big|\Big) \leq \sum_{k=1}^{\infty} S_g(|f_k|),$$

as desired.

Last of all, we verify (iii). If $s : \mathbf{R} \to \mathbf{R}$ is a step function, then $S_g(s) \leq A_g(s)$. Assume now that $(s_k)_{k=1}^{\infty}$ is any admissible sequence for s and let $t_n = s - \sum_{j=1}^{n} s_j$. Then $t_n : \mathbf{R} \to \mathbf{R}$ is a step function, decreasing and convergent to $\lim_{n\to\infty} t_n \leq 0$. Consequently, $t_n^+ = \max\{t_n, 0\}$ decreases and converges to 0. Since

$$K_{1,+} = \{x \in \mathbf{R} : \ t_1^+(x) > 0\} \quad \text{and} \quad K_{n,\epsilon} = \{x \in \mathbf{R} : \ t_n^+(x) \geq \epsilon\}$$

are simple sets for any given $\epsilon > 0$, we conclude

$$\begin{aligned} A_g(t_n^+) &\leq \big(\sup_{x\in K_{n,\epsilon}} t_n^+(x)\big)m_g(K_{n,\epsilon}) + \big(\sup_{x\in \mathbf{R}\setminus K_{n,\epsilon}} t_n^+(x)\big)m_g(\mathbf{R}\setminus K_{n,\epsilon}) \\ &\leq \big(\sup_{x\in\mathbf{R}} t_1^+(x)\big)m_g(K_{n,\epsilon}) + \epsilon m_g(K_{1,+}). \end{aligned}$$

Since

$$K_{n+1,\epsilon} \subseteq K_{n,\epsilon} \quad \text{and} \quad \cap_{n=1}^{\infty} K_{n,\epsilon} = \emptyset,$$

we employ Theorem 4.4 to achieve

$$m_g(K_{1,\epsilon}) = \lim_{n\to\infty} \sum_{j=1}^{n} \big(m_g(K_{j,\epsilon}) - m_g(K_{j+1,\epsilon})\big) = m_g(K_{1,\epsilon}) - \lim_{n\to\infty} m_g\big(K_{n,\epsilon}\big),$$

whence $\lim_{n\to\infty} m_g\big(K_{n,\epsilon}\big) = 0$. The previous discussion implies immediately

$$\lim_{n\to\infty} \sup_{k\geq n} A_g(t_k^+) \leq \epsilon m_g\big(K_{1,+}\big),$$

which yields $\lim_{n\to\infty} A_g(t_n^+) = 0$ since $\epsilon > 0$ is arbitrary. But,

$$s = t_n + \sum_{j=1}^{n} s_j \leq t_n^+ + \sum_{j=1}^{n} s_j \Rightarrow A_g(s) \leq A_g(t_n^+) + \sum_{j=1}^{n} A_g(s_j).$$

Letting $n \to \infty$ we obtain $A_g(s) \leq \sum_{j=1}^{n} A_g(s_j)$ which, together with the definition of $S_g(s)$, yields $A_g(s) \leq S_g(s)$. Accordingly, $A_g(s) = S_g(s)$. $\square$

Thirdly, the Lebesgue–Radon–Stieltjes integrals are founded on the following assertion.

Theorem 4.8. *Given an increasing function $g : \mathbf{R} \to \mathbf{R}$. For $k \in \mathbf{N}$ let $f_k : \mathbf{R} \to \mathbf{R}$ be a function with $S_g(|f_k|) < \infty$. If $f : \mathbf{R} \to \mathbf{R}$ satisfies $\lim_{k\to\infty} S_g(|f - f_k|) = 0$ then:*

(i)

$$S_g(|f|) < \infty \quad \textit{and} \quad S_g(f^{\pm}) < \infty;$$

(ii)

$$\lim_{k\to\infty} S_g(\big||f| - |f_k|\big|) = 0 \quad \textit{and} \quad \lim_{k\to\infty} S_g(|f^{\pm} - f_k^{\pm}|) = 0;$$

(iii)

$$\lim_{k\to\infty} S_g(|f_k|) = S_g(|f|) \quad \textit{and} \quad \lim_{k\to\infty} S_g(f_k^{\pm}) = S_g(f^{\pm}).$$

Proof. (i) By hypothesis, there is an $N \in \mathbf{N}$ such that $S_g(|f - f_N|) < \infty$ and $S_g(|f_N|) < \infty$. So by Theorem 4.7 (ii) (d),

$$S_g(f^{\pm}) \leq S_g(|f|) \leq S_g(|f - f_N|) + S_g(|f_N|) < \infty.$$

(ii) Note that for each k,

$$\max\{\big||f| - |f_k|\big|, |f^+ - f_k^+|, |f^- - f_k^-|\} \leq |f - f_k|.$$

So this inequality and $\lim_{k\to\infty} S_g(|f - f_k|) = 0$ imply the desired limits.

(iii) It follows from Theorem 4.7 (ii) (d) that for each $k \in \mathbf{N}$,

$$S_g(|f_k|) \leq S_g(|f|) + S_g(|f_k - f|)$$

and

$$S_g(|f|) \leq S_g(|f_k|) + S_g(|f - f_k|)$$

and so that

$$\big|S_g(|f_k|) - S_g(|f|)\big| \leq S_g(|f - f_k|).$$

This inequality yields

$$\lim_{k\to\infty} \big|S_g(|f_k|) - S_g(|f|)\big| = 0.$$

Since $f_k^{\pm} = f^{\pm} + (f_k^{\pm} - f^{\pm})$, we can prove $\lim_{k\to\infty} S_g(f_k^{\pm}) = S_g(f^{\pm})$ in a way similar to showing $\lim_{k\to\infty} \big|S_g(|f_k|) - S_g(|f|)\big| = 0$. □

Now, we are in a position to introduce the definition of a Lebesgue–Radon–Stieltjes integral.

Definition 4.9. Let $g : \mathbf{R} \to \mathbf{R}$ be an increasing function.

(i) For a step function $f : \mathbf{R} \to \mathbf{R}$, we define the Lebesgue–Radon–Stieltjes integral of f on $\mathbf{R}$ with respect to m_g by

$$\int_{\mathbf{R}} f(x)dm_g(x) = A_g(f^+) - A_g(f^-).$$

(ii) For an arbitrary function $f : \mathbf{R} \to \mathbf{R}^e$, we say that f is Lebesgue–Radon–Stieltjes integrable on $\mathbf{R}$ with respect to m_g, denoted $f \in LRS_g(\mathbf{R})$ provided there exists a sequence $(s_k)_{k=1}^{\infty}$ of step functions on $\mathbf{R}$ such that $\lim_{k\to\infty} S_g(|f - s_k|) = 0$. In this case, we write

$$\int_{\mathbf{R}} f(x)dm_g(x) = S_g(f^+) - S_g(f^-)$$

for the Lebesgue–Radon–Stieltjes integral of f on $\mathbf{R}$.

We close this section by making two important comments on the above notion.

Remark 4.10.

(i) If g in Definition 4.9 is the identity on $\mathbf{R}$, then $\int_{\mathbf{R}} f(x)dm_g(x)$ is called the Lebesgue integral of $f : \mathbf{R} \to \mathbf{R}^e$ on $\mathbf{R}$, denoted $\int_{\mathbf{R}} f(x)dm_{id}(x)$. It is clear that if f equals the function discussed in Example 4.1 on $[0, 1]$ and 0 elsewhere, then f is Lebesgue integrable on $\mathbf{R}$.

(ii) Definition 4.9 produces the following three facts:

(a) $\int_{\mathbf{R}} f(x)1_I(x)dm_g(x) = 0$ when I is any open interval in $\mathbf{R}$ and g equals any constant on I;

(b) $\int_{\mathbf{R}} 1_{[c,c]}(x)f(x)dm_g(x) = f(c)\big(g(c^+) - g(c^-)\big)$ for any $c \in \mathbf{R}$;

(c) $\int_{\mathbf{R}} 1_I(x)dm_g(x) = m_g(I)$ for any finite interval I in $\mathbf{R}$.

4.2 Essential Properties

After introducing the concept of the Lebesgue–Radon–Stieltjes integration, we seek to show some basic properties of these integrals.

Theorem 4.11. *Let $g : \mathbf{R} \to \mathbf{R}$ be increasing. If $f \in LRS_g(\mathbf{R})$ then $|f|, f^+, f^- \in LRS_g(\mathbf{R})$ with*

$$\int_{\mathbf{R}} f(x)dm_g(x) = \int_{\mathbf{R}} f^+(x)dm_g(x) - \int_{\mathbf{R}} f^-(x)dm_g(x),$$

$$\int_{\mathbf{R}} |f(x)|dm_g(x) = \int_{\mathbf{R}} f^+(x)dm_g(x) + \int_{\mathbf{R}} f^-(x)dm_g(x),$$

and

$$\Big|\int_{\mathbf{R}} f(x)dm_g(x)\Big| \le \int_{\mathbf{R}} |f(x)|dm_g(x).$$

Proof. Because of $f \in LRS_g(\mathbf{R})$, we can take a sequence $(s_k)_{k=1}^{\infty}$ of step functions on $\mathbf{R}$ such that $\lim_{k\to\infty} S_g(|f - s_k|) = 0$. Since each s_k is a step function $\mathbf{R}$, so is $|s_k|$ and it follows that $S_g(|s_k|) < \infty$. From Theorem 4.8 (ii) it turns out that

$$\lim_{k\to\infty} S_g(\big||f| - |s_k|\big|) = 0 \quad \text{and} \quad \lim_{k\to\infty} S_g(|f^{\pm} - s_k^{\pm}|) = 0.$$

By definition, we have $|f|, f^+, f^- \in LRS_g(\mathbf{R})$ with

$$\int_{\mathbf{R}} f(x)dm_g(x) = S_g(f^+) - S_g(f^-) = \int_{\mathbf{R}} f^+(x)dm_g(x) - \int_{\mathbf{R}} f^-(x)dm_g(x).$$

Meanwhile, note by Theorem 4.7 (i) (c) that

$$A_g(|s_k|) = A_g(s_k^+) + A_g(s_k^-) = A_g(s_k^+) + A_g(s_k^-).$$

So it follows that $S_g(|s_k|) = S_g(s_k^+) + S_g(s_k^-)$. This, along with Theorem 4.8 (iii), implies

$$\int_{\mathbf{R}} |f(x)|dm_g(x) = S_g(f^+) + S_g(f^-) = \int_{\mathbf{R}} f^+(x)dm_g(x) + \int_{\mathbf{R}} f^-(x)dm_g(x),$$

as required.

Finally, the foregoing argument yields the inequality in Theorem 4.11 right away. □

Theorem 4.12. *Let $g : \mathbf{R} \to \mathbf{R}$ be increasing. If $f_k \in LRS_g(\mathbf{R})$ and $\lim_{k\to\infty} S_g(|f - f_k|) = 0$, then $f \in LRS_g(\mathbf{R})$ with:*

$$\lim_{k\to\infty} \int_{\mathbf{R}} f_k(x)dm_g(x) = \int_{\mathbf{R}} f(x)dm_g(x);$$

$$\lim_{k\to\infty} \int_{\mathbf{R}} f_k^{\pm}(x)dm_g(x) = \int_{\mathbf{R}} f^{\pm}(x)dm_g(x);$$

$$\lim_{k\to\infty} \int_{\mathbf{R}} |f_k(x)|dm_g(x) = \int_{\mathbf{R}} |f(x)|dm_g(x).$$

Proof. By Theorem 4.7 (ii) (d), $f_k \in LRS_g(\mathbf{R})$ induces a sequence $(s_{k,j})_{j=1}^{\infty}$ of step functions on $\mathbf{R}$ such that

$$\lim_{j\to\infty} S_g(|f_k - s_{k,j}|) = 0.$$

Thus, for some $j \in \mathbf{N}$ we must have $S_g(|f_k - s_{k,j}|) < 1/k$. For any $\epsilon > 0$, there is an $N \in \mathbf{N}$ such that $S_g(|f - f_k|) < \epsilon/2$ as $k \geq N$. Accordingly, if $k \geq 2/\epsilon$ then $S_g(|f_k - s_{k,j}|) < \epsilon/2$. Using Theorem 4.7 (ii) (d) again, we obtain that $k \geq \max\{N, 2/\epsilon\}$ implies

$$S_g(|f - s_{k,j}|) \leq S_g(|f - f_k|) + S_g(|f_k - s_{k,j}|) < \epsilon,$$

namely, $f \in LRS_g(\mathbf{R})$.

The limit formulas may be verified by Theorems 4.11 and 4.8 (iii), along with the definition of Lebesgue–Radon–Stieltjes integration. □

Theorem 4.13. *Let $g : \mathbf{R} \to \mathbf{R}$ be increasing.*

(i) *If $0 \leq f \in LRS_g(\mathbf{R})$, then $\int_{\mathbf{R}} f(x)dm_g(x) \geq 0$.*

(ii) *If $f_1, f_2 \in LRS_g(\mathbf{R})$ satisfy $f_1 \leq f_2$ on $\mathbf{R}$, then*

$$\int_{\mathbf{R}} f_1(x)dm_g(x) \leq \int_{\mathbf{R}} f_2(x)dm_g(x).$$

(iii) *If $f_1, \ldots, f_n \in LRS_g(\mathbf{R})$ and $c_1, \ldots, c_n \in \mathbf{R}$, then $\sum_{k=1}^{n} c_k f_k \in LRS_g(\mathbf{R})$ with*

$$\int_{\mathbf{R}} \Big(\sum_{k=1}^{n} c_k f_k(x)\Big) dm_g(x) = \sum_{k=1}^{n} c_k \int_{\mathbf{R}} f_k(x)dm_g(x).$$

Proof. (ii) follows from (i) and (iii), but (i) is derived easily from that

$$\int_{\mathbf{R}} f(x)dm_g(x) = S_g(f) \geq 0$$

whenever $f \geq 0$. To prove (iii), we may assume $f_k \geq 0$. The condition $f_k \in LRS_g(\mathbf{R})$ produces a sequence $(s_{k,j})_{j=1}^{\infty}$ of step functions on $\mathbf{R}$ such that $\lim_{j\to\infty} S_g(|f_k - s_{k,j}|) = 0$. Now for each $j \in \mathbf{N}$ we use Theorem 4.7 (ii) (d) to get

$$0 \leq S_g\Big(\Big|\sum_{k=1}^{n} c_k f_k - \sum_{k=1}^{n} c_k s_{k,j}\Big|\Big) \leq \sum_{k=1}^{n} |c_k| S_g(|f_k - s_{k,j}|).$$

Since n is finite, we conclude from $\lim_{j\to\infty} S_g(|f_k - s_{k,j}|) = 0$ that

$$\lim_{j\to\infty} S_g\Big(\Big|\sum_{k=1}^{n} c_k f_k - \sum_{k=1}^{n} c_k s_{k,j}\Big|\Big) = 0$$

and so that $\sum_{k=1}^{n} c_k f_k \in LRS_g(\mathbf{R})$. An application of Theorem 4.12 implies

$$\lim_{j\to\infty} \int_{\mathbf{R}} s_{k,j}(x)dm_g(x) = \int_{\mathbf{R}} f_k(x)dm_g(x)$$

and hence

$$\lim_{j\to\infty}\int_{\mathbf{R}}\Big(\sum_{k=1}^{n}c_k s_{k,j}(x)\Big)dm_g(x)=\int_{\mathbf{R}}\sum_{k=1}^{n}c_k f_k(x)dm_g(x).$$

By virtue of these limits and the following equalities

$$\int_{\mathbf{R}}\Big(\sum_{k=1}^{n}c_k s_{k,j}(x)\Big)dm_g(x)=A_g\Big(\sum_{k=1}^{n}c_k s_{k,j}\Big)=\sum_{k=1}^{n}c_k\int_{\mathbf{R}}s_{k,j}(x)dm_g(x),$$

we obtain the desired result. □

The following result, a consequence of Theorem 4.13, will be very useful in evaluating some Lebesgue–Radon–Stieltjes integrals.

Corollary 4.14. *Let* $g:\mathbf{R}\to\mathbf{R}$ *be increasing and* $I\subseteq\mathbf{R}$ *a union of finitely many disjoint finite intervals* $\{I_k\}_{k=1}^{n}$. *Then* $1_I f\in LRS_g(\mathbf{R})$ *if and only if* $1_{I_k}f\in LRS_g(\mathbf{R})$ *for any* $k=1,\dots,n$. *In this case,*

$$\int_{\mathbf{R}}1_I(x)f(x)dm_g(x)=\sum_{k=1}^{n}\int_{\mathbf{R}}1_{I_k}(x)f(x)dm_g(x).$$

Proof. If $1_I f\in LRS_g(\mathbf{R})$, then there is a sequence of step functions $(s_k)_{k=1}^{\infty}$ on $\mathbf{R}$ such that $\lim_{k\to\infty}S_g(|1_I f-s_k|)=0$. So, $\lim_{k\to\infty}S_g(|1_{I_j}f-1_{I_j}s_k|)=0$ and $1_{I_j}f\in LRS_g(\mathbf{R})$ for each $j=1,2,\dots,n$. Note that $1_I f=\sum_{k=1}^{n}1_{I_k}f$ on $\mathbf{R}$. Then by Theorem 4.13 (iii) we get

$$\int_{\mathbf{R}}1_I(x)f(x)dm_g(x)=\int_{\mathbf{R}}\sum_{k=1}^{n}1_{I_k}(x)f(x)dm_g(x)=\sum_{k=1}^{n}\int_{\mathbf{R}}1_{I_k}(x)f(x)dm_g(x).$$

Conversely, if $1_{I_k}f\in LRS_g(\mathbf{R})$ for each $k=1,2,\dots,n$, then there is a sequence of step functions $(s_{k,j})_{j=1}^{\infty}$ on $\mathbf{R}$ such that $\lim_{j\to\infty}S_g(|1_{I_k}f-s_{k,j}|)=0$. This yields $\lim_{j\to\infty}S_g(|f1_I-\sum_{k=1}^{n}s_{k,j}|)=0$. Since $\big(\sum_{k=1}^{n}s_{k,j}\big)_{j=1}^{\infty}$ is also a sequence of step functions on $\mathbf{R}$, $f1_I\in LRS_g(\mathbf{R})$ follows. □

We give an example to show how Corollary 4.14 is applied.

Example 4.15. Let

$$g(x)=\begin{cases}0, & x<2,\\ 1, & x\ge 2.\end{cases}$$

Then an application of Corollary 4.14 and Remark 4.10 (ii) gives

$$\begin{aligned}&\int_{\mathbf{R}}x^6 1_{[2,4]}(x)dm_g(x)\\ &=\int_{\mathbf{R}}x^6 1_{[2,2]}(x)dm_g(x)+\int_{\mathbf{R}}x^6 1_{(2,4)}(x)dm_g(x)+\int_{\mathbf{R}}x^6 1_{[4,4]}(x)dm_g(x)\\ &=2^6\big(g(2^+)-g(2^-)\big)+0+4^6\big(g(4^+)-g(4^-)\big)=2^6.\end{aligned}$$

Motivated by Theorem 4.13 (i), we consider the so-called null functions and sets with respect to m_g.

Definition 4.16. Let $g : \mathbf{R} \to \mathbf{R}$ be increasing.

(i) $f : \mathbf{R} \to \mathbf{R}^e$ is called an m_g-null function provided $f \in LRS_g(\mathbf{R})$ and

$$\int_{\mathbf{R}} |f(x)| dm_g(x) = 0.$$

(ii) $E \subseteq \mathbf{R}$ is called an m_g-null set provided

$$1_E \in LRS_g(\mathbf{R}) \quad \text{and} \quad \int_{\mathbf{R}} 1_E(x) dm_g(x) = 0.$$

(iii) A property $\mathcal{P}$ on a function $f : \mathbf{R} \to \mathbf{R}^e$ is said to hold almost everywhere with respect to m_g (denoted m_g-a.e.) on $\mathbf{R}$ provided $\mathcal{P}$ holds everywhere in $\mathbf{R}$ except possibly on some m_g-null subset of $\mathbf{R}$.

Clearly, f is an m_g-null function if and only if $S_g(|f|) = 0$. Further, the following result not only gives the visible description of an m_g-null function, but also shows that changing the values of a function on an m_g-null set does not affect the integral of the function – two functions that are equal m_g-a.e. can be regarded as identical in the context of integration theory.

Theorem 4.17. *Let $g : \mathbf{R} \to \mathbf{R}$ be increasing.*

(i) *$f : \mathbf{R} \to \mathbf{R}^e$ is an m_g-null function if and only if $f = 0$ m_g-a.e. on $\mathbf{R}$.*

(ii) *If $f_1, f_2 : \mathbf{R} \to \mathbf{R}^e$ satisfy $f_1 = f_2$ m_g-a.e. on $\mathbf{R}$, and $f_1 \in LRS_g(\mathbf{R})$, then*

$$f_2 \in LRS_g(\mathbf{R}) \quad \textit{and} \quad \int_{\mathbf{R}} f_1(x) dm_g(x) = \int_{\mathbf{R}} f_2(x) dm_g(x).$$

Proof. (i) Suppose $f : \mathbf{R} \to \mathbf{R}^e$ is an m_g-null function. Then $S_g(|f|) = 0$. For each $n - 1 \in \mathbf{N}$ let

$$E_1 = \{x \in \mathbf{R} : |f(x)| \geq 1\} \quad \text{and} \quad E_n = \{x \in \mathbf{R} : 1/n \leq |f(x)| < 1/(n-1)\}.$$

It is evident that $0 \leq 1_{E_n} \leq n|f|$ for $n \in \mathbf{N}$ and so that

$$0 \leq S_g(1_{E_n}) \leq S_g(n|f|) = nS_g(|f|) = 0.$$

Let $E = \{x \in \mathbf{R} : f(x) \neq 0\}$. Then for any $x \in E$ there is a unique $N \in \mathbf{N}$ such that $x \in E_N$ and hence $1_{E_n}(x) = 1$ whenever $n = N$ and $1_{E_n}(x) = 0$ whenever $n \neq N$. This means that $1_E(x) = 1 = \sum_{n=1}^{\infty} 1_{E_n}(x)$ for $x \in E$. However, if $x \notin E$ then $x \notin E_n$ for all $n \in \mathbf{N}$ and hence $1_E(x) = 0 = \sum_{n=1}^{\infty} 1_{E_n}(x)$. Therefore, $1_E = \sum_{n=1}^{\infty} 1_{E_n}$. This, together with Theorem 4.7 (ii) (d), implies

$$0 \leq S_g(1_E) \leq \sum_{n=1}^{\infty} S_g(1_{E_n}) = 0,$$

and so 1_E is an m_g-null function; that is, E is an m_g-null set; i.e., $f = 0$ m_g-a.e. on $\mathbf{R}$.

Conversely, suppose $f = 0$ m_g-a.e. on $\mathbf{R}$. Then $E = \{x \in \mathbf{R} : f(x) \neq 0\}$ is an m_g-null set. For $n \in \mathbf{N}$ set $F_n = \{x \in \mathbf{R} : n - 1 < |f(x)| \leq n\}$. Naturally, each F_n is an m_g-null set. Set $f_n = n1_{F_n}$. Then to any $x \in E$ there corresponds a unique $N \in \mathbf{N}$ such that $x \in F_N$, and so

$$f_n(x) = \begin{cases} N\,, & n = N, \\ 0\,, & n \neq N. \end{cases}$$

Consequently, $\sum_{n=1}^{\infty} f_n(x) = N \geq |f(x)|$ for $x \in E$. Of course, if $x \in \mathbf{R} \setminus E$, then $x \notin F_n$ for all $n \in \mathbf{N}$ and hence $\sum_{n=1}^{\infty} f_n(x) = 0 = f(x)$. Thus, $|f| \leq \sum_{n=1}^{\infty} f_n$ on $\mathbf{R}$. Using Theorem 4.7 (ii) (c)-(d), we find

$$0 \leq S_g(|f|) \leq \sum_{n=1}^{\infty} S_g(f_n) = \sum_{n=1}^{\infty} n S_g(1_{F_n}) = 0,$$

which means that f is an m_g-null function.

(ii) Since $f_1 = f_2$ m_g-a.e. on $\mathbf{R}$ is equivalent to $f_1 - f_2 = 0$ m_g-a.e. on $\mathbf{R}$. So the result follows from the foregoing (i) and Theorem 4.13 (iii). □

4.3 Convergence Theorems

In this section, we will present the dominated convergence theorem and its consequent monotone convergence theorem as well as Pierre Fatou's lemma for the Lebesgue–Radon–Stieltjes integrals. As an application of the monotone convergence theorem, we will prove that the Lebesgue–Radon–Stieltjes integrals actually generalize the Riemann–Stieltjes ones.

Here is the dominated convergence theorem.

Theorem 4.18. *Let $g : \mathbf{R} \to \mathbf{R}$ be increasing. Suppose $(f_k)_{k=1}^{\infty}$ is a sequence in $LRS_g(\mathbf{R})$ such that $|f_k| \leq h \in LRS_g(\mathbf{R})$. If $\lim_{k\to\infty} f_k = f$ m_g-a.e on $\mathbf{R}$, then $f \in LRS_g(\mathbf{R})$ and*

$$\int_{\mathbf{R}} \lim_{k\to\infty} f_k(x)dm_g(x) = \int_{\mathbf{R}} f(x)dm_g(x) = \lim_{k\to\infty} \int_{\mathbf{R}} f_k(x)dm_g(x).$$

Proof. To prove the conclusion, we need two auxiliary facts.

Fact 1. If $(s_k)_{k=1}^{\infty}$ is a decreasing and nonnegative sequence of step functions on $\mathbf{R}$ and $\lim_{k\to\infty} s_k = 0$ m_g-a.e. on $\mathbf{R}$, then $\lim_{k\to\infty} \int_{\mathbf{R}} s_k(x)dm_g(x) = 0$.

Indeed, $\lim_{k\to\infty} s_k(x) = s(x) \geq 0$ exists for all $x \in \mathbf{R}$ due to the above-given condition. Note that $\lim_{k\to\infty} s_k = 0$ m_g-a.e. on $\mathbf{R}$. So s is an m_g-null function. Further, from Definitions 4.5 and 4.9, and Theorem 4.7 (d)'s it follows that

$$\begin{aligned} 0 &\leq \int_{\mathbf{R}} (s_k(x) - s(x))dm_g(x) \\ &= S_g(s_k - s) \end{aligned}$$

$$
\begin{aligned}
&= S_g\Big(\sum_{n=k+1}^{\infty}(s_{n-1}-s_n)\Big)\\
&\le \sum_{n=k+1}^{\infty}\big(S_g(s_{n-1})-S_g(s_n)\big)\\
&= S_g(s_k)-\lim_{m\to\infty}S_g(s_m)\\
&\to 0 \quad \text{as} \quad k\to\infty.
\end{aligned}
$$

This implies $\lim_{k\to\infty}\int_{\mathbf{R}} s_k(x)dm_g(x)=0$.

Fact 2. If each t_n is the limit of an increasing and nonnegative sequence of step functions on $\mathbf{R}$, if $S_g(t_1)<\infty$, and if $(t_n)_{n=1}^{\infty}$ is a decreasing sequence and tends to 0 m_g-a.e. on $\mathbf{R}$, then $\lim_{n\to\infty}S_g(t_n)=0$.

To check *Fact 2*, let $\epsilon>0$ and $\epsilon_m=2^{-m}\epsilon$ for $m\in\mathbf{N}$. Using the assumptions on $(t_n)_{n=1}^{\infty}$ and *Fact 1*, we can get step functions u_m on $\mathbf{R}$ such that $S_g(t_m-u_m)<\epsilon_m$, $0\le u_m\le t_m$. Then $v_n=\inf_{1\le m\le n}u_m$ is a step function on $\mathbf{R}$, $(v_n)_{n=1}^{\infty}$ is decreasing and since $0\le v_n\le u_n\le t_n$, it follows that $\lim_{n\to\infty}v_n=0$ m_g-a.e. on $\mathbf{R}$, and therefore, by *Fact 1*, one has

$$\lim_{n\to\infty}S_g(v_n)=\lim_{n\to\infty}\int_{\mathbf{R}}v_n(x)dm_g(x)=0.$$

However, $(t_n)_{n=1}^{\infty}$ is a decreasing sequence and enjoys the estimation

$$t_n=\inf_{1\le m\le n}t_m=\inf_{1\le m\le n}\big(u_m+(t_m-u_m)\big)\le v_n+\sum_{m=1}^{n}(t_m-u_m),$$

which implies that there is an $N\in\mathbf{N}$ such that

$$S_g(t_n)\le S_g(v_n)+\sum_{m=1}^{n}S_g(t_m-u_m)\le 2\epsilon \quad \text{as} \quad n>N.$$

Thus, the result follows.

Now, let us prove the desired convergence result. Let $\epsilon>0$ and $\epsilon_k=\epsilon/2^k$ for $k\in\mathbf{N}$. To each k there corresponds a step function s_k with $S_g(|f_k-s_k|)\le\epsilon_k$. Then

$$\sup_{k\ge n}|f_k-s_k|\le\sum_{k=n}^{\infty}|f_k-s_k|$$

and hence

$$
\begin{aligned}
S_g\big(\lim_{m\to\infty}\sup_{k\ge m}|f_k-s_k|\big) &\le S_g\big(\sup_{k\ge n}|f_k-s_k|\big)\\
&\le \sum_{k=n}^{\infty}S_g(f_k-s_k)\\
&\le 2^{1-n}\epsilon\to 0 \quad \text{as} \quad n\to\infty.
\end{aligned}
$$

This last estimation tells us that $\lim_{n\to\infty} \sup_{k\geq n} |f_k - s_k|$ is an m_g-null function but also equals 0 m_g-a.e. on $\mathbf{R}$. Note that $\lim_{k\to\infty} f_k = f$ m_g-a.e. on $\mathbf{R}$. So it follows that $\lim_{k\to\infty} s_k = f$ m_g-a.e. on $\mathbf{R}$. Of course, this gives that if $t_n = \sup_{k,m\geq n} |s_k - s_m|$ then

$$\lim_{n\to\infty} t_n = \lim_{n\to\infty} \sup_{k,m\geq n} |s_k - s_m| = 0 \quad m_g\text{-a.e. on } \mathbf{R}.$$

In addition, $(t_n)_{n=1}^{\infty}$ is a decreasing sequence with the following property

$$t_1 \leq 2 \sup_{k\in\mathbf{N}} |s_k| \leq 2 \sup_{k\in\mathbf{N}} |f_k| + 2 \sup_{k\in\mathbf{N}} |f_k - s_k| \leq 2h + 2\sum_{k=1}^{\infty} |f_k - s_k|,$$

which gives

$$S_g(t_1) \leq 2S_g(h) + 2\sum_{k=1}^{\infty} S_g(|f_k - s_k|) \leq 2S_g(h) + 2\epsilon.$$

In other words, t_n satisfies the conditions of *Fact 2*. So, $\lim_{n\to\infty} S_g(t_n) = 0$. Nevertheless, since

$$|f - s_n| = \lim_{k\to\infty} |s_k - s_n| \leq t_n \quad m_g\text{-a.e. on } \mathbf{R},$$

it follows that $\lim_{k\to\infty} S_g(|f - s_k|) = 0$. This means that $f \in LRS_g(\mathbf{R})$. Finally, $S_g(|f_k - s_k|) \leq \epsilon_k$, together with Theorems 4.7 (ii) (d) and 4.8, implies

$$\lim_{k\to\infty} \int_{\mathbf{R}} f_k(x)dm_g(x) = \int_{\mathbf{R}} f(x)dm_g(x). \qquad \square$$

As a direct consequence of the dominated convergence theorem, we have the following monotone convergence theorem.

Theorem 4.19. *Let $g : \mathbf{R} \to \mathbf{R}$ be increasing. Suppose that $(f_k)_{k=1}^{\infty}$ is an increasing sequence in $LRS_g(\mathbf{R})$ such that $\lim_{k\to\infty} f_k = f$ m_g-a.e. on $\mathbf{R}$. Then $f \in LRS_g(\mathbf{R})$ if and only if $\lim_{k\to\infty} \int_{\mathbf{R}} f_k(x)dm_g(x)$ exists. In this case,*

$$\lim_{k\to\infty} \int_{\mathbf{R}} f_k(x)dm_g(x) = \int_{\mathbf{R}} f(x)dm_g(x).$$

Proof. If $f \in LRS_g(\mathbf{R})$, then $\int_{\mathbf{R}} f(x)dm_g(x)$ is finite, and hence the estimate $|f_k - f_1| \leq |f - f_1|$ and Theorem 4.18 give $\lim_{k\to\infty} \int_{\mathbf{R}} f_k(x)dm_g(x) = \int_{\mathbf{R}} f(x)dm_g(x)$.

On the other hand, if $\lim_{k\to\infty} \int_{\mathbf{R}} f_k(x)dm_g(x)$ is finite, then by Theorems 4.7

(ii) (d) and 4.13 (iii) we have

$$\begin{aligned} S_g(f - f_1) &= S_g\Big(\sum_{k=2}^{\infty}(f_k - f_{k-1})\Big) \\ &\le \sum_{k=2}^{\infty} S_g(f_k - f_{k-1}) \\ &= \lim_{n\to\infty}\sum_{k=2}^{n}\int_{\mathbf{R}}\big(f_k(x) - f_{k-1}(x)\big)dm_g(x) \\ &= \lim_{n\to\infty}\sum_{k=2}^{n}\Big(\int_{\mathbf{R}} f_k(x)dm_g(x) - \int_{\mathbf{R}} f_{k-1}(x)dm_g(x)\Big) \\ &= -\int_{\mathbf{R}} f_1(x)dm_g(x) + \lim_{n\to\infty}\int_{\mathbf{R}} f_k(x)dm_g(x) < \infty. \end{aligned}$$

Consequently, there exists a sequence of nonnegative step functions $(s_j)_{j=1}^{\infty}$ on $\mathbf{R}$ such that

$$f - f_1 \le h = \sum_{j=1}^{\infty} s_j = \lim_{n\to\infty}\sum_{j=1}^{n} s_j$$

and

$$S_g(f - f_1) \le \sum_{j=1}^{\infty} A_g(s_j) < \infty.$$

With the last result, we have

$$S_g\big(h - \sum_{j=1}^{n} s_j\big) \le \sum_{j=n+1}^{\infty} S_g(s_j) \le \sum_{j=n+1}^{\infty} A_g(s_j) \to 0 \quad \text{as} \quad n \to \infty.$$

This, plus Theorem 4.12, implies $h \in LRS_g(\mathbf{R})$. Since

$$f_1 \in LRS_g(\mathbf{R}) \quad \text{and} \quad \lim_{k\to\infty}(f_k - f_1) = f - f_1 \ m_g - a.e. \text{ on } \mathbf{R},$$

we conclude from Theorem 4.18 that $f \in LRS_g(\mathbf{R})$ and

$$\int_{\mathbf{R}}\big(f(x) - f_1(x)\big)dm_g(x) = \lim_{k\to\infty}\int_{\mathbf{R}}\big(f_k - f_1(x)\big)(x)dm_g(x),$$

as desired. □

Given a sequence $(a_n)_{n=1}^{\infty}$ in $\mathbf{R}$ bounded from below. If $b_n = \inf\{a_m : m \ge n\}$ then $(b_n)_{n=1}^{\infty}$ is an increasing sequence of real numbers, and hence $\lim_{n\to\infty} b_n \in \mathbf{R}^e$. Using this notion, we have the following Fatou's lemma.

Lemma 4.20. *Let $g : \mathbf{R} \to \mathbf{R}$ be increasing. If $(f_k)_{k=1}^{\infty}$ is a nonnegative function sequence in $LRS_g(\mathbf{R})$ such that $\lim_{k\to\infty} f_k = f$ m_g-a.e. on $\mathbf{R}$ and*

$$\lim_{n\to\infty}\inf_{m\ge n}\int_{\mathbf{R}} f_m(x)dm_g(x)$$

is finite, then $f \in LRS_g(\mathbf{R})$ *with*

$$\int_{\mathbf{R}} f(x)dm_g(x) \leq \lim_{n\to\infty} \inf_{m\geq n} \int_{\mathbf{R}} f_m(x)dm_g(x).$$

Proof. For each $k \in \mathbf{N}$ let $h_k = \inf_{j\geq k} f_j$. Then $(h_k)_{k=1}^{\infty}$ is increasing and satisfied with

$$f = \lim_{k\to\infty} h_k = \sup_{k\in\mathbf{N}} h_k \quad m_g - a.e. \text{ on } \mathbf{R}.$$

By Theorem 4.19 and the fact that $0 \leq h_k \leq f_j$ for each $j \geq k$, we derive

$$\int_{\mathbf{R}} f(x)dm_g(x) = \lim_{k\to\infty} \int_{\mathbf{R}} h_k(x)dm_g(x) \leq \lim_{k\to\infty} \inf_{j\geq k} \int_{\mathbf{R}} f_j(x)dm_g(x),$$

as desired. □

In the rest of this section, we use the above-discussed convergence results to show that the Lebesgue–Radon–Stieltjes integrals is a generalization of the Riemann–Stieltjes integrals.

Theorem 4.21. *Let* $g : \mathbf{R} \to \mathbf{R}$ *be increasing and continuous, and suppose* $f : \mathbf{R} \to \mathbf{R}$ *equals* 0 *outside the finite interval* $[a, b] \subset \mathbf{R}$. *If* $f \in RS_g[a, b]$, *then* $f \in LRS_g(\mathbf{R})$ *with*

$$\int_{\mathbf{R}} f(x)dm_g(x) = \int_a^b f(x)dg(x).$$

Proof. Assume $f \in RS_g[a, b]$. For each $k \in \mathbf{N}$, partition $[a, b]$ into k subintervals with equal length k^{-1}. Denote this partition by $P = \{x_j\}_{j=0}^{k}$. Define

$$G_k = \sum_{j=1}^{k} m_j 1_{[x_{j-1},x_j)} \quad \text{and} \quad H_k = \sum_{j=1}^{k} M_j 1_{[x_{j-1},x_j)},$$

where

$$m_j = \inf\{f(x) : x \in [x_{j-1}, x_j]\} \text{ and } M_j = \sup\{f(x) : x \in [x_{j-1}, x_j]\}.$$

Clearly, $(G_k)_{k=1}^{\infty}$ and $(H_k)_{k=1}^{\infty}$ are increasing and decreasing sequences respectively, but also G_k and H_k belong to $LRS_g(\mathbf{R})$ thanks to both that g is continuous on $\mathbf{R}$ and that $f \in RS_g[a, b]$ implies

$$\begin{aligned}
\lim_{k\to\infty} \int_{\mathbf{R}} G_k(x)dm_g(x) &= \lim_{k\to\infty} A_g(G_k) \\
&= \lim_{k\to\infty} \sum_{j=1}^{k} m_j \big(g(x_j) - g(x_{j-1})\big) \\
&= \int_a^b f(x)dg(x)
\end{aligned}$$

and

$$\begin{aligned}\lim_{k\to\infty}\int_{\mathbf{R}} H_k(x)dm_g(x) &= \lim_{k\to\infty} A_g(H_k)\\ &= \lim_{k\to\infty}\sum_{j=1}^{k} M_j\big(g(x_j)-g(x_{j-1})\big)\\ &= \int_a^b f(x)dg(x).\end{aligned}$$

Putting $G=\lim_{k\to\infty} G_k$ and $H=\lim_{k\to\infty} H_k$, we employ Theorem 4.19 to deduce $G,H\in LRS_g(\mathbf{R})$ for which $G\le f\le H$ m_g-a.e. on $\mathbf{R}$. Notice also that

$$H_k-G_k\ge 0 \quad\text{and}\quad \lim_{k\to\infty}(H_k-G_k)=H-G \quad m_g-a.e.\ \text{ on }\ \mathbf{R}.$$

So, from Theorems 4.17 and 4.19 it follows that

$$\begin{aligned}0 &\le \int_{\mathbf{R}}\big(H(x)-G(x)\big)dm_g(x)\\ &= \lim_{k\to\infty}\int_{\mathbf{R}}\big(H_k(x)-G_k(x)\big)dm_g(x)\\ &= \lim_{k\to\infty}\int_{\mathbf{R}} H_k(x)dm_g(x)-\lim_{k\to\infty}\int_{\mathbf{R}} G_k(x)dm_g(x)=0.\end{aligned}$$

The above estimates indicate that $H-G=0$ and so $G=f=H$ m_g-a.e. on $\mathbf{R}$. Accordingly, $f\in LRS_g(\mathbf{R})$ with

$$\int_{\mathbf{R}} f(x)dm_g(x)=\lim_{k\to\infty}\int_{\mathbf{R}} G_k(x)dm_g(x)=\int_a^b f(x)dg(x). \qquad \square$$

Theorem 4.21 provides a practical way to evaluate many Lebesgue–Radon–Stieltjes integrals.

Example 4.22. Let

$$g(x)=\begin{cases} 0\,, & x<0,\\ 1-e^{-x}\,, & x\ge 0.\end{cases}$$

Then

$$\begin{aligned}&\int_{\mathbf{R}} 1_{[-1,1]}(x)e^x dm_g(x)\\ &=\int_{\mathbf{R}} 1_{[-1,-1]}(x)e^x dm_g(x)+\int_{\mathbf{R}} 1_{(-1,0)}(x)e^x dm_g(x)+\int_{\mathbf{R}} 1_{[0,1]}(x)e^x dm_g(x)\\ &=e^{-1}\big(g((-1)^+)-g((-1)^-)\big)+0+\int_0^1 e^x dg(x)\\ &=\int_0^1 e^x e^{-x}dx=1.\end{aligned}$$

It is worth mentioning that the generalization breaks down whenever Riemann–Stieltjes integration is improper. For instance, when $p \in (0,1]$, $\int_1^\infty x^{-p}\sin x dx$ is convergent – see also Example 3.40, but $\int_1^\infty x^{-p}|\sin x|dx = \infty$ which means that $\int_{[1,\infty)} x^{-p}\sin x dx$ does not exist. However, the following assertion is valid.

Corollary 4.23. *Let $f, g : \mathbf{R} \to \mathbf{R}$ be two functions such that g is increasing and continuous and that f belongs to $RS_g[-n,n]$ for any $n \in \mathbf{N}$ with*

$$\lim_{n\to\infty} \int_{-n}^{n} |f(x)|dg(x) < \infty.$$

Then $f \in LRS_g(\mathbf{R})$ and $\int_{\mathbf{R}} f(x)dm_g(x) = \lim_{n\to\infty} \int_{-n}^{n} f(x)dg(x)$.

Proof. Since $\{|f1_{[-n,n]}|\}_{n=1}^\infty$ is an increasing sequence and convergent to $|f|$ but also both $|f1_{[-n,n]}|$ and $f1_{[-n,n]}$ lie in $LRS_g(\mathbf{R})$ due to Theorem 4.21, a further application of Theorem 4.21 yields

$$\lim_{n\to\infty} \int_{\mathbf{R}} |f(x)1_{[-n,n]}(x)|dm_g(x) = \lim_{n\to\infty} \int_{-n}^{n} |f(x)|dg(x) < \infty.$$

This limit result and Theorem 4.19 derive $|f| \in LRS_g(\mathbf{R})$. Consequently, the pointwise convergence $\lim_{n\to\infty} f(x)1_{[-n,n]}(x) = f(x)$, via Theorem 4.18, gives $f \in LRS_g(\mathbf{R})$ with

$$\int_{\mathbf{R}} f(x)dm_g(x) = \lim_{n\to\infty} \int_{-n}^{n} f(x)dg(x).$$

□

4.4 Extension via Measurability

This section deals with the Lebesgue–Radon–Stieltjes integration on any subset of the real line in terms of measurable functions.

Definition 4.24. Let $g : \mathbf{R} \to \mathbf{R}$ be increasing. A function $f : \mathbf{R} \to \mathbf{R}^e$ is called m_g-measurable provided there is a sequence $(s_k)_{k=1}^\infty$ of step functions on $\mathbf{R}$ such that $\lim_{k\to\infty} s_k = f$ m_g-a.e. on $\mathbf{R}$.

A good but important thing is that integrability can be characterized in terms of measurability.

Theorem 4.25. *Let $g : \mathbf{R} \to \mathbf{R}$ be increasing. Then $f \in LRS_g(\mathbf{R})$ if and only if f is m_g-measurable and $S_g(|f|) < \infty$.*

Proof. The necessity follows from the proof of Theorem 4.18 with $f_k = f$ for all $k \in \mathbf{N}$. To argue the sufficiency, suppose $(s_k)_{k=1}^\infty$ is a sequence of step functions on $\mathbf{R}$ with $\lim_{k\to\infty} s_k = f$ m_g-a.e. on $\mathbf{R}$, and let $S_g(|f|) < \infty$. Using the second part of the argument of Theorem 4.19 we can obtain $h \in LRS_g(\mathbf{R})$ such that $|f| \le h$. If

$$t_k = \begin{cases} s_k\,, & |s_k| \le h, \\ h\,, & s_k > h, \\ -h\,, & s_k < -h, \end{cases}$$

then $|t_k| \le h$ and $t_k \in LRS_g(\mathbf{R})$ by Theorem 4.13 (iii). It is easy to see that $\lim_{k\to\infty} t_k = f$ m_g-a.e. on $\mathbf{R}$. So Theorem 4.18 is used to deduce $f \in LRS_g(\mathbf{R})$. □

Any step function on $\mathbf{R}$ is obviously m_g-measurable and consequently $1 = \lim_{n\to\infty} 1_{(-n,n)}$ is m_g-measurable. Moreover, the m_g-measurability is preserved under the usual analytic operations – more precisely, we have the following property.

Theorem 4.26. *Let $g : \mathbf{R} \to \mathbf{R}$ be increasing.*

(i) *If $f : \mathbf{R} \to \mathbf{R}^e$ is m_g-measurable, so are $|f|$, f^+ and f^-.*

(ii) *If $f_1, f_2 : \mathbf{R} \to \mathbf{R}^e$ are m_g-measurable, so are $f_1 \pm f_2$, $f_1 f_2$, f_1/f_2 (where $f_2 \neq 0$ m_g-a.e. on $\mathbf{R}$), $\max\{f_1, f_2\}$, and $\min\{f_1, f_2\}$.*

(iii) *If $(f_j)_{j=1}^{\infty}$ is a sequence of m_g-measurable functions from $\mathbf{R}$ to $\mathbf{R}^e$, so are $\limsup f_j$ and $\liminf f_j$. In particular, if the m_g-measurable sequence $(f_j)_{j=1}^{\infty}$ converges to f m_g-a.e. on $\mathbf{R}$, then f is m_g-measurable.*

Proof. (i) This follows from the definitions.

(ii) It suffices to verify that $1/f$ is m_g-measurable whenever $f : \mathbf{R} \to \mathbf{R}^e$ is m_g-measurable and $f \neq 0$ m_g-a.e. on $\mathbf{R}$. Assuming the statement after the whenever, we get a sequence of step functions $(s_k)_{k=1}^{\infty}$ on $\mathbf{R}$ such that $\lim_{k\to\infty} s_k = f$ m_g-a.e. on $\mathbf{R}$. If

$$t_k(x) = \begin{cases} \frac{1}{s_k(x)}, & s_k(x) \neq 0, \\ 1, & s_k(x) = 0,\ x \in (-k, k), \\ 0, & s_k(x) = 0,\ x \in \mathbf{R} \setminus (-k, k), \end{cases}$$

then $(t_k)_{k=1}^{\infty}$ is a sequence of step functions on $\mathbf{R}$ and convergent to $1/f$ m_g-a.e. on $\mathbf{R}$, and hence $1/f$ is m_g-measurable.

(iii) Noticing the following formulas

$$\limsup f_j = \lim_{j\to\infty} \sup_{k\geq j} f_k = \lim_{j\to\infty} \lim_{l\to\infty} \sup_{l\geq k\geq j} f_k$$

and

$$\liminf f_j = \lim_{j\to\infty} \inf_{k\geq j} f_k = \lim_{j\to\infty} \lim_{l\to\infty} \inf_{l\geq k\geq j} f_k,$$

we just prove the special case that the m_g-a.e. limit function f of the m_g-measurable function sequence $(f_j)_{j=1}^{\infty}$ is m_g-measurable. To do so, let $\mathcal{S} = (S_k)_{k=1}^{\infty}$ be a sequence of disjoint simple sets such that $\mathbf{R} = \cup_{k=1}^{\infty} S_k$ and $0 < m_g(S_k) < \infty$. Then the positive function $h : \mathbf{R} \to \mathbf{R}^e$, defined via putting $h(x) = \left(k^2 m_g(S_k)\right)^{-1}$ for $x \in S_k$, belongs to $LRS_g(\mathbf{R})$ thanks to Theorem 4.19. Since f_j is m_g-measurable, by Definition 4.24 there exists a sequence of step functions $(s_{j,k})_{k=1}^{\infty}$ on $\mathbf{R}$ such that $s_{j,k}$ equals 0 outside a finite union of sets from $\mathcal{S}$, and $\lim_{k\to\infty} s_{j,k} = f_j$ m_g-a.e. on $\mathbf{R}$. Accordingly, if

$$q_{j,k} = \frac{h s_{j,k}}{h + |s_{j,k}|}$$

and

$$q_j = \begin{cases} \frac{h f_j}{h+|f_j|}, & f_j \neq \pm\infty, \\ \pm h, & f_j = \pm\infty, \end{cases}$$

then $\lim_{k\to\infty} q_{j,k} = q_j$ m_g-a.e. on $\mathbf{R}$; $q_{j,k}$ is a step function on $\mathbf{R}$ and hence q_j is m_g-measurable; moreover $|q_j| \le h$ and $(q_j)_{j=1}^{\infty}$ converges m_g-a.e. on $\mathbf{R}$ to the following function:

$$q = \begin{cases} \frac{hf}{h+|f|}, & f \neq \pm\infty, \\ \pm h, & f_j = \pm\infty. \end{cases}$$

From $h \in LRS_g(\mathbf{R})$, Theorems 4.18 and 4.25 it follows that q is m_g-measurable, and one can define a sequence of step functions $(s_j)_{j=1}^{\infty}$, each being 0 outside a finite union of sets from $\mathcal{S}$, so that $|s_j| < h$ and $\lim_{j\to\infty} s_j = q$ m_g-a.e. on $\mathbf{R}$. Accordingly, $s_j h/(h - |s_j|)$ is a step function on $\mathbf{R}$ and convergent to f (see also the definition of q) m_g-a.e. on $\mathbf{R}$, and consequently, f is m_g-measurable. $\square$

In the light of Theorem 4.25, we introduce the following concept.

Definition 4.27. Let $g : \mathbf{R} \to \mathbf{R}$ be increasing.

(i) A subset E of $\mathbf{R}$ is called the Lebesgue–Radon–Stieltjes g-measurable or m_g-measurable provided 1_E is m_g-measurable.

(ii) If $E \subseteq \mathbf{R}$ is m_g-measurable, then

$$m_g(E) = \int_{\mathbf{R}} 1_E(x)dm_g(x) = S_g(1_E)$$

is said to be the Lebesgue–Radon–Stieltjes g-measure of E.

(iii) Let $E \subseteq \mathbf{R}$ and $f : \mathbf{R} \to \mathbf{R}^e$. We say $f \in LRS_g(E)$ provided $f1_E \in LRS_g(\mathbf{R})$ and E is m_g-measurable. In this case, the Lebesgue–Radon–Stieltjes integral of f on E is defined by

$$\int_E f(x)dm_g(x) = \int_{\mathbf{R}} f(x)1_E(x)dm_g(x).$$

In particular, if $g = id$, i.e., $g(x) = x$ for all $x \in \mathbf{R}$, in (i)–(ii)–(iii), then the corresponding terms are Lebesgue measurable, the Lebesgue measure, the Lebesgue integral.

Remark 4.28. A few words on Definition 4.27 are arranged below:

(a) It is possible to have $m_g(E) = \infty$ – this means that E has infinite g-measure. Of course, if $m_g(E) < \infty$ then E is said to have finite g-measure – in particular, if $m_g(E) = m_g(S) < \infty$ whenever $E = S$ is a simple set;

(b) When $f \in LRS_g(\mathbf{R})$ and E is m_g-measurable, (a) and Theorem 4.25 are applied to imply that $f1_E$ is m_g-measurable with $S_g(|f1_E|) \le S_g(|f|) < \infty$, and hence $f1_E \in LRS_g(\mathbf{R})$ by Theorem 4.25;

(c) Given an m_g-measurable interval I in $\mathbf{R}$, the theorems about $LRS_g(\mathbf{R})$ given above have analogues for $LRS_g(I)$, obtained by multiplying all functions involved by 1_I. In order to avoid unnecessary repeating, we will not state such theorems explicitly, yet will use them freely.

Theorem 4.29. *Let $g : \mathbf{R} \to \mathbf{R}$ be increasing and $\mathcal{M}_g$ comprise all m_g-measurable subsets of* $\mathbf{R}$.

(i) *$\mathcal{M}_g$ is an σ-ring in the sense of: $\emptyset, \mathbf{R} \in \mathcal{M}_g$; $\mathbf{R} \setminus E \in \mathcal{M}_g$ for $E \in \mathcal{M}_g$; $\cup_{j=1}^{\infty} E_j \in \mathcal{M}_g$ for $\{E_j\}_{j=1}^{\infty} \subseteq \mathcal{M}_g$.*

(ii) *m_g is a measure on $\mathcal{M}_g$ in the sense of: $m_g(\emptyset) = 0$ and $m_g(\cup_{j=1}^{\infty} E_j) = \sum_{j=1}^{\infty} m_g(E_j)$ for any sequence $(E_j)_{j=1}^{\infty}$ of disjoint sets in $\mathcal{M}_g$.*

(iii) *$m_g(\mathbf{R}) < \infty$ if and only if m_g is bounded on all simple sets if and only if $\lim_{n\to\infty} g(\pm n) < \infty$.*

(iv) *If $f \in LRS_g(\mathbf{R})$, then $L_g(E) = \int_E f dm_g$ and $L_g^{\pm}(E) = \int_E f^{\pm} dm_g$ are countably additive in the sense of:*

$$L_g(\cup_{j=1}^{\infty} E_j) = \sum_{j=1}^{\infty} L_g(E_j) \quad \textit{and} \quad L_g^{\pm}(\cup_{j=1}^{\infty} E_j) = \sum_{j=1}^{\infty} L_g^{\pm}(E_j)$$

for any sequence $(E_j)_{j=1}^{\infty}$ of disjoint sets in $\mathcal{M}_g$.

(v) *If $\int_E f dm_g = 0$ for any $E \in \mathcal{M}_g$, then f is an m_g-null function.*

(vi) *A function $f : \mathbf{R} \to \mathbf{R}^e$ is m_g-measurable if and only if $E(f; c) = \{x \in \mathbf{R} : f(x) > c\}$ is m_g-measurable for any $c \in \mathbf{R}$.*

Proof. (i) Below is a simple observation. If $f \geq 0$ is m_g-measurable and $E, E_1, E_2 \in \mathcal{M}_g$, then $1_E f$ is m_g-measurable by Theorem 4.26 (ii), and the following two formulas are valid:

$$1_{\mathbf{R}\setminus E} f = (1 - 1_E) f; \quad 1_{E_1 \cup E_2} f = \max\{1_{E_1} f, 1_{E_2} f\}.$$

The preceding observation, along with Definition 4.27 and Theorems 4.25-4.26, establishes the desired result.

(ii) Trivially, we have $m_g(\emptyset) = 0$. Suppose $(E_j)_{j=1}^{\infty}$ is a sequence of disjoint sets in $\mathcal{M}_g$. Then it is easy to see that $1_{\cup_{j=1}^{\infty} E_j}$ is the pointwise limit of the increasing sequence $\left(\sum_{j=1}^{n} 1_{E_j}\right)_{n=1}^{\infty}$ and so that

$$\begin{aligned} m_g\big(\cup_{j=1}^{\infty} E_j\big) &= \int_{\mathbf{R}} 1_{\cup_{j=1}^{\infty} E_j} dm_g \\ &= \lim_{n\to\infty} \int_{\mathbf{R}} 1_{\cup_{j=1}^{n} E_j} dm_g \\ &= \lim_{n\to\infty} \sum_{j=1}^{n} \int_{\mathbf{R}} 1_{E_j} dm_g \\ &= \sum_{j=1}^{\infty} m_g(E_j). \end{aligned}$$

(iii) This follows from $\mathbf{R} = \cup_{j=1}^{\infty}(-j,j)$ and

$$\begin{aligned} m_g(\mathbf{R}) &= m_g\big((-1,1)\big) + \sum_{j=2}^{\infty} m_g\big((-j,j)\setminus(-j+1,j-1)\big) \\ &= m_g\big((-1,1)\big) + \lim_{n\to\infty}\sum_{j=2}^{n}\Big(m_g\big((-j,j)\big) - m_g\big((-j+1,j-1)\big)\Big) \\ &= \lim_{n\to\infty} m_g\big((-n,n)\big) \end{aligned}$$

due to (ii) above.

(iv) Since $f \in LRS_g(\mathbf{R})$, the result follows from Theorems 4.13 (iii) and 4.18 for $L_g^+(\cdot)$ as well as for $L_g^-(\cdot)$ and $L_g(\cdot)$.

(v) The sufficiency is evident. The necessity follows from the fact that $L_g(E) = 0$ implies $L_g^{\pm}(E) = 0$, for any $E \in \mathcal{M}_g$.

(vi) Assume the statement after the if and only if. Then

$$E(f;\infty) = \{x \in \mathbf{R} :\ f(x) = \infty\} = \cap_{j=1}^{\infty} E(f;j)$$

and

$$E(f;-\infty) = \{x \in \mathbf{R} :\ f(x) = -\infty\} = \cap_{j=1}^{\infty}\big(\mathbf{R}\setminus E(f;-j)\big)$$

are m_g-measurable. Moreover,

$$E(f;j,k) = \Big\{x \in \mathbf{R} :\ \frac{j}{k} < f(x) \le \frac{j+1}{k}\Big\} = E(f;\frac{j}{k}) \cap \big(\mathbf{R}\setminus E(f;\frac{j+1}{k})\big)$$

is m_g-measurable for $k \in \mathbf{N}$ and $j \in \mathbf{Z}$. Consequently, the characteristic functions $1_{E(f;\pm\infty)}$ and $1_{E(f;j,k)}$ are m_g-measurable. This gives that

$$f_k = k^{-1}\sum_{j=-\infty}^{\infty} j 1_{E(f;j,k)} + k 1_{E(f;\infty)} - k 1_{E(f;-\infty)}$$

is m_g-measurable and so is $f = \lim_{k\to\infty} f_k$ (m_g-a.e. on $\mathbf{R}$).

Conversely, fix $c \in \mathbf{R}$ and suppose f is m_g-measurable. Then there exists a sequence of step functions $(s_k)_{k=1}^{\infty}$ which converges to f m_g-a.e. on $\mathbf{R}$. Note that

$$\begin{aligned} \{x \in \mathbf{R} : \liminf s_k(x) > c\} &= \bigcup_{j=1}^{\infty} \liminf_{k\to\infty}\Big\{x \in \mathbf{R} :\ s_k(x) \ge c + \frac{1}{j}\Big\} \\ &= \bigcup_{j=1}^{\infty}\bigcup_{n=1}^{\infty}\bigcap_{m=n}^{\infty}\Big\{x \in \mathbf{R} :\ s_m(x) \ge c + \frac{1}{j}\Big\} \end{aligned}$$

is m_g-measurable since each $\{x \in \mathbf{R} :\ s_m(x) \ge c + \frac{1}{j}\}$ is a simple set. So, it follows that f is m_g-measurable since $f - \liminf_{k\to\infty} s_k$ is an m_g-null function. □

4.5 Double and Iterated Integrals with Applications

Motivated by Theorems 4.13 (iii) and 4.18 or 4.19 as well as Remark 3.19 or Theorem 3.18, in this section we settle the question of exchanging the order of the integration in a double integral, and of evaluating an integral as an iterated one, but also employ the established results to introduce an integration over an abstract set.

Definition 4.30. Let $g_1, g_2 : \mathbf{R} \to \mathbf{R}$ be increasing.

(i) A rectangle in $\mathbf{R}^2 = \mathbf{R} \times \mathbf{R}$ is a set of the form $I_1 \times I_2$ where I_1, I_2 are finite intervals in $\mathbf{R}$. A simple set in $\mathbf{R}^2$ is a union of finitely many disjoint rectangles.

(ii) The $g_1 \otimes g_2$-measure of a rectangle $I_1 \times I_2$ in $\mathbf{R}^2$ is determined by $m_{g_1 \otimes g_2}(I_1 \times I_2) = m_{g_1}(I_1) m_{g_2}(I_2)$. The $g_1 \otimes g_2$-measure of a simple set $S = \cup_{k=1}^n (I_{1,k} \times I_{2,k})$ in $\mathbf{R}^2$ is defined by

$$m_{g_1 \otimes g_2}(S) = \sum_{k=1}^n m_{g_1 \otimes g_2}(I_{1,k} \times I_{2,k}) = \sum_{k=1}^n m_{g_1}(I_{1,k}) m_{g_2}(I_{2,k}).$$

(iii) A function $f : \mathbf{R}^2 \to \mathbf{R}$ is said to be a step function on $\mathbf{R}^2$ provided $\{x = (x_1, x_2) \in \mathbf{R}^2 : f(x) \neq 0\}$ is a simple set $S = \cup_{k=1}^n I_{1,k} \times I_{2,k}$ for which f equals a constant c_k on $I_{1,k} \times I_{2,k}$.

(iv) The Lebesgue–Radon–Stieltjes double integral on $\mathbf{R}^2$ of a function $f : \mathbf{R}^2 \to \mathbf{R}^e$, denoted

$$\int_{\mathbf{R}^2} f \, dm_{g_1 \otimes g_2} = \int_{\mathbf{R}^2} f^+ dm_{g_1 \otimes g_2} - \int_{\mathbf{R}^2} f^- dm_{g_1 \otimes g_2},$$

is defined by a process similar to that used for the one-variable Lebesgue–Radon–Stieltjes integral in Section 4.1. The class of all functions f with $\int_{\mathbf{R}^2} f \, dm_{g_1} \otimes m_{g_2}$ being finite is written as $LRS_{g_1 \otimes g_2}(\mathbf{R}^2)$.

Under this definition, we can analogously establish the two-dimensional concepts and results corresponding to those presented in Sections 4.1-4.4. For instance, a function $f : \mathbf{R}^2 \to \mathbf{R}^e$ is $m_{g_1 \otimes g_2}$-measurable if there is a sequence of step functions $(s_k)_{k=1}^\infty$ on $\mathbf{R}^2$ such that $\lim_{k \to \infty} s_k = f$ $m_{g_1 \otimes g_2}$-a.e. on $\mathbf{R}^2$. When evaluating a Lebesgue–Radon–Stieltjes double integral, we are naturally led to a problem how to convert the integral to iterated integrals. This problem can be handled via Fubini–Tonelli's theorem (named in honor of Guido Fubinias and Leonida Tonelli) as follows.

Theorem 4.31. *For two increasing functions $g_1, g_2 : \mathbf{R} \to \mathbf{R}$, let $f : \mathbf{R}^2 \to \mathbf{R}^e$ be $m_{g_1 \otimes g_2}$-measurable.*

(i) *$f(\cdot, x_2)$ and $f(x_1, \cdot)$ are m_{g_1}-measurable for m_{g_2}-almost all $x_2 \in \mathbf{R}$ and m_{g_2}-measurable for m_{g_1}-almost all $x_1 \in \mathbf{R}$ respectively.*

(ii) *The following three conditions are equivalent:*

(a) $\int_{\mathbf{R}} \left(\int_{\mathbf{R}} |f| dm_{g_1} \right) dm_{g_2} < \infty$;

(b) $\int_{\mathbf{R}^2} |f| dm_{g_1 \otimes g_2} < \infty$;

(c) $\int_{\mathbf{R}} \left(\int_{\mathbf{R}} |f| dm_{g_2} \right) dm_{g_1} < \infty$.

Under any one of (a)-(b)-(c), the following three integrals

$$\int_{\mathbf{R}}\Big(\int_{\mathbf{R}} f dm_{g_1}\Big)dm_{g_2};\ \int_{\mathbf{R}^2} f dm_{g_1\otimes g_2};\ \int_{\mathbf{R}}\Big(\int_{\mathbf{R}} f dm_{g_2}\Big)dm_{g_1}$$

are finite and equal.

Proof. First of all, if f is a step function on $\mathbf{R}^2$, then there are real numbers $\{c_k\}_{k=1}^n$ and disjoint rectangles $\{I_{1,k}\times I_{2,k}\}_{k=1}^n$ such that

$$f=\sum_{k=1}^{n} c_k 1_{I_{1,k}\times I_{2,k}}.$$

Accordingly, (i) follows right away, and (ii) follows from the related definitions and properties of the integrals via

$$\begin{aligned}
\int_{\mathbf{R}^2} f dm_{g_1\otimes g_2} &= \sum_{k=1}^{n} c_k \int_{\mathbf{R}^2} 1_{I_{1,k}\times I_{2,k}} dm_{g_1\otimes g_2}\\
&= \sum_{k=1}^{n} c_k m_{g_1}(I_{1,k}) m_{g_2}(I_{2,k})\\
&= \sum_{k=1}^{n} c_k \int_{\mathbf{R}}\Big(\int_{\mathbf{R}} 1_{I_{1,k}} dm_{g_1}\Big) 1_{I_{2,k}} dm_{g_2}\\
&= \sum_{k=1}^{n} c_k \int_{\mathbf{R}}\Big(\int_{\mathbf{R}} 1_{I_{2,k}} dm_{g_2}\Big) 1_{I_{1,k}} dm_{g_1}\\
&= \int_{\mathbf{R}}\Big(\int_{\mathbf{R}} f dm_{g_2}\Big) dm_{g_1}\\
&= \int_{\mathbf{R}}\Big(\int_{\mathbf{R}} f dm_{g_1}\Big) dm_{g_2}.
\end{aligned}$$

Next, we consider the general case. Since $f=f^+-f^-$ and $|f|=f^++f^-$, without loss of generality we may assume $f\geq 0$.

(i) Note that $f=\lim_{n\to\infty} 1_{Q_n}\min\{f,n\}$ holds $m_{g_1\otimes g_2}$-a.e. on $\mathbf{R}^2$ where Q_n is the rectangle $\{(x_1,x_2)\in\mathbf{R}^2 : |x_1|,|x_2|\leq n\}$ for $n\in\mathbf{N}$. If $f_n=1_{Q_n}\min\{f,n\}$, then $0\leq f_n\leq n$ on Q_n and $f=0$ on $\mathbf{R}^2\setminus Q_n$. Since f is $m_{g_1\otimes g_2}$-measurable, so is f_n. Therefore, it suffices to verify (i) for each f_n.

By definition there are a sequence of step functions $(s_{n,k})_{k=1}^\infty$ on $\mathbf{R}^2$ and a set $E_n\subseteq Q_n$ such that $m_{g_1\otimes g_2}(E_n)=0$, $0\leq s_{n,k}\leq n$ and $\lim_{k\to\infty} s_{n,k}(x)=f_n(x)$ for $x\in Q_n\setminus E_n$.

Since E_n is an $m_{g_1\otimes g_2}$-null set, for any $\epsilon>0$ there are a sequence of rectangles $(R_{n,j})_{j=1}^\infty$ and a sequence of numbers $(c_{n,j})_{j=1}^\infty$ such that

$$1_{E_n}\leq \sum_{j=1}^{\infty} c_{n,j} 1_{R_{n,j}} \quad\text{and}\quad \sum_{j=1}^{\infty} c_{n,j} m_{g_1\otimes g_2}(R_{n,j})<\epsilon.$$

Accordingly,

$$\begin{aligned}\int_{\mathbf{R}}\Big(\int_{\mathbf{R}} 1_{E_n} dm_{g_2}\Big) dm_{g_1} &\le \sum_{j=1}^{\infty}\int_{\mathbf{R}}\Big(\int_{\mathbf{R}} c_{n,j}1_{R_{n,j}} dm_{g_2}\Big) dm_{g_1}\\ &= \sum_{j=1}^{\infty}\int_{R_{n,j}} c_{n,j}1_{R_{n,j}} dm_{g_1\otimes g_2} < \epsilon\end{aligned}$$

and

$$\begin{aligned}\int_{\mathbf{R}}\Big(\int_{\mathbf{R}} 1_{E_n} dm_{g_1}\Big) dm_{g_2} &\le \sum_{j=1}^{\infty}\int_{\mathbf{R}}\Big(\int_{\mathbf{R}} c_{n,j}1_{R_{n,j}} dm_{g_1}\Big) dm_{g_2}\\ &= \sum_{j=1}^{\infty}\int_{R_{n,j}} c_{n,j}1_{R_{n,j}} dm_{g_1\otimes g_2} < \epsilon.\end{aligned}$$

Since $\epsilon > 0$ is arbitrary, it follows that

$$\int_{\mathbf{R}} 1_{E_n}(x_1,\cdot) dm_{g_2} = 0 \quad \text{for } m_{g_1} - \text{almost all} \quad x_1 \in \mathbf{R}$$

and

$$\int_{\mathbf{R}} 1_{E_n}(\cdot,x_2) dm_{g_1} = 0 \quad \text{for } m_{g_2} - \text{almost all} \quad x_2 \in \mathbf{R}.$$

In other words, $1_{E_n}(x_1,\cdot)$ and $1_{E_n}(\cdot,x_2)$ are m_{g_2}-null and m_{g_1}-null functions for almost all x_1 and x_2 in $\mathbf{R}$ respectively, and consequently,

$$\lim_{j\to\infty} s_{n,j}(x_1,\cdot) = f_n(x_1,\cdot) \quad \text{for } m_{g_1} - \text{almost all} \quad x_1 \in \mathbf{R}$$

and

$$\lim_{j\to\infty} s_{n,j}(\cdot,x_2) = f_n(\cdot,x_2) \quad \text{for } m_{g_2} - \text{almost all} \quad x_2 \in \mathbf{R}.$$

Hence (i) is valid for f_n and then for f.

(ii) It is enough to show that $\int_{\mathbf{R}}\Big(\int_{\mathbf{R}} f dm_{g_1}\Big) dm_{g_2} < \infty$ if and only if

$$\int_{\mathbf{R}^2} f dm_{g_1\otimes g_2} < \infty.$$

To this end, let $f_n = 1_{Q_n}\min\{f,n\}$ be as above. Then

$$\int_{\mathbf{R}^2} f_n dm_{g_1\otimes g_2} = \int_{\mathbf{R}}\Big(\int_{\mathbf{R}} f_n dm_{g_1}\Big) dm_{g_2}$$

which follows from the dominated convergence theorem and the validity of this formula for the step functions $(s_{n,j})_{j=1}^{\infty}$ above.

Suppose $\int_{\mathbf{R}}\Big(\int_{\mathbf{R}} f dm_{g_1}\Big) dm_{g_2} < \infty$. Since $f_n = \min\{f,n\}1_{Q_n}$ belongs to $LRS_{g_1\otimes g_2}(\mathbf{R}^2)$ for each $n \in \mathbf{N}$ and converges to f as $n \to \infty$, we use the last formula for f_n to obtain

$$\int_{\mathbf{R}^2} f_n dm_{g_1\otimes g_2} \le \int_{\mathbf{R}}\Big(\int_{\mathbf{R}} f dm_{g_1}\Big) dm_{g_2} < \infty,$$

which ensures $f \in LRS_{g_1 \otimes g_2}(\mathbf{R}^2)$.

Conversely, if $f \in LRS_{g_1 \otimes g_2}(\mathbf{R}^2)$, then a combination of both the last formula for f_n and the monotone convergence theorem gives

$$\begin{aligned}\lim_{n\to\infty}\int_{\mathbf{R}}\Big(\int_{\mathbf{R}} f_n dm_{g_1}\Big)dm_{g_2} &= \lim_{n\to\infty}\int_{\mathbf{R}^2} f_n dm_{g_1\otimes g_2}\\ &= \int_{\mathbf{R}^2} f dm_{g_1\otimes g_2} < \infty.\end{aligned}$$

Since $(f_n)_{n=1}^{\infty}$ increases to f, for each fixed $x_2 \in \mathbf{R}$ the sequence $\big(f_n(\cdot, x_2)\big)_{n=1}^{\infty}$ increases to $f(\cdot, x_2)$, and consequently, if

$$F_n(x_2) = \int_{\mathbf{R}} f_n(\cdot, x_2)dm_{g_1} \quad \text{and} \quad F(x_2) = \int_{\mathbf{R}} f(\cdot, x_2)dm_{g_1},$$

then $\big(F_n(x_2)\big)_{n=1}^{\infty}$ increases to $F(x_2)$. Since each F_n is m_{g_2}-measurable by the argument for (i), so is F. This fact and the monotone convergence theorem yield

$$\lim_{n\to\infty}\int_{\mathbf{R}} F_n dm_{g_2} = \int_{\mathbf{R}} F dm_{g_2}.$$

The previous argument actually implies

$$\int_{\mathbf{R}}\Big(\int_{\mathbf{R}} f dm_{g_1}\Big)dm_{g_2} = \int_{\mathbf{R}^2} f dm_{g_1\otimes g_2} < \infty.$$

□

Example 4.32. Let $g_1(x) = g_2(x) = x$ on $\mathbf{R}$ and

$$f(x_1, x_2) = \begin{cases} x_1 \exp\big(-x_1^2(1+x_2^2)\big), & (x_1, x_2) \in [0,\infty)\times[0,\infty),\\ 0, & (x_1,x_2) \in \mathbf{R}^2 \setminus [0,\infty)\times[0,\infty).\end{cases}$$

Then

$$\begin{aligned}\int_{\mathbf{R}}\Big(\int_{\mathbf{R}} f dm_{g_1}\Big)dm_{g_2} &= \int_0^{\infty}\Big(\int_0^{\infty} x_1\exp\big(-x_1^2(1+x_2^2)\big)dx_1\Big)dx_2\\ &= \int_0^{\infty}\frac{dx_2}{2(1+x_2^2)} = \frac{\pi}{4},\end{aligned}$$

and hence by Theorem 4.31 (ii) and the substitution $z_1 = x_1 x_2$ we get

$$\begin{aligned}\frac{\pi}{4} &= \int_0^{\infty}\Big(\int_0^{\infty} x_1\exp\big(-x_1^2(1+x_2^2)\big)dx_2\Big)dx_1\\ &= \int_0^{\infty}\exp(-x_1^2)\Big(\int_0^{\infty}\exp(-z_1^2)dz_1\Big)dx_1\\ &= \Big(\int_0^{\infty}\exp(-t^2)dt\Big)^2,\end{aligned}$$

namely, $\int_0^{\infty}\exp(-t^2)dt = \sqrt{\pi}/2$.

The Fubini–Tonelli theorem can be used to establish the well-known Hermann Minkowski's inequality. To this end, we need the following Hölder's inequality which is named after Otto Hölder and viewed as a fundamental inequality in analysis.

Theorem 4.33. *Let $g : \mathbf{R} \to \mathbf{R}$ be increasing, $1 < p < \infty$ and $q = p/(p-1)$. If $f_1, f_2 : \mathbf{R} \to \mathbf{R}^e$ are m_g-measurable, then*

$$\int_{\mathbf{R}} |f_1 f_2| dm_g \le \Big(\int_{\mathbf{R}} |f_1|^p dm_g\Big)^{\frac{1}{p}} \Big(\int_{\mathbf{R}} |f_2|^q dm_g\Big)^{\frac{1}{q}}.$$

Proof. Case 1: $\int_{\mathbf{R}} |f_1|^p dm_g = \infty$ or $\int_{\mathbf{R}} |f_2|^q dm_g = \infty$. The desired inequality is trivial.

Case 2: $0 < \int_{\mathbf{R}} |f_1|^p dm_g < \infty$ and $0 < \int_{\mathbf{R}} |f_2|^q dm_g < \infty$. For this, we consider $f(t) = 1/p + t^q/q - t$ for $t \in [0, \infty)$ and get

$$f'(t) = t^{q-1} - 1 \begin{cases} < 0\,, & t \in [0,1), \\ > 0\,, & t \in (1, \infty), \end{cases}$$

which ensures that $f(t)$ has minimum 0 at $t = 1$, and hence $f(t) \ge 0$ for all $t \in [0, \infty)$ – in particular $f(ba^{1-p}) \ge 0$ for $a, b \in (0, \infty)$. Consequently,

$$ab \le \frac{a^p}{p} + \frac{b^q}{q} \quad \text{for} \quad a, b \in [0, \infty).$$

Taking

$$a = \frac{|f_1(x)|}{\big(\int_{\mathbf{R}} |f_1|^p dm_g\big)^{\frac{1}{p}}} \quad \text{and} \quad b = \frac{|f_2(x)|}{\big(\int_{\mathbf{R}} |f_2|^q dm_g\big)^{\frac{1}{q}}} \quad \text{for} \quad x \in \mathbf{R}$$

in the last inequality, we get

$$\frac{|f_1(x) f_2(x)|}{\big(\int_{\mathbf{R}} |f_1|^p dm_g\big)^{\frac{1}{p}} \big(\int_{\mathbf{R}} |f_2|^q dm_g\big)^{\frac{1}{q}}} \le \frac{|f_1(x)|^p}{p \int_{\mathbf{R}} |f_1|^p dm_g} + \frac{|f_2(x)|^q}{q \int_{\mathbf{R}} |f_2|^q dm_g},$$

whence deriving the required inequality via an integration with respect to m_g. □

Remark 4.34.

(i) The case $p = q = 2$ of Hölder's inequality is the so-called Cauchy–Schwarz's inequality.

(ii) When $p = 1$ and $q = p/(p-1) = \infty$, the Hölder inequality is still valid in the sense of

$$\int_{\mathbf{R}} |f_1 f_2| dm_g \le \Big(\int_{\mathbf{R}} |f_1| dm_g\Big) \inf\Big\{c \ge 0 : \ m_g\big(\{x \in \mathbf{R} : |f_2(x)| > c\}\big) = 0\Big\}.$$

(iii) The Hölder inequality has the following generalization: If $p_1, \ldots, p_n \in (1, \infty)$ with $\sum_{j=1}^n p_j^{-1} = 1$, and $f_1, \ldots, f_n$ are m_g-measurable, then

$$\int_{\mathbf{R}} \prod_{j=1}^n |f_j| dm_g \le \prod_{j=1}^n \Big(\int_{\mathbf{R}} |f_j|^{p_j} dm_g\Big)^{\frac{1}{p_j}}.$$

This can be proved by Hölder's inequality for f_1 and $\prod_{j=2}^n f_j$ and induction on

$$\int_{\mathbf{R}} \prod_{j=2}^{n} |f_j|^{\frac{p_1}{p_1-1}} dm_g.$$

Now, we can establish the following general form of Minkowski's inequality.

Theorem 4.35. *Let $g_1, g_2 : \mathbf{R} \to \mathbf{R}$ be increasing and $1 \le p < \infty$. If $f : \mathbf{R}^2 \to \mathbf{R}^e$ is $m_{g_1 \otimes g_2}$-measurable, then*

$$\Big(\int_{\mathbf{R}} \Big(\int_{\mathbf{R}} |f| dm_{g_2}\Big)^p dm_{g_1}\Big)^{\frac{1}{p}} \le \int_{\mathbf{R}} \Big(\int_{\mathbf{R}} |f|^p dm_{g_1}\Big)^{\frac{1}{p}} dm_{g_2}.$$

Proof. The case $p = 1$ follows immediately from the Fubini–Tonell's theorem. Next, let $p \in (1, \infty)$. Suppose $F(x_1) = \int_{\mathbf{R}} |f(x_1, x_2)| dm_{g_2}(x_2)$. Then a combination of Fubini–Tonelli's theorem and Hölder's inequality gives

$$\begin{aligned}
\int_{\mathbf{R}} F^p dm_{g_1} &= \int_{\mathbf{R}} F^{p-1} F dm_{g_1} \\
&= \int_{\mathbf{R}} (F(x_1))^{p-1} \Big(\int_{\mathbf{R}} |f(x_1, x_2)| dm_{g_2}(x_2)\Big) dm_{g_1}(x_1) \\
&= \int_{\mathbf{R}} \Big(\int_{\mathbf{R}} |f(x_1, x_2)| F^{p-1}(x_1) dm_{g_1}(x_1)\Big) dm_{g_2}(x_2) \\
&\le \int_{\mathbf{R}} \Big(\int_{\mathbf{R}} |f(x_1, x_2)|^p dm_{g_1}(x_1)\Big)^{\frac{1}{p}} \Big(\int_{\mathbf{R}} F^p dm_{g_1}\Big)^{p-1} dm_{g_2}(x_2),
\end{aligned}$$

whence deriving the required inequality. □

Remark 4.36. In Theorem 4.35, if $f(x_1, 1) = f_1(x_1)$ and $f(x_1, 2) = f_2(x_1)$ are m_{g_1}-measurable, and if g_2 is a step function with two steps as follows:

$$g_2(x_2) = \begin{cases} 0\,, & x_2 \in (-\infty, 1), \\ 1\,, & x_2 \in [1, 2], \\ 2\,, & x_2 \in (2, \infty), \end{cases}$$

then the well-known Minkowski inequality of the triangle type:

$$\Big(\int_{\mathbf{R}} |f_1 + f_2|^p dm_{g_1}\Big)^{\frac{1}{p}} \le \Big(\int_{\mathbf{R}} |f_1|^p dm_{g_1}\Big)^{\frac{1}{p}} + \Big(\int_{\mathbf{R}} |f_2|^p dm_{g_1}\Big)^{\frac{1}{p}}$$

holds for $p \in [1, \infty)$ by Remark 4.10 (ii) (a)-(b). In case of $p = \infty$, we can readily get

$$\begin{aligned}
&\inf\Big\{c \ge 0 : \; m_g\big(\{x \in \mathbf{R} : |f_1(x) + f_2(x)| > c\}\big) = 0\Big\} \\
&\le \inf\Big\{c \ge 0 : \; m_g\big(\{x \in \mathbf{R} : |f_1(x)| > c\}\big) = 0\Big\} \\
&+ \inf\Big\{c \ge 0 : \; m_g\big(\{x \in \mathbf{R} : |f_2(x)| > c\}\big) = 0\Big\}.
\end{aligned}$$

Furthermore, it is easy to verify that

$$\int_{\mathbf{R}} |f_1 + f_2|^p dm_{g_1} \leq \int_{\mathbf{R}} |f_1|^p dm_{g_1} + \int_{\mathbf{R}} |f_2|^p dm_{g_1}$$

holds for $p \in (0, 1)$.

Based on Remark 4.36 and Definition 4.9, we consider the class of Lebesgue–Radon–Stieltjes p-integral functions.

Definition 4.37. Let $g : \mathbf{R} \to \mathbf{R}$ be increasing and $p \in (0, \infty]$.

(i) When $p \in (0, \infty)$, the so-called Lebesgue–Radon–Stieltjes space $LRS_g^p(\mathbf{R})$, often denoted $L^p(m_g, \mathbf{R})$, comprises all functions $f : \mathbf{R} \to \mathbf{R}^e$ satisfying $|f|^p \in LRS_g(\mathbf{R})$ or $S_g(|f|^p) < \infty$. Regarding the limiting case $p = \infty$, $LRS_g^\infty(\mathbf{R})$, often denoted $L^\infty(m_g, \mathbf{R})$, stands for the class of all functions $f : \mathbf{R} \to \mathbf{R}^e$ with $\inf\{c \geq 0 : m_g(\{x \in \mathbf{R} : |f(x)| \leq c\})\}$ being finite.

(ii) If $E \subseteq \mathbf{R}$ is m_g-measurable, then $LRS_g^p(E)$ is defined to be the class of all functions $f : \mathbf{R} \to \mathbf{R}^e$ with $f1_E \in LRS_g^p(\mathbf{R})$.

Remark 4.38. For the purpose of integration it does not make any difference whenever one changes function values on m_g-null sets. Actually, one can integrate functions f that are only defined on an m_g-measurable set E for which $m_g(E^c) = 0$ simply by taking f to be 0 on $E^c = \mathbf{R} \setminus E$. In this manner, extended real-valued functions that are finite m_g-a.e can be treated freely as real-valued functions.

Minkowski's inequality in Remark 4.36 is used to produce the following convergence theorem in $LRS_g^p(\mathbf{R})$.

Theorem 4.39. *Let $g : \mathbf{R} \to \mathbf{R}$ be increasing, $p \in [1, \infty)$, and $C_0(\mathbf{R})$ the class of all continuous functions on $\mathbf{R}$ vanishing outside a bounded and closed subset of $\mathbf{R}$.*

(i) *If $f_j, f \in LRS_g^p(\mathbf{R})$, $\lim_{j\to\infty} S_g(|f_j - f|^p) = 0$, and $h \in LRS_g^{\frac{p}{p-1}}(\mathbf{R})$, then*

$$\lim_{j\to\infty} S_g(|f_j|^p) = S_g(|f|^p), \quad \lim_{j\to\infty} S_g(|f_j h - fh|^p) = 0,$$

and

$$\lim_{j\to\infty} \int_{\mathbf{R}} f_j h dm_g = \int_{\mathbf{R}} f h dm_g.$$

(ii) *If $f_j \in LRS_g^p(\mathbf{R})$ and $\lim_{j,k\to\infty} S_g(|f_j - f_k|^p) = 0$, then there exist a function $f \in LRS_g^p(\mathbf{R})$ and a subsequence $(f_{j_n})_{n=1}^\infty$ such that $\lim_{j\to\infty} S_g(|f_j - f|^p) = 0$ and $\lim_{n\to\infty} f_{j_n} = f$ m_g-a.e. on $\mathbf{R}$.*

(iii) *If $f \in LRS_g^p(\mathbf{R})$ and $\epsilon \in (0, 1)$, then there exists a function $h \in C_0(\mathbf{R})$ such that $S_g(|f - h|^p) < \epsilon^p$.*

Proof. (i) It suffices to handle the case $p \in (1, \infty)$ since $p/(p-1)$ is treated as ∞ when $p = 1$. Minkowski's inequality in Remark 4.36 gives

$$\left(S_g(|f_j|^p)\right)^{\frac{1}{p}} \leq \left(S_g(|f_j - f|^p)\right)^{\frac{1}{p}} + \left(S_g(|f|^p)\right)^{\frac{1}{p}}$$

and

$$\left(S_g(|f|^p)\right)^{\frac{1}{p}} \le \left(S_g(|f_j - f|^p)\right)^{\frac{1}{p}} + \left(S_g(|f_j|^p)\right)^{\frac{1}{p}},$$

whence deriving the first limit result. The second and third limit assertions follow from an application of Hölder's inequality to

$$\begin{aligned}\left|\int_{\mathbf{R}} f_j h dm_g - \int_{\mathbf{R}} f h dm_g\right| &\le \int_{\mathbf{R}} |f_j - f||h| dm_g \\ &\le \left(S_g(|f_j - f|^p)\right)^{\frac{1}{p}} \left(S_g(|h|^{\frac{p}{p-1}})\right)^{\frac{p-1}{p}}.\end{aligned}$$

(ii) Choose $(j_n)_{n=1}^{\infty}$ in $\mathbf{N}$ such that $\left(S_g(|f_j - f_{j_n}|^p)\right)^{\frac{1}{p}} \le 2^{-n}$ for all $j \ge j_n$ and $n \in \mathbf{N}$. Then $F_n(x) = \sum_{k=1}^{n-1} |f_{j_{k+1}} - f_{j_k}|$ increases with $n \ge 2$ and hence by Minkowski's inequality in Remark 4.36,

$$\left(S_g(|F_n|^p\right)^{\frac{1}{p}} \le \sum_{k=1}^{n-1} \left(S_g(|f_{j_{k+1}} - f_{j_k}|^p\right)^{\frac{1}{p}} \le \sum_{k=1}^{n-1} 2^{-k} < 1.$$

By Fatou's lemma (i.e., Lemma 4.20) there is an $F \in LRS_g^p(\mathbf{R})$ such that $\lim_{n\to\infty} F_n = F$ m_g-a.e. on $\mathbf{R}$ – this means that $f_{j_1} + \sum_{k=1}^{\infty} \left(f_{j_{k+1}} - f_{j_k}\right)$ is absolutely convergent and its partial sum sequence $(f_{j_n})_{n=1}^{\infty}$ converges (m_g-a.e. on $\mathbf{R}$) to a function $f \in LRS_g^p(\mathbf{R})$ thanks to $|f_{j_n}| \le F_n \le F$ m_g-a.e. on $\mathbf{R}$. A further application of the Minkowski inequality in Remark 4.36 gives

$$\begin{aligned}\left(S_g(|f_j - f|^p)\right)^{\frac{1}{p}} &\le \left(S_g(|f_j - f_{j_n}|^p)\right)^{\frac{1}{p}} + \left(S_g(|f_{j_n} - f|^p)\right)^{\frac{1}{p}} \\ &\le 2^{-n} + \sum_{k=n}^{\infty} \left(S_g(|f_{j_{k+1}} - f_{j_k}|^p\right)^{\frac{1}{p}} \le 2^{2-n},\end{aligned}$$

which deduces the desired conclusion.

(iii) For $f \in LRS_g^p(\mathbf{R})$ and $j \in \mathbf{N}$ let

$$f_j(x) = \begin{cases} f(x)\,, & |f(x)| \le j, \\ j\,, & f(x) \ge j, \\ -j\,, & f(x) < -j. \end{cases}$$

Then

$$|f_j - f| \le |f| \quad \text{and} \quad \lim_{j\to\infty} |f_j - f| = 0 \quad m_g - \text{a.e. on } \mathbf{R},$$

and hence for any $\epsilon \in (0,1)$ there is a $j \in \mathbf{N}$ such that $S_g(|f_j - f|^p) < \epsilon/2$ due to Theorem 4.18, and at the same time, there is a step function s on $\mathbf{R}$ such that

$$\left(S_g(|s - f_j|^p)\right)^{\frac{1}{p}} \le (2j)^{1-\frac{1}{p}} \left(\int_{\mathbf{R}} |s - f_j| dm_g\right)^{\frac{1}{p}} \le \frac{\epsilon}{2}.$$

Accordingly, the Minkowski's inequality in Remark 4.36 yields

$$\left(S_g(|f - s|^p)\right)^{\frac{1}{p}} \le \left(S_g(|f - f_j|^p)\right)^{\frac{1}{p}} + \left(S_g(|f_j - s|^p\right)^{\frac{1}{p}} < \epsilon.$$

Note that $s = \sum_{k=1}^{n} c_k 1_{I_k}$ where $\{c_k\}_{k=1}^{n}$ are constants and $\{I_k\}_{k=1}^{n}$ are disjoint finite intervals in $\mathbf{R}$. So, if each 1_{I_k} can be approximated by $C_0(\mathbf{R})$-functions, then the argument is finished. Without loss of generality (see also the argument for Theorem 2.41), we may assume $I_k = [0,1]$. For any $\epsilon > 0$ let

$$\phi_\epsilon(x) = \begin{cases} 0\,, & x \in (-\infty, -\epsilon), \\ 1 + \frac{x}{\epsilon}\,, & x \in [-\epsilon, 0), \\ 1\,, & x \in [0,1], \\ \frac{1+\epsilon-x}{\epsilon}\,, & x \in (1, 1+\epsilon], \\ 0\,, & x \in (1+\epsilon, \infty). \end{cases}$$

Then $\phi \in C_0(\mathbf{R})$ and

$$1_{[0,1]} \le \phi \quad \text{and} \quad \int_{\mathbf{R}} |\phi_\epsilon - 1_{[0,1]}|^p dm_g \le m_g\big([-\epsilon, 0)\big) + m_g\big((1, 1+\epsilon]\big).$$

Note that the right-hand side of the last inequality tends to zero as ϵ approaches zero since $\cap_{\epsilon>0}[-\epsilon, 0) = \emptyset = \cap_{\epsilon>0}(1, 1+\epsilon]$. So, the desired conclusion follows. □

The next application of Fubini–Tonelli's theorem is to provide a very useful way evaluating a Lebesgue–Radon–Stieltjes integral via the classical Lebesgue one or reducing a problem about an integral of a general function to a problem about the integration of characteristic functions.

Theorem 4.40. *Let $g : \mathbf{R} \to \mathbf{R}$ be increasing and $p \in (0, \infty)$. If $f : \mathbf{R} \to \mathbf{R}^e$ is m_g-measurable, then*

$$\int_{\mathbf{R}} |f|^p dm_g = p \int_0^\infty m_g\big(\{x \in \mathbf{R} : |f(x)| > t\}\big) t^{p-1} dt.$$

Proof. Using Fubini–Tonelli's theorem we have

$$\begin{aligned} \int_{\mathbf{R}} |f|^p dm_g &= \int_{\mathbf{R}} \Big(\int_0^{|f|} dt^p \Big) dm_g \\ &= p \int_{\mathbf{R}} \Big(\int_0^\infty 1_{\{0<t<|f|\}} t^{p-1} dt \Big) dm_g \\ &= p \int_0^\infty \Big(\int_{\mathbf{R}} 1_{\{x \in \mathbf{R} : |f(x)| > t\}} dm_g \Big) t^{p-1} dt \\ &= p \int_0^\infty t^{p-1} m_g\big(\{x \in \mathbf{R} : |f(x)| > t\}\big) dt. \end{aligned}$$

□

Remark 4.41. For a fixed point $c \in \mathbf{R}$, let

$$g(x) = \begin{cases} 0\,, & x < c, \\ 1\,, & x \ge c. \end{cases}$$

Then Remark 4.10 (ii) (b) and Theorem 4.40 are employed to deduce the well-known layer cake representation of a function $f : \mathbf{R} \to [0, \infty]$:

$$f(c) = \int_0^\infty 1_{\{x \in \mathbf{R}:\ f(x) > t\}}(c) dt.$$

Even more interesting and important is that Theorem 4.40 suggests a useful approach to define an integral on an abstract set.

Definition 4.42. For a given set X, let $\mathbf{P}(X)$ be the collection of all subsets of X and $\mu : \mathbf{P}(X) \to [0,\infty]$ be an increasing set function – μ satisfy both $\mu(\emptyset) = 0$ and $\mu(E_1) \le \mu(E_2)$ for $E_1 \subseteq E_2 \subseteq X$. Suppose $f : X \to [0,\infty]$. Then $\mu\big(\{x \in X : f(x) > t\}\big)$ is an increasing function of $t \in (0,\infty)$, and hence

$$\int_X f d\mu = \int_0^\infty \mu\big(\{x \in X : \ f(x) > t\}\big) dt$$

can be used to define the integral of f on X. In general, for $f : X \to \mathbf{R}^e$ we write

$$\int_X f d\mu = \int_X f^+ d\mu - \int_X f^- d\mu.$$

Theorem 4.43. *The integral introduced in Definition 4.42 has the following four properties:*

(i) $f_1, f_2 : X \to [0,\infty]$ *and* $f_1 \le f_2$ *implies* $\int_X f_1 d\mu \le \int_X f_2 d\mu$;

(ii) $\int_X \min\{f, c\} d\mu + \int_X (f-c)^+ d\mu = \int_X f d\mu$ *for any* $c \in [0,\infty)$;

(iii) $\int_X f d\mu = \lim_{\epsilon \to 0^+} \int_X \min\{(f-\epsilon)^+, \epsilon^{-1}\} d\mu$;

(iv) $\int_X c f d\mu = c \int_X f d\mu$ *for* $c \in [0,\infty)$.

Conversely, if a real-valued function L *defined on the family of functions from* $\mathbf{P}(X)$ *to* $[0,\infty]$ *obeys (i)-(ii)-(iii)-(iv) above, and* $\mu(E) = L(1_E)$ *is defined for any* $E \in \mathbf{P}(X)$*, then*

$$L(f) = \int_X f d\mu \quad \text{for} \quad f : X \to [0,\infty].$$

Proof. (i) This follows from the definition.

(ii) This follows from the following two formulas:

$$\int_X \min\{f, c\} d\mu = \int_0^c \mu\big(\{x \in X : \ f(x) > t\}\big) dt$$

and

$$\int_X (f-c)^+ d\mu = \int_c^\infty \mu\big(\{x \in X : \ f(x) > t\}\big) dt.$$

(iii) This follows from the monotone property of the function $t \to \mu\big(\{x \in X : f(x) > t\}\big)$ and the following calculation

$$\int_X \min\{(f-\epsilon)^+, \epsilon^{-1}\} d\mu = \int_\epsilon^{\epsilon+\epsilon^{-1}} \mu\big(\{x \in X : \ f(x) > t\}\big) dt.$$

(iv) This follows from the substitution $t = cs$.

For the reversed result, suppose L satisfies (i)-(ii)-(iii)-(iv) and set $\mu(E) = L(1_E)$ for $E \in \mathbf{P}(X)$. Fix $f : X \to [0,\infty]$. Then $f \ge \epsilon 1_{\{x \in X: \ f(x) > \epsilon\}}$ for any $\epsilon > 0$, and hence we may assume that $\mu(\{x \in X: \ f(x) > \epsilon\})$ is finite – otherwise it follows from (i) that

$$L(f) \geq \epsilon L(1_{\{x\in X: \ f(x)>\epsilon\}}) = \infty = \int_X f d\mu$$

and so that the above inequality becomes an equality.

Given $\epsilon > 0$ and $n \in \mathbf{N}$, set

$$c = \epsilon + \epsilon^{-1}, \ T_\epsilon(f) = \min\{(f-\epsilon)^+, \epsilon^{-1}\},$$

and

$$X_{n,j} = \left\{x \in X: \ T_\epsilon(f) > \frac{jc}{n}\right\} \quad \text{for} \quad j \in \{0, \ldots, n-1\}.$$

Using (ii) we obtain

$$\begin{aligned} & L(T_\epsilon(f)) - \int_X T_\epsilon(f) d\mu \\ & = \sum_{j=0}^{n-1} \left(L\Big(\min\Big\{T_\epsilon(f) - \frac{jc}{n}, \frac{c}{n} 1_{X_{n,j}}\Big\}\Big) - \int_X \min\Big\{T_\epsilon(f) - \frac{jc}{n}, \frac{c}{n} 1_{X_{n,j}}\Big\} d\mu \right). \end{aligned}$$

Meanwhile, using (i) and (iv) we find the following two estimates:

$$\frac{c}{n}\mu(X_{n,j+1}) \leq L\Big(\min\Big\{T_\epsilon(f) - \frac{jc}{n}, \frac{c}{n} 1_{X_{n,j}}\Big\}\Big) \leq \frac{c}{n}\mu(X_{n,j})$$

and

$$\frac{c}{n}\mu(X_{n,j+1}) \leq \int_X \Big(\min\Big\{T_\epsilon(f) - \frac{jc}{n}, \frac{c}{n} 1_{X_{n,j}}\Big\}\Big) d\mu \leq \frac{c}{n}\mu(X_{n,j}).$$

Therefore

$$\left|L(T_\epsilon(f)) - \int_X T_\epsilon(f) d\mu\right| \leq \frac{c}{n}\mu(X_{n,0}) = \frac{c}{n}\mu(\{x \in X: \ f(x) > \epsilon\}).$$

Since $\epsilon > 0$ and $n \in \mathbf{N}$ are arbitrary, this last estimate, along with (iii), must ensure $L(f) = \int_X f d\mu$. □

As an aside of Theorem 4.43, we can establish the following additive and subadditive properties of the above-defined integrals.

Corollary 4.44. *Given a set X, let $\mu : \mathbf{P}(X) \to [0, \infty]$ be an increasing set function, $f : X \to [0, \infty]$ and $E \subseteq X$.*

(i) If $c \in [0, \infty)$, then $\int_X (f + c)1_E d\mu = \int_X f 1_E d\mu + c\mu(E)$.

(ii) If μ is subadditive; that is, $\mu(E_1 \cup E_2) \leq \mu(E_1) + \mu(E_2)$ whenever $E_1, E_2 \subseteq X$, then

$$\int_X f 1_S d\mu \leq \int_X f 1_{S\cap E} d\mu + \int_{\mathbf{X}} f 1_{S\setminus E} d\mu \quad \textit{for} \quad S \subseteq X$$

with equality if E is μ-measurable; that is, $\mu(A) = \mu(A \cap E) + \mu(A \setminus E)$ for all $A \subseteq X$.

Proof. (i) This follows from Theorem 4.43 (ii) applied to $\min\{(f+c)1_E, c\} = c1_E$ and $\big((f+c)1_E - c\big)^+ = f1_E$.

(ii) Using both the subadditivity of μ and the equality $S = (S\cap E)\cup(S\setminus E)$ for any $S \subseteq X$, we have

$$\begin{aligned}\int_X f1_S d\mu &= \int_0^\infty \mu\big(\{x\in X:\ 1_S(x)f(x)>t\}\big)dt\\ &\le \int_0^\infty \mu\big(\{x\in X:\ 1_S(x)f(x)>t\}\big)dt\\ &+ \int_0^\infty \mu\big(\{x\in X:\ 1_{S\setminus E}(x)f(x)>t\}\big)dt\\ &= \int_X f1_{S\cap E}d\mu + \int_X f1_{S\setminus E}d\mu,\end{aligned}$$

where equality occurs when E is μ-measurable since $1_S = 1_{S\cap E} + 1_{S\setminus E}$. □

Remark 4.45. We can develop a measure theoretic based theory of integration via establishing countable subadditivity/additivity, dominated convergence theorem, monotone convergence theorem and Fatou's lemma, Fubini–Tonelli's theorem and so on.

Problems

4.1. Let $g: \mathbf{R} \to \mathbf{R}$ be determined by

$$g(x) = \begin{cases} x\,, & x<0,\\ 2\,, & x=0,\\ 3-e^{-x}\,, & x>0.\end{cases}$$

Find $m_g(I)$ when $I = (0,1); [0,1]; (-1,1); [0,0]$.

4.2. Suppose $g: \mathbf{R}\to\mathbf{R}$ is an increasing function.

(i) Prove that if S_1 and S_2 are disjoint simple subsets of $\mathbf{R}$ then $m_g(S_1\cup S_2) = m_g(S_1) + m_g(S_2)$. Construct examples to show that if S_1 and S_2 are not disjoint, then $m_g(S_1\cup S_2)$ may or may not equal $m_g(S_1)+m_g(S_2)$.

(ii) Prove that if S_1 and S_2 are simple subsets of $\mathbf{R}$ such that $S_1\subseteq S_2$ then $m_g(S_2\setminus S_1) = m_g(S_2) - m_g(S_1)$. Construct examples to show that if S_1 and S_2 are simple with $S_1 \not\subseteq S_2$ then $m_g(S_2\setminus S_1)$ may or may not equal $m_g(S_2)-m_g(S_1)$.

4.3. Let $g: \mathbf{R}\to\mathbf{R}$ be given by

$$g(x) = \begin{cases} \frac{x}{2}\,, & x<0,\\ 1\,, & x\ge 0.\end{cases}$$

Are the following step functions on $\mathbf{R}$? If the answer is yes, find the corresponding $A_g(\cdot)$'s:

(i)

$$s_1(x) = \begin{cases} 0\,, & x \in \mathbf{R} \setminus (-\infty, -1), \\ 1\,, & x \in [-1, 0); \end{cases}$$

(ii)

$$s_2(x) = \begin{cases} -2\,, & x \in [-1, 0), \\ 1\,, & x \in [0, 1], \\ 0\,, & x \in [-1, 1]; \end{cases}$$

(iii)

$$s_3(x) = \begin{cases} 2\,, & x \in [-1, 3], \\ 1\,, & x \in (3, \infty), \\ 0\,, & x \in \mathbf{R} \setminus (-\infty, -1); \end{cases}$$

(iv)

$$s_4(x) = \begin{cases} 3\,, & x \in (-2, -1), \\ -3\,, & x \in [-1, 1), \\ 0\,, & x \in \mathbf{R} \setminus (-2, 1); \end{cases}$$

(v)

$$s_5(x) = \begin{cases} -1\,, & x \in (-\infty, 0), \\ 1\,, & x \in [0, \infty). \end{cases}$$

4.4. Give a sequence of step functions $(s_k)_{k=1}^{\infty}$on $\mathbf{R}$ such that $f = \sum_{k=1}^{\infty} s_k$ is not a step function and $S_{id}(f) = 0$.

4.5. Let $f : \mathbf{R} \to \mathbf{R}$ be the following function

$$f(x) = \begin{cases} \frac{1}{n}\,, & x \in [n-1, n-\frac{1}{2}),\ n \in \mathbf{N}, \\ -\frac{1}{n}\,, & x \in [n-\frac{1}{2}, n),\ n \in \mathbf{N}, \\ 0\,, & x \in (-\infty, 0). \end{cases}$$

(i) Evaluate $\int_0^b f(x)dx$ for any $b > 0$.

(ii) Prove that $\int_0^\infty f(x)dx$ exists.

(iii) Prove that $\lim_{b\to\infty} \int_0^b |f(x)|dx$ and $\int_{\mathbf{R}} 1_{[0,\infty)}(x) f(x) dm_{id}(x)$ do not exist.

4.6. Prove the following mean value inequality for the Lebesgue–Radon–Stieltjes integrals. Let $g : \mathbf{R} \to \mathbf{R}$ be increasing and $I \subseteq \mathbf{R}$ be an finite interval. If $1_I f \in LRS_g(\mathbf{R})$ and $c_1 \le f \le c_2$ on I for some finite constants c_1, c_2, then

$$c_1 m_g(I) \le \int_{\mathbf{R}} f(x) 1_I(x) dm_g(x) \le c_2 m_g(I).$$

4.7.

(i) Given an increasing function $g : \mathbf{R} \to \mathbf{R}$. Show that if $f_1, f_2, \cdots, f_n \in LRS_g(\mathbf{R})$ then

$$\Big|\int_{\mathbf{R}} \Big(\sum_{k=1}^{n} f_k(x)\Big) dm_g(x)\Big| \le \sum_{k=1}^{n} \int_{\mathbf{R}} |f_k(x)| dm_g(x).$$

(ii) Suppose $g=\sum_{k=1}^{n} c_k g_k$, where each $g_k:\mathbf{R}\to\mathbf{R}$ is increasing and each $c_k\ge 0$. Prove that if $f\in\cap_{k=1}^{n} LRS_{g_k}(\mathbf{R})$ then $f\in LRS_g(\mathbf{R})$ and

$$\int_{\mathbf{R}} f(x)dm_g(x)=\sum_{k=1}^{n} c_k\int_{\mathbf{R}} f(x)dm_{g_k}(x).$$

4.8.

(i) Show that the union of two m_g-null sets is an m_g-null set.

(ii) Give an example of a finite subset $E\subseteq\mathbf{R}$ and an increasing function $g:\mathbf{R}\to\mathbf{R}$ such that E is not an m_g-null set.

(iii) Let $g:\mathbf{R}\to\mathbf{R}$ be an increasing function. Verify that if $f_1,f_2\in LRS_g(\mathbf{R})$ and $f_1\le f_2$ m_g-a.e. on $\mathbf{R}$, then

$$\int_{\mathbf{R}} f_1(x)dm_g(x)\le\int_{\mathbf{R}} f_2(x)dm_g(x).$$

4.9. Let $g:\mathbf{R}\to\mathbf{R}$ be an increasing function. Suppose that $(f_k)_{k=1}^{\infty}$ is a sequence in $LRS_g(\mathbf{R})$ and $\sum_{k=1}^{\infty} f_k=f$ exists m_g-a.e. on $\mathbf{R}$. Prove the following results:

(i) If there is a function $F\in LRS_g(\mathbf{R})$ such that $\left|\sum_{k=1}^{n} f_k\right|\le F$ on $\mathbf{R}$, then $f\in LRS_g(\mathbf{R})$ and

$$\int_{\mathbf{R}} f(x)dm_g(x)=\sum_{k=1}^{\infty}\int_{\mathbf{R}} f_k(x)dm_g(x);$$

(ii) If $f_k\ge 0$ or $f_k\le 0$ on $\mathbf{R}$ and $\sum_{k=1}^{\infty}\int_{\mathbf{R}} f_k(x)dm_g(x)$ converges, then $f\in LRS_g(\mathbf{R})$ and

$$\int_{\mathbf{R}} f(x)dm_g(x)=\sum_{k=1}^{\infty}\int_{\mathbf{R}} f_k(x)dm_g(x).$$

4.10. For $n\in\mathbf{N}$ let

$$f_n(x)=\begin{cases}1, & x\in[n,n+1),\\ 0, & x\in\mathbf{R}\setminus[n,n+1).\end{cases}$$

(i) Find $f=\lim_{n\to\infty} f_n$.

(ii) Prove

$$\lim_{n\to\infty}\int_{\mathbf{R}} f_n(x)dm_{id}(x)\ne\int_{\mathbf{R}} f(x)dm_{id}(x).$$

(iii) Point out which hypothesis of the monotone convergence theorem is not valid in this case, and write down the reasoning why it is not valid.

4.11. If $\alpha>0$, prove the following two formulas:

(i)

$$\lim_{n\to\infty}\int_{\mathbf{R}} 1_{[0,n]}(x)\Big(1-\frac{x}{n}\Big)^n|x|^{\alpha-1}dm_{id}(x)=\int_{\mathbf{R}} 1_{(0,\infty)}(x)e^{-x}|x|^{\alpha-1}dm_{id}(x);$$

(ii)

$$\sum_{n=1}^{\infty}\int_{\mathbf{R}} 1_{(0,\infty)}(x)e^{-nx}|x|^{\alpha}dm_{id}(x) = \int_{\mathbf{R}} 1_{(0,\infty)}(x)(e^{x}-1)|x|^{\alpha}dm_{id}(x)$$

$$= \Gamma(1+\alpha)\sum_{n=1}^{\infty} n^{-(1+\alpha)}.$$

4.12. Prove the following formulas:

(i)

$$\int_{\mathbf{R}} 1_{(0,1]}(x)|x|^{-p}dm_{id}(x) = \begin{cases} (1-p)^{-1}, & p \in (0,1), \\ \infty, & p \in [1,\infty); \end{cases}$$

(ii)

$$\lim_{n\to\infty}\int_{\mathbf{R}} 1_{(0,\infty)}(x)|x|^{-1/n}\Big(1+\frac{|x|}{n}\Big)^{-n}dm_{id}(x) = 1.$$

4.13. For each $n \in \mathbf{N}$ and all $x \in \mathbf{R}$, let $f_n(x) = e^{-nx} - 2e^{-2nx}$.

(i) Prove that $f(x) = \sum_{n=1}^{\infty} f_n(x)$ is convergent for all $x > 0$, and calculate $f(x)$.

(ii) Prove that $1_{(0,\infty)}f_n$ and $1_{(0,\infty)}f$ are Lebesgue integrable on $\mathbf{R}$.

(iii) Compare

$$\int_{\mathbf{R}} 1_{(0,\infty)}(x)f(x)dm_{id}(x) \quad \text{and} \quad \sum_{n=1}^{\infty}\int_{\mathbf{R}} 1_{(0,\infty)}(x)f_n(x)dm_{id}(x).$$

4.14.

(i) For each $n \in \mathbf{N}$ let

$$f_n = \begin{cases} 1_{[0,\frac{1}{4}]}, & n \text{ is even}, \\ 1_{[\frac{1}{4},1]}, & n \text{ is odd}. \end{cases}$$

Calculate the following four numbers:

$$N_1 = \lim_{k\to\infty}\inf_{n\geq k}\int_0^{\infty} f_n(x)dx; \quad N_2 = \int_0^{\infty}\lim_{k\to\infty}\inf_{n\geq k} f_n(x)dx;$$

$$N_3 = \lim_{k\to\infty}\sup_{n\geq k}\int_0^{\infty} f_n(x)dx; \quad N_4 = \int_0^{\infty}\lim_{k\to\infty}\sup_{n\geq k} f_n(x)dx.$$

(ii) If $(f_n)_{n=1}^{\infty}$ is a sequence of positive Lebesgue measurable functions, what can be said of the four numbers above, and more particularly about N_3 and N_4?

4.15. Let $g(x) = x$ on $\mathbf{R}$. If $f \in LRS_g\big((0,\infty)\big)$ is uniformly continuous on $(0,\infty)$, prove $\lim_{x\to\infty} f(x) = 0$.

4.16. Let $g : \mathbf{R} \to \mathbf{R}$ be increasing. Assume $f : [a,b] \times [c,d] \to \mathbf{R}$ and $f(\cdot, t) \in LRS_g[a,b]$ for each $t \in [c,d]$. Suppose $F(y) = \int_{[a,b]} f(x,y)dm_g(x)$.

(i) If there is an $h \in LRS_g([a,b])$ such that $|f(x,y)| \le h(x)$ for all $(x,y) \in [a,b] \times [c,d]$, and if $\lim_{y \to y_0} f(x,y) = f(x,y_0)$ for every $x \in [a,b]$ and any $y_0 \in [c,d]$, prove that $\lim_{y\to y_0} F(y) = F(y_0)$; in particular, if $f(x,\cdot)$ is continuous for every $x \in [a,b]$, then F is continuous.

(ii) If $\partial f(x,y)/\partial y$ exists and there is an $h \in LRS_g([a,b])$ such that

$$\left|\frac{\partial f(x,y)}{\partial y}\right| \le h(x), \quad (x,y) \in [a,b] \times [c,d],$$

prove that F is differentiable and

$$F'(y) = \int_{[a,b]} \frac{\partial f(x,y)}{\partial y} dm_g(x).$$

4.17. Let $g : \mathbf{R} \to \mathbf{R}$ be increasing and $\mathcal{M}_g$ the σ-ring of all m_g-measurable sets. Prove that if $(E_j)_{j=1}^\infty$ is a sequence of sets in $\mathcal{M}_g$ then $m_g(\cup_{j=1}^\infty E_j) \le \sum_{j=1}^\infty m_g(E_j)$.

4.18. Let $g : \mathbf{R} \to \mathbf{R}$ be increasing. For an m_g-measurable set $E \subseteq \mathbf{R}$ let $L_g(E) = \int_E dm_g < \infty$. If $1_E f : \mathbf{R} \to \mathbf{R}^e$ is m_g-measurable and $E_j = \{x \in E : j-1 \le f(x) < j\}$ for each $j \in \mathbf{Z}$, prove that $\int_E |f| dm_g < \infty$ if and only if $\sum_{j=-\infty}^\infty |j| m_g(E_j) < \infty$.

4.19. Let $g : \mathbf{R} \to \mathbf{R}$ be increasing. Prove that $f : \mathbf{R} \to \mathbf{R}^e$ is m_g-measurable if and only if $\{x \in \mathbf{R} : f(x) \ge c\}$ is m_g-measurable for any $c \in \mathbf{R}$.

4.20. Let $g : \mathbf{R} \to \mathbf{R}$ be increasing and $(f_n)_{n=1}^\infty$ be a sequence of m_g-measurable functions on $\mathbf{R}$. Then we say that:

(i) $(f_n)_{n=1}^\infty$ is convergent to f in the Lebesgue–Radon–Stieltjes g-measure provided

$$\lim_{n\to\infty} m_g\big(\{x \in \mathbf{R} : |f_n(x) - f(x)| \ge \epsilon\}\big) = 0 \quad \text{for every} \quad \epsilon > 0;$$

(ii) $(f_n)_{n=1}^\infty$ is a Cauchy sequence in the Lebesgue–Radon–Stieltjes g-measure provided

$$\lim_{k,n\to\infty} m_g\big(\{x \in \mathbf{R} : |f_k(x) - f_n(x)| \ge \epsilon\}\big) = 0 \quad \text{for every} \quad \epsilon > 0.$$

Prove the following facts:

(iii) If $\lim_{n\to\infty} \int_{\mathbf{R}} |f_n - f| dm_g = 0$ then $f_n \to f$ in the Lebesgue–Radon–Stieltjes g-measure m_g;

(iv) If $(f_n)_{n=1}^\infty$ is a Cauchy sequence in the Lebesgue–Radon–Stieltjes g-measure m_g, there exists an m_g-a.e. unique function f such that $(f_n)_{n=1}^\infty$ is convergent to f in m_g, and there exists a subsequence $(f_{n_k})_{k=1}^\infty$ of $(f_n)_{n=1}^\infty$ which is convergent to f m_g-a.e. on $\mathbf{R}$;

(v) If $(f_n)_{n=1}^\infty$ is a sequence of nonnegative m_g-measurable functions which converges to f m_g-a.e. on $\mathbf{R}$, then $\lim_{n\to\infty} \int_{\mathbf{R}} f_n dm_g = 0$ implies $f = 0$ m_g-a.e. on $\mathbf{R}$;

(vi) Give an example of g to show that $f_n \to f$ m_g-a.e. on $\mathbf{R}$ does not ensure $f_n \to f$ in the Lebesgue–Radon–Stieltjes g-measure m_g.

4.21. For $p \in (0,1)$ let

$$f_1(x) = |x|^{-p} 1_{\{x\in\mathbf{R}:\ |x|<1\}} \quad \text{and} \quad f_2(x) = (-\ln|x|) 1_{\{x\in\mathbf{R}:\ |x|<1\}}.$$

Calculate $\int_{\mathbf{R}} f_j dm_{id}$ for $j = 1, 2$ in two ways:

(i) Use the standard calculus method;

(ii) Compute $m_{id}\big(\{x \in \mathbf{R} : f_j(x) > t\}\big)$.

Chapter 5

Metric Spaces

The objective of this chapter is to build a base which is general enough to acquaint ourselves with some limit concepts in such an abstract setting as functional analysis. In this case, the word *abstract* implies that the objects we deal with do not have to be numbers or even have arithmetic properties like numbers. The one property that is fundamental to our idea of limits is the concept of distance between elements. Each limit concept that we have seen thus far is based on the question of whether two numbers are close enough to each other whenever certain conditions hold. So our abstraction is developed in a system whose elements enjoy the most essential properties of a distance function.

5.1 Metrizable Topology

To begin with, we introduce the definition of a metric space followed by some useful examples, and consider topological properties such as open and closed sets induced by a metric space.

Definition 5.1. A metric space is a system (X, d) that consists of a set X whose elements are called points and a function d whose domain is all of $X \times X$ and whose range is in $[0, \infty)$ such that the following three properties hold:

(i) $d(x, y) \geq 0$ for all $x, y \in X$ and $d(x, y) = 0$ if and only if $x = y$;

(ii) $d(x, y) = d(y, x)$ for every $x, y \in X$;

(iii) $d(x, z) \leq d(x, y) + d(y, z)$ for every $x, y, z \in X$.

Remark 5.2.

(i) Thanks to these three properties whose (ii) and (iii) mean respectively the symmetry and the triangle inequality of the metric space, the function d is usually called a distance function.

(ii) If $d(\cdot, \cdot)$ has all the properties (i)-(ii)-(iii) except that $d(x, y) = 0$ does not necessarily enforce $x = y$, then we call d a pseudo-distance and (X, d) a pseudo-metric space.

Example 5.3.

(i) For $n \in \mathbf{N}$ let $\mathbf{R}^n$ be the set of all finite number sequences $x = (x_k)_{k=1}^n$ where the real number x_k is called the kth coordinate of x. Define

$$d_n(x,y) = \Big(\sum_{k=1}^n |x_k - y_k|^2\Big)^{1/2}, \quad x = (x_k)_{k=1}^n,\ y = (y_k)_{k=1}^n \in \mathbf{R}^n.$$

Then $\mathbf{R}^n$ with this distance function is called the n-dimensional Euclidean space, or, more briefly, the Euclidean n-space. Our immediate goal, however, is to verify that d_n does indeed provide $\mathbf{R}^n$ with a metric distance via proving the Cauchy–Schwarz inequality for $\mathbf{R}^n$ (see also Theorem 2.18 for a continuous form):

$$\sum_{k=1}^n |x_k y_k| \le \Big(\sum_{k=1}^n |x_k|^2\Big)^{1/2}\Big(\sum_{k=1}^n |y_k|^2\Big)^{1/2}.$$

To see this, consider the quadratic polynomial $Q(t) = At^2 + Bt + C$, where

$$A = \sum_{k=1}^n |x_k|^2, \quad B = 2\sum_{k=1}^n |x_k||y_k|, \quad C = \sum_{k=1}^n |y_k|^2.$$

Then

$$Q(t) = \sum_{k=1}^n (|x_k|t + |y_k|)^2 \ge 0.$$

This infers that $Q(t)$ cannot have two distinct zeros. Therefore, by the quadratic formula, its discriminant $B^2 - 4AC \le 0$. In other words,

$$\Big(\sum_{k=1}^n |x_k||y_k|\Big)^2 - \Big(\sum_{k=1}^n |x_k|^2\Big)\Big(\sum_{k=1}^n |y_k|^2\Big) \le 0.$$

Using the Cauchy–Schwarz inequality, we derive that if $x, y, z \in \mathbf{R}^n$, then

$$\begin{aligned}
\big(d_n(x,y) + d_n(y,z)\big)^2 &= d_n(x,y)^2 + 2d_n(x,y)d_n(y,z) + d_n(y,z)^2 \\
&\ge \sum_{k=1}^n \big((x_k - y_k) + (y_k - z_k)\big)^2 \\
&= \big(d_n(x,z)\big)^2.
\end{aligned}$$

Taking the square root of the first and last members, we further obtain

$$d_n(x,z) \le d_n(x,y) + d_n(y,z),$$

whence verifying that $(\mathbf{R}^n, d_n)$ is a metric space.

(ii) For $n \in \mathbf{N}$ let $\mathbf{Q}^n = \mathbf{Q} \times \mathbf{Q} \times \cdots \mathbf{Q} = \{(x_1, \ldots, x_n) \in \mathbf{R}^n : x_1, x_2, \ldots, x_n \in \mathbf{Q}\}$. Then $(\mathbf{Q}^n, d_n)$ is also a metric space.

(iii) Let $g : \mathbf{R} \to \mathbf{R}$ be an increasing function, $E \subseteq \mathbf{R}$ an m_g-measurable set, and $p \in (0, \infty]$. If $\mathbf{F}$ is $\mathbf{R}$ or $\mathbf{C}$, then the Lebesgue–Radon–Stieltjes space $LRS_g^p(E, \mathbf{F})$ is defined as the collection of all $\mathbf{F}$-valued functions $f = \Re f + i\Im f$ for which $|f| = \sqrt{(\Re f)^2 + (\Im f)^2}$; and

$$\|f\|_{p,m_g,E} = \begin{cases} \left(\int_E |f(x)|^p dm_g(x)\right)^{\frac{1}{p}}, & p \in (0,\infty), \\ \inf\left\{c \geq 0 : \ m_g(\{x \in E : \ |f(x)| > c\}) = 0\right\}, & p = \infty \end{cases}$$

is finite. If

$$d_{p,m_g,E}(f_1, f_2) = \begin{cases} \|f_1 - f_2\|_{p,m_g,E}^p, & p \in (0,1), \\ \|f_1 - f_2\|_{p,m_g,E}, & p \in [1,\infty], \end{cases}$$

then $d_{p,m_g,E}(f_1, f_2) = 0$ if and only if $f_1 = f_2$ m_g-a.e. on E. Meanwhile, Minkowski's inequality yields that

$$d_{p,m_g,E}(f_1, f_2) \leq d_{p,m_g,E}(f_1, f_3) + d_{p,m_g,E}(f_3, f_2)$$

holds for $f_1, f_2, f_3 \in LRS_g^p(E, \mathbf{F})$. Accordingly, $\left(LRS_g^p(E, \mathbf{F}), d_{p,m_g,E}\right)$ is a pseudo-metric space.

Example 5.3 leads to a general fact about metric spaces.

Theorem 5.4.

(i) *Let X be any nonempty set and define the discrete distance $d(x, y)$, $x, y \in X$, by*

$$d(x,y) = \begin{cases} 1, & x \neq y, \\ 0, & x = y. \end{cases}$$

Then (X, d) is a metric space.

(ii) *If (X, d) is a metric space and Y is a subset of X, then (Y, d) is a metric space for which the domain of d is now restricted to $Y \times Y$.*

Proof. (i) It is clear that this d satisfies Definition 5.1 (i) and (ii). To verify Definition 5.1 (iii), consider any points $x, y, z \in X$. If $d(x, z) = 0$, then Definition 5.1 (iii) is trivial. If $d(x, z) > 0$, then $x \neq z$ and $d(x, z) = 1$, and hence y cannot equal both x and z, so at least one of the distances $d(x, y)$ and $d(y, z)$ must equal 1. Therefore, Definition 5.1 (iii) follows.

(ii) This truth is an immediate consequence of the definition of metric space and the concept of subset. □

The topology for a space of points provides a theory of cluster points and convergence for sets of points in the space. In a metric space, this convergence theory is based on the concept of distance between points. For more abstract spaces it is based on a system of open sets, and there may be no distance concept associated with the notion of a limit. We here take the former approach and use the metric distance function to define certain open sets, which are generalizations of the open intervals in $\mathbf{R}$.

In the rest of this section, we always assume that X is a metric space with distance function d.

Definition 5.5. If $x \in X$ and $r > 0$, then $B_r(x) = B_r^X(x) = \{y \in X : d(x,y) < r\}$, $\overline{B}_r(x) = \overline{B}_r^X(x) = \{y \in X : d(x,y) \le r\}$, and $S_r(x) = S_r^X(x) = \{y \in X : d(x,y) = r\}$ are called the open ball, closed ball, and sphere of radius r about x respectively. A neighborhood of x is any subset of X that contains some open ball about x.

Remark 5.6. Note that $B_0(x) = \emptyset$ and $\overline{B}_0(x) = \{x\}$.

Example 5.7. Let $X = \mathbf{R}^n$, $x \in \mathbf{R}^n$ and $r > 0$.

(i) If $n = 1$, then $B_r(x) = (x - r, x + r)$ and $\overline{B}_r(x) = [x - r, x + r]$

(ii) If $n = 2$, then $B_r(x)$ and $\overline{B}_r(x)$ are the open and closed disks of radius r centered at x, respectively.

(iii) If $n = 3$, then $B_r(x)$ and $\overline{B}_r(x)$ are the open and closed (3-dimensional) balls of radius r centered at x, respectively.

Definition 5.8. Let $A \subseteq X$.

(i) $x \in X$ is called an interior point of A, denoted $x \in A^\circ$, provided there exists $r > 0$ such that $B_r(x) \subseteq A$.

(ii) A is said to be open provided $A \subseteq A^\circ$.

(iii) $x \in X$ is called a cluster point of A, denoted $x \in A'$, provided for every $r > 0$ one has $B_r(x) \cap (A \setminus \{x\}) \neq \emptyset$.

(iv) $x \in X$ is called an isolated point of A provided there exists an $r_0 > 0$ such that $B_{r_0}(x) \cap A = \{x\}$.

(v) A is said to be closed provided $A' \subseteq A$.

(vi) A is said to be bounded provided $A \subseteq B_r(x)$ for certain $r > 0$ and some $x \in X$.

Remark 5.9. It is clear that A is open or closed if and only if $A = A^\circ$ or $A = \overline{A} = A \cup A'$.

Example 5.10.

(i) Any open ball $B_r(x)$ in a given metric space X is a bounded open set.

(ii) In $\mathbf{R}^2$, let $A = B_2(0)$ and $x = (\sqrt{2}, \sqrt{2})$. Then $x \in A'$ – this is because

$$(\sqrt{2} - \epsilon/2, \sqrt{2} - \epsilon/2) \in B_2(0) \cap B_\epsilon(x),$$

where $B_\epsilon(x)$ is an open disk about x with radius $\epsilon > 0$. However, in $\mathbf{R}^2$, if $A = B_1(0) \cup \{x\}$ where $x = (2, 0)$. Then $x \notin A'$, for the open disk $B_{1/2}(x)$ contains no point of A except x itself.

(iii) Any singleton $\{x\}$ of X is closed.

(iv) X and $\emptyset$ are not only open, but also closed.

(v) Let F be the subset of $\mathbf{R}^2$ consisting of

$$\Big\{(1,0), (1/2,0), (1/3,0), \ldots, (1/k,0), \ldots\Big\}.$$

Then $(0,0)$ is a cluster point of F, and since $(0,0)$ is not in F we infer that F is not closed. Also, the point $(1,0)$ is not an interior point of F, so F is not open.

The forthcoming theorem is the fundamental relationship between the notions of an open set and a closed set.

Theorem 5.11. *For a subset A of X let $A^c = X \setminus A$ be the complement of a set A in X. Then A is open if and only if A^c is closed.*

Proof. Suppose A is open. To show that A^c is closed, we use the contrapositive method to prove that if $x \notin A^c$ then x is not a cluster point of A^c. Suppose now $x \notin A^c$. Then $x \in A$. Since A is open, there is a ball $B_r(x) \subseteq A$. Thus x is not a cluster point of A^c, as desired.

Conversely, suppose A^c is closed. If A is not open. Then A contains some point y that is not an interior point of A. Thus every ball $B_r(y)$ contains a point of A^c. Consequently, y is a cluster point of A^c, and since y is in $A \setminus A^c$, we conclude that A^c is not closed, a contradiction to the assumption. □

Remark 5.12. Perhaps the greatest value of Theorem 5.11 is that it gives us an alternative method for proving that a set is open or closed. It is sometimes easier to work with the complement of a set than with the set itself. For instance, we know immediately that $X \setminus \{x\}$ is open because $\{x\}$ is closed.

Theorem 5.13.

(i) *The intersection of a finite number of open sets is itself an open set.*

(ii) *The union of any collection of open sets is an open set.*

Proof. (i) Suppose each of $A_1, \ldots, A_n$ is open, and let $x \in A = \cap_{k=1}^n A_k$. Then x is in each of $A_1, \ldots, A_n$, so for each $1 \leq k \leq n$ there exists a positive radius r_k such that $B_{r_k}(x) \subseteq A_k$. Define $r = \min\{r_1, \ldots, r_n\}$. Then for each k, $B_r(x) \subseteq B_{r_k}(x) \subseteq A_k \subseteq A$. Hence x is in A°, and so A is open.

(ii) Suppose that for each j in an index set I, A_j is an open set. Let $x \in \cup_{j \in I} A_j$. Then x belongs to some A_j, say, A_{j_0}. Since it is open, there exists an open ball $B_r(x)$ such that $B_r(x) \subseteq A_{j_0} \subseteq \cup_{j \in I} A_j$. Hence $\cup_{j \in I} A_j$ is open. □

This theorem leads to a result regarding closed sets.

Corollary 5.14.

(i) *The union of a finite number of closed sets is a closed set.*

(ii) *The intersection of any collection of closed sets is itself a closed set.*

Proof. It suffices to prove (i). Suppose that $F_1, \ldots, F_n$ are closed sets. It is easy to verify that $X \setminus \cup_{k=1}^n F_k = \cap_{k=1}^n (X \setminus F_k)$. By Theorem 5.13, each $X \setminus F_k$ is open. Thus, according to Theorem 5.13 (i) their intersection is open. Hence $\cup_{k=1}^n F_k$ is closed since its complement is open. □

Remark 5.15.

(i) The union of an infinite collection of closed sets need not be closed. For instance, let F_k be the singleton $(1/k, 0)$ in $\mathbf{R}^2$. It is clear that $(0,0)$ is a cluster point of $\cup_{k=1}^{\infty} F_k$, but $(0,0)$ is not in this union. So the union is not closed. Of course, it is not hard to give an example of an infinite collection of open sets whose intersection is not open. For example, $A_k = B_{1/k}(0)$. Clearly, $\cap_{k=1}^{\infty} A_k = \{0\}$ which is not open.

(ii) We should take particular notice of the fact that the collections of sets in Theorem 5.13 and Corollary 5.14 may be arbitrarily large. In particular, the collections may contain so many sets that is impossible to describe them as an infinite sequence of sets. This is why we use the device of an index set I to describe each collection. Had we written $\{A_n\}_{n=1}^{\infty}$ for the collection of sets, this would have indicated a sequence of sets and therefore limited our discussion to countable collections.

We finish this section with applying the formula

$$\overline{A} = \{x \in X : \ B_r(x) \cap A \neq \emptyset \text{ for all } r > 0\}$$

to discussing the connectedness of a metric space – the phenomenon of a set that cannot be naturally separated into two subsets.

The vagueness of the phrase "naturally separated" suggests that it is not easy to give a precise definition of the property we want. Indeed, we define it by first stating when a set does not possess this property.

Definition 5.16. The set $S \subseteq X$ is disconnected if there exist nonempty sets S_1 and S_2 such that $S_1 \cup S_2 = S$, $\overline{S}_1 \cap S_2 = \emptyset$ and $\overline{S}_2 \cap S_1 = \emptyset$. If S is not disconnected, then S is said to be connected.

It is worth pointing out that the above S_1 and S_2 satisfy a property that is stronger than being disjoint. Not only must S_1 and S_2 fail to contain any point of the other set, they must also fail to contain any cluster point of the other set. Note that this extra stipulation in Definition 5.16 is significant because any set containing two or more points can be written as the union of two nonempty disjoint subsets – for $x \in S$, let $S_1 = \{x\}$ and $S_2 = S \setminus \{x\}$. But as we see in the next theorem, when we are dealing with open sets, disjointness is sufficient to imply that their union is disconnected.

Theorem 5.17. *Let $S \subseteq X$. Then S is disconnected if and only if there are disjoint open sets A and B such that $S \subseteq A \cup B$, $A \cap S \neq \emptyset$, and $B \cap S \neq \emptyset$.*

Proof. Suppose that A and B exist as in the statement of Theorem 5.17 and let $S_1 = A \cap S$ and $S_2 = B \cap S$. Clearly, S_1 and S_2 are nonempty, and $S_1 \cup S_2 = S$. Consider an arbitrary point $x \in S_1$. Clearly, x is in the open set A, so for some $r > 0$, $B_r(x) \subseteq A$. Thus $B_r(x) \cap B = \emptyset$ because $A \cap B = \emptyset$, so $B_r(x) \cap S_2 = \emptyset$. Thus $x \notin \overline{S}_2$; hence $S_1 \cap \overline{S}_2 = \emptyset$. Similarly, $\overline{S}_1 \cap S_2 = \emptyset$, and we conclude that S is disconnected.

Now assume that S is disconnected, say, $S = S_1 \cup S_2$ and $S_1 \cap \overline{S}_2 = \overline{S}_1 \cap S_2 = \emptyset$. Then no point of S_1 is in S_2'. For $x \in S_1$, choose $B_r(x)$ such that $B_r(x) \cap S_2 = \emptyset$.

Thus $A = \cup_{x \in S_1} B_{r/2}(x)$ is an open set that contains no point of S_2. Similarly, we can take a ball $B_s(y)$ for each $y \in S_2$ that satisfies $B_s(y) \cap S_1 = \emptyset$ and define $B = \cup_{x \in S_2} B_{s/2}(x)$, which is open. It remains only to show that $A \cap B = \emptyset$. Suppose not, and let $p \in A \cap B$. Then for some $x \in S_1$ and $y \in S_2$, $p \in B_{r/2}(x) \cap B_{s/2}(y)$. But this implies that

$$d(x, y) \leq d(x, p) + d(p, y) < r/2 + s/2 \leq \max\{r, s\}.$$

Therefore either $y \in B_r(x)$ or $x \in B_s(y)$, which contradicts the choice of either r or s, respectively. □

Corollary 5.18. *Let $S \subseteq X$. If S is connected, then $\overline{S}$ is connected.*

Proof. Assume that $\overline{S}$ is disconnected, and let A and B be disjoint open sets in Theorem 5.17: $\overline{S} \subseteq A \cup B$, $A \cap \overline{S} \neq \emptyset$, and $B \cap \overline{S} \neq \emptyset$. Since S is obviously contained in $A \cup B$, we need to prove only that $A \cap S \neq \emptyset$ and $B \cap S \neq \emptyset$. Let $x \in \overline{S} \cap A$. Since A is open, there is a ball about x such that $B_r(x) \subseteq A$. But $x \in \overline{S}$ too, so $B_r(x)$ must contain some point y of S. Therefore $y \in B_r(x) \cap S \subseteq A \cap S$, so $A \cap S \neq \emptyset$. Similarly, $B \cap S \neq \emptyset$, so by Theorem 5.17, S is disconnected. This contradicts the assumption that S is connected. □

5.2 Completeness

To discuss the completeness of a metric space, we start with the definition of the convergence of a point sequence in the metric space.

A point sequence is a function from $\mathbf{N}$ into a metric space (X, d); this is, it is a sequence whose terms are points in X. Since our principal examples of metric spaces are the Euclidean spaces and we use subscripts to designate the coordinates of points in $\mathbf{R}^n$, we use superscripts to index the terms of a point sequence – $(x^{(k)})_{k=1}^{\infty}$ represents a point sequence in a metric space.

Definition 5.19. Given a metric space (X, d). The point sequence $(x^{(k)})_{k=1}^{\infty}$ in X is said to converge to the point $x \in X$, denoted $\lim_{k \to \infty} x^{(k)} = x$, provided for every $\epsilon > 0$ there is an $N \in \mathbf{N}$ such that $d(x^{(k)}, x) < \epsilon$ whenever $k > N$.

Our first task is to establish a connection between convergent point sequences and cluster points.

Theorem 5.20. *Given a metric space (X, d) and $A \subseteq X$. Then $x \in A'$ if and only if there is a non-repeating point sequence in A that converges to x.*

Proof. Suppose $x \in A'$ and $r_1 = 1$. Then there exists a point $x^{(1)}$ in $B_{r_1}(x) \cap (A \setminus \{x\})$. Let $r_2 = \min\{1/2, d(x^{(1)}, x)\}$, and choose a point $x^{(2)}$ in $(A \setminus \{x\}) \cap B_{r_2}(x)$. After $x^{(1)}, \ldots, x^{(k)}$ have been defined, let $r_{k+1} = \min\{1/(k+1), d(x^{(k)}, x)\}$ and choose $x^{(k+1)}$ as a point of $A \setminus \{x\}$ in the open ball $B_{r_{k+1}}(x)$. Since $r_k \leq 1/k$, it is clear that $\lim_{k \to \infty} x^{(k)} = x$; and since $r_k \leq d(x^{(k-1)}, x)$, it follows that no two $x^{(k)}$'s are the same.

To prove the converse, we simply observe that if A contains such a point sequence that converges to x, then it is obvious from the definition that every open ball about x contains infinitely many points of A. □

Example 5.21. In $\mathbf{R}^n$ there is a very strong connection between convergent point sequences and convergent number sequences. More precisely, $x^{(k)} \to x$ in $\mathbf{R}^n$ if and only if $\lim_{k\to\infty} x_j^{(k)} = x_j$ for each $j = 1, \ldots, n$. This is because $x^{(k)} \in B_\epsilon(x)$ if and only if

$$d_n(x^{(k)}, x) = \Big(\sum_{j=1}^{n} |x_j^{(k)} - x_j|^2\Big)^{1/2} < \epsilon.$$

Definition 5.22. Suppose (X, d) is a metric space. A point sequence $(x^{(k)})_{k=1}^{\infty}$ in X is a Cauchy sequence provided for every $\epsilon > 0$ there is an $N > 0$ such that $d(x^{(k)}, x^{(m)}) < \epsilon$ whenever $k > m > N$.

This definition is obviously a generalization of the concept of Cauchy number sequences treated in Chapter 1.

Example 5.23. A point sequence in $\mathbf{R}^n$ is a Cauchy sequence if and only if it converges to a point in $\mathbf{R}^n$. To verify this, suppose $(x^{(k)})_{k=1}^{\infty}$ is a Cauchy sequence. Since $d_n(x^{(k)}, x^{(m)}) \ge |x_j^{(k)} - x_j^{(m)}|$ for each $j = 1, \cdots, n$, it follows that $(x_j^{(k)})_{k=1}^{\infty}$ forms a Cauchy number sequence. Thus such a sequence converges to a point in $\mathbf{R}$, say, $\lim_{k\to\infty} x_j^{(k)} = x_j$. Now Example 5.21 ensures that $(x^{(k)})_{k=1}^{\infty}$ converges to $x = (x_1, \ldots, x_n)$ in $\mathbf{R}^n$. The converse assertion is true in any metric space, and therefore we give it as the next theorem.

Theorem 5.24. *Suppose (X, d) is a metric space.*

(i) *If $(x^{(k)})_{k=1}^{\infty}$ in X is convergent, then $(x^{(k)})_{k=1}^{\infty}$ is a Cauchy sequence.*

(ii) *If $(x^{(k)})_{k=1}^{\infty}$ in X is a Cauchy sequence, then it is bounded.*

(iii) *If $x \in X$ and $Y = X \setminus \{x\}$, then any sequence $(x^{(k)})_{k=1}^{\infty}$ in Y satisfying*

$$\lim_{k\to\infty} d(x^{(k)}, x) = 0$$

is a Cauchy but not a convergent sequence in Y with respect to d.

Proof. (i) Assume that $(x^{(k)})_{k=1}^{\infty}$ converges to x, and suppose $\epsilon > 0$. Choose $N > 0$ so that $d(x^{(k)}, x) < \epsilon/2$ as $k > N$. This implies that

$$d(x^{(k)}, x^{(m)}) \le d(x^{(k)}, x) + d(x^{(m)}, x) < \epsilon,$$

whenever $k > m > N$. Therefore, $(x^{(k)})_{k=1}^{\infty}$ is a Cauchy sequence in X.

(ii) Let $(x^{(k)})_{k=1}^{\infty}$ be a Cauchy sequence. By definition, we find an $N > 0$ such that $d(x^{(k)}, x^{(m)}) < 1$ whenever $k > m > N$. In particular, if $m = N + 1$ this property becomes $d(x^{(k)}, x^{(N+1)}) < 1$ whenever $k > N$. Therefore all the points $x^{(k)}$ for $k > N$ lie in the open ball $B_1(x^{(N+1)})$. Now we simply enlarge the radius of the ball until it also includes the first N points of the sequence. Define

$$r = 1 + \max\big\{1, d(x^{(1)}, x^{(N+1)}), \ldots, d(x^{(N)}, x^{(N+1)})\big\}.$$

Thus r is at least one unit more than the distance between $x^{(N+1)}$ and $x^{(k)}$ for every $k = 1, 2, \ldots$; so $B_r(x^{(N+1)})$ contains every point $x^{(k)}$ of the sequence.

(iii) Now suppose that $x \in X$ is the limit of $(x^{(k)})_{k=1}^{\infty}$ under d. Then $(x^{(k)})_{k=1}^{\infty}$ is a sequence in both X and Y, and it converges in X; so by (i) it is a Cauchy sequence in X. The distance function d on $Y \times Y$ is the same one as on $X \times X$, so $(x^{(k)})_{k=1}^{\infty}$ is also a Cauchy sequence in Y. But in Y there is no point to which $(x^{(k)})_{k=1}^{\infty}$ can converge, because x has been removed and the limit of a sequence is unique. □

Accordingly, we see from Theorem 5.24 that Example 5.23 cannot be generalized to all metric spaces. This idea is the general principle behind the following example.

Example 5.25.

(i) Let $X = B_1(0)$ be the open unit ball in $\mathbf{R}^2$ with the usual Euclidean distance. Consider a sequence in $B_1(0)$ that converges to a point on its boundary, say, $x^{(k)} = (1 - 1/k, 0)$, so that it has cluster point $(1, 0)$. Then this sequence is a Cauchy sequence in X, but it has no limit in X, so it does not converge in X.

(ii) Again for $n \in \mathbf{N}$ let $\mathbf{Q}^n$ be the subset of $\mathbf{R}^n$ consisting of all points for which all coordinates are rational numbers. The point $x = (\sqrt{2}, 0, \ldots, 0)$ is in $\mathbf{R}^n \setminus \mathbf{Q}^n$, but if $(r_k)_{k=1}^{\infty}$ is a sequence of rational numbers such that $\lim_{k\to\infty} r_k = \sqrt{2}$, and $x^{(k)} = (r_k, 0, \ldots, 0)$, then $\lim_{k\to\infty} x^{(k)} = x$. Therefore $(x^{(k)})_{k=1}^{\infty}$ is a Cauchy sequence but does not converge in $\mathbf{Q}^n$.

Naturally, we can give the definition of the completeness of a metric space.

Definition 5.26. Suppose (X, d) is a metric space. $S \subseteq X$ is said to be complete with respect to d provided every Cauchy sequence in S converges to a point in S with respect to d. In particular, if X is complete with respect to d, then we say that (X, d) is a complete metric space.

Theorem 5.27. *Let (X, d) be a complete metric space. Then $S \subseteq X$ is complete with respect to d if and only if S is a closed subset of X.*

Proof. Suppose that S is closed and $(x_k)_{k=1}^{\infty}$ is a Cauchy sequence in S. Since X is complete, there is an $x \in X$ such that $x_k \to x$. But because S is closed, one gets $x \in S$. Conversely, if S is complete, then for any sequence $(x_k)_{k=1}^{\infty}$ converging to $x \in X$, one has that this sequence is a Cauchy sequence in S and, therefore, converges to a point $y \in S$. So $x = y \in S$ and S is closed. □

In the terminology of Definition 5.26, $\mathbf{R}^n$ is a complete metric space. The next result gives four alternative properties that are equivalent to completeness in $\mathbf{R}^n$. Each is an important result in its own right, and collectively they are the most important tools of analysis. They are immediately recognizable as multidimensional extensions of the corresponding four theorems in the $\mathbf{R}^1$-case.

Theorem 5.28. *For $n \in \mathbf{N}$ let $X = \mathbf{R}^n$ be equipped with the distance $d_n(\cdot, \cdot)$. Then the following statements are equivalent:*

(i) *X is complete;*

(ii) *Heine-Borel property: If F is a closed and bounded subset of X and $\{A_\mu\}_{\mu\in I}$ is a collection of open sets whose union contains F, then there is a finite subcollection $\{A_{\mu_j}\}_{j=1}^m$ such that $F\subseteq\cup_{j=1}^m A_{\mu_j}$;*

(iii) *Bolzano-Weierstrass property: If S is an infinite bounded subset of X, then $S'\neq\emptyset$;*

(iv) *Bounded sequence property: If $(x^{(k)})_{k=1}^\infty$ is a bounded sequence in X, then it has a convergent subsequence;*

(v) *Nested set property: If $(F_k)_{k=1}^\infty$ is a sequence of closed and bounded nonempty sets such that $F_{k+1}\subseteq F_k\subseteq X$ for each $k\in\mathbf{N}$, then $\cap_{k=1}^\infty F_k\neq\emptyset$.*

Proof. Since statements (ii)-(v) refer to bounded sets, it will be more convenient to use another formulation of the boundedness; that is, a set S is bounded in X if and only if it is contained in an n-cube Q with side-length $2r>0$, i.e.,

$$S\subseteq Q=\{x\in\mathbf{R}^n: |x_j|\le r \quad\text{for}\quad j=1,\dots,n\}.$$

(i)$\Rightarrow$(ii) Let F be a closed and bounded set and suppose that we are given that $\{A_\mu\}_{\mu\in I}$ is an open cover of F as in (ii). Since F is bounded, there is an n-cube Q_1 containing F. Assume that F cannot be covered by any finite number of the A_μ's. Subdivide Q_1 into 2^n n-cubes by halving each of the coordinate intervals of Q_1; that is, the jth coordinate of a point x in one of the n-cubes is restricted to either $[0,r]$ or $[-r,0]$ instead of $[-r,r]$. If it were possible to cover those parts of F that lie in each one of the 2^n n-cubes with finitely many A_μ's, then the union of all of these A_μ's would still be only a finite number and would cover F. Therefore one of these 2^n n-cubes must contain a subset of F that cannot be covered by any finite number of the A_μ's. Call this n-cube Q_2. Now subdivide Q_2 into 2^n n-cubes and repeat the process. The result is a sequence of n-cubes such that $Q_{k+1}\subseteq Q_k$, and the jth coordinate of each point in Q_k is restricted on an interval whose length is $r2^{2-k}$. Choose a point sequence $(x^{(k)})_{k=1}^\infty$ such that $x^{(k)}$ is in $F\cap Q_k$. Then $(x_j^{(k)})_{k=1}^\infty$ – the sequence of jth coordinates forms a Cauchy number sequence in $\mathbf{R}$ thanks to

$$|x_j^{(k)}-x_j^{(m)}|\le r(2^{2-k}+\cdots+2^{2-m})<r2^{3-m}\to 0\quad\text{as}\quad k>m\to\infty.$$

Consequently, $(x^{(k)})_{k=1}^\infty$ is a Cauchy sequence in $\mathbf{R}^n$. Assuming (i), we conclude that there is a point $x\in\mathbf{R}^n$ such that $\lim_{k\to\infty}x^{(k)}=x$. Since each $x^{(k)}$ is in F and F is closed, we have $x\in F$. Therefore x is in one of the A_μ's, say, $x\in A_{\mu_x}$. But A_{μ_x} is open, so for some $s>0$, $x\in B_s(x)\subseteq A_{\mu_x}$, which means that $B_s(x)$ contains all but a finite number of the n-cubes Q_k's. But this derives that the points of F in all these Q_k's are contained in A_{μ_x}, and this contradicts the choice of Q_k.

(ii)$\Rightarrow$(iii) Suppose that S is a bounded set which has no cluster point. We show that S must be finite, which establishes (iii). Let $\overline{B}$ be a closed and bounded ball containing S. Since no point of $\overline{B}$ is a cluster point of S, we can choose a open ball $B_{r_x}(x)$ for each $x\in\overline{B}$ such that $B_{r_x}(x)$ contains no point of S except possibly x itself. Now $\overline{B}\subseteq\cup_{x\in\overline{B}}B_{r_x}(x)$, so $\{B_{r_x}(x): x\in\overline{B}\}$ is a collection of open sets whose union contains $\overline{B}$. Therefore from (ii) we conclude that there is a finite subcollection of these open balls that covers $\overline{B}$. But this subcollection must also cover S due to $S \subseteq \overline{B}$, and since each open ball contains at most one point of S, we conclude that S is finite.

(iii)⇒(iv) Assume that $(x^{(k)})_{k=1}^{\infty}$ is a bounded point sequence, and let S be the range of this sequence; that is, $S = \{p \in \mathbf{R}^n : p = x^{(k)} \text{ for some } k\}$. If S is a finite set, then at least one of its points must appear infinitely many times as a term of the sequence, in which case $(x^{(k)})_{k=1}^{\infty}$ has a constant subsequence. If S has infinitely many points, then (iii) implies that S has a cluster point, and in proving Theorem 5.20 we have seen how to construct a sequence in S that converges to that cluster point.

(iv)⇒(v) Let $(F_k)_{k=1}^{\infty}$ be a nested sequence of closed and bounded sets as in the hypothesis of (v). For each k, choose a point $x^{(k)}$ in F_k. Every such point is in F_1, so $(x^{(k)})_{k=1}^{\infty}$ is bounded sequence. By (iv), $(x^{(k)})_{k=1}^{\infty}$ has a convergent subsequence whose limit we here call x. We see that the nested property of the sets guarantees that each F_k contains all but possibly a finite number of the points $x^{(k)}$. Therefore for each k there is a sequence of points in F_k that converges to x. Since they are closed sets, x must belong to each F_k. Hence $\cap_{k=1}^{\infty} F_k$ contains x, so the intersection is nonempty.

(v)⇒(i) Let $(x^{(k)})_{k=1}^{\infty}$ be a Cauchy sequence, and for each m set F_m be the closure of the collection of points $\{x^{(k)} : k \geq m\}$. Thus $(F_m)_{m=1}^{\infty}$ is a nested sequence of closed sets. By Theorem 5.24 (ii) we see that $(x^{(k)})_{k=1}^{\infty}$ is bounded, and therefore F_1 is bounded. By (v) there is a point x in all sets F_m's. Let $B_\epsilon(x)$ be any open ball about x, and choose a number N such that $k > m > N$ implies that $d_n(x^{(k)}, x^{(m)}) < \epsilon/2$. Since x is in F_N, which is the closure of the subsequence $(x^{(k)})_{k=N}^{\infty}$, there is some point $x^{(m)}$, where $m > N$, such that $x^{(m)}$ is in $B_{\epsilon/2}(x)$. Now if $k > N$, then

$$d_n(x^{(k)}, x) \leq d_n(x^{(k)}, x^{(m)}) + d_n(x^{(m)}, x) < \epsilon,$$

and hence $\lim_{k\to\infty} x^{(k)} = x$ in X. □

Remark 5.29.

(i) In examining the proof of Theorem 5.28, we find that the Euclidean distance formula was used only in proving that (i) implies (ii). Therefore we conclude that the other four implications hold in any metric space.

(ii) For $x \in \mathbf{R}^n$ let $X = \mathbf{R}^n \setminus \{x\}$ and the distance between points in X be the same Euclidean distance as in $\mathbf{R}^n$. Now if $(x^{(k)})_{k=1}^{\infty}$ is a sequence that converges to x in $\mathbf{R}^n$ and $x^{(k)} \neq x$, then it is still a Cauchy sequence in X. But because there is no point in X to which it converges, $(x^{(k)})_{k=1}^{\infty}$ is not convergent in X. Thus X is not complete. Since completeness is implied by the other four statements, it follows that all five are false.

(iii) Of course, the fact that all five statements in Theorem 5.28 are valid for $X = \mathbf{R}^n$ is quite dependent upon the distance formula. The use of the distance formula in proving that (i) implies (ii) is very subtle. It is inherent in the notions of boundedness and n-cubes that were used.

Example 5.30. Let X be an infinite set and define d by

$$d(x,y) = \begin{cases} 1, & x \neq y, \\ 0, & x = y. \end{cases}$$

Since each point in X can be written as $\{x\} = B_{1/2}(x)$, we see that every singleton set is an open set in X. Also $X = B_2(x)$ for any $x \in X$, so X is bounded. Therefore X is a bounded and closed set, and $\cup_{x\in X}\{x\}$ is an open cover of X that obviously cannot be reduced to a finite number of open sets. We now assert that X is complete, because it is not hard to show that if $(x^{(k)})_{k=1}^{\infty}$ is a Cauchy sequence, then there is an N such that $x^{(k)} = x^{(N)}$ whenever $k \geq N$. Therefore $\lim_{k\to\infty} x^{(k)} = x^{(N)}$, so X is complete even though the Heine-Borel property does not hold.

5.3 Compactness, Density and Separability

As for an expansion of the Heine-Borel property, we discuss the compactness, density and countability of sets in a given metric space.

The first important notion induced by the Heine-Borel property is that of compact sets. To see this picture clearly, we first consider two examples that enable us to describe some important and attractive results in the theory of functions.

Example 5.31. A set $K \subseteq \mathbf{R}^n$ is said to be compact provided every sequence in K contains a subsequence that converges to a point in K. This notion can be characterized by the equivalence of the following three statements:

(i) K is compact;

(ii) K is closed and bounded;

(iii) Every open cover of K has a finite subcover – if $K \subseteq \cup_{\alpha\in I} G_\alpha$ where $G_\alpha \subseteq \mathbf{R}^n$ is open, then there exists a finite subset J of the index set I such that $K \subseteq \cup_{\alpha\in J} G_\alpha$.
In fact, suppose (i) holds. Then every convergent sequence in K converges to a point in K. Using the fact that a subset E of $\mathbf{R}^n$ is closed if and only if E is equal to its closure, we obtain that K is closed. If K is not bounded, then for each $k \in \mathbf{N}$, there exists an $x_k \in K$ such that $d_n(x_k, 0) > k$. Consequently, no subsequence of $(x_k)_{k=1}^{\infty}$ can converge and so K is not compact, a contradiction – in other words, (ii) is true. Next, if (ii) holds, then an application of Theorem 5.28 (i) yields that (iii) is true. Finally, suppose that (iii) holds. To verify (i), it suffices to prove that K is bounded and closed since Theorems 5.27 and 5.28 (iv) imply that every sequence in such K has a subsequence which converges to a point in K. To see that K is bounded, set $G_x = B_1(x)$. Then $\{G_x : x \in K\}$ is an open cover of K and so has a finite subcover, say, $G_{x_1}, \ldots, G_{x_k}$. Let $M = \max\{d_n(x_j, 0) : j = 1, \ldots, k\}$. If $x \in K$, then $x \in G_{x_j}$ for some j and $d_n(x, 0) \leq d_n(x_j, 0) + 1 \leq M + 1$. Thus, K is bounded. To show that K is closed, fix a point $x \in \mathbf{R}^n \setminus K$. For any $y \in K$, there are disjoint open balls B_y and V_y about y and x, respectively. Note that these two balls will generally depend on x. The family $\{B_y : y \in K\}$ is an open over of K and so has a finite subcover, say, $B_{y_1}, \ldots, B_{y_k}$. Then $K \subseteq \cup_{j=1}^{k} B_{y_j}$, which is disjoint from the open ball $B = \cap_{j=1}^{k} V_{y_j}$ centered at x. This ball B must be contained entirely in $\mathbf{R}^n \setminus K$:

Otherwise, $B \cap K \neq \emptyset$ and hence $B \cap \left(\cup_{j=1}^{k} B_{y_j} \right) \neq \emptyset$, a contradiction. It follows that $\mathbf{R}^n \setminus K$ is open and so K is closed.

Example 5.32. The family $\mathcal{F} = \{(1/k, 2) : k \in \mathbf{N}\}$ is an open cover of $(0, 1]$ and the family $\mathcal{G} = \{(2^{-k}, 2) : k \in \mathbf{N}\}$ is a subfamily of $\mathcal{F}$. Each point of $(0, 1]$ belongs to $(2^{-k}, 2)$ for k sufficiently large, and so $\mathcal{G}$ is a subcover for $(0, 1]$. If $\mathcal{H}$ is a finite subfamily of $\mathcal{F}$, then there is a largest value of k, say k_1 such that $(2^{-k_1}, 2) \in \mathcal{H}$. Since $2^{-k_1-1} \in (0, 1]$ and does not belong to any element of $\mathcal{H}$, $\mathcal{H}$ is not a subcover for $(0, 1]$. A close look at this example reveals that the problem lies in the fact that $(0, 1]$ is not closed. Other examples, which the reader should construct, show that similar problems can arise with unbounded sets.

Remark 5.33. There is an important result generalizing the nested set property – if $\mathcal{F} = \{K_j\}_{j \in I}$ is a class of compact subsets of $\mathbf{R}^n$, $n \in \mathbf{N}$, and the intersection of any finite subclass of $\mathcal{F}$ is nonempty then $\cap_{j \in I} K_j \neq \emptyset$. To this end, let $K \in \mathcal{F}$ be such that $K \cap (\cap_{j \in I} K_j) = \emptyset$. Then $K \subseteq \cup_{j \in I} (\mathbf{R}^n \setminus K_j)$. Since K is compact, there are finitely many indices $j_1, \ldots, j_k$ such that

$$K \subseteq \cup_{l=1}^{k} (\mathbf{R}^n \setminus K_{j_l}) = \mathbf{R}^n \setminus \cap_{l=1}^{k} K_{j_l},$$

so $K \cap (\cap_{l=1}^{k} K_{j_l}) = \emptyset$, a contradiction. Accordingly, $K \cap (\cap_{j \in I} K_j) \neq \emptyset$.

An advantage of the last characterization of compactness in Example 5.31 is that it remains meaningful when the discussion is extended to the topological spaces which are much more general than $\mathbf{R}^n$, and thus serves as the basis for a definition of the compactness in these more general spaces.

Definition 5.34. Suppose (X, d) is a metric space. We say that $S \subseteq X$ is compact provided that, whenever S is contained in the union of a collection of open subsets of X, S is contained in the union of a finite number of these open subsets. In particular, if $S = X$ then (X, d) is called a compact metric space.

It is very natural to give an alternate description of this definition in terms of cluster point.

Theorem 5.35. *Let (X, d) be a metric space and $S \subseteq X$. Then the following statements are equivalent:*

(i) *S is compact;*

(ii) *Any infinite subset of S has at least one cluster point in S;*

(iii) *Any sequence of points in S has a subsequence which is convergent to a point in S.*

Proof. (i)⇒(ii) Suppose (i) is true. If (ii) is false, then there is an infinite subset S of X that has no cluster point in S. Now for each $x \in S$, we can find an open ball having x as center and containing only a finite number of points of S. Note that S is compact and covered by all such open balls centered at x. So it is subset of the union of a finite number of such open balls of which each contains only a finite number of points of S. This implies that S is finite, a contradiction.

(ii)⇒(iii) This implication is trivial.

(iii)⇒(i) Suppose (iii) is valid, but (i) is not true. Given $\epsilon > 0$ and $x_1 \in S$. Choose $x_2 \in S$ such that $d(x_2, x_1) \geq \epsilon$. For $k = 1, 2$ choose $x_3 \in S$ such that $d(x_3, x_k) \geq \epsilon$. Continuing the previous selection, we can find $x_{n+1} \in S$ such that $d(x_{n+1}, x_k) \geq \epsilon$ for $k = 1, 2, \ldots, n$ and $n \in \mathbf{N}$. This process can be done because S is covered by all open balls centered at points in S of radius ϵ but this cover has no a finite subcover thanks to the assumption that S is not compact. According to (iii), $(x_n)_{n=1}^{\infty}$ must possess a subsequence $(x_{n_j})_{j=1}^{\infty}$ which is convergent to a point in S, so $d(x_{n_j}, x_{n_k}) < \epsilon$ whenever n_j and n_k are big enough. This contradicts $d(x_{n_j}, x_{n_k}) \geq \epsilon$. □

Here is an interesting aside of Theorem 5.35 and Remark 5.29.

Corollary 5.36. *Let (X, d) be a complete metric space. Then a closed subset S of X is compact if and only if S is totally bounded; that is, for any $\epsilon > 0$ there exist finitely many open balls $\{B_\epsilon(x_j)\}_{j=1}^{n}$ in X such that $S \subseteq \cup_{j=1}^{n} B_\epsilon(x_j)$.*

Proof. Suppose $S \subseteq X$ is closed. If S is compact, then S can be covered by open balls $\{B_\epsilon(x)\}_{x \in S}$ for any $\epsilon > 0$, and hence by the definition of compactness there are finitely many elements $\{B_\epsilon(x_j)\}_{j=1}^{n}$ such that S is covered by $\{B_\epsilon(x_j)\}_{j=1}^{n}$.

Conversely, suppose S is totally bounded. Let S be covered by a collection of open sets $\{O_\alpha\}_{\alpha \in I}$. To reach a contradiction, assume S cannot be covered by any finite sub-collection of $\{O_\alpha\}_{\alpha \in I}$. Since S is closed and totally bounded, for $\epsilon = 1$ there are finitely many open balls $\{B_1(x_j)\}_{j=1}^{n_1}$ such that $S = \cup_{j=1}^{n_1} S \cap \overline{B}_1(x_j)$. According to the assumption, one of closed sets in $\{S \cap \overline{B}_1(x_j)\}_{j=1}^{n_1}$, say, $S_1 = S \cap \overline{B}_1(x_1)$, cannot be covered by finitely many elements of $\{O_\alpha\}_{\alpha \in I}$. Do the same with $\epsilon = 1/2$ and S_1 in place of $\epsilon = 1$ and S respectively, and continue this process. The result is that there exists a sequence of closed sets $(S_k)_{k=1}^{\infty}$ such that:

(a) $S \supseteq S_1 \supseteq S_2 \supseteq \cdots$;

(b) $\sup_{x,y \in S_k} d(x, y) \leq 2/k$;

(c) S_k cannot be covered by finitely many elements of $\{O_\alpha\}_{\alpha \in I}$.

Choose $x_k \in S_k$. By (a), (b) and the fact that X is complete and each S_k is closed, $(x_k)_{k=1}^{\infty}$ is a Cauchy sequence which is convergent to an element $x \in \cap_{k=1}^{\infty} S_k$. This implies $x \in S_k \subset O_\alpha$ for some $\alpha \in I$ and for sufficiently large $k \in \mathbf{N}$, contradicting (c). Therefore, S must be covered by finitely many elements of $\{O_\alpha\}_{\alpha \in I}$, i.e., S is compact. □

One example of a compact metric space will give us many more, by means of the following result.

Theorem 5.37. *Let (X, d) be a compact metric space. Then X is complete with respect to d. Furthermore:*

(i) *Any closed subset S of X is compact;*

(ii) *For any sequence of nonempty closed subsets $(S_j)_{j=1}^{\infty}$ of X, with $S_1 \supseteq S_2 \supseteq S_3 \supseteq \ldots$, there is at least one point in $\cap_{j \in \mathbf{N}} S_j$.*

Proof. By Theorem 5.35 it follows that any Cauchy sequence has a convergent subsequence and therefore is itself convergent. Thus, (X, d) is complete.

(i) Let S be closed. Then S^c is open. If $S \subseteq \cup_{\alpha\in I} U_\alpha$ where $U_\alpha \subseteq X$ is open for each $\alpha \in I$. Then $X \subseteq (\cup_{\alpha\in I} U_\alpha) \cup S^c$. Since X is compact, we can find a finite subset $J \subseteq I$ such that $X \subseteq (\cup_{\alpha\in J} U_\alpha) \cup S^c$. Hence $S \subseteq \cup_{\alpha\in J} U_\alpha$. This shows that S is compact.

(ii) If $\cap_{j\in\mathbf{N}} S_j = \emptyset$, then $X = \emptyset^c = \cup_{j\in\mathbf{N}} S_j^c$. Since X is compact, it is the union of a finite number of the open subsets $(S_j^c)_{j=1}^\infty$. Note that since $S_1^c \subseteq S_2^c \subseteq S_3^c \subseteq \cdots$, we must have $X = S_k^c$ for some k, which produces the contradiction $S_k = X^c = \emptyset$. □

Remark 5.38. Here, we point out that (ii) does not hold if the word "compact" is replaced by "complete" – for example, $X = \mathbf{R}$ and $S_k = \{x \in \mathbf{R} : x \geq k\}$, $k \in \mathbf{N}$.

In addition to this counterexample, we have the following interesting consequence.

Corollary 5.39. *Suppose (X, d) is a metric space. If $S \subseteq X$ is compact, then it is bounded and closed, but not conversely.*

Proof. Since X is the union of its open balls, if $S \subseteq X$ is compact then S is covered by a finite number of those balls and hence S is bounded. To establish the closedness of S, we note that (S, d) is a compact metric space and so it is complete, by Theorem 5.37. Accordingly, S is closed.

For the converse, consider the distance d defined by $d(x, y) = 1$ or $d(x, y) = 0$ if $x \neq y$ or $x = y$. Clearly, any infinite set X is bounded and closed under d, but X is not compact since $X = \cup_{x\in X} B_{1/2}(x)$ has no finite cover. □

Next we deal with the density and the separability of metric spaces.

Definition 5.40. Suppose (X, d) is a metric space.

(i) $D \subseteq X$ is said to be dense in X provided every open ball in X contains a point of D.

(ii) X is called separable provided there is a countable set $S = \{x_1, x_2, \cdots\} \subseteq X$ that is dense in X.

To give an example, we turn immediately to $\mathbf{R}^n$, $C[a, b]$ and ℓ_∞.

Example 5.41.

(i) For $n \in \mathbf{N}$, $\mathbf{Q}^n$ is a countable dense subset of $\mathbf{R}^n$. This fact can be deduced from the countability of $\mathbf{Q}$. To show that $\mathbf{Q}^n$ is dense in $\mathbf{R}^n$, let $B_\epsilon(x)$ be any open ball of radius $\epsilon > 0$ and center $x = (x_1, .., x_n) \in \mathbf{R}^n$ and use the density of $\mathbf{Q}$ in $\mathbf{R}$ to choose rational numbers $r_1, \ldots, r_n$ such that

$$|x_j - r_j| < \epsilon/\sqrt{n} \quad \text{for} \quad j = 1, \ldots, n.$$

Then

$$d_n(x, r) = \Big(\sum_{j=1}^n |x_j - r_j|^2\Big)^{1/2} < \epsilon \quad \text{and so} \quad r = (r_1, \ldots, r_n) \in \mathbf{Q}^n \cap B_\epsilon(x).$$

(ii) Let ℓ_2 and ℓ_∞ be the spaces of real-valued sequences $(x_k)_{k=1}^\infty$ with $\sum_{j=1}^\infty x_j^2 < \infty$ and $\sup_{k\in\mathbf{N}} |x_k| < \infty$, respectively. For two sequences $x = (x_j)_{j=1}^\infty$ and $y = (y_j)_{j=1}^\infty$, define

$$d_p(x,y) = \begin{cases} \left(\sum_{j=1}^\infty |x_j - y_j|^2\right)^{\frac{1}{2}}, & p = 2, \\ \sup_{1\le j<\infty} |x_j - y_j|, & p = \infty. \end{cases}$$

Then (ℓ_2, d_2) and (ℓ_∞, d_∞) are metric spaces, but the former is separable and the latter is not separable. It is enough to check the statement after the but. Let S be the collection of all sequences of rational numbers that are eventually 0. If $\epsilon > 0$ is given, then for any $x = (x_j)_{j=1}^\infty \in \ell_2$ there is some $N \in \mathbf{N}$ such that $\sum_{j=N}^\infty |x_j|^2 < (\epsilon/2)^2$; at the same time, for each $j \in \{1, \ldots, N\}$ there is an $r_j \in \mathbf{Q}$ such that $|r_j - x_j| < \epsilon/(2N)$. Accordingly, the sequence $r = (r_1, \ldots, r_{N-1}, 0, 0, 0, 0 \ldots) \in S$ satisfies

$$d_2(x,r) \le \sum_{j=1}^{N-1} |x_j - r_j| + \left(\sum_{j=N}^\infty x_j^2\right)^{\frac{1}{2}} < \epsilon.$$

This implies that S is dense in ℓ_2. As for the latter, given $n \in \mathbf{N}$ let $x^{(n)} = (x_1^{(n)}, x_2^{(n)}, \cdots, x_j^{(n)}, \cdots)$ be an element in ℓ_∞. Define $x = (x_1, \cdots, x_j, \cdots)$, where

$$x_j = \begin{cases} x_j^{(j)} + 1, & |x_j^{(j)}| \le 1, \\ 0, & |x_j^{(j)}| > 1. \end{cases}$$

Thus $x \in \ell_\infty$. Moreover,

$$d_\infty(x, x^{(n)}) \ge |x_n - x_n^{(n)}| \ge 1, \quad n \in \mathbf{N}.$$

This shows that the set $\{x^{(n)}\}_{n=1}^\infty$ cannot be dense in ℓ_∞.

(iii) For any finite closed interval $[a,b] \subset \mathbf{R}$, $C[a,b]$ of all real-valued continuous functions on $[a,b]$ is a metric space under the sup-distance:

$$d(f,g) = \sup_{x\in[a,b]} |f(x) - g(x)| < \infty \quad \text{for} \quad f, g \in C[a,b].$$

Moreover, it is separable. In fact, let S be the collection of piecewise linear functions of the form

$$f(t) = s_k + \frac{s_{k+1} - s_k}{t_{k+1} - t_k}(t - t_k), \quad t_k \le t \le t_{k+1},$$

where $a = t_0 < t_1 < \cdots < t_n = b$ is a partition of $[a,b]$, and the s_k, t_k are rational (with the possible exceptions of $t_0 = a$ and $t_n = b$). The set S is enumerable. Suppose $g \in C[a,b]$. For any $\epsilon > 0$, there is a $\delta > 0$ such that

$$|t - s| < \delta \Rightarrow |g(t) - g(s)| < \frac{\epsilon}{4}.$$

Let $a = t_0 < t_1 < \cdots < t_n = b$ be a partition of $[a,b]$ with $t_1, \cdots, t_{n-1}$ rational and such that $\max_{0\le k\le n-1}(t_{k+1} - t_k) < \delta$. Let $s_0, \cdots, s_n$ be rational numbers such that $\max_{0\le k\le n} |g(t_k) - s_k| < \frac{\epsilon}{4}$. Then for $t_k \le t \le t_{k+1}$ we have

$$f(t) - g(t) = \frac{t_{k+1} - t}{t_{k+1} - t_k}(s_k - g(t)) + \frac{t - t_k}{t_{k+1} - t_k}(s_{k+1} - g(t)),$$

and hence

$$|f(t) - g(t)|$$
$$\leq |s_k - g(t_k)| + |g(t_k) - g(t)| + |s_{k+1} - g(t_{k+1})| + |g(t_{k+1}) - g(t)| < \epsilon.$$

Thus S is dense in $C[a, b]$.

Motivated by the foregoing example, we can establish a relationship between compactness and separability.

Theorem 5.42. *Let (X, d) be a metric space. If X is compact, then it is separable.*

Proof. Suppose $n \in \mathbf{N}$ and X is compact. Since $X = \cup_{x \in X} B_{1/n}(x)$, it follows that there is an $N_n \in \mathbf{N}$ such that $X = \cup_{j=1}^{N_n} B_{1/n}(x_j)$. Now, the countable set $S = \cup_{n=1}^{\infty} \cup_{j=1}^{N_n} \{x_j\}$ is dense in X. As a matter of fact, if $x \in X$ then $x \in B_{1/n}(x_k)$ for some $k \in \{1, \ldots, N_n\}$. Now for any $\epsilon > 0$ there exists an $n \in \mathbf{N}$ such that $n^{-1} < \epsilon$ and hence $x_k \in B_{1/n}(x) \subseteq B_\epsilon(x)$, i.e., $B_\epsilon(x) \cap S \neq \emptyset$. Therefore, X is separable. □

The next result is Lebesgue's property which is of great generality and combines the concepts of open sets, density and separability. This theorem should be compared to the Heine-Borel property, for each statement makes an assertion about reducing an open covering of a set.

Theorem 5.43. *For $n \in \mathbf{N}$ let $X = \mathbf{R}^n$ be equipped with the distance $d_n(\cdot, \cdot)$.*

(i) *There is a countable collection $\mathcal{B}$ of open balls in X such that any open subset of X can be expressed as the union of some subcollection of $\mathcal{B}$.*

(ii) *If D is any subset of X and $\{A_\mu\}_{\mu \in I}$ is a collection of open sets whose union contains D, then there is a countable subcollection $\{A_{\mu_k}\}_{k=1}^{\infty}$ whose union contains D.*

Proof. (i) As a matter of fact, if $\mathcal{B}$ stands for the collection of all open balls $B_r(q)$ with $r > 0$ being a rational number and $q \in \mathbf{Q}^n$, then for a given open set A we can consider the subcollection $\mathcal{B}_A$ consisting of those open balls such that $B_r(q) \subseteq A$. Their union is obviously contained in A, and the collection is countable because both $\mathbf{Q}^n$ and $\mathbf{Q}$ are countable. Therefore it remains only to show that A is contained in the union of this collection. If x is a point in A, then there is an open ball about x with rational radius r such that $B_r(x) \subseteq A$. Since $\mathbf{Q}^n$ is dense, there is a point q of $\mathbf{Q}^n$ in $B_{r/2}(x)$. Then x is in $B_{r/2}(q)$, and $B_{r/2}(q)$ is in $\mathcal{B}_A$ because it is contained in $B_r(x)$, which lies in A. This last assertion is verified by observing that if $y \in B_{r/2}(q)$, then $d_n(x, y) \leq d_n(x, q) + d_n(q, y) < r$. We have shown that an arbitrary point $x \in A$ is contained in some open ball in $\mathcal{B}_A$, so A is contained in the union of all balls in $\mathcal{B}_A$.

(ii) Suppose $D \subseteq \cup_{\mu \in I} A_\mu$. By (i), each of the open sets A_μ can be written as the union of all the balls $B_{r_k}^{\mu}$ about points of $\mathbf{Q}^n$ that have rational radii and are contained in A_μ, say, $A_\mu = \cup_{k=1}^{\infty} B_{r_k}^{\mu}$. If $x \in D$ then there is some r_k such that $x \in B_{r_k}^{\mu} \subseteq A_\mu$. For each of the open balls $B_{r_k}^{\mu}$, choose just one A_μ that contains $B_{r_k}^{\mu}$ and call it $A_{r_k}^{\mu}$. The subcollection of all such $A_{r_k}^{\mu}$ is countable because there is only one $A^{\mu}_{r_k}$ for each $B^{\mu}_{r_k}$. Also, the union of this subcollection contains the union of the $B^{\mu}_{r_k}$'s, which in turn contains D. Hence there is a countable subcollection of $\{A_\mu\}_{\mu\in I}$ whose union contains D. □

Remark 5.44. It is worth remarking that the hypothesis of Theorem 5.43 (ii) makes no restrictive assumption about D. That is the strength and generality of this result; it applies to any subset D of $\mathbf{R}^n$. If it is given, in addition, that D is closed and bounded, then the countable subcollection obtained from the Lebesgue property can be further reduced to a finite subcollection whose union still contains D.

Definition 5.45. Suppose (X, d) is a metric space.

(i) A set $S \subseteq X$ is said to be nowhere dense if $\overline{S}$ contains no open ball, i.e., $\overline{S}^{\circ} = \emptyset$.

(ii) A set $S \subseteq X$ is said to be of first category in X if S is a countable union of nowhere dense sets.

(iii) A set $S \subseteq X$ is said to be of second category in X if S is not of first category.

Example 5.46.

(i) The Georg Cantor set K is nowhere dense. To see this, let us recall the construction of the Cantor set. Set $I = [0,1]$. K is constructed by removing open intervals from I. The first step, which for notational convenience we call the zeroth step, is the removal of the "middle third" of I: $E_{0,1} = (1/3, 2/3)$. At the next step (i.e., the real first step) we remove the "middle thirds" of the remaining two intervals. We continue in this way, at each step removing the "middle thirds" of the remaining intervals. At the kth step there will be 2^k intervals remaining and then we remove 2^k "middle thirds"; our notation for the deleted open intervals is then $E_{k,j}$, $j = 1, 2, \ldots, 2^k$. Note that the length $m_{id}(E_{k,j}) = 3^{-(k+1)}$ of $E_{k,j}$. The set remaining after removal of the middle thirds is called the Cantor set, K. Explicitly, $K = I \setminus \cup_{k=0}^{\infty} \cup_{j=1}^{2^k} E_{k,j}$. It is clear that K is closed since K^c is open. Note that $\{E_{k,j}\}$ are disjoint one from another. So it follows from Theorem 4.4 that

$$m_{id}\big(\cup_{k=0}^{\infty} \cup_{j=1}^{2^k} E_{k,j}\big) = \sum_{k=0}^{\infty}\sum_{j=1}^{2^k} m_{id}(E_{k,j}) = \sum_{k=0}^{\infty}\sum_{j=1}^{2^k} \frac{1}{3^{j+1}} = 1.$$

Since $m_{id}(I) = 1$, one has

$$1 = m_{id}(I) = m_{id}(K) + m_{id}\big(\cup_{k=0}^{\infty} \cup_{j=1}^{2^k} E_{k,j}\big) = m_{id}(K) + 1,$$

which implies $m_{id}(K) = 0$. If $(\overline{K})^{\circ} = K^{\circ}$ were not empty, then K would contain a finite open interval (a, b), then $b - a \le m_{id}(K) = 0$, and hence $a = b$, a contradiction. Thus, $K^{\circ} = \emptyset$.

(ii) $\mathbf{Q}$ is of first category in $\mathbf{R}$ – this follows from the definition.

(iii) $\mathbf{R}$ is of second category in itself – this assertion is not obvious, and in fact it can only be deduced as a consequence of the so-called Baire category theorem (named after René-Louis Baire) as follows.

Theorem 5.47. *Given a metric (X, d). If X is complete, then it is of second category, and hence the complement of a first category set in X is of second category and dense in X*

Proof. Let A_k be nowhere dense in X for every $k \in \mathbf{N}$, and let $E = \cup_{k=1}^{\infty} A_k$. We shall show that there is $x \in X \setminus E = E^c$ and this will establish the result. Let $x^{(0)} \in X$. Since A_1 is nowhere dense, there is a closed ball B_1 of radius less than $1/2$ inside the open ball $B_1(x^{(0)})$ and such that $B_1 \cap A_1 = \emptyset$. Since A_2 is nowhere dense, there is also a closed ball B_2 of radius smaller than $1/3$ such that $B_2 \subseteq B_1$ and $B_2 \cap A_2 = \emptyset$. Continuing this construction produces a nested sequence of closed balls: $(B_k)_{k=1}^{\infty}$ such that the radius of B_k is less than $1/(k+1)$. By the proof for Theorem 5.28 and its immediate Remark 5.29, there is $x \in \cap_{k=1}^{\infty} B_k \subseteq B_1(x^{(0)})$. But $x \notin A_k$ for any k; so $x \notin E$.

If S is of first category, then the density of S^c can be worked out by replacing $B_1(x^{(0)})$ by $B_\epsilon(x^{(0)})$ (for any $\epsilon > 0$) in the foregoing argument. Of course, S^c must be second category: Otherwise, $X = S \cup S^c$ is of first category, a contradiction. □

Problems

5.1. For each of the following functions on $\mathbf{R}^2$, determine which of the properties (i), (ii), and (iii) in Definition 5.1 will be satisfied:

(i) $d(x, y) = |x_1 - y_1| + |x_2 - y_2|$;

(ii) $d(x, y) = \max\{|x_1 - y_1|, |x_2 - y_2|\}$;

(iii)

$$d(x, y) = \begin{cases} ((x_1 - y_1)^2 + (x_2 - y_2)^2)^{1/2}, & x_2 \geq y_2, \\ |x_1 - y_1| + |x_2 - y_2|, & x_2 \leq y_2. \end{cases}$$

5.2. Prove that if $x^{(1)}, \ldots, x^{(m)}$ are points in a metric space (X, d), then

$$d(x^{(1)}, x^{(m)}) \leq \sum_{j=2}^{m} d(x^{(j)}, x^{(j-1)}).$$

5.3. Given $n \in \mathbf{N}$.

(i) Let $d_n^*(x, y) = \sum_{k=1}^{n} |x_k - y_k|$ for $x, y \in \mathbf{R}^n$. Prove that d_n^* satisfies (i)-(ii)-(iii) of Definition 5.1. In addition, show that $d_n(x, y) \leq d_n^*(x, y)$ for $x, y \in \mathbf{R}^n$.

(ii) Let $d_{*,n}(x, y) = \max_{1 \leq k \leq n} |x_k - y_k|$ for $x, y \in \mathbf{R}^n$. Prove that $d_{*,n}$ satisfies (i)-(ii)-(iii) of Definition 5.1. Discuss the relationship between d_n and $d_{*,n}$.

5.4. Prove that A° and $\overline{A}$ are the largest open subset of A and the smallest closed set containing A, respectively.

5.5. In $\mathbf{R}^2$, show that the closure of $B_1(0)$ is $\overline{B}_1(0)$.

5.6. Suppose (X, d) is a metric space. Prove that if S is a finite subset of X, then S is disconnected.

5.7. Prove that, if $f, g > 0$ on $\mathbf{R}$ so that their graphs

$$G_1 = \{x \in \mathbf{R}^2 : \ x_2 = f(x_1)\} \quad \text{and} \quad G_2 = \{x \in \mathbf{R}^2 : \ x_2 = -g(x_1)\}$$

are sets in $\mathbf{R}^2$, then $S = G_1 \cup G_2$ is disconnected.

5.8. Decide whether or not each of the following sequences $(x^{(k)})_{k=1}^{\infty}$ in $\mathbf{R}^2$ where:
(i) $x^{(k)} = \left(\frac{k-1}{k}, \frac{k+1}{k}\right)$;
(ii) $x^{(k)} = \left(\frac{1}{k}, \sin \pi k\right)$;
(iii) $x^{(k)} = \left(\frac{1}{k}, k\right)$;
converges and, if so, find its limit.

5.9. Let X be the interval $(0, 1)$ in $\mathbf{R}$ with the usual distance $|x-y|$. Find a Cauchy sequence in X that does not converge in X.

5.10. For $n \in \mathbf{N}$, prove the following two equivalent statements:
(i) $(x^{(k)})_{k=1}^{\infty}$ is a bounded sequence in $\mathbf{R}^n$ if and only if each coordinate sequence $(x_j^{(k)})_{k=1}^{\infty}$ $(j = 1, \ldots, n)$ is bounded in $\mathbf{R}$;
(ii) A is a bounded set in $\mathbf{R}^n$ when and only when there exists an n-cube containing A.

5.11. Prove that if X is an infinite set and its distance function d is given by

$$d(x, y) = \begin{cases} 1, & x \neq y, \\ 0, & x = y, \end{cases}$$

then every Cauchy sequence in X is eventually constant – there exists an $N \in \mathbf{N}$ such that $x^{(k)} = x^{(N)}$ whenever $k \geq N$.

5.12. For $n \in \mathbf{N}$, prove that $\{(x_1, \ldots, x_n) \in \mathbf{R}^n : \ x_1, \ldots, x_n \in \mathbf{R} \setminus \mathbf{Q}\}$ is dense in $\mathbf{R}^n$.

5.13. Let (X, d) be a metric space. Show that if $(x^{(k)})_{k=1}^{\infty}$ is a Cauchy sequence in X and has a subsequence $(x^{(k_j)})_{j=1}^{\infty}$ that converges to a point $x \in X$, then $d(x_k, x) \to 0$.

5.14. Let (X, d) be a metric space. Prove that X is complete if and only if every closed nested sequence of closed balls $\left(\overline{B}_{r_k}(x_k)\right)_{k=1}^{\infty}$ with $r_k \to 0$ has non-void intersection.

5.15. Let (X, d) be a complete metric space. Prove that if $(S_j)_{j=1}^{\infty}$ is nonempty closed subsets of X with $S_{j+1} \subseteq S_j$ for any $j \in \mathbf{N}$ and if $\text{diam} S_j = \sup\{d(x, y) : x, y \in S_j\} \to 0$ as $j \to \infty$ then $\cap_{j=1}^{\infty} S_j \neq \emptyset$.

5.16. Suppose (X, d) is a metric space. Show that $S \subseteq X$ is nowhere dense if and only if every open ball O contains an open ball O' such that $O' \cap S = \emptyset$.

5.17. Suppose (X, d) is a metric space. Prove that if $E_\alpha \subseteq X$ is compact for any $\alpha \in I$, then $\cap_{\alpha \in I} E_\alpha$ is compact.

5.18. Let (X, d) be a metric space and $\lim_{n \to \infty} d(x_n, x_0) = 0$. Prove that the set $\{x_j\}_{j=0}^{\infty}$ is compact.

Chapter 6

Continuous Maps

Since every metric space is automatically a topological space with the set of all open sets as the metrizable topology, we have a notion of continuous mappings between metric spaces. Note that a function between topological spaces is said to be continuous if the inverse image of every open set is open – this is an attempt to capture the intuition that there are no breaks or separations in the function. Without referring to the topology, this notion can also be directly defined using limits of sequences. In this chapter, we consider properties of continuous mappings, contractions with straightforward applications to integral and differential equations, and equivalence of metric spaces.

6.1 Criteria for Continuity

By a mapping on a metric space (X, d), frequently written as (X, d_X) in what follows, we mean a mapping on the set of points in X, and by a mapping with values in a metric space Y we mean a mapping with values in the set of points in Y. Thus if $f : X \to Y$ is a mapping from the metric space X into the metric space Y, then to each point $x \in X$ is associated a point $f(x) \in Y$. The mapping f will be called continuous at a point $x_0 \in X$ if, roughly speaking, points of X that are near x_0 are mapped by f into points of Y that are near $f(x_0)$. Below is the precise definition.

Definition 6.1. Let (X, d_X) and (Y, d_Y) be two metric spaces, let $f : X \to Y$ be a mapping, and let $x_0 \in X$. Then f is said to be continuous at x_0 if, given any $\epsilon > 0$, there exists a $\delta > 0$ such that if $x \in X$ and $d_X(x, x_0) < \delta$, then $d_Y\big(f(x), f(x_0)\big) < \epsilon$. Moreover, if f is continuous at all points in X, then f is said to be continuous on X.

Here we would like to emphasize that δ depends on ϵ as well as x_0. Therefore, we could more exactly have written $\delta(\epsilon, x_0)$ instead of δ. We are faithful to δ rather than $\delta(\epsilon, x_0)$ for the notational simplicity, always bearing in mind that for a given x_0 each ϵ should have its own δ.

Example 6.2.

(i) The mapping $f : \mathbf{R} \to \mathbf{R}$ given by $f(x) = x^2$ is continuous.

(ii) Let X be any metric space with the distance $d(\cdot,\cdot)$, and x_0 a fixed point in X. Then the mapping $f : X \to \mathbf{R}$ given by $f(x) = d(x, x_0)$ for all $x \in X$ is continuous. This follows from the easily-obtained inequality $|f(x) - f(y)| \le d(x, y)$. The special case $X = \mathbf{R}$ and $x_0 = 0$ shows that the absolute value function $|x|$ is continuous.

(iii) If $f : X \to Y$ is continuous and S is a subspace of X, then the restriction of f to S is continuous on S. This is clear from Definition 6.1. One of the curious consequences of Definition 6.1 occurs at a point in $x_0 \in S$ that is not a cluster point of S. Since x_0 is an isolated point of S, there is an open ball $B_\delta(x_0)$ that contains no point of S other than x_0. Accordingly, the mapping is always continuous at x_0.

Let us have a look at another example.

Example 6.3. For $n, m \in \mathbf{N}$, let $T : \mathbf{R}^n \to \mathbf{R}^m$ be a linear mapping; that is,

$$T(ax + by) = aT(x) + bT(y) \quad \text{for all} \quad x, y \in \mathbf{R}^n.$$

Then there exists an $m \times n$ real-valued matrix $A = [a_{kj}]$ such that $y = T(x) = Ax$, i.e.,

$$T\left(\begin{pmatrix} x_1 \\ \vdots \\ x_n \end{pmatrix}\right) = \begin{pmatrix} y_1 \\ \vdots \\ y_m \end{pmatrix},$$

where

$$y_j = \sum_{k=1}^{n} a_{jk} x_k, \quad a_{kj} \in \mathbf{R}, \quad k = 1, \ldots, n \quad \text{and} \quad j = 1, \ldots, m.$$

Thus T is continuous. To prove this result, we first consider the case $m = 1$, and see that $T : \mathbf{R}^n \to \mathbf{R}$ is a function. Let $e^{(k)}$, $k = 1, \ldots, n$ be the standard basis vectors of $\mathbf{R}^n$: Its kth coordinate is 1 and others are 0. And set $A_k = T(e^{(k)})$. Since $x = \sum_{k=1}^n x_k e^{(k)}$, by the definition of T we have

$$T(x) = \sum_{k=1}^{n} x_k T(e^{(k)}) = \sum_{k=1}^{n} x_k A_k.$$

Thus T is represented by the row matrix $[A_1, \ldots, A_n]$ whenever x is written as the column matrix

$$x = \begin{pmatrix} x_1 \\ \vdots \\ x_n \end{pmatrix}$$

Suppose now $m > 1$. Then

$$T(x) = \begin{pmatrix} y_1 \\ \vdots \\ y_m \end{pmatrix},$$

where y_j is a function of x, say $y_j = f_j(x)$. The linearity of T implies that T is linear in each coordinate; that is, each f_j is a linear function from $\mathbf{R}^n$ into $\mathbf{R}$. Therefore, by the first case, each f_j is determined through

$$y_j = f_j(x) = \sum_{k=1}^{n} a_{jk}x_k.$$

This set of m linear functions $f_1, \ldots, f_m$ determines the m rows of the matrix $[a_{jk}]$. Thus $T(x) = Ax$. In order to prove the continuity of T, let

$$M = \Big(\sum_{j=1}^{m}\sum_{k=1}^{n} a_{jk}^2\Big)^{1/2}; \ ||x||_l = \Big(\sum_{k=1}^{l} x_k^2\Big)^{1/2}; \ d_l(x,y) = ||x-y||_l$$

for

$$x = \begin{pmatrix} x_1 \\ \vdots \\ x_l \end{pmatrix} \quad \text{and} \quad y = \begin{pmatrix} y_1 \\ \vdots \\ y_l \end{pmatrix} \quad \text{in } \mathbf{R}^l.$$

Then

$$||T(x)||_m = \left(\Big(\sum_{k=1}^{n} a_{1k}x_k\Big)^2 + \cdots + \Big(\sum_{k=1}^{n} a_{mk}x_k\Big)^2\right)^{1/2}.$$

Using the Cauchy–Schwarz inequality, we get

$$\Big(\sum_{k=1}^{n} a_{jk}x_k\Big)^2 \le \Big(\sum_{k=1}^{n} a_{jk}^2\Big)\Big(\sum_{k=1}^{n} x_k^2\Big), \quad j = 1, 2, \ldots, m,$$

whence deriving $||T(x)||_m \le M||x||_n$. Consequently, for any fixed point $x_0 \in \mathbf{R}^n$ we have

$$d_m\big(T(x), T(x_0)\big) = ||T(x) - T(x_0)||_m \le M d_n(x, x_0).$$

If $\epsilon > 0$ is given, then we can define $\delta = \frac{\epsilon}{1+M}$, and this implies that

$$d_m\big(T(x), T(x_0)\big) < \epsilon \ \text{ whenever } \ d_n(x, x_0) < \delta.$$

Remark 6.4. Here two facts are pointed out: The first is that the choice of δ above does not depend on x_0 where the continuity is established. The second is that M independently appears in front of $d_n(x, x_0)$ when controlling $d_m\big(T(x), T(x_0)\big)$.

Definition 6.1 may be reformulated by saying that f is continuous at x_0 if, given any open ball in Y of center $f(x_0)$, there exists an open ball in X centered at x_0 whose image under f is contained in the former ball. Clearly, these open balls can be replaced by open sets. The forthcoming criterion for the continuity of a mapping from one metric space into another is often useful.

Theorem 6.5. *Let (X, d_X) and (Y, d_Y) be two metric spaces and let $f : X \to Y$ be a mapping. Then f is continuous on X if and only if the pre-image $f^{-1}(V) = \{x \in X : f(x) \in V\}$ of every open set $V \subseteq Y$ is an open subset of X.*

Proof. To prove this theorem, first suppose f is continuous. We have to show that if $V \subset Y$ is open, then also $f^{-1}(V)$ is open. Let $x_0 \in f^{-1}(V)$. Then $f(x_0) \in V$. Since V is open, it contains the open ball in Y of center $f(x_0)$ and some radius $\epsilon > 0$. Since f is continuous at x_0, there is a $\delta > 0$ such that if $x \in X$ and $d_X(x, x_0) < \delta$ then $d_Y\big(f(x), f(x_0)\big) < \epsilon$. This means that if x is in the open ball in X of center x_0 and radius δ then $f(x)$ belongs to the open ball in Y of center $f(x_0)$ and radius ϵ, so that $f(x) \in V$. That is, $f^{-1}(V)$ contains the open ball in X of center x_0 and radius δ. Since x_0 is an arbitrarily chosen point in $f^{-1}(V)$, the set $f^{-1}(V)$ is open.

Conversely, suppose that for every open $V \subset Y$, the set $f^{-1}(V)$ is an open subset of X. We must show that f is continuous at any point $x_0 \in X$. For any $\epsilon > 0$ let $B_\epsilon\big(f(x_0)\big) \subseteq Y$ be the open ball of center $f(x_0)$ and radius ϵ. Then $f^{-1}\Big(B_\epsilon\big(f(x_0)\big)\Big)$ is an open subset of X that contains x_0, and hence contains the open ball in X of center x_0 and some radius $\delta > 0$. Thus if $x \in X$ and $d_X(x, x_0) < \delta$, then $d_Y\big(f(x), f(x_0)\big) < \epsilon$. This means that f is continuous at x_0, and this completes the proof. □

Remark 6.6. As an immediate consequence of this theorem, we have that if $f : X \to \mathbf{R}$ is continuous then for any $c \in \mathbf{R}$

$$\{x \in X : \ f(x) > c\} \quad \text{and} \quad \{x \in X : \ f(x) < c\}$$

are open subsets of X. Additionally, it is not hard to see that a continuous mapping of a continuous mapping is a continuous mapping; that is, if $f : X \to Y$ and $g : Y \to Z$ are continuous, so is the mapping $g \circ f : X \to Z$.

The next result is the sequence criterion for continuity.

Theorem 6.7. *Let (X, d_X) and (Y, d_Y) be two metric spaces. Then a mapping $f : X \to Y$ is continuous at $x_0 \in X$ if and only if for every sequence $(x_k)_{k=1}^\infty$ of points in X that converges to $x_0 \in X$, the sequence $\big(f(x_k)\big)_{k=1}^\infty$ converges to $f(x_0)$ in Y.*

Proof. Suppose first that f is continuous at $x_0 \in X$ and that $(x_k)_{k=1}^\infty$ converges to x_0 in X. We have to show that $\big(f(x_k)\big)_{k=1}^\infty$ converges to $f(x_0)$ in Y. Given $\epsilon > 0$, the continuity of f at x_0 implies that there is a $\delta > 0$ such that $d_Y\big(f(x), f(x_0)\big) < \epsilon$ whenever $x \in X$ and $d_X(x, x_0) < \delta$. Because $(x_k)_{k=1}^\infty$ converges to x_0, there exists a positive integer N such that $d_X(x_k, x_0) < \delta$ for all $k > N$. Hence if $k > N$ then $d_Y\big(f(x_k), f(x_0)\big) < \epsilon$, which shows that $\big(f(x_k)\big)_{k=1}^\infty$ converges to $f(x_0)$.

Conversely, suppose the statement after the if and only if is valid. If f is not continuous at x_0, then by the negation of Definition 6.1 there is some $\epsilon_0 > 0$ such that for any $\delta > 0$ one can choose $x \in X$ to ensure $d_X(x, x_0) < \delta$ but $d_Y\big(f(x), f(x_0)\big) \geq \epsilon_0$. Hence for any $k \in \mathbf{N}$ we can find a point $x_k \in X$ such that $d_X(x_k, x_0) < 1/k$ and $d_Y\big(f(x_k), f(x_0)\big) \geq \epsilon_0$. Since $d_X(x_k, x_0) < 1/k$, the sequence $(x_k)_{k=1}^\infty$ converges to x_0. However $\big(f(x_k)\big)_{k=1}^\infty$ does not converge to $f(x_0)$ since $d_Y\big(f(x_k), f(x_0)\big) \geq \epsilon_0$ for all k. This completes the proof. □

Example 6.8. Let f be defined on $\mathbf{R}^2$ by

$$f(x) = f(x_1, x_2) = \begin{cases} 0\,, & x = (x_1, x_2) = (0,0), \\ \frac{x_1 x_2}{x_1^2 + x_2^2}\,, & x = (x_1, x_2) \neq (0,0). \end{cases}$$

Then as $(x^{(k)})_{k=1}^{\infty}$ tends to the origin $(0,0)$ along the axes, we see that $\big(f(x^{(k)})\big)_{k=1}^{\infty}$ converges to 0. But if $x^{(k)} = (1/k, 1/k)$, then $f(x^{(k)}) = 1/2$. Thus f is not continuous at the point $(0,0)$.

6.2 Continuous Mappings on Compact or Connected Spaces

First, we consider continuous mappings on a compact metric space.

Theorem 6.9. *Let (X, d_X) and (Y, d_Y) be two metric spaces. Suppose $f : X \to Y$ is a continuous mapping. If X is compact, so is its image $f(X)$.*

Proof. We must prove that if $f(X) = \{f(x) : \ x \in X\}$ is covered by the union of a collection of open subsets of Y then it is covered by the union of a finite number of these open subsets. So, suppose $f(X) \subseteq \cup_{j \in I} V_j$ where I is an index set and V_j is open. Because f is continuous, each inverse image $f^{-1}(V_j)$ is open. Also, for any $x \in X$ we have $f(x) \in V_j$ for some $j \in I$, in which case $x \in f^{-1}(V_j)$, so that $X = \cup_{j \in I} f^{-1}(V_j)$. By the compactness of X we can find a finite subset $J \subseteq I$ such that $X = \cup_{j \in J} f^{-1}(V_j)$. Therefore

$$f(X) = \cup_{j \in J} f\big(f^{-1}(V_j)\big) \subseteq \cup_{j \in J} V_j.$$

Thus $f(X)$ is compact. □

This theorem has two extremely important immediate consequences.

Corollary 6.10. *Let (X, d_X) and (Y, d_Y) be two metric spaces. Suppose $f : X \to Y$ is a continuous mapping. If X is compact, then f is bounded.*

Proof. Since $f(X)$ is compact, it is bounded according to Corollary 5.39. □

The example $f(x) = x$ on the open interval $(0,1)$ of $\mathbf{R}$ shows that a bounded continuous real-valued function need not assume either its least upper bound or its greatest lower bound on its domain of definition. If, however, the domain is compact, then these values are actually taken on by the continuous function.

Corollary 6.11. *Let (X, d_X) be a nonempty compact metric space. Suppose $f : X \to \mathbf{R}$ is a continuous mapping. Then:*

(i) $\sup\{f(x) : x \in X\} = M$ *and* $\inf\{f(x) : x \in X\} = m$ *are finite;*

(ii) *There are points $x, y \in X$ such that $f(x) = M$ and $f(y) = m$.*

Proof. (i) By Theorem 6.9 it follows that $f(X)$ is a compact subset of $\mathbf{R}$, hence closed and bounded. Since $f(X)$ is not empty, $f(X)$ has both a greatest and a least element.

(ii) By the definition of M we derive that for each $k \in \mathbf{N}$ there is $x_k \in X$ such that $M - 1/k < f(x_k) \le M$. Since X is compact, $(x_k)_{k=1}^{\infty}$ has a convergent subsequence $(x_{k_j})_{j=1}^{\infty}$, which converges to a point $x \in X$. Since f is continuous, $f(x) = \lim_{j\to\infty} f(x_{k_j}) = M$. The argument for the existence of the point y such that $f(y) = m$ is similar. □

Continuing from Examples 6.2 (ii) and 6.3, we get the following concept.

Definition 6.12. Let (X, d_X) and (Y, d_Y) be two metric spaces. Then a mapping $f : X \to Y$ is said to be uniformly continuous if, given any $\epsilon > 0$, there exists a $\delta > 0$ such that if $x, y \in X$ and $d_X(x, y) < \delta$ then $d_Y\big(f(x), f(y)\big) < \epsilon$. Moreover, if it happens that a mapping $f : X \to Y$ is such that for a subset S of X, the restriction of f to S is uniformly continuous, we say that f is uniformly continuous on S.

Clearly, a uniformly continuous mapping is continuous. To check continuity at a point $x_0 \in X$ just set $y = x_0$ in the definition. The next theorem states that conversely if f is continuous then f is actually uniformly continuous, provided X is compact.

Theorem 6.13. *Let (X, d_X) and (Y, d_Y) be two metric spaces. Suppose $f : X \to Y$ is a continuous mapping. If X is compact, then f is uniformly continuous, equivalently, $\big(f(x_j)\big)_{j=1}^{\infty}$ is a Cauchy sequence in Y whenever $(x_j)_{j=1}^{\infty}$ is a Cauchy sequence in X.*

Proof. Suppose f is not uniformly continuous on X. Then there are an $\epsilon > 0$ and sequences $(x_k)_{k=1}^{\infty}$ and $(y_k)_{k=1}^{\infty}$ of points in X such that

$$d_X(x_k, y_k) < 1/k \quad \text{and} \quad d_Y\big(f(x_k), f(y_k)\big) \ge \epsilon.$$

Since X is compact, $(x_k)_{k=1}^{\infty}$ has a subsequence $(x_{k_j})_{j=1}^{\infty}$, which converges to a point $x \in X$. Then $y_{k_j} \to x$ since

$$0 \le d_X(y_{k_j}, x) \le d_X(y_{k_j}, x_{k_j}) + d_X(x_{k_j}, x) < {k_j}^{-1} + d_X(x_{k_j}, x).$$

Since f is continuous, we have

$$\lim_{j\to\infty} d_Y\big(f(x_{k_j}), f(x)\big) = 0 \quad \text{and} \quad \lim_{j\to\infty} d_Y\big(f(y_{k_j}), f(x)\big) = 0.$$

Noticing

$$d_Y\big(f(x_{k_j}), f(y_{k_j})\big) \le d_Y\big(f(x_{k_j}), f(x)\big) + d_Y\big(f(y_{k_j}), f(x)\big),$$

we then get $\lim_{j\to\infty} d_Y\big(f(x_{k_j}), f(y_{k_j})\big) = 0$, which contradicts $d_Y\big(f(x_{k_j}), f(y_{k_j})\big) \ge \epsilon$.

Next, we prove the equivalence. The above argument indicates that if f is not uniformly continuous on X, then the sequence $(x_{k_1}, y_{k_1}, x_{k_2}, y_{k_2}, \ldots)$ is a Cauchy sequence in X but $(f(x_{k_1}), f(y_{k_1}), f(x_{k_2}), f(y_{k_2}), \ldots)$ is not a Cauchy sequence in Y. On the other hand, if f is uniformly continuous, then we conclude that for any $\epsilon > 0$ there is a $\delta > 0$ such that $d_X(x, y) < \delta$ implies $d_Y\big(f(x), f(y)\big) < \epsilon$. Now if $(x_j)_{j=1}^{\infty}$ is a Cauchy sequence in X then for the above-obtained $\delta > 0$ there exists $N > 0$ such that $d_X(x_j, x_k) < \delta$ as $k, j > N$ and consequently, $d_Y\big(f(x_j), f(x_k)\big) < \epsilon$, i.e., $\big(f(x_j)\big)_{j=1}^{\infty}$ is a Cauchy sequence in Y. □

Remark 6.14. The compactness of the domain is important. For instance, the function f, defined by $f(x) = 1/x$ on $(0, 1]$, is continuous but is not uniformly continuous on the noncompact set $(0, 1]$. The problem, of course, lies at the left end-point of the interval. The function values are arbitrarily large in every open ball of center 0.

Secondly, we discuss continuous mappings on a connected metric space.

Theorem 6.15. *Let (X, d_X) and (Y, d_Y) be two metric spaces. Suppose $f : X \to Y$ is a continuous mapping. If X is connected, so is its image $f(X)$.*

Proof. If $f(X)$ is not connected, then $f(X) = A \cup B$, where A and B are disjoint nonempty open subsets of Y. It is clear that $f^{-1}(A)$ and $f^{-1}(B)$ are disjoint nonempty open subsets of X. We therefore have the expression of X as $X = f^{-1}(A) \cup f^{-1}(B)$. This contradicts the fact that X is connected, proving the theorem. □

Below is the intermediate value property as a consequence of the above theorem.

Example 6.16. Suppose $[a, b]$ is a finite interval of $\mathbf{R}$. Let $f : [a, b] \to \mathbf{R}$ be continuous with $f(a) < f(b)$. If $f(a) < \zeta < f(b)$, then there exists $c \in [a, b]$ such that $f(c) = \zeta$. In fact, since $[a, b]$ is connected, so is $f([a, b])$. Moreover, any open subset of $\mathbf{R}$ which contains α and β and does not contain some point between α and β is not connected. To see this, suppose that $\alpha < \gamma < \beta$ and S is an open subset of $\mathbf{R}$ with $\alpha, \beta \in S$, $\gamma \notin S$, then

$$S = (S \cap \{x \in \mathbf{R} : x < \gamma\}) \cup (S \cap \{x \in \mathbf{R} : x > \gamma\})$$

expresses S as the union of two disjoint nonempty open subsets. In other words, any connected subset of $\mathbf{R}$ contains all points between any two of its points. Since ζ is between $f(a)$ and $f(b)$ which belong to the connected set $f([a, b])$, we have $\zeta \in f([a, b])$ as desired.

6.3 Sequences of Mappings

Definition 6.17. Let (X, d_X) and (Y, d_Y) be two metric spaces, and for $k \in \mathbf{N}$ let $f_k : X \to Y$ be a mapping. We say that:

(i) $(f_k)_{k=1}^{\infty}$ converges at $x \in X$ provided $\big(f_k(x)\big)_{k=1}^{\infty}$ converges in Y;

(ii) $(f_k)_{k=1}^{\infty}$ converges on X, provided $\big(f_k(x)\big)_{k=1}^{\infty}$ converges at any $x \in X$;

(iii) $(f_k)_{k=1}^{\infty}$ converges to a mapping $f : X \to Y$, denoted $f = \lim_{k\to\infty} f_k$, provided $f(x) = \lim_{k\to\infty} f_k(x)$ whenever $x \in X$.

Example 6.18.

(i) Let $f_k : [0,1] \to \mathbf{R}$ be given by $f_k(x) = x - x/k$. Then $\lim_{k\to\infty} f_k(x) = x$.

(ii) Let $f_k : [0,1] \to \mathbf{R}$ be given by $f_k(x) = x^k$. Then $\lim_{k\to\infty} f_k(x) = f(x)$ where $f(x) = 0$ or 1 if $x \in [0,1)$ or $x = 1$. Note that f_k is continuous, but f is not.

Definition 6.19. Let (X, d_X) and (Y, d_Y) be two metric spaces, for $k \in \mathbf{N}$ let $f_k : X \to Y$ be a mapping, and let $f : X \to Y$ be another mapping. Then we say that $(f_k)_{k=1}^{\infty}$ converges uniformly to f on X if, given any $\epsilon > 0$, there is an $N \in \mathbf{N}$ such that $d_Y\big(f_k(x), f(x)\big) < \epsilon$ whenever $k > N$ for all $x \in X$. If the restrictions of $(f_k)_{k=1}^{\infty}$ to a certain subset S of X converge uniformly to some mapping on S, we say that $(f_k)_{k=1}^{\infty}$ converges uniformly on S.

Uniform convergence clearly implies convergence. Having a look at Example 6.18, we have that the first one is uniform, but not the second. Moreover, we have the following Cauchy criterion for uniform convergence.

Theorem 6.20. *Let (X, d_X) and (Y, d_Y) be two metric spaces, let Y be complete, and for $k \in \mathbf{N}$ let $f_k : X \to Y$ be a mapping. Then $(f_k)_{k=1}^{\infty}$ converges uniformly to f on X when and only when for any $\epsilon > 0$ there is an $N \in \mathbf{N}$ such that $d_Y\big(f_k(x), f_l(x)\big) < \epsilon$ whenever $k, l > N$ for all $x \in X$.*

Proof. It is enough to verify the sufficiency. Suppose the statement after the when and only when is true. So, for any $x \in X$, $\big(f_k(x)\big)_{k=1}^{\infty}$ is a Cauchy sequence in Y. Since Y is complete, this sequence has a limit. Thus $(f_k)_{k=1}^{\infty}$ converges to some mapping f. Given $\epsilon > 0$, choose an integer N so that we have $d_Y\big(f_k(x), f_l(x)\big) < \epsilon/2$ whenever $k, l > N$, for all $x \in X$. Then for any fixed $k > N$ and fixed $x \in X$ the sequence $\big(f_l(x)\big)_{l=1}^{\infty}$ is such that all terms after the N-th are within distance $\epsilon/2$ of $f_k(x)$, and are therefore in the closed ball in Y of center $f_k(x)$ and radius $\epsilon/2$. Since closed balls are closed sets, the limit $f(x)$ of the convergent sequence $\big(f_l(x)\big)_{l=1}^{\infty}$ is also in this closed ball, so that $d_Y\big(f_k(x), f(x)\big) \le \epsilon/2$. Hence if $k > N$ we have $d_Y\big(f_k(x), f(x)\big) < \epsilon$ for all $x \in X$, proving uniform convergence. □

Interestingly, the continuity is preserved under the uniform convergence.

Theorem 6.21. *Let (X, d_X) and (Y, d_Y) be two metric spaces. If $(f_k)_{k=1}^{\infty}$ is a uniformly convergent sequence of continuous mappings from X into Y, then $f = \lim_{k\to\infty} f_k$ is a continuous mapping from X into Y.*

Proof. Fix $x_0 \in X$. Let $\epsilon > 0$. Take a $k \in \mathbf{N}$ such that $d_Y\big(f_k(x), f(x)\big) < \epsilon/3$ for all $x \in X$, which is possible by the uniform convergence. Since f_k is continuous at x_0, there is a $\delta > 0$ such that if $x \in X$ and $d_X(x, x_0) < \delta$ then $d_Y\big(f_k(x), f_k(x_0)\big) < \epsilon/3$. Hence if $x \in X$ and $d_X(x, x_0) < \delta$ we have

$$\begin{aligned} d_Y\big(f(x), f(x_0)\big) &\le d_Y\big(f(x), f_k(x)\big) + d_Y\big(f_k(x), f_k(x_0)\big) + d_Y\big(f_k(x_0), f(x_0)\big) \\ &< \epsilon. \end{aligned}$$

Thus f is continuous at x_0. We are done. □

If f_1 and f_2 are mappings from X into Y, it is natural to try to find some measure of the extent to which f_1 and f_2 differ; that is, to find some sort of distance between f_1 and f_2. For any specific $x \in X$ we may say that f_1 and f_2 differ at x by the distance $d_Y(f_1(x), f_2(x))$, but we would really like to measure how much f_1 and f_2 differ over all points of X, not just at x. There are various ways to do this, depending on the circumstances and purposes in mind, but the most simple-minded method turns out to be one of the most useful. It is to take the distance between f_1 and f_2 to be $\sup\{d_Y(f_1(x), f_2(x)) : x \in X\}$ when this supremum is finite. In order to develop this idea we turn aside for a simple lemma which is motivated by Example 6.2 (ii).

Lemma 6.22. *Let (X, d_X) and (Y, d_Y) be two metric spaces. If f_1 and f_2 are continuous mappings from X into Y, then the function $x \to d_Y(f_1(x), f_2(x))$ is continuous on X.*

Proof. This follows from

$$\begin{aligned}
&|d_Y(f_1(x), f_2(x)) - d_Y(f_1(x_0), f_2(x_0))| \\
&\leq |d_Y(f_1(x), f_2(x)) - d_Y(f_1(x), f_2(x_0))| \\
&+ |d_Y(f_1(x), f_2(x_0)) - d_Y(f_1(x_0), f_2(x_0))| \\
&\leq d_Y(f_2(x), f_2(x_0)) + d_Y(f_1(x), f_1(x_0)).
\end{aligned}$$

□

Now we consider the set $C(X, Y)$ of all continuous mappings from X into Y. If X is a nonempty compact space, then it is clear that for $f_1, f_2 \in C(X, Y)$ the following notion

$$d_{C(X,Y)}(f_1, f_2) = \max_{x \in X} d_Y(f_1(x), f_2(x))$$

makes sense thanks to Corollary 6.11, especially saying that any continuous real-valued function on a compact metric space attains a maximum. Moreover, it is easy to prove that $C(X, Y)$ is a metric space under $d_{C(X,Y)}(\cdot, \cdot)$. However, it is abstract in the sense that its points are mappings on another metric space. A sequence of points in $C(X, Y)$ is a sequence of continuous mappings $(f_k)_{k=1}^{\infty}$ from X into Y. This sequence converges to a point $f \in C(X, Y)$ if and only if $\lim_{k \to \infty} d_{C(X,Y)}(f_k, f) = 0$ – in other words – if and only if for each $\epsilon > 0$ there is an $N \in \mathbf{N}$ such that for any integer $k > N$ one has $d_{C(X,Y)}(f_k, f) < \epsilon$; that is, $d_Y(f_k(x), f(x)) < \epsilon$ for all $x \in X$. Equivalently, $(f_k)_{k=1}^{\infty}$ converges uniformly to f on X.

An application of the last two theorems gives the following result covering the well-known Arzela–Ascoli theorem which comes about as this is a generalization going back to Cesare Arzelá's theorem – if f_n is a uniformly bounded sequence of Riemann integrable functions that converge pointwise to a Riemann integrable function f on the finite interval $[a, b]$, then

$$\int_a^b f(x)dx = \lim_{n \to \infty} \int_a^b f_n(x)dx.$$

Theorem 6.23. *Let (X, d_X) and (Y, d_Y) be two metric spaces. Suppose X and Y are compact and complete respectively. Then:*

(i) *$C(X,Y)$ is a complete metric space with respect to the distance $d_{C(X,Y)}(\cdot,\cdot)$;*

(ii) *A closed subset E of $C(X,Y)$ is compact if and only if E is bounded and equicontinuous in the sense of that for any $\epsilon > 0$ there is a $\delta > 0$ such that*

$$d_X(x_1,x_2) < \delta \Rightarrow d_Y\big(f(x_1), f(x_2)\big) < \epsilon \quad \textit{for all} \quad f \in E.$$

Proof. (i) Suppose $(f_k)_{k=1}^{\infty}$ is a Cauchy sequence in $C(X,Y)$. Then for any $\epsilon > 0$ there is an $N \in \mathbf{N}$ such that if $k, l > N$ then $d_{C(X,Y)}(f_k, f_l) < \epsilon$; that is, $d_Y\big(f_k(x), f_l(x)\big) < \epsilon$ for all $x \in X$. Since Y is complete, Theorem 6.20 is applied to derive that $(f_k)_{k=1}^{\infty}$ converges uniformly on X to some mapping $f : X \to Y$. However, Theorem 6.21 tells us that f is continuous. Thus $f \in C(X,Y)$ and $\lim_{k\to\infty} f_k = f$ in the sense of points of the metric space $\big(C(X,Y), d_{C(X,Y)}\big)$. Thus $C(X,Y)$ is complete under $d_{C(X,Y)}(\cdot,\cdot)$.

(ii) Let E be a closed subset of $C(X,Y)$. If E is compact, then E is totally bounded by Corollary 5.36, and hence for $\epsilon > 0$ there are finite many open balls $\{B_{\epsilon/3}^{C(X,Y)}(f_k)\}_{k=1}^{n}$ of $C(X,Y)$ such that $E \subseteq \bigcup_{j=1}^{n} B_{\epsilon/3}^{C(X,Y)}(f_k)$. Since each $f_k : X \to Y$ is uniformly continuous, there exists a $\delta_k > 0$ such that

$$d_X(x_1,x_2) < \delta_k \Rightarrow d_Y\big(f_k(x_1), f_k(x_2)\big) < \epsilon/3.$$

Let $\delta = \min\{\delta_k : \ k = 1, 2, \ldots, n\}$. Then for a given $f \in E$, choose an f_k such that $d_{C(X,Y)}(f, f_k) < \epsilon/3$. Hence, $d_X(x_1,x_2) < \delta$ yields

$$\begin{aligned} & d_Y\big(f(x_1), f(x_2)\big) \\ & \le d_Y\big(f(x_1), f_k(x_1)\big) + d_Y\big(f_k(x_1), f_k(x_2)\big) + d_Y\big(f_k(x_2), f(x_2)\big) < \epsilon. \end{aligned}$$

Conversely, assume the statement after the if and only if. Since E is closed and $C(X,Y)$ is complete, according to Corollary 5.36 and Theorem 5.35 it remains to check that each sequence $(f_k)_{k=1}^{\infty}$ in E has a Cauchy subsequence. Since X is separable, there is a countable set $\{x_k\}_{k=1}^{\infty}$ which is dense in X. Note that $\big(f_k(x_1)\big)_{k=1}^{\infty}$ is bounded in the complete space Y. So this sequence has a convergent subsequence, denoted $\big(f_k^{(1)}(x_1)\big)_{k=1}^{\infty}$. Similarly, suppose $(f_k^{(2)})_{k=1}^{\infty}$ is a subsequence of $(f_k^{(1)})_{k=1}^{\infty}$ such that $\big(f_k^{(2)}(x_2)\big)_{k=1}^{\infty}$ converges. In this way, for each $j \in \mathbf{N}$ we can inductively obtain subsequence $(f_k^{(j)})_{k=1}^{\infty}$ of $(f_k)_{k=1}^{\infty}$ such that $\lim_{k\to\infty} f_k^{(j)}(x_l)$ exists for $l = 1, 2, \ldots, j$. Now $(f_k^{(k)})_{k=1}^{\infty}$ ensures that $\big(f_k^{(k)}(x_j)\big)_{k=1}^{\infty}$ is convergent for each j. Now for $\epsilon > 0$, there is a $\delta > 0$ such that $d_X(x_1,x_2) < \delta$ implies $d_Y\big(f_k^{(k)}(x_1), f_k^{(k)}(x_2)\big) < \epsilon/3$. Note that $\{x_k\}_{k=1}^{\infty}$ is dense in the compact space X. So, it follows that $X = \cup_{l=1}^{N} B_{\delta}^{X}(x_l)$ for some natural number N, where $B_{\delta}^{X}(x_l)$ is the open ball in X centered at x_l with radius δ. Furthermore, the definition of $f_k^{(k)}$ yields a natural number M such that

$$m, n > M \Rightarrow d_Y\big(f_m^{(m)}(x_j), f_n^{(n)}(x_j)\big) < \epsilon/3, \quad j = 1, 2, \ldots, N.$$

Finally, for $x \in X$ there is an x_j such that $x \in B_\delta^X(x_j)$. Accordingly, if $m, n > M$ then

$$\begin{aligned} & d_Y\big(f_m^{(m)}(x), f_n^{(n)}(x)\big) \\ & \le d_Y\big(f_m^{(m)}(x), f_m^{(m)}(x_j)\big) + d_Y\big(f_m^{(m)}(x_j), f_n^{(n)}(x_j)\big) + d_Y\big(f_m^{(m)}(x_j), f_n^{(n)}(x)\big) \\ & < \epsilon. \end{aligned}$$

Therefore, $(f_k^{(k)})_{k=1}^\infty$ is convergent to an element of E and so E is compact. □

Remark 6.24. Theorem 6.23 extends (from a closed interval to a compact metric space) Guido Ascoli's theorem – every bounded equi-continuous sequence of real-valued functions on the unit interval $[0, 1]$ has a uniformly convergent subsequence.

6.4 Contractions

In general, a fixed point of a mapping f from a set X to itself is a point $x_0 \in X$ such that $f(x_0) = x_0$. For example, 0 is a fixed point of the mapping $f(x) = x^2 + x$ from $\mathbf{R}$ to $\mathbf{R}$. But, not all mappings have fixed points – for instance, the mapping $f(x) = x + 1$ has no fixed point on $\mathbf{R}$. So, "What mappings have fixed points?" is an interesting question. In what follows, we introduce an important tool – the so-called Banach fixed point theorem (named after Stefan Banach) – which ensures the existence and uniqueness of fixed points of certain self mappings of metric spaces, but also provides a constructive method to find those fixed points.

Definition 6.25. Let (X, d_X) be a metric space. A mapping f from X to itself is a contraction map if there exists a so-called contraction constant $\alpha \in (0, 1)$ such that

$$d_X\big(f(x_1), f(x_2)\big) \le \alpha d_X(x_1, x_2) \quad \text{for all} \quad x_1, x_2 \in X.$$

A contraction mapping contracts or shrinks the distance between points by the factor α. Clearly, any contraction map is uniformly continuous on X. This property actually suggests the following Banach's theorem on contraction mappings and fixed points.

Theorem 6.26. *Let (X, d_X) be a complete metric space. If $f : X \to X$ is a contraction mapping, then f has a unique fixed point.*

Proof. Let $x_0 \in X$. Define $x_{k+1} = f(x_k)$ for $k \in \mathbf{N} \cup \{0\}$. We claim that $(x_k)_{k=1}^\infty$ is a Cauchy sequence in X. In fact,

$$d_X(x_2, x_1) = d_X\big(f(x_1), f(x_0)\big) \le \alpha d_X(x_1, x_0),$$

and so

$$d_X(x_3, x_2) = d_X\big(f(x_2), f(x_1)\big) \le \alpha d_X(x_2, x_1) \le \alpha^2 d_X(x_1, x_0).$$

Generally, we have that if $k > j$ then

$$d_X(x_k, x_j) \le \sum_{n=j}^{k-1} \alpha^n d_X(x_1, x_0) \le \Big(\frac{\alpha^j}{1-\alpha}\Big) d_X(x_1, x_0).$$

This, together with $\alpha \in (0,1)$, implies $(x_k)_{k=1}^{\infty}$ is a Cauchy sequence and hence it converges to a point $x \in X$: $\lim_{k\to\infty} x_k = x$ in X. Since f is uniformly continuous, one has

$$f(x) = \lim_{k\to\infty} f(x_k) = \lim_{k\to\infty} x_{k+1} = x;$$

that is, x is a fixed point of f.

Regarding the uniqueness, suppose y is also a fixed point of f. Then

$$d_X(x,y) = d_X\big(f(x), f(y)\big) \le \alpha d_X(x,y)$$

and hence $d_X(x,y) = 0$; that is, $x = y$, thanks to $\alpha \in (0,1)$. □

Remark 6.27. The above proof is constructive in the sense that the fixed point is the limit of the iterations given by $x_{k+1} = f(x_k)$, where the initial point x_0 is an arbitrary point in X. The previous estimate gives the rapidity of the convergence $x_k \to x_0$:

$$d_X(x, x_j) \le \Big(\frac{\alpha^j}{1-\alpha}\Big) d_X\big(f(x_0), x_0\big).$$

Below is an interesting example which shows an application of Theorem 6.26 in integral equations.

Example 6.28. For a finite interval $[a,b]$ of $\mathbf{R}$, let $k : [a,b] \times [a,b] \to \mathbf{R}$ be continuous and $\phi \in C[a,b]$. An equation of the type:

$$f(x) = \lambda \int_a^b k(x,y) f(y) dy + \phi(x), \quad \lambda \in \mathbf{R},$$

where f is unknown, is called a Fredholm integral equation (of the second kind). This equation introduced by Ivar Fredholm has a unique solution $f \in C[a,b]$ for some λ. To check this example, define a mapping $T : C[a,b] \to C[a,b]$ by

$$T(f)(x) = \lambda \int_a^b k(x,y) f(y) dy + \phi(x), \quad \lambda \in \mathbf{R}.$$

We write the distance function on $C[a,b]$ as

$$d_{C[a,b]}(f_1, f_2) = \max_{x\in[a,b]} |f_1(x) - f_2(x)| \quad \text{for all} \quad f_1, f_2 \in C[a,b].$$

Solving the desired equation is equivalent to showing that T has a fixed point. Now

$$d_{C[a,b]}\big(T(f_1), T(f_2)\big) \le |\lambda| \max_{x,y\in[a,b]} |k(x,y)|(b-a) d_{C[a,b]}(f_1, f_2).$$

Thus, if $|\lambda| \max_{x,y\in[a,b]} |k(x,y)|(b-a) < 1$, then T is a contraction map and, therefore, has a unique fixed point by Theorem 6.26.

As a consequence of Theorem 6.26, we can obtain a more general fixed point theorem.

Corollary 6.29. *Let (X, d_X) be a complete metric space and $n-1 \in \mathbf{N}$. If the n-th iteration $f_{(n)}(x) = \underbrace{f(f(f(\cdots(f}_{n}(x)))))$ is a contraction map, then f has a unique fixed point.*

Proof. Since $f_{(n)}$ is a contraction mapping, it has a unique fixed point x by Theorem 6.26. If α is the contraction constant for $f_{(n)}$, then

$$\begin{aligned} d_X(f(x), x) &= d_X(f(f_{(n)}(x)), f_{(n)}(x)) \\ &= d_X(f_{(n)}(f(x)), f_{(n)}(x)) \le \alpha d_X(f(x), x) \end{aligned}$$

and hence $f(x) = x$.

If y is another fixed point of f then it is also a fixed point of $f_{(n)}$ since

$$f_{(n)}(y) = f_{(n-1)}(f(y)) = f_{(n-1)}(y) = \cdots = y.$$

The uniqueness of the fixed point of $f_{(n)}$ implies $y = x$. □

Remark 6.30. In Corollary 6.29, f is not necessarily a contraction map. In fact, there is a discontinuous function f from $[0, 1]$ to itself such that its second iteration becomes a contraction map. For instance, if

$$f(x) = \begin{cases} \frac{1}{4}, & x \in [0, 1/2], \\ \frac{1}{2}, & x \in (1/2, 1], \end{cases}$$

then $f_{(2)}(x) = 1/4$ for $x \in [0, 1]$.

Example 6.31. Consider the following Volterra integral equation (VIE), named after Vito Volterra:

$$f(x) = \lambda \int_a^x k(x, y) f(y) dy + \phi(x),$$

for which the notations are the same as in Example 6.28. If $T : C[a, b] \to C[a, b]$ is defined by

$$T(f)(x) = \lambda \int_a^x k(x, y) f(y) dy + \phi(x),$$

then the VIE has a unique solution in $C[a, b]$ for any $\lambda \in \mathbf{R}$. To see this assertion, it is enough to show that T in the above has a unique fixed point in $C[a, b]$. A simple computation implies that if $f_1, f_2 \in C[a, b]$ and $M = \max_{x,y \in [a,b]} |k(x, y)|$ then

$$|T(f_1)(x) - T(f_2)(x)| \le |\lambda| M d_{C[a,b]}(f_1, f_2)(x - a),$$

$$|T_{(2)}(f_1)(x) - T_{(2)}(f_2)(x)| \le (|\lambda| M)^2 d_{C[a,b]}(f_1, f_2) \frac{(x-a)^2}{2},$$

and

$$|T_{(n)}(f_1)(x) - T_{(n)}(f_2)(x)| \le (|\lambda| M)^n d_{C[a,b]}(f_1, f_2) \frac{(x-a)^n}{n!}.$$

Hence

$$d_{C[a,b]}(T_{(n)}(f_1), T_{(n)}(f_2)) \le \frac{(|\lambda|(b-a)M)^n}{n!} d_{C[a,b]}(f_1, f_2).$$

Because $\lim_{n\to\infty} \big(|\lambda|(b-a)M\big)^n/n! = 0$, for large $n \in \mathbf{N}$ the iteration $T_{(n)}$ is a contraction mapping and thus has a unique fixed point for any value of the parameter λ by Corollary 6.29.

As a consequence of Remark 6.27, we consider a family of contraction mappings that vary continuously with respect to a parameter and prove that the corresponding fixed points also vary continuously.

Corollary 6.32. *Let (X, d_X) be a complete metric space and let (Y, d_Y) be a metric space. Suppose $f : Y \times X \to X$ is such that $f(\cdot, x)$ is continuous on Y for any point $x \in X$ and there exists $\alpha \in (0,1)$ such that*

$$d_X\big(f(y,x_1), f(y,x_2)\big) \le \alpha d_X(x_1,x_2) \quad \textit{for all} \quad y \in Y \quad \textit{and} \quad x_1, x_2 \in X.$$

For $y \in Y$ let $x_y \in X$ be the unique fixed point of the contraction mapping $f(y,\cdot)$. Then the mapping $y \to x_y$ is continuous from Y to X.

Proof. For $y \in Y$, consider the equation $x = f(y,x)$. Let $y_0 \in Y$. Construct a solution of the equation starting with the initial point $x_0 = x_{y_0}$ so that $x_{k+1} = f(y, x_k) \to x_y$. From Remark 6.27 it follows that

$$d_X(x_{y_0}, x_y) \le \frac{d_X\big(x_{y_0}, f(y, x_{y_0})\big)}{1-\alpha} = \frac{d_X\big(f(y_0, x_{y_0}), f(y, x_{y_0})\big)}{1-\alpha}$$

so that the mapping $y \to x_y$ is continuous at y_0 since the mapping $y \to f(y, x_{y_0})$ is continuous at y_0. We are done. □

As a further application of the contraction mapping theorem, we give the following Charles Emile Picard's existence and uniqueness theorem for a frist-order system of nonlinear ordinary differential equations based on the Rudolf Lipschitz continuity.

Theorem 6.33. *For $n \in \mathbf{N}$ equip $\mathbf{R}^n$ with the distance*

$$d_n(x,y) = \|x-y\|_n = \sqrt{\sum_{k=1}^{n}(x_k-y_k)^2}$$

between both $x = (x_1, \ldots, x_n)$ and $y = (y_1, \ldots, y_n)$ in $\mathbf{R}^n$. Let $[a,b] \subseteq \mathbf{R}$ and $D \subseteq \mathbf{R}^n$ be a finite interval and an open set respectively. Suppose $f : [a,b] \times D \to \mathbf{R}^n$ is a continuous and satisfies a Lipschitz condition with the constant $\kappa > 0$ below:

$$d_n\big(f(t,y_1), f(t,y_2)\big) \le \kappa d_n(y_1,y_2) \quad \textit{for all} \quad (t,y_1),\ (t,y_2) \in [a,b] \times D.$$

Then there exists a $\delta \in (a,b]$ such that the initial value problem (IVP):

$$\frac{du(t)}{dt} = f\big(t, u(t)\big), \quad u(a) = y_0 \in \mathbf{R}^n$$

has a unique solution in the interval $[a,\delta]$.

Proof. Clearly, solving this IVP is equivalent to solving the integral equation

$$u(t) = y_0 + \int_a^t f\big(s, u(s)\big)ds.$$

So, it is our aim to show the existence and uniqueness of a solution to this integral equation.

Assuming that $\overline{B}_r(y_0) \subseteq D$ is the closed ball centered at y_0 with radius $r > 0$, we have

$$M = \max_{(t,y)\in[a,b]\times\overline{B}_r(y_0)} \|f(t,y)\|_n < \infty.$$

Now choose $\delta \in (a, b]$ such that $(\delta - a)\kappa < 1$ and $(\delta - a)M \leq r$. Set S be the class of continuous mappings from $[a, \delta]$ to $\overline{B}_r(y_0)$. It is clear that S is complete under the distance defined by

$$d_S(\phi_1, \phi_2) = \max_{t\in[a,\delta]} d_n\big(\phi_1(t), \phi_2(t)\big) \quad \text{for all} \quad \phi_1, \phi_2 \in S.$$

Define a mapping $F : S \to S$ by

$$F(\phi)(t) = y_0 + \int_a^t f\big(s, \phi(s)\big)ds.$$

Obviously, $F(\phi)$ is continuously differentiable. If $\phi \in S$ and $t \in [a, \delta]$, then

$$d_n\big(F(\phi)(t), y_0\big) = \left\|\int_a^t f\big(s, \phi(s)\big)ds\right\|_n \leq M|t - a| \leq (\delta - a)M \leq r.$$

This implies $F(\phi) \in S$. Now, our problem amounts to showing that F has a unique fixed point in S. Thus, it suffices to verify that F is a contraction map. To do so, we note that $t \in [a, \delta]$ and $\phi_1, \phi_2 \in S$ imply

$$\begin{aligned} d_n\big(F(\phi_1)(t) - F(\phi_2)(t)\big) &\leq \int_a^t \big\|f\big(s, \phi_1(s)\big) - f\big(s, \phi_2(s)\big)\big\|_n ds \\ &\leq (\delta - a)\kappa d_S(\phi_1, \phi_2), \end{aligned}$$

whence obtaining

$$d_S\big(F(\phi_1), F(\phi_2)\big) \leq (\delta - a)\kappa d_S(\phi_1, \phi_2).$$

Accordingly, the assertion follows. □

Remark 6.34.

(i) Note that any existence theorem for the nonlinear IVP in the above must be local in nature. For example,

$$y'(t) = y^2(t), \quad y(1) = -1$$

has the solution $y(t) = -1/t$, which is not defined at $t = 0$ even though $f(t, y) = y^2$ is satisfied with the required condition on D which is assumed to be an open and bounded subset of $\mathbf{R}$.

(ii) If the Lipschitz condition is dropped, then it is still possible for the IVP to have one and even many more solutions – for instance, the IVP:

$$y'(t) = y^{1/3}(t), \quad y(0) = 0$$

has an infinite number of solutions

$$y_c(t) = \begin{cases} 0\,, & 0 \le t \le c, \\ \left(\frac{2(t-c)}{3}\right)^{3/2}, & c < t \le 1, \end{cases}$$

where $c \in [0, 1]$.

6.5 Equivalence of Metric Spaces

It is often necessary to compare two metric spaces and decide in what sense they are equivalent or to analyze how the structure of a metric space changes when changing the metric. Note that every metric space is a set with additional topological structure induced by the metric. So to decide in what sense two metric spaces are equivalent we have to use continuous mappings between them.

Definition 6.35. Let (X, d_X) and (Y, d_Y) be two metric spaces. Then they are called:

(i) Topologically isomorphic or homeomorphic provided there exists a homeomorphism between them – a mapping $f : X \to Y$ which is bijective and continuous, and has continuous inverse;

(ii) Uniformly isomorphic provided there exists a uniform isomorphism between them – a mapping $f : X \to Y$ which is bijective and uniformly continuous, and has uniformly continuous inverse;

(iii) Isometrically isomorphic provided there exists a bijective mapping $f : X \to Y$ such that the isometry $d_Y\big(f(x_1), f(x_2)\big) = d_X(x_1, x_2)$ holds for all $x_1, x_2 \in X$;

(iv) Similar provided there exists a positive constant $\kappa > 0$ and a bijective mapping $f : X \to Y$ such that $d_Y\big(f(x_1), f(x_2)\big) = \kappa d_X(x_1, x_2)$ holds for all $x_1, x_2 \in X$.

(v) Equivalent provided as sets $X = Y$ and there exist two positive constants κ_1 and κ_2 independent of all $x_1, x_2 \in X$ such that

$$\kappa_1 d_X(x_1, x_2) \le d_Y(x_1, x_2) \le \kappa_2 d_X(x_1, x_2).$$

The following example helps us grasp Definition 6.35.

Example 6.36.

(i) Let $f : [-\frac{\pi}{2}, \frac{\pi}{2}] \to [-1, 1]$ be defined by $f(x) = \sin x$. Then it is a uniform isomorphism, and hence any two finite closed subintervals of $\mathbf{R}$ are uniformly isomorphic.

(ii) For $x = (x_1, \cdots, x_n), y = (y_1, \cdots, y_n) \in \mathbf{R}^n$ and $n \in \mathbf{N}$, recall

$$d_n(x,y) = \|x-y\|_n = \sqrt{\sum_{k=1}^{n} |x_k - y_k|^2}$$

and let

$$d_\infty(x,y) = \|x-y\|_\infty = \max\{|x_k - y_k| : k = 1, \cdots, n\}.$$

Then

$$d_n(x,y) \le d_\infty(x,y) \le n d_n(x,y).$$

This means that $(\mathbf{R}^n, d_n)$ and $(\mathbf{R}^n, d_\infty)$ are equivalent. Of course, d_n and d_∞ define the same notions of continuity and convergence and do not need to be distinguished for most purposes. In other words, the identity mapping is uniformly isomorphic from $(\mathbf{R}^n, d_n)$ to $(\mathbf{R}^n, d_\infty)$.

(iii) In $(\mathbf{R}^n, d_n)$, an isometrically isomorphic mapping is a rotation (the movement of a body in such a way that the distance between a certain fixed point and any given point of that body remains constant), a reflection (to invert a geometric figure, respect to a line or plane, but not a point), or a translation (to move every point by a fixed distance in the same direction).

(iv) $(\mathbf{R}^n, d_n)$ is similar to itself. This is because the mapping $f(x) = \kappa x + x_0$, where $\kappa > 0$ is constant and $x_0 \in \mathbf{R}^n$, is bijective and satisfies $d_n\big(f(x), f(y)\big) = \kappa d_n(x,y)$ for any $x, y \in \mathbf{R}^n$.

Both a uniform isomorphism and an isometric isomorphism are certainly homeomorphisms which are not only open mappings (from open sets to open sets) but also closed mappings (from closed sets to closed sets). Intuitively, a homeomorphism not only maps points in the first object that are close together to points in the second object that are close together, but also sends points in the first object that are not close together to points in the second object that are not close together. Topology is the study of those properties of objects that do not change when homeomorphisms are applied. Below is a classical and important result.

Theorem 6.37. *For $n+1 \in \mathbf{N}$ let $\mathbf{R}^{n+1}$ be equipped with the Euclidean distance*

$$d_{n+1}(x,y) = \|x-y\|_{n+1} = \sqrt{\sum_{k=1}^{n+1} (x_k - y_k)^2}$$

for $x = (x_1, \cdots, x_{n+1})$ and $y = (y_1, \cdots, y_{n+1})$ in $\mathbf{R}^{n+1}$.

(i) *If $n = 0$, then $\mathbf{R}^{n+1}$ is homeomorphic to the open interval $(-1,1) \subseteq \mathbf{R}$.*

(ii) *If $n \ge 1$, then $\mathbf{R}^n$ is homeomorphic to the punctured sphere $\mathbf{S}^n \setminus \{(0, \cdots, 1)\}$, where*

$$\mathbf{S}^n = \{x \in \mathbf{R}^{n+1} : \|x\|_{n+1} = d_{n+1}(x, 0) = 1\}$$

is the compact unit sphere in $\mathbf{R}^{n+1}$.

Proof. To check (i), we just take $f(x) = \frac{2}{\pi}\arctan x$.

As with (ii), we define the mapping $f : \mathbf{S}^n \setminus \{(0,\cdots,1)\} \to \mathbf{R}^n$ by letting

$$y = (y_1,\cdots,y_n) = f\big((x_1,\cdots,x_{n+1})\big) = f(x)$$

be the point in $\mathbf{R}^n$ such that

$$y_k = \frac{x_k}{1-x_{n+1}} \quad \text{for} \quad k = 1,2,\ldots,n.$$

Next we define $h : \mathbf{R}^n \to \mathbf{R}^{n+1}$ by letting $x = h(y)$ be the point in $\mathbf{R}^{n+1}$ such that

$$x_k = \frac{2y_k}{1+\big(d_n(y,0)\big)^2} \quad \text{for } k = 1,\cdots,n, \quad \text{and} \quad x_{n+1} = 1 - \frac{2}{1+\big(d_n(y,0)\big)^2}.$$

Note that $d_{n+1}(h(y),0) = 1$ and $x_{n+1} \neq 1$. So, $h(\mathbf{R}^n) \subseteq \mathbf{S}^n \setminus \{(0,0,\cdots,1)\}$. It is easy to see that both f and h are continuous and satisfy $f \circ h(y) = y$ and $h \circ f(x) = x$. Thus, h is the inverse of f, and f is a homeomorphism of $\mathbf{S}^n \setminus \{(0,\cdots,1)\}$ onto $\mathbf{R}^n$.

Regarding the compactness of $\mathbf{S}^n$, we define a function $F : \mathbf{R}^{n+1} \to \mathbf{R}$ via $F(x) = \|x\|_{n+1}$. The triangle inequality for d_{n+1} yields that F is continuous. With this and the closedness of the single point $\{1\}$, we see that $\mathbf{S}^n = F^{-1}(\{1\})$ is closed. Since $d_{n+1}(0,x) = 1$ for $x \in \mathbf{S}^n$, $\mathbf{S}^n$ is bounded. Being closed, $\mathbf{S}^n$ is therefore compact. □

Problems

6.1. Let $f : \mathbf{R}^3 \to \mathbf{R}^2$ be given by $f(x) = (x_1,x_2)$ for $x = (x_1,x_2,x_3) \in \mathbf{R}^3$. Prove that f is continuous on $\mathbf{R}^3$.

6.2. Given $f(x) = d_X(x,0)$ for every point x in the subset $X \setminus \{0\}$ of a metric space X with distance d_X, define $f(0)$ so that f is continuous at 0.

6.3. For $n \in \mathbf{N}$ let $f : \mathbf{R}^n \to \mathbf{R}$ be given by $f(x) = (\sum_{j=1}^n x_j^2)^{1/2}$ for $x = (x_1,\ldots,x_n) \in \mathbf{R}^n$, and let $S = (-3,-2)$. Find $f^{-1}(S)$.

6.4. Define $D = \{x = (x_1,x_2,x_3) \in \mathbf{R}^3 : 0 < x_3 < x_1^2 + x_2^2\}$ and let f be the mapping from $\mathbf{R}^3$ into $\mathbf{R}$ given by

$$f(x) = \begin{cases} 1, & x \in D, \\ 0, & x \notin D. \end{cases}$$

Show that $f(x^{(k)})$ tends to $f(0)$ as $x^{(k)}$ approaches 0 along any linear path, but f is discontinuous at 0.

6.5. Let T be the linear transformation from $\mathbf{R}^2$ into itself such that

$$T\big((1,1)\big) = (3,-1) \quad \text{and} \quad T\big((1,-1)\big) = (1,7).$$

Find the matrix representation of T.

6.6. Given $n \in \mathbf{N}$. If K is a compact subset of $\mathbf{R}^n$, $f : K \to \mathbf{R}$ is continuous, and $f(x) > 0$ for any $x \in K$, show that there is a $\delta > 0$ such that $f(x) \geq \delta$ for any $x \in K$.

6.7. Show that the function $f : [0, 1] \to [0, 1]$, defined by

$$f(x) = \begin{cases} x\,, & x \in \mathbf{Q} \cap [0, 1], \\ 1 - x\,, & x \in (\mathbf{R} \setminus \mathbf{Q}) \cap [0, 1], \end{cases}$$

is onto and thus satisfies the intermediate value property. Show, however, that f is continuous only at $x = 1/2$.

6.8. Define

$$T : C[0, 1] \to C[0, 1] \quad \text{by} \quad T(f)(x) = \int_0^x f(t)dt.$$

Verify the following three facts:

(i) T is not a contraction map;

(ii) T has a unique fixed point;

(iii) $T \circ T$ is a contraction map.

6.9. Let $f : \mathbf{R} \to \mathbf{R}$ be differentiable with $|f'(x)| \leq \alpha$, where $\alpha \in (0, 1)$. Prove that f is a contraction mapping.

6.10. For a complete metric space (X, d_X), let $T : X \to X$ be a mapping. If

$$\sum_{k=1}^{\infty} \sup_{x_1 \neq x_2} \frac{d_X\big(T_{(k)}(x_1), T_{(k)}(x_2)\big)}{d_X(x_1, x_2)} < \infty,$$

prove that T has a unique fixed point, where $T_{(k)} = \underbrace{T \circ T \cdots \circ T}_{k}$.

6.11. Let (X, d_X) be a metric space. Suppose K is a nonempty compact subset of X. If the mapping $T : K \to K$ satisfies

$$d_X\big(T(x_1), T(x_2)\big) < d_X(x_1, x_2) \quad \text{for all} \quad x_1 \neq x_2 \quad \text{in} \quad K,$$

prove that there exists precisely one point $x \in K$ such that $x = T(x)$.

6.12. Let $h \in C[0, 1]$. Show that there is an $f \in C[0, 1]$ such that

$$f(x) - \int_0^x f(x - t) \exp(-t^2)dt = h(x).$$

6.13. Let (X, d_X) be a complete metric space, and let

$$f : D \subseteq X \to X = f(D)$$

be a mapping. Suppose there is a number $\kappa > 1$ such that

$$d_X\big(f(x_1), f(x_2)\big) \geq \kappa d_X(x_1, x_2) \quad \text{for all} \quad x_1, x_2 \in D.$$

Prove that there exists exactly one point $x \in D$ such that $f(x) = x$.

6.14. Let (X, d_X) and (Y, d_Y) be two metric spaces and $f : X \to Y$ bijective. Prove that the following three conditions are equivalent:

(i) f is a homeomorphism;

(ii) f is continuous, and maps closed subsets of X to closed subsets of Y;

(iii) f is continuous and maps open subsets of X to open subsets of Y.

6.15. Suppose $\mathbf{R}$ is equipped with the usual Euclidean distance. If $f : \mathbf{R} \to \mathbf{R}$ is defined by

$$f(x) = \begin{cases} x + \frac{3}{2}, & x \in (-\infty, \frac{1}{2}], \\ \frac{1}{x}, & x \in (\frac{1}{2}, \infty), \end{cases}$$

prove that f is not homeomorphic.

6.16. Let (X, d_X) be a metric space. Prove that there is a complete metric space (Y, d_Y) and a mapping $f : X \to Y$ such that f is an isometry, i.e.,

$$d_Y\big(f(x_1), f(x_2)\big) = d_X(x_1, x_2) \quad \text{for all} \quad x_1, x_2 \in X,$$

and $f(X)$ is a dense subset of Y.

6.17. Let (X, d_X) be a metric space and let K be a nonempty closed subset of X. If $f : X \to \mathbf{R}$ is defined by $f(x) = \inf_{y \in K} d_X(x, y)$, prove that f is continuous, and that $f(x) = 0$ if and only if $x \in K$.

Chapter 7

Normed Linear Spaces

In contrast to the previous practice of examining functions individually, functional analysis is initially treated as studying common and distinct properties of various spaces of functions, but actually it can be considered as proceeding from an interplay between both linear algebra and topology (based on the Euclidean spaces), resulting in the notion of a normed linear space. Accordingly we begin our discussion with this fundamental concept which, when combined with increasingly specialized assumptions, will lead to various increasingly specialized spaces and results. Here we would like to say that our investigation will involve only linear functional analysis whose relation to the developing nonlinear counterpart is similar to and arises from the connection between the Euclidean spaces and manifolds.

7.1 Linear Spaces, Norms and Quotient Spaces

From now on, we always use $\mathbf{F}$ as either $\mathbf{R}$ or $\mathbf{C} = \mathbf{R} + i\mathbf{R}$ – the field of real or complex numbers.

Definition 7.1. A linear (or vector) space over $\mathbf{F}$ is a set X equipped with two functions

$$+ : \ X \times X \to X \quad \text{and} \quad \cdot : \ \mathbf{F} \times X \to X$$

with the properties below:

(i) $x + y = y + x$ for all $x, y \in X$;

(ii) $(x + y) + z = x + (y + z)$ for all $x, y, z \in X$;

(iii) There exists $0 \in X$ such that $x + 0 = 0 + x = x$ for all $x \in X$;

(iv) There exists $-x \in X$ such that $x + (-x) = (-x) + x = 0$ for all $x \in X$;

(v) $\alpha \cdot (\beta \cdot x) = (\alpha\beta) \cdot x$ for all $\alpha, \beta \in \mathbf{F}, x \in X$;

(vi) $(\alpha + \beta) \cdot x = (\alpha \cdot x) + (\beta \cdot x)$ for all $\alpha, \beta \in \mathbf{F}, x \in X$;

(vii) $\alpha \cdot (x + y) = (\alpha \cdot x) + (\alpha \cdot y)$ for all $\alpha \in \mathbf{F}, x, y \in X$;

(viii) $1 \cdot x = x$ for all $x \in X$ where 1 is the multiplicative identity in $\mathbf{F}$.

Although our main purpose is to study linear spaces over $\mathbf{R}$ or $\mathbf{C}$, we frequently state that the spaces are over $\mathbf{F}$ whenever both $\mathbf{R}$ and $\mathbf{C}$ may be handled in the same way.

Example 7.2.

(i) For $n \in \mathbf{N}$, $\mathbf{F}^n$ is a linear space with the usual vector addition and scalar multiplication over $\mathbf{F}$.

(ii) Let X be the set of all polynomials with coefficients in $\mathbf{R}$ of degree less than $n \in \mathbf{N}$. Then X is a linear space with usual addition of polynomials and scalar multiplication over $\mathbf{R}$.

(iii) For $m, n \in \mathbf{N}$ let $M_{m,n}(\mathbf{C})$ be the set of all complex-valued $m \times n$ matrices. Then $M_{m,n}(\mathbf{C})$ is a linear space with usual addition of matrices and scalar multiplication over $\mathbf{C}$.

(iv) Recall that ℓ_∞ represents the set of infinite real-valued sequences $(x_j)_{j=1}^\infty$ which are bounded: $\sup_{j\in\mathbf{N}} |x_j| < \infty$. Then ℓ_∞ is a linear space over $\mathbf{R}$ with:

$$\sup_{j\in\mathbf{N}} |x_j + y_j| \le \sup_{j\in\mathbf{N}} |x_j| + \sup_{j\in\mathbf{N}} |y_j|; \quad \sup_{j\in\mathbf{N}} |\alpha x_j| = |\alpha| \sup_{j\in\mathbf{N}} |x_j| < \infty.$$

(v) Let $C(S, \mathbf{R})$ be the class of all continuous functions $f : S \to \mathbf{R}$ with

$$(f+g)(x) = f(x) + g(x) \quad \text{and} \quad (\alpha \cdot f)(x) = \alpha f(x).$$

Here S is any nonempty subset of $\mathbf{R}$. Then $C(S, \mathbf{R})$ is a linear space over $\mathbf{R}$.

(vi) Let $C^\infty[a, b]$ be the space of all infinitely differentiable real-valued functions on the finite interval $[a, b]$ of $\mathbf{R}$. Then it is linear space over $\mathbf{R}$ with the same addition and scalar multiplication as in (v).

(vii) For any closed interval $[a, b] \subset \mathbf{R}$ and any increasing function $g : \mathbf{R} \to \mathbf{R}$, the classes $R[a, b]$, $RS_g[a, b]$ and $LRS_g([a, b])$ are also linear spaces over $\mathbf{R}$ with the same addition and scalar multiplication as in (v).

For convenience, we will drop the special notation $+$, $\cdot$ for vector addition and scalar multiplication, and simply refer to X as a linear space over $\mathbf{F}$. Moreover, if $\mathbf{F} = \mathbf{R}$ then we will say that X is a real linear space; whereas if $\mathbf{F} = \mathbf{C}$, then we will say that X is a complex linear space.

As in the linear algebra of finite-dimensional vector spaces, we have the concept of a linear subspace which is often called simply a subspace (when the context serves to distinguish it from other kinds of subspaces) and plays an important role in functional analysis and related fields of mathematics.

Definition 7.3. Let X be a linear space over $\mathbf{F}$.

(i) A subset $Y \subseteq X$ is called a linear subspace of X provided that

$$\alpha, \beta \in \mathbf{F} \quad \text{and} \quad x, y \in Y \quad \text{imply} \quad \alpha x + \beta y \in Y.$$

(ii) If $Y = \{x + x_0 : x \in S\}$ where S is a linear subspace of X and x_0 is a fixed element of X, then Y is called an affine subset of X.

Example 7.4.

(i) For $n - 2 \in \mathbf{N}$, the vectors in $\mathbf{R}^n$ of the form $(x_1, x_2, x_3, 0, \ldots, 0)$ form a linear subspace of $\mathbf{R}^n$.

(ii) For $m, n \in \mathbf{N}$ and $m \leq n$, the set of polynomials of degree $\leq m$ forms a linear subspace of the set of polynomials of degree $\leq n$.

(iii) If $Y = \{(x_1, x_2, 1, \ldots, 1) \in \mathbf{R}^n\}$ for $n - 2 \in \mathbf{N}$, then Y is an affine subset of $\mathbf{R}^n$.

(iv) In Example 7.2 (iii), let Y be the set of matrices with certain blocks of 1's. Then Y is an affine subset of $M_{m,n}(\mathbf{C})$.

(v) In $\mathbf{R}^3$ all lines and planes through the origin are linear subspaces, whereas all lines and planes not passing through the origin are affine subsets.

A fundamental concept for linear spaces is that of dimension. To see this, suppose X is a linear space over $\mathbf{F}$. Elements $e_1, e_2, \ldots, e_n$ of X are linearly dependent provided there are scalars $\alpha_1, \alpha_2, \ldots, \alpha_n$ (not all zero) such that $\sum_{j=1}^{n} \alpha_j e_j = 0$. If there is no such set of scalars, then they are linearly independent. The linear span of the vectors $\{e_j\}_{j=1}^{n}$ is the linear subspace of X as follows:

$$\text{span}\{e_j\}_{j=1}^{n} = \text{span}\{e_1, \ldots, e_n\} = \Big\{\sum_{j=1}^{n} \alpha_j e_j : \ \alpha_1, \ldots, \alpha_n \in \mathbf{F}\Big\}.$$

In general, the linear span of a subset S of X is defined to be the set of all finite linear combinations of elements in S; that is, the intersection of all linear subspaces of X containing S.

Definition 7.5. Let $n \in \mathbf{N}$. If the linear space X is equal to the space spanned by a linearly independent set of n vectors in X, then X is said to have the dimension n. If there is no such set of vectors, then X is infinite-dimensional. Furthermore, a linearly independent set of vectors that spans X is called a basis for X.

Example 7.6.

(i) For $n \in \mathbf{N}$, the space $\mathbf{R}^n$ has dimension n; the standard basis is given by the vectors $e_1 = (1, 0, \cdots, 0)$, $e_2 = (0, 1, 0, \cdots, 0)$, $\cdots$, $e_n = (0, 0, \cdots, 0, 1)$.

(ii) For $n \in \mathbf{N}$, the set $\{1, t, t^2, \cdots, t^n\}$ is a basis for the linear space of real-valued polynomials of degree $\leq n$ which has dimension $n + 1$.

(iii) All linear spaces given in Example 7.2 (iv)-(vii) are infinite-dimensional.

Next, we equip a linear space with a norm. The norm on a linear space is a way of measuring the length of a vector and hence the distance between two vectors.

Definition 7.7. Let X be a linear space over $\mathbf{F}$. Then a norm on X is a nonnegative function $\|\cdot\| : X \to \mathbf{R}$ with the following three properties:

(i) $\|x\| = 0$ if and only if $x = 0$;

(ii) $\|x + y\| \leq \|x\| + \|y\|$ for all $x, y \in X$;

(iii) $\|\alpha x\| = |\alpha|\|x\|$ for all $x \in X$ and $\alpha \in \mathbf{F}$.
In this case, $(X, \|\cdot\|)$ is called a normed linear space.

Remark 7.8.

(i) In the definition we are assuming that $|\cdot|$ denotes the usual absolute value. If $\|\cdot\|$ is a nonnegative function only with both (ii) – the triangle inequality and (iii) – homogeneity, then it is called a semi-norm. For instance, $\|\cdot\|_{p,m_g,E}$ defined in Example 5.3 (iii) is a semi-norm whenever $p \in [1, \infty)$.

(ii) Whenever $(X, \|\cdot\|)$ is a normed linear space over $\mathbf{F}$, via defining

$$d_X(x_1, x_2) = \|x_1 - x_2\| \quad \text{for all} \quad x_1, x_2 \in X$$

we find that (X, d_X) is a metric space since d_X is a distance function which can be sufficiently demonstrated by

$$d_X(x_1, x_3) = \|x_1 - x_3\| \leq \|x_1 - x_2\| + \|x_2 - x_3\| = d_X(x_1, x_2) + d_X(x_2, x_3).$$

(iii) Clearly, if Y is a linear subspace of the linear space X (over $\mathbf{F}$) which is equipped with norm $\|\cdot\|$, then $(Y, \|\cdot\|)$ is also a normed linear space and hence it can be regarded as a linear subspace of $(X, \|\cdot\|)$.

Example 7.9.

(i) For $n \in \mathbf{N}$ and $x = (x_1, \dots, x_n) \in \mathbf{R}^n$ let $d_n(x, 0) = \sqrt{\sum_{j=1}^n |x_j|^2}$. Then $d_n(\cdot, 0)$ defines a norm on $\mathbf{R}^n$ – the only difficulty to verify this fact is the triangle inequality – for this we use the Cauchy–Schwarz inequality:

$$\sum_{j=1}^n |x_j y_j| \leq \sqrt{\Big(\sum_{j=1}^n |x_j|^2\Big)\Big(\sum_{j=1}^n |y_j|^2\Big)}.$$

(ii) For $n \in \mathbf{N}$ there are many other norms on $\mathbf{R}^n$, called the (n,p)-norms. More precisely, if $p \in [1, \infty)$, then

$$\|x\|_{n,p} = \Big(\sum_{j=1}^n |x_j|^p\Big)^{\frac{1}{p}}$$

is a norm on $\mathbf{R}^n$. To see this, it suffices to verify the triangle inequality, i.e., the following Hermann Minkowski's inequality (see also Problem 7.1 (i))

$$\|x + y\|_{n,p} \leq \|x\|_{n,p} + \|y\|_{n,p} \quad \text{for} \quad x, y \in \mathbf{R}^n.$$

If $p = \infty$, then

$$\|x\|_{n,\infty} = \sup_{1 \leq j \leq n} |x_j|$$

defines a norm on $\mathbf{R}^n$. It is conventional to write ℓ_p^n for these normed spaces. Note that ℓ_p^n and ℓ_q^n have exactly the same elements which are just ones of $\mathbf{R}^n$.

(iii) Recall that ℓ_∞ is the linear space of bounded infinite sequences of real numbers. For $x = (x_j)_{j=1}^\infty \in \ell_\infty$, define

$$\|x\|_p = \begin{cases} \left(\sum_{j=1}^\infty |x_j|^p\right)^{\frac{1}{p}}, & 1 \le p < \infty, \\ \sup_{1\le j<\infty} |x_j|, & p = \infty. \end{cases}$$

If our attention is restricted to the linear subspace on which $\|\cdot\|_p$ is finite, then $\|\cdot\|_p$ is a norm – the somewhat difficult triangle inequality follows from the Minkowski inequality for the infinite sequences which can be established by the Minkowski inequality for $\mathbf{R}^n$ in (ii) – see also Problem 7.1 (ii). This yields an infinite family of normed linear spaces:

$$\ell_p = \{x \in \ell_\infty : \ \|x\|_p < \infty\}, \quad p \in [1, \infty].$$

Let $p, q \in [1, \infty]$ and $p < q$. Then there is a strict inclusion: $\ell_p \subset \ell_q$ and hence ℓ_p is a linear subspace of ℓ_q. Moreover, $(\ell_p, \|\cdot\|_p)$ is separable for $p \in [1, \infty)$ – for a proof see also Example 5.41 (ii).

(iv) For a finite closed interval $[a, b]$ in $\mathbf{R}$, $C[a, b]$ becomes a normed space with the p-norm below

$$\|f\|_p = \begin{cases} \left(\int_a^b |f(t)|^p dt\right)^{\frac{1}{p}}, & 1 \le p < \infty, \\ \sup_{a\le t\le b} |f(t)|, & p = \infty. \end{cases}$$

Note that the triangle inequality for $p \in [1, \infty)$ follows from the Minkowski inequality $\|f_1 + f_2\|_p \le \|f_1\|_p + \|f_2\|_p$ – see also Remark 4.36.

As an application of the above concepts, quotients of normed linear spaces may be formulated. Note that we need both the algebraic structure (linear subspace of a linear space) and a topological property (closedness) to make them all work.

Definition 7.10. Let X be a linear space over $\mathbf{F}$ and Y be a linear subspace of X. Then the linear space X/Y – the quotient or factor space is formed as follows. The elements of X/Y are cosets of Y – sets of the form

$$x + Y = \{x + y : \ y \in Y\} \quad \text{where} \quad x \in X.$$

The set of cosets is a linear space under the operations:

$$(x_1 + Y) + (x_2 + Y) = x_1 + x_2 + Y \quad \text{and} \quad \lambda \cdot (x + Y) = \lambda x + Y$$

for any $x_1, \ x_2, \ x \in X$ and $\lambda \in \mathbf{F}$. In addition, $\dim(X/Y)$ is called the codimension of a linear subspace $Y \subseteq X$.

Remark 7.11. The above-defined two operations make sense precisely because Y is itself a linear space, so for instance,

$$Y + Y = \{y_1 + y_2 : \ y_1, y_2 \in Y\} = Y$$

and

$$\lambda Y = \{\lambda y : y \in Y\} = Y \quad \text{for} \quad \lambda \neq 0.$$

Moreover, $x_1 + Y$ and $x_2 + Y$ are equal if and only if as sets $x_1 + Y = x_2 + Y$; this is true if and only if $x_1 - x_2 \in Y$, denoted $x_1 \sim x_2$, which reads: x_1 is equivalent to x_2 with respect to Y.

Example 7.12.

(i) Let $X = \mathbf{R}^3$, and let Y be the linear subspace spanned by $(1, 1, 0)$. Then X/Y is a two-dimensional real vector space since $(1, 0, 1) + Y$ and $(0, 0, 1) + Y$ generate X/Y.

(ii) The linear space Y of finitely supported sequences (of which all but a finite number of entries vanish) in ℓ_1 is a linear subspace. Each element of the quotient space ℓ_1/Y is an equivalence class under the relation $(x_j)_{j=1}^{\infty} \sim (y_j)_{j=1}^{\infty}$ whenever $(x_j)_{j=1}^{\infty}$ and $(y_j)_{j=1}^{\infty}$ differ in finitely many coordinates.

(iii) For $n \in \mathbf{N}$ let Y be the set of ℓ_1-sequences of $(0, \cdots, 0, x_{n+1}, \cdots)$ (first n coordinates are zero). Then Y is a linear subspace of ℓ_1 and ℓ_1/Y is an n-dimensional quotient space.

(iv) Recall that if $p, q \in [1, \infty]$ and $p < q$ then $\ell_p \subset \ell_q$ – this implies that ℓ_q/ℓ_p exists as a quotient space.

(v) Let $X = C[0, 1]$ and $Y = \{f \in X : f(0) = 0\}$. Then X/Y is a quotient space.

(vi) $Y = C[0, 1]$ is a linear subspace of $X = R[0, 1]$. The quotient X/Y is again a linear space.

Evidently, these examples indicate that not all linear subspaces are equally good: Example 7.12 (i), (iii) and (v) are quite reasonable, whereas Example 7.12 (ii), (iv) and (vi) are examples of linear spaces unlike any we have seen. The reason is the following: The space X/Y is guaranteed to be a normed space with a norm related to the original norm $\|\cdot\|$ on X only when the subspace Y is itself closed. Notice that Example 7.12 (i), (iii) and (v) are precisely the ones in which the linear subspace is closed whenever the space X is treated as a metric space with the distance

$$d_X(x_1, x_2) = \|x_1 - x_2\| \quad \text{for all} \quad x_1,\ x_2 \in X.$$

Theorem 7.13. *Let $(X, \|\cdot\|_X)$ be a normed linear space over* $\mathbf{F}$ *and Y a linear subspace of X. Then X/Y is a normed linear space over* $\mathbf{F}$ *under the norm*

$$\|x + Y\|_{X/Y} = \inf_{z \in x+Y} \|z\|_X$$

when and only when Y is a closed subset of X; that is, if $(y_j)_{j=1}^{\infty}$ is a sequence in Y with $\lim_{j\to\infty} \|y_j - y\|_X = 0$ then $y \in Y$.

Proof. On the one hand, suppose that Y is closed and note that

$$\|x + Y\|_{X/Y} = \inf_{z \in x+Y} \|z\|_X = \inf_{y \in Y} \|x - y\|_X.$$

Firstly, if $\|x+Y\|_{X/Y}=0$ then there are countably many vectors $y_j\in Y$ such that $\lim_{j\to\infty}\|x-y_j\|_X=0$. Since Y is closed, $x\in Y$ and then $x+Y=0+Y$. Conversely, $\|0+Y\|_{X/Y}=0$.

Secondly, the homogeneity is clear from $\lambda\in\mathbf{F}$ and

$$\|\lambda(x+Y)\|_{X/Y}=\inf_{z\in x+Y}\|\lambda z\|_X=|\lambda|\inf_{z\in x+Y}\|z\|_X=|\lambda|\|x+Y\|_{X/Y}.$$

Finally, the triangle inequality is clear from

$$\begin{aligned}\|(x_1+Y)+(x_2+Y)\|_{X/Y} &= \inf_{z_1\in x_1+Y, z_2\in x_2+Y}\|z_1+z_2\|_X\\ &\le \inf_{z_1\in x_1+Y}\|z_1\|_X+\inf_{z_2\in x_2+Y}\|z_2\|_X\\ &= \|x_1+Y\|_{X/Y}+\|x_2+Y\|_{X/Y}.\end{aligned}$$

On the other hand, suppose Y is not closed. Let x be a point that is not in Y but is in the closure of Y with respect to the distance $\|x_1-x_2\|_X$. If $(y_j)_{j=1}^\infty$ is a sequence of points of Y that converges to x, then

$$0\le\|x+Y\|_{X/Y}=\inf_{z\in x+Y}\|z\|_X\le\inf_{j\in\mathbf{N}}\|x-y_j\|_X=0,$$

and consequently, $x\in Y$ which contradicts $x\notin Y$. Therefore $\|\cdot\|_{X/Y}$ could not be a norm on X/Y. We are done. □

Example 7.14.

(i) If $X=\mathbf{R}^2$ and $Y=\{(0,y):y\in\mathbf{R}\}$, then X/Y consists of lines in X of the form $(s,t)+Y$. Furthermore, if X is equipped with the norm $\|\cdot\|_{2,2}$, then $\|(s,t)+Y\|_{X/Y}=\inf_{(u,v)\in(s,t)+Y}\sqrt{u^2+v^2}=|s|$.

(ii) The quotient space may be a little odd. For instance, let $\ell_{\infty,c}$ denote the space of all sequences $(x_j)_{j=1}^\infty$ with the property that $\lim_{j\to\infty}x_j$ exists. This is a closed linear subspace of ℓ_∞. It is a good practice to give a representation of the quotient $\ell_\infty/\ell_{\infty,c}$.

(iii) Let $g:\mathbf{R}\to\mathbf{R}$ be increasing, $E\subseteq\mathbf{R}$ an m_g-measurable set, $p\in[1,\infty]$. Then each set $LRS_g^p(E,\mathbf{F})$ defined in Example 5.3 (iii), is a linear space. If

$$\mathcal{N}_g(E)=\{f:E\to\mathbf{F}:\ f=0\ m_g-\text{a.e. on } E\},$$

then $\mathcal{LRS}_g^p(E,\mathbf{F})=LRS_g^p(E,\mathbf{F})/\mathcal{N}_g(E)$ forms a linear quotient space whose elements can be written as $f+\mathcal{N}_g(E)$ where $f\in LRS_g^p(E,\mathbf{F})$. In particular, if $g:\mathbf{R}\to\mathbf{R}$ is the identity, then $\mathcal{LRS}_{id}^p(E,\mathbf{F})$ is employed to represent $\mathcal{LRS}_g^p(E,\mathbf{F})$. More importantly, when $1\le p\le\infty$ the space $\mathcal{LRS}_g^p(E,\mathbf{F})$ is a normed linear space under the following norm:

$$\|f+\mathcal{N}_g(E)\|_{\mathcal{LRS}_g^p(E,\mathbf{F})}=\|f\|_{p,m_g,E}.$$

The three properties required by a norm can be easily checked – in particular, the triangle inequality follows from Minkowski's inequality presented in Remark 4.36. Even though $\mathcal{LRS}_g^p(E,\mathbf{F})$ exists as a space of equivalence classes of m_g-a.e.-defined $LRS_g^p(E,\mathbf{F})$-functions, for the sake of simplicity of notation, we will act according to the customary language to speak of it as a space of functions – this unimportant abuse of language is uniformly accepted and almost never results in any confusion.

7.2 Finite Dimensional Spaces

From the last section we have seen that any normed linear space generates a metric space and consequently brings the notions such as continuity and convergence (discussed in Chapter 6) into play. Therefore, it is unnecessary to deal with this issue again. But, to put it more abstractly, we want to emphasize that every normed linear space is a topological vector space and thus carries a topological structure which is induced by the norm and a linear mapping.

Definition 7.15.

(i) Two linear spaces X and Y over $\mathbf{F}$ are called algebraically isomorphic provided there is a bijection $T : X \to Y$ that is linear:

$$T(\alpha x + \beta y) = \alpha T(x) + \beta T(y) \quad \text{for all} \quad \alpha, \beta \in \mathbf{F} \quad \text{and} \quad x, y \in X.$$

(ii) Two normed linear spaces over $\mathbf{F}$: $(X, \|\cdot\|_X), (Y, \|\cdot\|_Y)$ are called topologically isomorphic provided there is a linear bijection $T : X \to Y$ with the property that there exist two positive constants c_1 and c_2 independent of $x \in X$ with

$$c_1\|x\|_X \leq \|T(x)\|_Y \leq c_2\|x\|_X.$$

If $c_1 = c_2 = 1$ then T is called an isometry and the normed spaces $(X, \|\cdot\|_X)$ and $(Y, \|\cdot\|_Y)$ are called isometric.

(iii) $\|\cdot\|_{(1)}$ and $\|\cdot\|_{(2)}$ defined on a given linear normed space X are equivalent provided there are two constants $c_1, c_2 > 0$ such that

$$c_1\|\cdot\|_{(1)} \leq \|\cdot\|_{(2)} \leq c_2\|\cdot\|_{(1)}.$$

Example 7.16.

(i) Let Y be the set of all real polynomials of the form $f(t) = y_1 + y_2 t + \frac{y_3}{2}t^2$ with the norm $\|f\|_Y = \max\{|y_1|, |y_2|, |y_3|\}$, and X the set of all vectors $x = (x_1, x_2, x_3) \in \mathbf{R}^3$ with the norm $\|x\|_X = \sqrt{x_1^2 + x_2^2 + x_3^2}$. If $T : X \to Y$ is given by $T(x) = x_1 + x_2 t + 2^{-1}x_3 t^2$, then T is linearly bijective but also enjoys

$$\|T(x)\|_Y = \max\{|x_1|, |x_2|, |x_3|\} \leq \sqrt{|x_1|^2 + |x_2|^2 + |x_3|^2} = \|x\|_X$$

and

$$\frac{1}{\sqrt{3}}\|x\|_X \leq \|T(x)\|_Y \leq \|x\|_X.$$

So, the two spaces are topologically isomorphic.

(ii) Given $p \in [1, \infty]$ and $n \in \mathbf{N}$, the previously-defined norm $\|\cdot\|_{n,p}$ and the following norm $\|\cdot\|_{n,*}$ defined via

$$\|x\|_{n,*} = \max_{1 \leq k \leq n} |x_k| \quad \text{for} \quad x = (x_1, \ldots, x_n) \in \mathbf{R}^n,$$

are equivalent.

In fact, we have the following more general result.

Theorem 7.17. *Let $n \in \mathbf{N}$.*

(i) *Any two norms on a given n-dimensional linear space X over $\mathbf{F}$ are equivalent.*

(ii) *If X and Y are n-dimensional normed linear spaces over $\mathbf{F}$ then X and Y are topologically isomorphic.*

Proof. (i) Let $\|\cdot\|_{(k)}$, $k = 1, 2$, be two norms on X. Choose a basis $\{e_1, \cdots, e_n\}$ for X and define a third norm $\|\cdot\|_{(3)}$ as follows. For each $x \in X$ there is a unique set of scalars $\alpha_1, \cdots, \alpha_n$ in $\mathbf{F}$ such that $x = \sum_{j=1}^{n} \alpha_j e_j$. Let $\|x\|_{(3)} = \sum_{j=1}^{n} |\alpha_j|$. Suppose each of the norms $\|\cdot\|_{(k)}$, $k = 1, 2$ is equivalent to $\|\cdot\|_{(3)}$. Then there are positive constants c_1, C_1 and c_2, C_2 such that

$$c_k\|\cdot\|_{(k)} \leq \|\cdot\|_{(3)} \leq C_k\|\cdot\|_{(k)}, \quad k = 1, 2.$$

It follows that

$$\frac{c_1}{C_2}\|\cdot\|_{(1)} \leq \|\cdot\|_{(2)} \leq \frac{C_1}{c_2}\|\cdot\|_{(1)},$$

implying the desired equivalence.

Now let $\|\cdot\|$ denote either $\|\cdot\|_{(1)}$ or $\|\cdot\|_{(2)}$. We show that $\|\cdot\|$ is equivalent to $\|\cdot\|_{(3)}$. If $x = \sum_{j=1}^{n} \alpha_j e_j$ then

$$\|x\| \leq \sum_{j=1}^{n} |\alpha_j|\|e_j\| \leq \big(\max_{1\leq j\leq n} \|e_j\|\big)\|x\|_{(3)}.$$

This implies a one-sided estimate. We shall prove that there is a constant $c > 0$ such that $\|\cdot\|_{(3)} \leq c\|\cdot\|$, i.e.,

$$\sum_{j=1}^{n} |\alpha_j| \leq c\Big\|\sum_{j=1}^{n} \alpha_j e_j\Big\|.$$

We may assume that $\|x\|_{(3)} = 1$ by dividing the last inequality by $\sum_{j=1}^{n} |\alpha_j|$. Now if the last inequality is not true then there would be a sequence $(y_k)_{k=1}^{\infty}$ where

$$y_k = \sum_{j=1}^{n} \alpha_{k,j} e_j \quad \text{with} \quad \|y_k\|_{(3)} = \sum_{j=1}^{n} |\alpha_{k,j}| = 1 \quad \text{but} \quad \lim_{k\to\infty} \|y_k\| = 0.$$

Note that $|\alpha_{k,j}| \leq 1$ for $j = 1, \cdots, n$ and every $k \in \mathbf{N}$. So there is a subsequence of $(y_k)_{k=1}^{\infty}$, denoted itself also, such that $\lim_{k\to\infty} \alpha_{k,j}$ exists and equals, say, α_j for $j = 1, 2, \cdots, n$ as well as

$$\lim_{k\to\infty} \Big\|y_k - \sum_{j=1}^{n} \alpha_j e_j\Big\| \leq \big(\max_{1\leq j\leq n} \|e_j\|\big) \lim_{k\to\infty} \sum_{j=1}^{n} |\alpha_{k,j} - \alpha_j| = 0.$$

Consequently,

$$\sum_{j=1}^{n} |\alpha_j| = 1 \quad \text{while} \quad \sum_{j=1}^{n} \alpha_j e_j = 0.$$

This is impossible, since $\{e_j\}_{j=1}^n$ are linearly independent. This completes the argument.

(ii) It suffices to show that X is topologically isomorphic to $\mathbf{F}^n$ with the following Euclidean norm:

$$\|\alpha\|_{n,2} = \Big(\sum_{k=1}^{n} |\alpha_k|^2\Big)^{\frac{1}{2}} \quad \text{for} \quad \alpha = (\alpha_1, \ldots, \alpha_n) \in \mathbf{F}^n.$$

By the argument for (i), there is an isomorphism T from X onto $\mathbf{F}^n$. We can use this map to define a new norm on X as follows: For each $x \in X$ let

$$|||x|||_X = \|T(x)\|_{n,2}\ .$$

When X is given this new norm, T becomes a topological isomorphism. Nevertheless, the assertion (i) indicates that $|||\cdot|||_X$ is equivalent to any norm $\|\cdot\|_X$ on X. Hence T is a topological isomorphism from $(X, \|\cdot\|_X)$ onto $\mathbf{F}^n$. □

Interestingly, Theorem 7.17 has some important consequences.

Corollary 7.18. *Let $n \in \mathbf{N}$ and X be a normed linear space over $\mathbf{F}$.*

(i) *If X is n-dimensional, then it is complete.*

(ii) *Any n-dimensional linear subspace of X is closed.*

(iii) *If X is n-dimensional, then every bounded closed subset S of X is compact.*

Proof. (i) Let $\{e_k\}_{k=1}^n$ be a basis for X. Then each $x \in X$ can be written as $x = \sum_{j=1}^n \alpha_j e_j$, $\alpha_j \in \mathbf{F}$. Set $\|x\|_{n,2} = \big(\sum_{j=1}^n |\alpha_j|^2\big)^{\frac{1}{2}}$. This is a norm on X, and by Theorem 7.17 it is equivalent to the given norm on X. Accordingly, if $\big(x^{(k)} = \sum_{j=1}^n \alpha_j^{(k)} e_j\big)_{k=1}^\infty$ is a Cauchy sequence in X, then $\big((\alpha_1^{(k)}, \ldots, \alpha_n^{(k)})\big)_{k=1}^\infty$ is a Cauchy sequence in $\mathbf{F}^n$ which is complete, and hence there exists a point $(\alpha_1, \ldots, \alpha_n) \in \mathbf{F}^n$ such that $(\alpha_1^{(k)}, \ldots, \alpha_n^{(k)}) \to (\alpha_1, \ldots, \alpha_n)$ as $k \to \infty$. Therefore $(x^{(k)})_{k=1}^\infty$ is convergent to $x = \sum_{j=1}^n \alpha_j e_j$ in X, whence X is complete.

(ii) Suppose S is an n-dimensional linear subspace of X. Then S is complete due to (i) and hence any sequence $(x^{(k)})_{k=1}^\infty$ in S which is convergent to $x \in X$ must be a Cauchy sequence in S – this yields $x \in S$ and so S is closed.

(iii) By Theorem 7.17 (ii) it follows that X is topologically isomorphic to $\mathbf{F}^n$ and hence every bounded closed subset S of X is topologically isomorphic to a compact (i.e., bounded and closed) subset of $\mathbf{F}^n$. Accordingly, S is compact. □

Even more interestingly, we can say something more about the converse of Corollary 7.18 (iii).

Theorem 7.19. *Let $(X, \|\cdot\|_X)$ be a normed linear space over $\mathbf{F}$.*

(i) *If S is a proper closed subspace of X, then for each number $\theta \in (0,1)$ there exists an element $x_\theta \in X$ such that*

$$\|x_\theta\|_X = 1 \quad \textit{and} \quad d(x_\theta, S) = \inf_{x \in S} \|x_\theta - x\|_X \geq \theta.$$

(ii) *If the unit sphere* $\{x \in X : \|x\|_X = 1\}$ *of* X *is compact, then* X *is finite dimensional.*

Proof. (i) Since S is closed and not equal to X, there exists an $x_1 \in X \setminus S$ such that $\delta = \inf_{x\in S} \|x_1 - x\|_X > 0$. Consequently, for any $\epsilon > 0$ there is an $x_2 \in S$ such that $\|x_2 - x_1\|_X < \delta + \epsilon$. Choosing

$$\epsilon = \frac{\delta(1-\theta)}{\theta} \quad \text{and} \quad x_\theta = \frac{x_2 - x_1}{\|x_2 - x_1\|_X},$$

we obtain $\|x_\theta\|_X = 1$ and

$$\|x - x_\theta\|_X = \frac{\|(\|x_2 - x_1\|_X x + x_1) - x_2\|_X}{\|x_2 - x_1\|_X} \geq \frac{\delta}{\|x_2 - x_1\|_X} \geq \frac{\delta}{\delta + \epsilon} = \theta$$

for any $x \in S$. Here we have used the fact that S is a linear subspace of X.

(ii) Suppose x_1 is any element of X with $\|x_1\|_X = 1$ and S_1 is the subspace spanned by x_1. If $S_1 = X$ then X is finite dimensional and we are done. Otherwise, by Theorem 7.19 (i), Corollary 7.18 (ii) and the fact that S_1 is finite dimensional, there exists an $x_2 \in X$ such that $\|x_2\|_X = 1$ and $d(x_2, S_1) \geq 1/2$. Suppose S_2 is the linear subspace of X spanned by x_1 and x_2. Then S_2 is a closed linear subspace of X and consequently, if $S_2 \neq X$ then by Theorem 7.19 (i) there exists an $x_3 \in X$ such that $\|x_3\|_X = 1$ and $d(x_3, S_2) \geq 1/2$. Continuing in this manner, we find inductively that if the closed linear subspace S_n spanned by $x_1, \ldots, x_n$ is not equal to X then by Theorem 7.19 (i) there exists an $x_{n+1} \in X$ such that $\|x_{n+1}\|_X = 1$ and $d(x_{n+1}, S_n) \geq 1/2$. However, this process must stop at some step – for otherwise there would be an infinite sequence $(x_j)_{j=1}^\infty$ with $\|x_j\|_X = 1$ but $\|x_j - x_k\|_X \geq 1/2$ when $j \neq k$. Of course, this sequence has no convergent subsequence, thereby deriving that the unit sphere of X is not compact thanks to Theorem 5.37 (iv), a contradiction. Accordingly, X equals some S_k, and the argument is complete. □

The foregoing discussion reveals that the unit sphere of a given normed linear space is compact if and only if the space is finite dimensional, but also leads naturally to the following concept.

Definition 7.20. If $(X, \|\cdot\|_X)$ and $(Y, \|\cdot\|_Y)$ are normed linear spaces over $\mathbf{F}$, then any one of:

(i) $\|(x, y)\| = (\|x\|_X^p + \|y\|_Y^p)^{\frac{1}{p}}$, $p \in [1, \infty)$;

(ii) $\|(x, y)\| = \max\{\|x\|_X, \|y\|_Y\}$;

may be defined as a norm on the Cartesian product $X \times Y$.

This certainly does not exhaust all the possible combinations of the norms $\|x\|_X$ and $\|y\|_Y$, and yet these are the most commonly used ones. An extension to the Cartesian product of n normed linear spaces is defined in the following manner.

Remark 7.21. For $n-1 \in \mathbf{N}$ let $\{X_k\}_{k=1}^n$ be a collection of linear spaces over $\mathbf{F}$ with norms $\{\|\cdot\|_{X_k}\}_{k=1}^n$. If their Cartesian product space is defined as

$$\prod_{k=1}^n X_k = X_1 \times \cdots \times X_n = \big\{(x_1, \ldots, x_n) : \; x_1 \in X_1, \ldots, x_n \in X_n\big\},$$

with vector addition

$$(x_1, \cdots, x_n) + (y_1, \cdots, y_n) = (x_1 + y_1, \cdots x_n + y_n)$$

and scalar multiplication

$$\alpha(x_1, \cdots, x_n) = (\alpha x_1, \cdots, \alpha x_n)$$

for

$$\alpha \in \mathbf{F};\ (x_1, \ldots, x_n),\ (y_1, \ldots, y_n) \in \prod_{k=1}^{n} X_k.$$

Then it is not hard to show that the function $\prod_{k=1}^{n} X_k \to \mathbf{R}$ defined by

$$\|(x_1, \cdots, x_n)\|_{\prod_{k=1}^{n} X_k} = \sum_{k=1}^{n} \|x_k\|_{X_k}$$

is a norm on X.

Example 7.22. If $n = m + k$ with $k, m, n \in \mathbf{N}$, then $\mathbf{R}^n$ may be viewed as the Cartesian product of $\mathbf{R}^m$ and $\mathbf{R}^k$.

7.3 Bounded Linear Operators

In this section, we discuss bounded operators, or equivalently, continuous operators, and inverse operators. To begin with, we give the definition for a bounded linear operator.

Definition 7.23. Let $(X, \|\cdot\|_X)$ and $(Y, \|\cdot\|_Y)$ be normed linear spaces over $\mathbf{F}$. A linear operator $T : X \to Y$ is said to be bounded provided there exists a constant $C \geq 0$ such that $\|T(x)\|_Y \leq C\|x\|_X$ for all $x \in X$. Define

$$\|T\| = \|T\|_{X \to Y} = \sup_{x \in X, x \neq 0} \frac{\|T(x)\|_Y}{\|x\|_X}.$$

According to this definition, we have $\|T\| = \sup_{\|x\|_X = 1} \|T(x)\|_Y$ which follows from

$$\big\|x\|x\|_X^{-1}\big\|_X = 1 \quad \text{for all} \quad x \neq 0.$$

Example 7.24.

(i) Equip ℓ_2 with the 2-norm, and let $T : \ell_2 \to \ell_2$ be given by $T(x) = (0, x_1, x_2, \cdots)$ when $x = (x_1, x_2, \cdots)$. Then it is easy to check that T is a bounded linear operator with $\|T\| = 1$.

(ii) Choose for both X and Y the real space $C[0, 1]$ with the sup-norm. Define $T : X \to Y$ by $T(f)(x) = e^x f(x)$, $x \in [0, 1]$. Then T is bounded with $\|T\| = e$.

The following result tells us that the boundedness amounts to the continuity as for a linear operator.

Theorem 7.25. *Let $(X, \|\cdot\|_X)$ and $(Y, \|\cdot\|_Y)$ be normed linear spaces over* $\mathbf{F}$, *and let $T : X \to Y$ be a linear operator. Then the following statements are equivalent:*

(i) *T is continuous on X;*

(ii) *T is continuous at 0;*

(iii) *T is bounded;*

(iv) *T maps bounded subsets of X to bounded subsets of Y.*

Proof. In the sequel, we will write $A \Leftrightarrow B$ for the statement – if A then B and vice versa, but also use the criterion for a linear map $T : X \to Y$ to be continuous at a point $x \in X$:

$$\|x_n - x\|_X \to 0 \Rightarrow \|T(x_n) - T(x)\|_Y = 0.$$

(i)$\Leftrightarrow$(ii) The implication (i) $\Rightarrow$ (ii) is trivial. Regarding the implication (ii) $\Rightarrow$ (i), we suppose T is continuous at $0 \in X$. If $x_n \to x$ then $x_n - x \to 0$. Hence

$$T(x_n - x) \to T(0) = 0 \quad \text{so that} \quad T(x_n) \to T(x) \quad \text{in} \quad Y.$$

(iii)$\Leftrightarrow$(i) If T is bounded and $x_n \to x$ in X, then $T(x_n) \to T(x)$ in Y as well. It follows that T is continuous at x. Conversely, assume that T is continuous on X. If T is not bounded, then for any $n \in \mathbf{N}$ there exists a point $x_n \in X$ with $\|T(x_n)\|_Y \geq n\|x_n\|_X$. Let $y_n = \frac{x_n}{n\|x_n\|_X}$, so that $\|y_n\|_X = n^{-1} \to 0$. However, $\|T(y_n)\|_Y > 1$ and $T(0) = 0$, contradicting the assumption that T is continuous at 0.

(iv)$\Leftrightarrow$(ii) Suppose (ii) is true. So T is bounded with $\|T\| \leq C_1$ for some constant $C_1 > 0$ due to (iii)$\Leftrightarrow$(ii). If S is a bounded subset of X, then there is a constant $C_2 > 0$ such that $\|x\|_X \leq C_2$ for all $x \in S$ and hence

$$\|T(x)\|_Y \leq C_1\|x\|_X \leq C_1 C_2 \quad \text{for all} \quad x \in S.$$

That is to say, $T(S)$ is a bounded subset of Y. Conversely, assume that (iv) is true. Given an open ball

$$B_\epsilon^Y(0) = \{y \in Y : \|y\|_Y < \epsilon\}$$

in Y, let

$$B_1^X(0) = \{x \in X : \|x\|_X < 1\}$$

denote the open unit ball in X. By (iv) it follows that $T(B_1^X)$ is bounded in Y. Thus, there is a $\lambda > 0$ such that

$$T(B_1^X) \subseteq \lambda B_\epsilon^Y(0) = \{y \in Y : \|y\|_Y < \lambda\epsilon\}.$$

This implies $T(B_{\lambda^{-1}}^X) \subseteq B_\epsilon^Y$ since T is linear, and so T is continuous at 0. $\square$

Example 7.26. For $n \in \mathbf{N}$ equip $X = \mathbf{R}^n$ with the $(n, 2)$-norm and let $\{e_j\}_{j=1}^n$ (for which the j-th coordinate of e_j is 1 and others are 0) be the standard basis for $\mathbf{R}^n$. Then any $x = (x_1, \ldots, x_n) \in \mathbf{R}^n$ has the form

$$x = \sum_{j=1}^n x_j e_j \quad \text{with} \quad \|x\|_{n,2}^2 = \sum_{j=1}^n |x_j|^2.$$

If $T : \mathbf{R}^n \to Y$ is a linear transformation, where $(Y, \|\cdot\|_Y)$ is a normed linear space over $\mathbf{F}$, then the Cauchy–Schwarz inequality implies

$$\|T(x)\|_Y \le \|x\|_{n,2}\Big(\sum_{j=1}^{n} \|T(e_j)\|_Y^2\Big)^{\frac{1}{2}}.$$

So, T is bounded with

$$\|T\| \le \Big(\sum_{j=1}^{n} \|T(e_j)\|_Y^2\Big)^{\frac{1}{2}}.$$

Indeed, Example 7.26 is a special case of the following result.

Theorem 7.27. *Let $(X, \|\cdot\|_X)$ and $(Y, \|\cdot\|_Y)$ be two normed linear spaces over $\mathbf{F}$. If X is finite dimensional, then any linear transformation $T : X \to Y$ is bounded.*

Proof. Note that any two norms on a finite dimensional linear space X over $\mathbf{F}$ are equivalent. So, we construct a new norm $\|\cdot\|$ via $\|\cdot\|_X$ and $\|\cdot\|_Y$:

$$\|x\| = \|x\|_X + \|T(x)\|_Y, \quad x \in X.$$

Of course, $\|\cdot\|$ is a norm on X and so it is equivalent to $\|\cdot\|_X$. This yields a constant $C > 0$ with $\|\cdot\| \le C\|\cdot\|_X$. It follows that $\|T(x)\|_Y \le \|x\| \le C\|x\|_X$ for all $x \in X$. In other words, $T : X \to Y$ is bounded. □

Next, we consider some basic algebraic properties of the space of all bounded linear operators.

Definition 7.28. Let $(X, \|\cdot\|_X)$ and $(Y, \|\cdot\|_Y)$ be two normed linear spaces over $\mathbf{F}$. Denote by $B(X, Y)$ the set of all bounded linear operators from X to Y. In particular, $B(X)$ is used as $B(X, X)$.

Theorem 7.29. *Let $(X, \|\cdot\|_X)$, $(Y, \|\cdot\|_Y)$ and $(Z, \|\cdot\|_Z)$ be normed linear spaces over $\mathbf{F}$. Then*

(i) *$B(X, Y)$ is a linear space over $\mathbf{F}$ with respect to the operations:*

$$(T + S)(x) = T(x) + S(x) \quad \text{and} \quad (\alpha T)(x) = \alpha T(x) \quad \text{for} \quad x \in X,\ \alpha \in \mathbf{F}.$$

(ii) *The function $\|\cdot\| : B(X, Y) \to \mathbf{R}$, defined by*

$$\|T\| = \sup_{x \in X, \|x\|_X \ne 0} \frac{\|T(x)\|_Y}{\|x\|_X} \quad \text{for} \quad T \in B(X, Y),$$

is a norm on $B(X, Y)$.

(iii) *If $T \in B(X, Y)$ and $S \in B(Y, Z)$, then the composition $ST = S \circ T$ belongs to $B(X, Z)$ with $\|ST\| \le \|S\|\|T\|$.*

(iv) *If $T, S \in B(X)$ are invertible; that is, there are two elements $T^{-1}, S^{-1} \in B(X)$ such that*

$$TT^{-1} = T^{-1}T = I \quad \text{and} \quad SS^{-1} = S^{-1}S = I,$$

where I stands for the identity element of $B(X)$, then $ST \in B(X)$ is invertible with $(ST)^{-1} = T^{-1}S^{-1}$.

Proof. (i) This follows from checking those conditions for a linear space with $B(X, Y)$.

(ii) We have to verify three conditions required for a norm. First, it is clear that $\|T\| \geq 0$. If $\|T\| = 0$ then $\|T(x)\|_Y = 0$ for all $x \in X$, and hence $T(x) = 0$ for all $x \in X$. This gives $T = 0$. Conversely, $T = 0$ implies $\|T\| = 0$.

Next,

$$\|\alpha T\| = \sup_{x \in X, \|x\|_X \neq 0} \frac{\|\alpha T(x)\|_Y}{\|x\|_X} = |\alpha| \|T\|.$$

Finally,

$$\begin{aligned} \|T + S\| &= \sup_{x \in X, \|x\|_X \neq 0} \frac{\|T(x) + S(x)\|_Y}{\|x\|_X} \\ &\leq \sup_{x \in X, \|x\|_X \neq 0} \frac{\|T(x)\|_Y}{\|x\|_X} + \sup_{x \in X, \|x\|_X \neq 0} \frac{\|S(x)\|_Y}{\|x\|_X} \\ &= \|T\| + \|S\|. \end{aligned}$$

(iii) Clearly, ST is a linear transformation from X to Z. Since T and S are bounded, we conclude

$$\|(ST)x\|_Z = \|S(T(x))\|_Z \leq \|S\| \|T(x)\|_Y \leq \|S\| \|T\| \|x\|_X \quad \text{for all} \quad x \in X.$$

This yields that ST is bounded and so in $B(X, Z)$ with $\|ST\| \leq \|S\| \|T\|$, as desired.

(iv) This follows from the following formula:

$$(ST)T^{-1}S^{-1} = I = T^{-1}S^{-1}(ST).$$

□

Example 7.30. Define $T : \ell_2 \to \ell_2$ by $T\big((x_1, x_2, \cdots)\big) = (0, x_1, x_2, \cdots)$. This map is bounded but not invertible, since it is clearly not onto. If $S : \ell_2 \to \ell_2$ is given by $S\big((x_1, x_2, \cdots)\big) = (x_2, x_3, \cdots)$, then it is bounded but not invertible, because it is clearly not one to one. Note that $ST = I \neq TS$.

7.4 Linear Functionals via Hahn–Banach Extension

Looking at the Lebesgue–Radon–Stieltjes integrals, we find that if $g : \mathbf{R} \to \mathbf{R}$ is increasing then $L_g(f) = \int_{\mathbf{R}} f dm_g$ defines a linear function from the real linear space $LRS_g(\mathbf{R})$ into $\mathbf{R}$. This observation suggests that we should work with the so-called linear functionals.

Definition 7.31. Let X be a linear space over $\mathbf{F}$. A linear map from X to $\mathbf{F}$ is called an $\mathbf{F}$-valued linear functional on X. If X is a normed linear space, then $X^* = B(X, \mathbf{F})$ and $X^{**} = (X^*)^*$ are respectively called the dual space and second dual space of X over $\mathbf{F}$. Moreover X is said to be reflexive whenever X^{**} and X are isometric.

The question is whether or not the class of $\mathbf{F}$-valued linear functionals on X consists only of the zero functional. To settle this question, let us consider the following example of Mahlon Marsh Day type.

Example 7.32. If L is a continuous linear functional on $\mathcal{LRS}^p_{id}([0,1],\mathbf{R})$, $p\in(0,1)$, then $L=0$. To see this conclusion, suppose, to the contrary, $L\neq 0$. Then, without loss of generality we may assume that there exists an $f\in\mathcal{LRS}^p_{id}([0,1],\mathbf{R})$ such that

$$L(f)=1 \quad \text{and} \quad \|f\|_{p,m_{id},[0,1]}\neq 0.$$

Since L is continuous, $\phi(x)=L(f1_{[0,x]})$ is a continuous function on $[0,1]$. Note that $\phi(0)=0$ and $\phi(1)=1$ and $f=f1_{[0,x]}+f1_{[x,1]}$. So by the intermediate value theorem for continuous functions (see also Theorem 2.20 (iii)) there is an $x_0\in(0,1)$ such that

$$\phi(x_0)=2^{-1} \quad \text{and} \quad L(f1_{[0,x_0]})=2^{-1}=L(f1_{[x_0,1]}).$$

Since

$$\|f1_{[0,x_0]}\|^p_{p,m_{id},[0,1]}+\|f1_{[x_0,1]}\|^p_{p,m_{id},[0,1]}=\|f\|^p_{p,m_{id},[0,1]},$$

one of two terms of the left-hand side of the last equation is not greater than $2^{-1}\|f\|^p_{p,m_{id},[0,1]}$, say,

$$\|f1_{[0,x_0]}\|^p_{p,m_{id},[0,1]}\leq 2^{-1}\|f\|^p_{p,m_{id},[0,1]},$$

and consequently,

$$L(2f1_{[0,x_0]})=1 \quad \text{and} \quad \|2f1_{[0,x_0]}\|^p_{p,m_{id},[0,1]}\leq 2^{p-1}\|f\|^p_{p,m_{id},[0,1]}.$$

Continuing the above argument, we obtain a sequence $(f_j)_{j=1}^{\infty}$ in $\mathcal{LRS}^p_{id}([0,1],\mathbf{R})$ such that for any $j\in\mathbf{N}$,

$$L(f_j)=1 \quad \text{and} \quad \|f_j\|^p_{p,m_{id},[0,1]}\leq 2^{j(p-1)}\|f\|^p_{p,m_{id},[0,1]}.$$

But, the last inequality cannot hold due to $0<p<1$, $2^{j(p-1)}\to 0$, and L being continuous.

Actually, the above question will be answered in great generality using the Hahn–Banach extension theorem which is stated below and named for Hans Hahn and Stefan Banach.

Theorem 7.33. *Let X be a linear space over $\mathbf{F}$, and $p: X\to[0,\infty)$ a function with*

$$p(x+y)\leq p(x)+p(y) \quad \text{and} \quad p(\lambda x)=|\lambda|p(x) \quad \text{for all} \quad \lambda\in\mathbf{F} \text{ and } x,y\in X.$$

If Y is a linear subspace of X and f is an $\mathbf{F}$-valued linear functional on Y with $|f(x)|\leq p(x)$ for all $x\in Y$, then there is an $\mathbf{F}$-valued linear functional F on X such that $F(x)=f(x)$ for all $x\in Y$ and $|F(x)|\leq p(x)$ for all $x\in X$.

Proof. First of all, we demonstrate the theorem for $\mathbf{F}=\mathbf{R}$. Under this situation, we find that $|f(x)|\leq p(x)$ amounts to $f(x)\leq p(x)$ thanks to $|f(x)|=\pm f(x)=f(\pm x)$ and $p(\pm x)=p(x)$. Thus, we consider the collection $\mathcal{K}$ of all pairs (Y_α,g_α) in which

Y_α is a linear subspace of X containing Y, and g_α is a real linear functional on Y_α with

$$g_\alpha(x) = f(x) \quad \text{for all} \quad x \in Y \quad \text{and} \quad g_\alpha(x) \le p(x) \quad \text{for all} \quad x \in Y_\alpha.$$

Making $\mathcal{K}$ into a partially ordered set by defining the relation:

$$(Y_\alpha, g_\alpha) \preceq (Y_\beta, g_\beta) \quad \text{if} \quad Y_\alpha \subseteq Y_\beta \quad \text{and} \quad g_\alpha = g_\beta \quad \text{on} \quad Y_\alpha,$$

we clearly see that every totally ordered subset $\{(Y_\lambda, g_\lambda)\}$ of $\mathcal{K}$, for which at least one of

$$(Y_\alpha, g_\alpha) \preceq (Y_\beta, g_\beta) \quad \text{and} \quad (Y_\beta, g_\beta) \preceq (Y_\alpha, g_\alpha)$$

holds, has an upper bound $\cup_\lambda Y_\lambda$ on which the functional is given by g_λ on each Y_λ. By Zorn's lemma we find that there is a maximal element (Y_0, g_0) in $\mathcal{K}$. Subsequently, we will prove $Y_0 = X$ and $g_0 = F$.

If $Y_0 \neq X$, then there is a $y_1 \in X \setminus Y_0$. Let Y_1 be the linear space spanned by Y_0 and y_1; that is,

$$Y_1 = \{y + \lambda y_1 : \ y \in Y_0, \ \lambda \in \mathbf{R}\}.$$

Note that Y_0 is a subset of Y_1, and if $x, y \in Y_0$ then

$$g_0(y) - g_0(x) = g_0(y - x) \le p(y - x) \le p(y + y_1) + p(-y_1 - x)$$

and hence

$$-p(-y_1 - x) - g_0(x) \le p(y + y_1) - g_0(y).$$

It follows that

$$a = \sup_{x \in Y_0} \big\{ -p(-y_1 - x) - g_0(x) \big\} \le \inf_{y \in Y_0} \{p(y + y_1) - g_0(y)\} = b.$$

Now for any number $c \in [a, b]$ define

$$g_1(y + \lambda y_1) = g_0(y) + \lambda c \quad \text{for all} \quad y \in Y_0 \quad \text{and} \quad \lambda \in \mathbf{R}.$$

Then g_1 is evidently linear. Furthermore, we have the following three cases:

Case 1: If $\lambda = 0$, then $g_1(y) = g_0(y) \le p(y)$.

Case 2: If $\lambda > 0$ and $y \in Y_0$, then

$$\begin{aligned} g_1(y + \lambda y_1) &= \lambda\Big(g_0(\frac{y}{\lambda}) + c\Big) \\ &\le \lambda\Big(g_0(\frac{y}{\lambda}) + p(\frac{y}{\lambda} + y_1) - g_0(\frac{y}{\lambda})\Big) \\ &= \lambda p(\frac{y}{\lambda} + y_1) \\ &= p(y + \lambda y_1), \end{aligned}$$

Case 3: If $\lambda < 0$, then

$$\begin{aligned} g_1(y+\lambda y_1) &= |\lambda|\Big(g_0\big(\frac{y}{|\lambda|}\big) - c\Big) \\ &\le |\lambda|\Big(g_0\big(\frac{y}{|\lambda|}\big) - g_0\big(\frac{y}{|\lambda|}\big) + p\big(-y_1 + \frac{y}{|\lambda|}\big)\Big) \\ &= |\lambda| p\big(-y_1 + \frac{y}{|\lambda|}\big) \\ &= p(y+\lambda y_1). \end{aligned}$$

Accordingly, we get

$$g_1(y+\lambda y_1) = g_0(y) + \lambda c \le p(y+\lambda y_1) \quad \text{for all} \quad \lambda \in \mathbf{R} \quad \text{and} \quad y \in Y_0.$$

This is to say,

$$(Y_1, g_1) \in \mathcal{K} \quad \text{and} \quad (Y_0, g_0) \preceq (Y_1, g_1) \quad \text{with} \quad Y_0 \ne Y_1.$$

This contradicts the maximality of (Y_0, g_0). The preceding argument indicates that if $x \in X$ and $\lambda = \text{sgn}F(x)$, the real number obeying $\lambda F(x) = |F(x)|$, then

$$|F(x)| = \lambda F(x) = F(\lambda x) \le p(\lambda x) \le p(x).$$

Next, we prove the theorem for the case $\mathbf{F} = \mathbf{C}$. Let f be a complex linear functional on Y such that $|f(x)| \le p(x)$ for $x \in Y$. Then $u = \Re f$ is clearly real linear on Y and $|u(x)| = |\Re f(x)| \le |f(x)| \le p(x)$. According to the above $\mathbf{R}$-case there is a real-valued linear functional U on X such that $U(x) = u(x)$ for $x \in Y$ and $|U(x)| \le p(x)$ for $x \in X$. Now if $F(x) = U(x) - iU(ix)$, then $\Im F(x) = -\Re(iF(x)) = -U(ix)$ and $F(ix) = U(ix) - iU(-x) = U(ix) + iU(x) = iF(x)$, and consequently, F is a complex linear extension of $f(x) = u(x) - iu(ix)$ to X. Furthermore, if

$$\alpha = \text{sgn}F(x) = \begin{cases} \exp\big(-i \arg F(x)\big), & F(x) \ne 0, \\ 0, & F(x) = 0, \end{cases}$$

then

$$|F(x)| = \alpha F(x) = F(\alpha x) = U(\alpha x) \le p(\alpha x) \le p(x). \qquad \square$$

Here is a series of important and interesting consequences of the Hahn–Banach extension theorem applied to normed linear spaces.

Corollary 7.34. *Let $(X, \|\cdot\|_X)$ be a normed space over $\mathbf{F}$, and Y a linear subspace of X.*

(i) *To any $f \in B(Y, \mathbf{F})$ there corresponds an $F \in X^*$ such that*

$$\|F\| = \|f\| \quad \textit{and} \quad F(y) = f(y) \quad \textit{for all} \quad y \in Y.$$

(ii) *If $x_0 \in X$ satisfies*

$$\inf_{y \in Y} \|y - x_0\|_X = d > 0,$$

then there is an $F \in X^*$ such that

$$F(x_0) = 1; \quad \|F\| = d^{-1}; \quad F(y) = 0 \quad \textit{for all} \quad y \in Y.$$

(iii) *If Y is not dense in X, then there is a nonzero $F \in X^*$ such that $F(y) = 0$ for all $y \in Y$.*

(iv) *If $x \in X$ is nonzero, then there is an $F \in X^*$ such that*

$$\|F\| = 1 \quad \text{and} \quad F(x) = \|x\|_X.$$

(v) *If $y, z \in X$ and $y \neq z$, then there exists an $F \in X^*$ such that $F(y) \neq F(z)$.*

(vi) *For any $x \in X$,*

$$\|x\|_X = \sup_{0 \neq F \in X^*} \frac{|F(x)|}{\|F\|} = \sup_{F \in X^*,\ \|F\|=1} |F(x)|.$$

(vii) *If $F \in X^*$ is nonzero and $\mathcal{N} = \{x \in X : F(x) = 0\}$, then there exists a one-dimensional subspace $\mathcal{M}$ of X such that*

$$X = \mathcal{N} + \mathcal{M} = \{x + y : \quad x \in \mathcal{N} \quad \text{and} \quad y \in \mathcal{M}\} \quad \text{and} \quad \mathcal{N} \cap \mathcal{M} = \{0\}.$$

(viii) *If X^* is separable, so is X.*

(ix) *If Y is closed and $Y^\perp = \{f \in X^* : f(y) = 0 \text{ for all } y \in Y\}$, then $Y^* = X^*/Y^\perp$ and $(X/Y)^* = Y^\perp$ in the sense that there exist isometries between the corresponding normed spaces.*

(x) *If X is reflexive and Y is closed, then Y is reflexive.*

Proof. (i) Given $f \in B(Y, \mathbf{F})$, let $p(x) = \|f\|\|x\|_X$ for all $x \in X$. Then

$$|f(x)| \leq \|f\|\|x\|_X = p(x) \quad \text{for all} \quad x \in Y.$$

Hence from Theorem 7.33 it turns out that there exists an extension $F \in B(X, \mathbf{F})$ with $F = f$ on Y and $|F| \leq p$ on X. Clearly, $\|F\| = \|f\|$ follows from $\|F\| \leq \|f\|$ and

$$\|f\| = \sup_{y \in Y,\ \|y\|_X = 1} |f(y)| = \sup_{y \in Y,\ \|y\|_X = 1} |F(y)| \leq \|F\|.$$

(ii) Let Y_1 be the linear space spanned by Y and x_0. Since $d > 0$, we conclude that $x_0 \notin Y$ and every point $x \in Y_1$ may be written uniquely as $x = y + \lambda x_0$ where $y \in Y$ and $\lambda \in \mathbf{F}$. Define a linear functional

$$f \in Y_1^* \quad \text{by} \quad f(y + \lambda x_0) = \lambda.$$

Then $f(y) = 0$ for $y \in Y$ and $f(x_0) = 1$. If $\lambda \neq 0$ and $x = y + \lambda x_0$, then

$$\|x\|_X = \|y + \lambda x_0\|_X = |\lambda| \left\|\lambda^{-1} y + x_0\right\|_X \geq |\lambda| d = |f(x)| d,$$

and hence $\|f\| \leq d^{-1}$. Pick a sequence $(y_n)_{n=1}^\infty$ in Y with $\|x_0 - y_n\|_X \to d$. Then

$$1 = f(x_0 - y_n) \leq \|f\|\|x_0 - y_n\|_X \to d\|f\|,$$

so $\|f\| \geq d^{-1}$. Therefore $\|f\| = d^{-1}$. Accordingly, a direct application of (i) produces an $F \in X^*$ such that $F(x) = f(x)$ when $x \in Y_1$, and $\|F\| = \|f\|$, as desired.

(iii) Since Y is not dense in X, we conclude that there is an $x_0 \in X$ such that

$$\inf_{y \in Y} \|y - x_0\|_X = d > 0.$$

An application of (ii) produces the conclusion in (iii).

(iv) Just apply (ii) with $Y = \{0\}$ and $x \in X$ to get an $f \in X^*$ such that

$$\|f\| = \|x\|_X^{-1} \quad \text{and} \qquad f(x) = 1.$$

We may then take $F = \|x\|_X f$.

(v) Apply (iv) to $x = y - z$.

(vi) If $x = 0$ then the assertion is trivial. So, suppose $x \neq 0$. Then

$$\sup_{F \in X^*,\ \|F\|=1} |F(x)| \leq \|x\|_X.$$

Meanwhile, by (iv) there is an $f \in X^*$ such that

$$f(x) = \|x\|_X \quad \text{and} \quad \|f\| = 1,$$

thus

$$\sup_{F \in X^*,\ \|F\|=1} |F(x)| = \|x\|_X.$$

(vii) If $F \neq 0$ then there is a point $x_0 \neq 0$ such that $F(x_0) = 1$. Note that any element $x \in X$ can then be written as

$$x = x - \lambda x_0 + \lambda x_0 \quad \text{with} \quad \lambda = F(x).$$

So, if $Y = \{\lambda x_0 : \lambda \in \mathbf{F}\}$ then the desired decomposition follows right away. It is clear that Y is the one-dimensional space spanned by x_0. If $x \in \mathcal{N} \cap Y$, then

$$x = \lambda x_0 \quad \text{and} \quad 0 = F(x) = \lambda F(x_0) = \lambda,$$

and hence $x = 0$.

(viii) Suppose $\{f_j\}_{j=1}^{\infty}$ is a dense subset of the unit sphere $\{f \in X^* : \ \|f\| = 1\}$ and choose $x_j \in \{x \in X : \ \|x\|_X = 1\}$ to obey $|f_j(x_j)| \geq 1/2$. Let $Y = \text{span}\{x_j\}_{j=1}^{\infty}$. If $\overline{Y} \neq X$, then the just-verified (ii) gives a functional $f \in X^*$ such that $\|f\| = 1$ and $f(x) = 0$ for all $x \in Y$. Now if $\epsilon \in (0, 1/2)$, then there exists a functional $f_{j_0} \in \{f_j\}_{j=1}^{\infty}$ such that $x_{j_0} \in Y$ and

$$2^{-1} \leq |f_{j_0}(x_{j_0})| = |f(x_{j_0}) - f_{j_0}(x_{j_0})| \leq \|f - f_{j_0}\| < \epsilon,$$

a contradiction. Accordingly, $\overline{Y} = X$, i.e., X is separable.

(ix) Suppose $f \in Y^*$. By (i) there is an $F \in X^*$ such that $F = f$ on Y and $\|F\| = \|f\|$. Then $\phi(F) = F + Y^{\perp}$ is a well-defined element in $X^*/Y^{\perp}$. It is easy to prove that ϕ establishes an isometry between Y^* and $X^*/Y^{\perp}$.

As with the second isometry, we define $\psi(f)(x) = f(x+Y)$ for any $f \in (X/Y)^*$, and then find that $\psi : (X/Y)^* \to Y^{\perp}$ is an isometry and so $(X/Y)^*$ and $Y^{\perp}$ are isometric.

(x) According to (vi), every $x \in X$ defines a unique element $\hat{x}$ in the second dual X^{**} of X and $\|\hat{x}\| = \|x\|_X$, and consequently, $\widehat{\cdot}$ is always linear and an isometry from X into X^{**}. Therefore, X is not only identified with $\widehat{X}$ but also regarded as a linear subspace of X^{**}. Since X is reflexive, every functional in X^{**} just arises in the fashion $\hat{x}(L) = L(x)$ for $L \in X^*$ and $x \in X$; that is, the mapping $\widehat{\cdot}$ is surjective.

Suppose Y is closed. Then (ix) tells us that $Y^* = X^*/Y^\perp$ and $(X^*/Y^\perp)^* = (Y^\perp)^\perp = \{f \in X^{**} : f(Y^\perp) = \{0\}\}$. Since X is viewed as a linear subspace of X^{**}, any element $y \in Y$ induces $f(y) = 0$ for all $f \in Y^\perp = \{f \in X^* : f(Y) = \{0\}\}$ and consequently, y is a member of $(Y^\perp)^\perp$. Meanwhile, if there is an element y_0 in $(Y^\perp)^\perp \setminus Y$, then the closedness of Y ensures $\inf_{y \in Y} \|y - y_0\|_X = \delta > 0$, and hence by (ii) there exists an $f \in X^*$ such that $f(y_0) = 1$, $f(y) = 0$ for all $y \in Y$ (this implies $f \in Y^\perp$), and $\|f\| = \delta^{-1}$. Note that X is reflexive. So $y_0 \in (Y^\perp)^\perp$ and $f \in Y^\perp$ yield $f(y_0) = 0$, contradicting $f(y_0) = 1$. Therefore, $(Y^\perp)^\perp = Y$, and consequently, $Y^{**} = Y$, as desired. □

Problems

7.1. Let $p \in (1, \infty)$ and $q = p/(p-1)$. Prove Hölder's and Minkowski's inequalities of the discrete forms:

(i) For vectors $(x_j)_{j=1}^n$ and $(y_j)_{j=1}^n$ in $\mathbf{R}^n$, one has

$$\sum_{j=1}^n |x_j y_j| \le \Big(\sum_{j=1}^n |x_j|^p\Big)^{\frac{1}{p}} \Big(\sum_{j=1}^n |y_j|^q\Big)^{\frac{1}{q}}$$

and

$$\Big(\sum_{j=1}^n |x_j + y_j|^p\Big)^{\frac{1}{p}} \le \Big(\sum_{j=1}^n |x_j|^p\Big)^{\frac{1}{p}} + \Big(\sum_{j=1}^n |y_j|^p\Big)^{\frac{1}{p}};$$

(ii) For real-valued sequences $(x_j)_{j=1}^\infty \in \ell_p$ and $(y_j)_{j=1}^\infty \in \ell_q$, one has

$$\sum_{j=1}^\infty |x_j y_j| \le \Big(\sum_{j=1}^\infty |x_j|^p\Big)^{\frac{1}{p}} \Big(\sum_{j=1}^\infty |y_j|^q\Big)^{\frac{1}{q}}$$

and

$$\Big(\sum_{j=1}^\infty |x_j + y_j|^p\Big)^{\frac{1}{p}} \le \Big(\sum_{j=1}^\infty |x_j|^p\Big)^{\frac{1}{p}} + \Big(\sum_{j=1}^\infty |y_j|^p\Big)^{\frac{1}{p}}.$$

7.2. Determine the dimension of:

(i) The set of vectors $x = (x_1, \cdots, x_n)$ in $\mathbf{R}^n$ with $\sum_{j=1}^n x_j = 0$;

(ii) The set $C[0,1]$ of all continuous functions $f : [0,1] \to \mathbf{R}$;

(iii) The set of all real-valued polynomials on $[0,1]$.

7.3. Prove the following two results:

(i) On $C[0,1]$ the sup-norm is not equivalent to any p-norm where $1 \le p < \infty$;

(ii) If $C[0,1]$ is equipped with the sup-norm, then the unit sphere of $C[0,1]$ is not compact.

7.4. Prove that if X is a linear space over $\mathbf{F}$ then any norm $\|\cdot\|: X \to \mathbf{R}$ is continuous on X, but also vector addition and scalar multiplication are continuous whenever $X \times Y$ is equipped with the norm $\|\cdot\|_X + \|\cdot\|_Y$.

7.5. Recall that ℓ_∞ is the space of all bounded infinite sequences $x = (x_j)_{j=1}^\infty$ of real numbers with $\|x\|_\infty = \sup_{j\in\mathbf{N}} |x_j|$. Prove that if ℓ_0 is the class of all infinite sequence of real numbers which have only finitely many non-zero terms, then ℓ_0 is not closed in ℓ_∞.

7.6. Verify the following results:

(i) $\lim_{p\to\infty} \|f\|_{p,m_{id},[0,1]} = \|f\|_{\infty,m_{id},[0,1]}$ whenever $\|f\|_{\infty,m_{id},[0,1]} < \infty$;

(ii) $\int_{[0,1]} |f_1 f_2| dm_{id} \le \|f_1\|_{1,m_{id},[0,1]} \|f_2\|_{\infty,m_{id},[0,1]}$ with equality if and only if $|f_2(x)| = \|f_2\|_{\infty,m_{id},[0,1]}$ for m_{id}-a.e. $x \in [0,1]$.

7.7. Prove that if $C[0,1]$ is equipped with the sup-norm and $T: C[0,1] \to \mathbf{R}$ is given by $T(f) = f(0)$, then T is bounded with $\|T\| = 1$.

7.8.

(i) Suppose the real infinite matrix $[a_{kj}]$ satisfies $\sup_{k\in\mathbf{N}} \sum_{j=1}^\infty |a_{kj}| < \infty$. Define

$$T: x = (x_1, x_2, \cdots) \to y = T(x) = \Big(\sum_{j=1}^\infty a_{1j}x_j, \sum_{j=1}^\infty a_{2j}x_j, \cdots\Big).$$

Prove that $T: \ell_\infty \to \ell_\infty$ is bounded and $\|T\| = \sup_{k\in\mathbf{N}} \sum_{j=1}^\infty |a_{kj}|$.

(ii) Let $T: \ell_2 \to \ell_2$ be defined by

$$T(x) = (0, x_1, x_2, \cdots) \quad \text{for} \quad x = (x_1, x_2, \cdots) \in \ell_2.$$

Prove $\|T(x)\|_2 = \|x\|_2$.

(iii) For a finite interval $[a,b]$ in $\mathbf{R}$, let $R^1[a,b]$ be the space of all real-valued Riemann integrable functions f on $[a,b]$ with $\|f\|_1 = \int_a^b |f(x)|dx < \infty$. Define $T(f)(x) = \int_a^x f(t)dt$. Prove that T is a bounded linear operator from $R^1[a,b]$ to itself with $\|T\| = b-a$.

7.9. Let $C(0,1)$ be the space of all real-valued continuous functions on $(0,1)$. Equip $C(0,1)$ with the 2-norm $\|f\|_2 = \big(\int_0^1 |f(t)|^2 dt\big)^{\frac{1}{2}}$. Define

$$T: C(0,1) \to C(0,1) \quad \text{by} \quad T(f)(t) = tf(t) \quad \text{for} \quad t \in (0,1).$$

Prove that T is bounded but not invertible.

7.10. Let $T: \mathbf{R}^2 \to \mathbf{R}^2$ be given by $T\big((x_1, x_2)\big) = (x_1, 0)$. Prove that T is linear, bounded, but not onto, and cannot map open sets to open sets in $\mathbf{R}^2$.

7.11. For a normed linear space X over $\mathbf{F}$, prove the following conclusions:

(i) If $T \in B(X)$ and T^{-1} exists and belongs to $B(X)$, then $(T^{-1})^n = (T^n)^{-1}$ holds for any $n \in \mathbf{N}$;

(ii) If $T, S \in B(X)$ and TS has an inverse in $B(X)$, then T and S must have inverses in $B(X)$.

7.12. Let K be a convex set in a normed linear space $(X, \|\cdot\|_X)$ over $\mathbf{R}$; that is,

$$x_1, x_2 \in K \quad \text{and} \quad \lambda \in (0,1) \Rightarrow \lambda x_1 + (1-\lambda)x_2 \in K.$$

If 0 is an interior point of K, then the Minkowski functional p of K is defined by

$$p(x) = \inf\{\lambda > 0 : x \in \lambda K\} \quad \text{where} \quad \lambda K = \{\lambda x : x \in K\}.$$

Prove the following results:

(i) The Minkowski functional of the unit ball in X is the norm $\|\cdot\|_X$;

(ii) The Minkowski functional p is positive homogeneous, i.e.,

$$p(\kappa x) = \kappa p(x) \quad \text{for} \quad \kappa > 0 \quad \text{and} \quad x \in X,$$

and subadditive, i.e.,

$$p(x+y) \le p(x) + p(y) \quad \text{for all} \quad x, y \in X;$$

(iii) For each $x_0 \notin K$ there exists an $L \in B(X, \mathbf{R})$ such that $L(x) \le L(x_0)$ for $x \in K$.

7.13. Let X be a real normed linear space. By a hyperplane in X is meant a set of the form $H = \{x \in X : f(x) = r\}$ where f is a continuous linear functional on X and $r \in \mathbf{R}$. Prove the following separation theorem: If E_1 and E_2 are disjoint convex subsets of X and E_1 has an interior point, then there is a hyperplane which separates E_1 and E_2; that is, there exist a continuous functional $f \in B(X, \mathbf{R})$ and an $r \in \mathbf{R}$ such that

$$E_1 \subseteq \{x \in X : f(x) \le r\} \quad \text{and} \quad E_2 \subseteq \{x \in X : f(x) \ge r\}.$$

7.14. Let X be a normed linear space over $\mathbf{F}$ and $f : X \to \mathbf{F}$ be a linear functional. Prove that $f \in B(X, \mathbf{F})$ if and only $f^{-1}(\{0\})$ is closed in X.

7.15. Let X be a normed linear space over $\mathbf{F}$. Prove that if $\mathcal{M}$ is a closed linear subspace of X and $x \in X \setminus \mathcal{M}$ then $\mathcal{M} + \mathbf{F}x$ is closed.

7.16. If $\mathcal{M}$ is a finite-dimensional subspace of a normed linear space X over $\mathbf{F}$, prove that there is a closed linear subspace $\mathcal{N}$ such that

$$\mathcal{M} \cap \mathcal{N} = \{0\} \quad \text{and} \quad \mathcal{M} + \mathcal{N} = X.$$

7.17. Verify the Krein extension theorem: Let X be a normed linear space over $\mathbf{R}$ and $Y \subseteq X$ such that if $y_1, y_2 \in Y$ and $c \ge 0$ then $y_1 + y_2 \in Y$ and $cy_1 \in Y$. Define a partial order on X by declaring that $x_1 \preceq x_2$ if and only if $x_2 - x_1 \in Y$, and say that a linear functional f on X is Y-positive when $f(x) \ge 0$ for $x \in Y$. Let $\mathcal{M}$ be a subspace of X such that for each $x \in X$ there exists $y \in \mathcal{M}$ with $x \preceq y$. Prove that if f is a $(Y \cap \mathcal{M})$-positive linear functional on $\mathcal{M}$, then there is a Y-positive linear functional F on X such that the restriction of F on $\mathcal{M}$ equals f.

Chapter 8

Banach Spaces via Operators and Functionals

Banach spaces, named after Stefan Banach who investigated them, are one of the central objects of study in linear functional analysis. Banach spaces are typically infinite-dimensional spaces containing functions. In this chapter we are concerned with the definition of a Banach space followed by some examples, some of the basic algebraic and topological properties of Banach spaces, continuous linear functionals, as well as bounded and compact linear operators in Banach spaces.

8.1 Definition and Beginning Examples

As previously indicated, $\mathbf{F}$ always means the real field $\mathbf{R}$ or the complex field $\mathbf{C}$.

Definition 8.1. A normed linear space over $\mathbf{F}$ which is complete in the metric generated by the norm is called a Banach space over $\mathbf{F}$.

Clearly, if a linear space is a Banach space under one norm, then it is also a Banach space under any equivalent norm, and hence for each $n \in \mathbf{N}$, $\mathbf{R}^n$ is complete under any norm. One more beginning example of Banach spaces is listed below.

Example 8.2.

(i) For a compact metric space (X, d_X), suppose $C(X, \mathbf{F})$ is equipped with the sup-norm $\|f\|_\infty = \sup_{x\in X} |f(x)|$ for $f \in C(X, \mathbf{F})$. Then it is a Banach space over $\mathbf{F}$, because of Theorem 6.23 (i).

(ii) For each $p \in [1, \infty]$, let $\ell_p(\mathbf{N}, \mathbf{F})$ be the space of all $\mathbf{F}$-valued sequences $(x_j)_{j=1}^\infty$ satisfying

$$\|(x_j)_{j=1}^\infty\|_p = \begin{cases} \left(\sum_{j=1}^\infty |x_j|^p\right)^{\frac{1}{p}}, & p \in [1, \infty), \\ \sup_{j\in\mathbf{N}} |x_j|, & p = \infty. \end{cases}$$

Then $\left(\ell_p(\mathbf{N}, \mathbf{F}), \|\cdot\|_p\right)$ is a Banach space over $\mathbf{F}$. To see this, assume $(x_j)_{j=1}^\infty$ is a Cauchy sequence in $\ell_p(\mathbf{N}, \mathbf{F})$, and write $x_j = (x_j^{(1)}, x_j^{(2)}, \ldots)$. Because of $\|\cdot\|_p \geq \|\cdot\|_\infty$, for any $\epsilon > 0$ we may find $N \in \mathbf{N}$ such that $m, n > N \Rightarrow \|x_n - x_m\|_p < \epsilon$

which in turn implies that $\|x_n - x_m\|_\infty < \epsilon$, so for each k, $|x_n^{(k)} - x_m^{(k)}| < \epsilon$. In other words, if $(x_j)_{j=1}^\infty$ is a Cauchy sequence in $\ell_p(\mathbf{N}, \mathbf{F})$ then $(x_j^{(k)})_{j=1}^\infty$ is a Cauchy sequence in $\mathbf{F}$. Since $\mathbf{F}$ is complete, for each k we have that $|x_j^{(k)} - y^{(k)}| \to 0$ as $j \to \infty$. Note that this does not imply by itself $x_j \to y = (y^{(1)}, y^{(2)}, \ldots)$. However, if we know that $(x_j)_{j=1}^\infty$ is a Cauchy sequence, then it does. In fact, we prove this for $p < \infty$ but the $p = \infty$ case is similar. Fix $\epsilon > 0$, and use the Cauchy criterion to find an $N \in \mathbf{N}$ such that

$$n, m > N \Rightarrow \sum_{k=1}^{\infty} |x_n^{(k)} - x_m^{(k)}|^p < \epsilon.$$

Now fix $n \in \mathbf{N}$ and let $m \to \infty$ to see $\sum_{k=1}^\infty |x_n^{(k)} - y^{(k)}|^p \leq \epsilon$. This inequality means $\|x_n - y\|_p \leq \epsilon^{\frac{1}{p}}$ and $y = (y^{(1)}, y^{(2)}, \ldots) \in \ell_p(\mathbf{N}, \mathbf{F})$.

To give another important class of Banach spaces, we need one more definition and theorem.

Definition 8.3. For a sequence $(x_j)_{j=1}^\infty$ in a normed linear space $(X, \|\cdot\|_X)$ over $\mathbf{F}$, we say that a series $\sum_{j=1}^\infty x_j$ is absolutely convergent provided $\sum_{j=1}^\infty \|x_j\|_X < \infty$. Moreover, a series $\sum_{j=1}^\infty x_j$ is said to converge to x in X provided

$$\lim_{n\to\infty} \Big\| \sum_{j=1}^{n} x_j - x \Big\|_X = 0.$$

Theorem 8.4. *Let $(X, \|\cdot\|_X)$ be a normed linear space over $\mathbf{F}$. Then it is a Banach space if and only if the absolute convergence of $\sum_{j=1}^\infty x_j$ implies its convergence.*

Proof. The argument is motivated by that for Theorem 4.40 (ii). On the one hand, suppose $(X, \|\cdot\|_X)$ is a Banach space and s_k stands for the partial sum $\sum_{j=1}^k x_j$. Since $\sum_{j=1}^\infty x_j$ is absolutely convergent, we conclude that

$$\|s_m - s_k\|_X \leq \sum_{j=k+1}^{m} \|x_j\|_X \to 0 \quad \text{as} \quad m > k \to \infty.$$

It follows that $(s_m)_{m=1}^\infty$ is a Cauchy sequence, and consequently this sequence converges since X is complete. Thus, $\sum_{j=1}^\infty x_j$ converges.

On the other hand, assume $(x_j)_{j=1}^\infty$ is a Cauchy sequence in $(X, \|\cdot\|_X)$. Then for each $k \in \mathbf{N}$ there is an $N_k \in \mathbf{N}$ such that

$$j, l \geq N_k \Rightarrow \|x_j - x_l\|_X < 2^{-k}.$$

Without loss of generality, we may assume $N_{k+1} \geq N_k$. This yields that $(x_{N_k})_{k=1}^\infty$ is a subsequence of $(x_k)_{k=1}^\infty$. Set $y_1 = x_{N_1}$ and $y_k = x_{N_k} - x_{N_{k-1}}$ when $k \geq 2$. Note that

$$\sum_{k=1}^{l} \|y_k\|_X < \|y_1\|_X + \sum_{k=2}^{l} 2^{1-k} \leq \|y_1\|_X + 1.$$

So the sequence $\left(\sum_{k=1}^{l}\|y_k\|_X\right)_{l=1}^{\infty}$ is increasing and bounded, and hence is convergent. By hypothesis, $\sum_{k=1}^{\infty} y_k$ is convergent. Since $\sum_{k=1}^{n} y_k = x_{N_n}$, it follows that $(x_{N_n})_{n=1}^{\infty}$ is convergent in $(X, \|\cdot\|_X)$. This, together with the fact that $(x_k)_{k=1}^{\infty}$ is a Cauchy sequence, infers that $(x_k)_{k=1}^{\infty}$ is convergent. Therefore, $(X, \|\cdot\|_X)$ is a Banach space. □

Remark 8.5. It is worthwhile to point out that Theorem 8.4 is clearly not true for general normed linear spaces. For example, for $j \in \mathbf{N}$ let

$$h_j(x) = \begin{cases} 0\,, & x \in [-1, -1/j], \\ 1 + jx\,, & x \in [-1/j, 0], \\ 1\,, & x \in [0, 1], \end{cases}$$

and $f_j = h_{j+1} - h_j$. Then $f_j \in C([-1,1], \mathbf{R})$ and

$$\sum_{j=1}^{\infty} \|f_j\|_{p,m_{id},[-1,1]} = \sum_{j=1}^{\infty} \frac{1}{j+1}\Big(\frac{1}{j(p+1)}\Big)^{\frac{1}{p}} < \infty \quad \text{for} \quad p \in [1, \infty),$$

but $\sum_{j=1}^{\infty} f_j = \lim_{n\to\infty}(h_{n+1} - h_1)$ with respect to $\|\cdot\|_{p,m_{id},[-1,1]}$ is outside $C([-1,1],\mathbf{R})$ since $\lim_{n\to\infty}\|h_{n+1} - 1_{[0,1]}\|_{p,m_{id},[-1,1]} = 0$. This example indicates that $C([-1,1],\mathbf{R})$ is not complete under $\|\cdot\|_{p,m_{id},[-1,1]}$. Actually, its completion is $\mathcal{LRS}^p_{id}([-1,1],\mathbf{R})$ – this fact can be verified by Theorem 4.39 (iii) since $C_0(\mathbf{R})$ is a subset of $C([-1,1],\mathbf{R})$.

Example 8.6. Let $\mathcal{LRS}^p_g(E,\mathbf{F})$ be as in Example 7.14. Then each $\mathcal{LRS}^p_g(E,\mathbf{F})$ is a Banach space whenever $p \in [1,\infty]$. Actually, in the case $p \in [1,\infty)$, the result can be demonstrated via Theorems 8.4 and 4.39 (ii). As with $p = \infty$, suppose $(f_j)_{j=1}^{\infty}$ is a Cauchy sequence in $\mathcal{LRS}^\infty_g(E,\mathbf{F})$. Clearly, we may assume $|f_j(x)| \le \|f_j\|_{\infty,m_g,E}$ for all $x \in E$ by replacing f_j with an equivalent function for which this is true. Then $\big(f_j(x)\big)_{j=1}^{\infty}$ is a Cauchy sequence in $\mathbf{F}$ for each $x \in E$ and we can thus get an $\mathbf{F}$-valued function f on E such that $\lim_{j\to\infty} f_j(x) = f(x)$ for each $x \in E$. This in turns yields $\lim_{j\to\infty}\|f - f_j\|_{\infty,m_g,E} = 0$.

Interestingly, Example 8.6 leads to a criterion for a quotient space to be complete.

Theorem 8.7. *Let $(X, \|\cdot\|_X)$ be a Banach space over $\mathbf{F}$. If Y is a linear subspace of X, then X/Y is a Banach space under the norm $\|x+Y\|_{X/Y} = \inf_{z\in x+Y}\|z\|_X$ when and only when Y is closed.*

Proof. If Y is not closed, then Theorem 7.13 tells us that $\|x+Y\|_{X/Y}$ is not a norm. So, it remains to prove that if Y is closed then X/Y is complete. In doing so, suppose $\sum_{k=1}^{\infty}(x_k + Y)$ is an absolutely convergent series in X/Y. For each $k \in \mathbf{N}$ choose $z_k \in x_k + Y$ such that

$$\|z_k\|_X \le \|x_k + Y\|_{X/Y} + 2^{-k}.$$

Since X is a Banach space, it follows that $\sum_{k=1}^{\infty} z_k$ is absolutely convergent and thus convergent to some $x \in X$ thanks to Theorem 8.4. Note that

$$\Big\|x + Y - \sum_{k=1}^{n}(x_k + Y)\Big\|_{X/Y} \le \Big\|x - \sum_{k=1}^{n} z_k\Big\|_X \to 0 \;\text{ as }\; n \to \infty.$$

So we obtain that $\sum_{k=1}^{\infty}(x_k + Y)$ converges to $x + Y \in X/Y$. Namely, X/Y is complete due to Theorem 8.4. □

In many situations it makes sense to multiply elements of a Banach space together.

Definition 8.8. Let $(X, \|\cdot\|_X)$ be a Banach space over $\mathbf{F}$. If there is a multiplication $(x, y) \to xy$ from $X \times X$ to X such that for any $x, y, z \in X$ and $\alpha \in \mathbf{F}$:

(i) $x(yz) = (xy)z$;

(ii) $x(y + z) = xy + xz$;

(iii) $(x + y)z = xz + yz$;

(iv) $\alpha(xy) = (\alpha x)y = x(\alpha y)$;

(v) $\|xy\|_X \le \|x\|_X \|y\|_X$,
then X is called a Banach algebra.

Example 8.9.
(i) $(C[0, 1], \|\cdot\|_\infty)$ is a Banach algebra with $(fg)(x) = f(x)g(x)$.

(ii) $\mathcal{LRS}^1_{id}(\mathbf{R}, \mathbf{F})$ is a Banach algebra under the convolution

$$f_1 * f_2(x) = \int_{\mathbf{R}} f_1(x - t) f_2(t) dm_{id}(t).$$

Here, we should note

$$f \in \mathcal{LRS}^1_{id}(\mathbf{R}, \mathbf{F}) \Rightarrow \int_{\mathbf{R}} f dm_{id} = \int_{\mathbf{R}} \Re f dm_{id} + i \int_{\mathbf{R}} \Im f dm_{id}.$$

(iii) If $X = \mathbf{R}^n$, $n \in \mathbf{N}$, then by choosing a basis for $\mathbf{R}^n$ we may identify $B(\mathbf{R}^n)$ with the space of $n \times n$ real matrices which is a Banach algebra under the usual matric multiplication.

(iv) If $(X, \|\cdot\|_X)$ is a Banach space over $\mathbf{F}$, then $(B(X), \|\cdot\|)$ is a Banach algebra under the composition $ST = S \circ T$.

Beyond Example 8.9 (iv), we can derive more information on all bounded linear operators on a given Banach space.

Theorem 8.10. *Let* $(X, \|\cdot\|_X)$ *be a Banach space over* $\mathbf{F}$.

(i) *If* $T \in B(X)$ *satisfies* $\|T\| < 1$ *and* I *is the identity element in* $B(X)$, *then* $I - T \in B(X)$ *is invertible and*

$$(I - T)^{-1} = \lim_{n \to \infty} (I + T + T^2 + \cdots + T^n) \quad in \quad \big(B(X), \|\cdot\|\big),$$

where T^k *is the* k*-th composition* $\underbrace{T \circ \cdots \circ T}_{k}$ *for* $k \in \mathbf{N}$.

(ii) *If* $\mathcal{I}$ *stands for the class of all invertible operators in* $B(X)$, *then* $\mathcal{I}$ *is an open set in* $B(X)$.

Proof. (i) Fix $x \in X$. Since $m, n \in \mathbf{N}$ and $m > n$ imply

$$\begin{aligned}
&\|(I + T + T^2 + \cdots + T^m)(x) - (I + T + T^2 + \cdots + T^n)(x)\|_X \\
&= \|T^{n+1}(x) + \cdots + T^m(x)\|_X \\
&\le \|T^{n+1}(x)\|_X + \cdots + \|T^m(x)\|_X \\
&\le \big(\|T^{n+1}\| + \cdots + \|T^m\|\big)\|x\|_X \\
&\le \Big(\sum_{j=n+1}^{\infty} \|T\|^j\Big)\|x\|_X \\
&= \Big(\frac{\|T\|^{n+1}}{1 - \|T\|}\Big)\|x\|_X \\
&\to 0 \quad \text{as} \quad n \to \infty,
\end{aligned}$$

we conclude that $\big((I + T + T^2 + \cdots + T^n)(x)\big)_{n=1}^{\infty}$ is a Cauchy sequence in X. Note that $(X, \|\cdot\|_X)$ is a Banach space. So the sequence converges to a limit $y \in X$. Let $y = A(x)$. It is not hard to show that $A : X \to X$ is a linear operator on X. Furthermore, letting $m \to \infty$, we have

$$\|A(x) - (I + T + T^2 + \cdots + T^n)(x)\|_X \le \Big(\frac{\|T\|^{n+1}}{1 - \|T\|}\Big)\|x\|_X,$$

so that $A - (I + T + T^2 + \cdots + T^n) \in B(X)$, and thus $A \in B(X)$. Because

$$\|A - (I + T + T^2 + \cdots + T^n)\| \le \frac{\|T\|^{n+1}}{1 - \|T\|} \to 0 \quad \text{as} \quad n \to \infty,$$

we derive that $I + T + T^2 + \cdots + T^n \to A$ as $n \to \infty$. It remains to verify $A = (I - T)^{-1}$. For any $x \in X$ we have

$$\begin{aligned}
\big((I - T)A\big)(x) &= \big((I - T)\lim_{n\to\infty}(I + T + T^2 + \cdots + T^n)\big)(x) \\
&= (I - T)\Big(\lim_{n\to\infty}\big(I(x) + T(x) + T^2(x) + \cdots + T^n(x)\big)\Big) \\
&= \lim_{n\to\infty}\big(x - T^{n+1}(x)\big).
\end{aligned}$$

But

$$\|T^{n+1}(x)\|_X \le \|T\|^{n+1}\|x\|_X \to 0 \quad \text{as} \quad n \to \infty,$$

so that $T^{n+1}(x) \to 0$ as $n \to \infty$, and consequently $\big((I - T)A(x)\big) = x$. Similarly, we have $\big(A(I - T)\big)(x) = x$, whence getting $A = (I - T)^{-1}$.

(ii) Note that $\|T^{-1}\| \ne 0$ for $T \in \mathcal{I}$. So, to prove that the open ball

$$\{S \in B(X) : \|T - S\| < \|T^{-1}\|^{-1}\}$$

is a subset of $\mathcal{I}$, we just show that every element S of this ball is invertible. Using

$$\|(T - S)T^{-1}\| \le \|T - S\|\|T^{-1}\| < 1,$$

we obtain that $ST^{-1} = I - (T - S)T^{-1}$ is invertible and thus $S = (ST^{-1})T$ is invertible. □

Remark 8.11. When $(X, \|\cdot\|_X)$ is a Banach space over $\mathbf{F}$ and T belongs to $B(X)$, we can define an operator

$$e^T = I + T + \frac{T^2}{2!} + \frac{T^3}{3!} + \cdots,$$

which makes sense since

$$\|e^T\| \le 1 + \|T\| + \frac{\|T\|^2}{2!} + \frac{\|T\|^3}{3!} + \cdots = \exp \|T\|.$$

With this notion, we have that if $x(t) = \big(x_1(t), x_2(t), \ldots, x_n(t)\big) \in \mathbf{R}^n$ and A is an $n \times n$ matrix, then the system

$$\frac{dx}{dt} = \Big(\frac{dx_1(t)}{dt}, \frac{dx_2(t)}{dt}, \ldots, \frac{dx_n(t)}{dt}\Big) = x(t)A, \quad x(0) = a \in \mathbf{R}^n$$

has a solution $x(t) = ae^{tA}$.

8.2 Uniform Boundedness, Open Mapping and Closed Graph

In this section, we proceed to discuss three fundamental results of functional analysis – the uniform boundedness principle (sometimes known as the Banach-Steinhaus theorem due to Stefan Banach and Hugo Dyonizy Steinhaus), open mapping theorem and closed graph theorem.

Below is the so-called uniform boundedness principle.

Theorem 8.12. *Let $(X, \|\cdot\|_X)$ be a Banach space and $(Y, \|\cdot\|_Y)$ a normed linear space over $\mathbf{F}$. Suppose $\{T_\alpha\}_{\alpha\in I}$ is a family of bounded linear operators $T_\alpha : X \to Y$ indexed by the nonempty set I. If $\sup_{\alpha\in I} \|T_\alpha(x)\|_Y < \infty$ for each $x \in X$, then $\sup_{\alpha\in I} \|T_\alpha\| < \infty$.*

Proof. For each $j \in \mathbf{N}$ let

$$X_j = \{x \in X : \sup_{\alpha\in I} \|T_\alpha(x)\|_Y \le j\} = \cap_{\alpha\in I}\{x \in X : \ \|T_\alpha(x)\|_Y \le j\}.$$

Then each X_j is a closed subset of X and $X = \cup_{j=1}^{\infty} X_j$. Since X is complete, X is of second category. By the Baire category theorem (i.e., Theorem 5.47) we see that $X_{j_0}^\circ \neq \emptyset$ for some $j_0 \in \mathbf{N}$ and consequently, there is an $x_0 \in X$ and an $r \in (0, \infty)$ such that $B_r(x_0)$ (the open ball in X with center x_0 and radius r) is a subset of X_{j_0}. This means that for $x \in B_r(x_0)$ we have $\sup_{\alpha\in I} \|T_\alpha(x)\|_Y \le j_0$. Consequently, for any $x \in B_r(0)$ we obtain $x_0 + x \in B_r(x_0)$ and so for any $\alpha \in I$,

$$\|T_\alpha(x)\|_Y \le \|T_\alpha(x + x_0)\|_Y + \|T_\alpha(-x_0)\|_Y \le 2j_0.$$

Thus, for each $x \in \overline{B}_1(0)$ we get $\|T_\alpha(x)\|_Y \le 4j_0/r$. This yields $\sup_{\alpha\in I} \|T_\alpha\| \le 4j_0/r$, as required. □

The boundedness of a sequence of linear operators is useful in the study of convergence of operator sequences. To see this, we introduce two types of convergence involving operator sequences.

Definition 8.13. Let $(X, \|\cdot\|_X)$ and $(Y, \|\cdot\|_Y)$ be normed linear spaces over $\mathbf{F}$.

(i) A sequence $(T_n)_{n=1}^{\infty}$ in $B(X,Y)$ is said to be uniformly convergent provided there is a $T \in B(X,Y)$ such that $\lim_{n\to\infty} \|T_n - T\| = 0$.

(ii) A sequence $(T_n)_{n=1}^{\infty}$ in $B(X,Y)$ is said to be strongly (or pointwise) convergent on X provided the sequence $\big(T_n(x)\big)_{n=1}^{\infty}$ is convergent in Y for any $x \in X$. Moreover, if there is a $T \in B(X,Y)$ such that $\lim_{n\to\infty} \|T_n(x) - T(x)\|_Y = 0$ for all $x \in X$, then $(T_n)_{n=1}^{\infty}$ is said to be strongly convergent to T.

Example 8.14. Clearly, the uniform convergence implies the strong convergence, but not conversely. Consider $\ell_p(\mathbf{N}, \mathbf{F})$, $p \in [1, \infty)$. For each $n \in \mathbf{N}$ define

$$T_n(x) = (x_n, x_{n+1}, \dots), \quad x = (x_1, x_2, \dots) \in \ell_p.$$

Then T_n is in $B\big(\ell_p(\mathbf{N}, \mathbf{F})\big)$ with $\|T_n\| \le 1$. Note that if $x = (x_1, x_2, \dots) \in \ell_p(\mathbf{N}, \mathbf{F})$ then

$$\lim_{n\to\infty} \|T_n(x)\|_p = \lim_{n\to\infty} \Big(\sum_{j=n}^{\infty} |x_j|^p\Big)^{\frac{1}{p}} = 0.$$

So $(T_n)_{n=1}^{\infty}$ is strongly convergent to 0. Meanwhile, for $n \in \mathbf{N}$ let $e_n = (\underbrace{0, \dots, 0}_{n-1}, 1, 0, \dots)$. Then $\|e_n\|_p = 1$ and $T_n(e_n) = (1, 0, 0, \dots)$ and hence $\|T_n\| \ge \|T_n(e_n)\|_p = 1$. This shows that $(T_n)_{n=1}^{\infty}$ is not uniformly convergent to 0.

Here is a special consequence of the uniform boundedness principle.

Theorem 8.15. *Let $(X, \|\cdot\|_X)$ be a Banach space over $\mathbf{F}$.*

(i) *Suppose $(Y, \|\cdot\|_Y)$ is a normed linear space over $\mathbf{F}$. If a sequence $(T_n)_{n=1}^{\infty}$ in $B(X,Y)$ is strongly convergent, then there exists a $T \in B(X,Y)$ such that $(T_n)_{n=1}^{\infty}$ is strongly convergent to T.*

(ii) *Suppose $(Y, \|\cdot\|_Y)$ is a Banach space over $\mathbf{F}$. Then a sequence $(T_n)_{n=1}^{\infty}$ in $B(X,Y)$ is strongly convergent if and only if $\sup_{n\in\mathbf{N}} \|T_n\| < \infty$ and $\big(T_n(x)\big)_{n=1}^{\infty}$ is convergent in Y for any x belonging to a dense subset D of X.*

Proof. (i) Let $(T_n)_{n=1}^{\infty}$ in $B(X,Y)$ be strongly convergent. Then for each $x \in X$ the sequence $\big(T_n(x)\big)_{n=1}^{\infty}$ is convergent in Y and hence defines a linear operator T on X by setting $T(x) = \lim_{n\to\infty} T_n(x)$. The key is to show that $T \in B(X,Y)$. Note that $\big(T_n(x)\big)_{n=1}^{\infty}$ is bounded in Y. So, from the uniform boundedness principle it turns out that there is a constant $C > 0$ such that $\sup_{n\in\mathbf{N}} \|T_n\| \le C$. Hence $\|T_n(x)\|_Y \le C\|x\|_X$ for all $x \in X$. This implies $\|T(x)\|_Y \le C\|x\|_X$ for all $x \in X$, showing that T is bounded. The definition of T means that $(T_n)_{n=1}^{\infty}$ converges strongly to T.

(ii) The necessity follows from the uniform boundedness principle. As for the sufficiency, we assume the statement after the if and only if. Given $\epsilon > 0$. Then for any $x \in X$ there is an element $z \in D$ such that $\|x - z\|_X < \epsilon$, and there is an $N \in \mathbf{N}$ such that $m > n > N$ implies $\|T_m(z) - T_n(z)\|_Y < \epsilon$. Consequently,

$$\begin{aligned}
&\|T_m(x) - T_n(x)\|_Y \\
&\leq \|T_m(x) - T_m(z)\|_Y + \|T_m(z) - T_n(z)\|_Y + \|T_n(z) - T_n(x)\|_Y \\
&\leq \|T_m\|\|x - z\|_X + \epsilon + \|T_n\|\|x - z\|_X \\
&\leq (1 + 2\sup_{n\in\mathbf{N}} \|T_n\|)\epsilon.
\end{aligned}$$

That is to say, $\left(T_n(x)\right)_{n=1}^{\infty}$ is a Cauchy sequence in Y and thus convergent thanks to the completeness of $(Y, \|\cdot\|_Y)$. □

Recall that a continuous map between normed linear spaces has the property that the pre-image of any open set is open, but in general the image of an open set is not open. Nevertheless, for continuous linear operators between Banach spaces there is the following open mapping theorem.

Theorem 8.16. *Let $(X, \|\cdot\|_X)$ and $(Y, \|\cdot\|_Y)$ be Banach spaces over $\mathbf{F}$. If T is a continuous linear operator from X onto Y, then $T(O)$ is open in Y whenever O is open in X.*

Proof. We split the argument into three steps. In what follows, we reuse $B_r^X(x)$ and $B_r^Y(y)$ to denote the balls of radius $r > 0$ centered at $x \in X$ and $y \in Y$, respectively. In particular, we write B_r^X and B_r^Y for $B_r^X(0)$ and $B_r^Y(0)$, respectively.

Step 1. We prove that for any $\epsilon > 0$ there is a $\delta > 0$ such that

$$B_\delta^Y \subseteq T(B_{2\epsilon}^X).$$

To see this, note that

$$X = \cup_{n=1}^{\infty} nB_\epsilon^X = \cup_{n=1}^{\infty}\{nx : x \in B_\epsilon^X\},$$

and $T \in B(X, Y)$ is surjective. So we have

$$Y = T(X) = \cup_{n=1}^{\infty} nT(B_\epsilon^X) = \cup_{n=1}^{\infty}\{ny : y \in T(B_\epsilon^X)\}.$$

Since $(Y, \|\cdot\|_Y)$ is a Banach space, we conclude that from the Baire category theorem (i.e., Theorem 5.47) that some $nT(B_\epsilon^X)$ is not nowhere dense in Y, and so that

$$B_r^Y(z) = \{y \in Y : \|y - z\|_Y < r\} \subseteq \overline{nT(B_\epsilon^X)} = \{ny : y \in T(\overline{B_\epsilon^X})\}$$

for some $z \in Y$ and some $r > 0$. Thus $T(\overline{B_\epsilon^X})$ must contain the ball $B_\delta^Y(y_0)$ where $y_0 = z/n$ and $\delta = r/n$. It follows that the set

$$V = \{y_1 - y_2 : \ y_1, y_2 \in B_\delta^Y(y_0)\}$$

is contained in $T(\overline{U})$, where

$$U = \{x_1 - x_2 : \ x_1, x_2 \in B_\epsilon^X\} \subseteq B_{2\epsilon}^X.$$

Thus, $T(\overline{B^X_{2\epsilon}}) \supseteq V$. Any point $y \in B^Y_\delta$ can be written as $y = (y + y_0) - y_0$, so $B^Y_\delta \subseteq V$, as desired.

Step 2. We further prove that for any $\epsilon > 0$ there is a $\delta > 0$ such that

$$B^Y_\delta \subseteq T(B^X_{2\epsilon}).$$

To do so, choose $(\epsilon_n)_{n=1}^\infty$ with $\epsilon_n > 0$ and $\sum_{n=1}^\infty \epsilon_n < \epsilon$. By *Step 1* there is a sequence of positive numbers $(\delta_n)_{n=1}^\infty$ such that $B^Y_{\delta_n} \subseteq T(\overline{B^X_{2\epsilon_n}})$. Without loss of generality, we may assume $\lim_{n\to\infty} \delta_n = 0$.

Let $y \in B^Y_{\delta_1}$. Then $y \in T(\overline{B^X_{2\epsilon_1}})$ and hence there is a point $x_1 \in B^X_{2\epsilon_1}$ with $\|y - T(x_1)\|_Y < \delta_2$. Since $y - T(x_1) \in B^Y_{\delta_2}$, we conclude that there is a point $x_2 \in B^X_{2\epsilon_2}$ such that $\|y - T(x_1) - T(x_2)\|_Y < \delta_3$. Continuing this process, we obtain a sequence $(x_n)_{n=1}^\infty$ such that $x_n \in B^X_{2\epsilon_n}$ and

$$\left\| y - T\Big(\sum_{k=1}^n x_k\Big)\right\|_Y < \delta_{n+1}.$$

Since $\|x_n\|_X < 2\epsilon_n$, we conclude that $\sum_{n=1}^\infty x_n$ is absolutely convergent and hence by Theorem 8.4 that $x = \sum_{n=1}^\infty x_n$ makes sense in $(X, \|\cdot\|_X)$. This implies

$$\|x\|_X \le \sum_{n=1}^\infty \|x_n\|_X < 2\sum_{n=1}^\infty \epsilon_n < 2\epsilon.$$

Since the map T is continuous and $\delta_n \to 0$, we get $y = T(x)$. In other words, for any $y \in B^Y_\delta$ where $\delta = \delta_1$, we have found a point $x \in B^X_{2\epsilon}$ such that $T(x) = y$, whence implying the desired inclusion.

Step 3. We prove that if O is open in X then for any point $x \in O$, there exists a $\delta > 0$ such that

$$B^Y_\delta\big(T(x)\big) \subseteq T(O).$$

In fact, if $x \in O$, then there exists an $\epsilon > 0$ such that $B^X_{2\epsilon}(x) \subseteq O$. By *Step 2*, we have $B^Y_\delta \subseteq T(B^X_{2\epsilon})$ for some $\delta > 0$. Hence

$$B^Y_\delta\big(T(x)\big) = T(x) + B^Y_\delta \subseteq T(x) + T(B^X_{2\epsilon}) = T(x + B^X_{2\epsilon}) = T\big(B^X_{2\epsilon}(x)\big) \subseteq T(O).$$

Of course, this step completes the proof of the theorem. □

As an application of the open mapping theorem we establish a general property of inverse maps.

Theorem 8.17. *Let X and Y be Banach spaces over $\mathbf{F}$. If $T \in B(X, Y)$ is bijective, then its inverse operator T^{-1} is a bounded linear map.*

Proof. It suffices to prove the continuity of T^{-1}. Since $T = (T^{-1})^{-1}$ maps the Banach space X onto the Banach space Y, we conclude from Theorem 8.16 that T maps open sets in X to open sets in Y. This amounts to saying that T^{-1} is continuous. □

Corollary 8.18. *Let $\|\cdot\|_{(1)}$ and $\|\cdot\|_{(2)}$ be two norms defined on a Banach space X over $\mathbf{F}$. If there is a constant $C_1 > 0$ such that $\|x\|_{(1)} \le C_1\|x\|_{(2)}$ for all $x \in X$, then there exists another constant $C_2 > 0$ such that $\|x\|_{(2)} \le C_2\|x\|_{(1)}$ for all $x \in X$. Consequently, both norms are equivalent.*

Proof. Consider the identity operator

$$I:\ (X, \|\cdot\|_{(2)}) \to (X, \|\cdot\|_{(1)}) \quad \text{where} \quad I(x) = x \quad \text{for all} \quad x \in X.$$

Clearly, I is bounded. By Theorem 8.17 we see that I^{-1} is also bounded, whence getting the norm inequality in the other direction. □

Definition 8.19. Given two normed linear spaces X and Y over $\mathbf{F}$, let $T : X \to Y$ be a linear operator. Then the graph of T is defined as

$$G(T) = \{(x, y) \in X \times Y : \quad y = T(x)\}.$$

Moreover, $G(T)$ is said to be closed when $G(T)$ is a closed subset of $X \times Y$.

The following result is called the closed graph theorem.

Theorem 8.20. *Let $(X, \|\cdot\|_X)$ and $(Y, \|\cdot\|_Y)$ be Banach spaces over $\mathbf{F}$. Then a linear operator $T : X \to Y$ is bounded if and only if $G(T)$ is closed.*

Proof. We initially observe that $X \times Y$ is a Banach space under the norm $\|(x, y)\| = \|x\|_X + \|y\|_Y$. Addition and scalar multiplication are defined in the expected manner:

$$(x_1, y_1) + (x_2, y_2) = (x_1 + x_2, y_1 + y_2) \quad \text{and} \quad \alpha(x, y) = (\alpha x, \alpha y).$$

The completeness of $(X \times Y, \|\cdot\|)$ follows readily from the completeness of $(X, \|\cdot\|_X)$ and $(Y, \|\cdot\|_Y)$.

On the one hand, suppose $T : X \to Y$ is bounded. To prove that $G(T)$ is closed, we assume $\lim_{n\to\infty} \|x_n - x\|_X = 0$ and $\lim_{n\to\infty} \|T(x_n) - y\|_Y = 0$. The boundedness of T implies $\lim_{n\to\infty} \|T(x_n) - T(x)\|_Y = 0$. Note that Y is Banach space. So $T(x) = y$. This means $(x, y) \in G(T)$. Thus $G(T)$ is closed.

On the other hand, suppose $G(T)$ is closed. To verify $T \in B(X, Y)$, we consider the projection map P from $G(T)$ onto X via: $P\big(x, T(x)\big) = x$. Clearly, P is linear, bijective and bounded. From Theorem 8.17 it turns out that P^{-1} is a bounded linear map from X onto $G(T)$, so there is a constant $C > 0$ such that

$$\|x\|_X + \|T(x)\|_Y = \big\|\big(x, T(x)\big)\big\| = \|P^{-1}(x)\| \le C\|x\|_X \quad \text{for all} \quad x \in X.$$

Consequently, T is bounded. □

8.3 Dual Banach Spaces by Examples

When dealing with a normed linear space X over the base field $\mathbf{F}$, one typically is only interested in the continuous linear functionals from the space into $\mathbf{F}$. According to Theorem 7.29 and Definition 7.31, these form a normed linear space. In this section, we will see that this new normed linear space is indeed a Banach space, but also completely describe the dual spaces of three typical Banach spaces.

We begin with a more general result.

Theorem 8.21. *Let $(X, \|\cdot\|_X)$ be a normed linear space over* $\mathbf{F}$. *If $(Y, \|\cdot\|_Y)$ is a Banach space over* $\mathbf{F}$, *then $B(X,Y)$ is a Banach space over* $\mathbf{F}$.

Proof. If $(T_j)_{j=1}^\infty$ is a Cauchy sequence in $B(X,Y)$, then it is bounded and so there is a constant $C > 0$ such that $\|T_j(x)\|_Y \le C\|x\|_X$ for all $x \in X$ and $j \in \mathbf{N}$. Since

$$\|T_j(x) - T_k(x)\|_Y \le \|T_j - T_k\|\|x\|_X \to 0 \quad \text{as} \quad j \ge k \to \infty,$$

$\big(T_j(x)\big)_{j=1}^\infty$ is a Cauchy sequence in Y. Moreover, since Y is a Banach space, $\big(T_j(x)\big)_{j=1}^\infty$ converges to $y \in Y$. Accordingly, $y = \lim_{j\to\infty} T_j(x) = T(x)$. Clearly, T is linear, and $\|T(x)\|_Y \le C\|x\|_X$ for all $x \in X$. This means $T \in B(X,Y)$.

Note that we have not yet proved that $(T_j)_{j=1}^\infty$ converges to T in norm. But, since $(T_j)_{j=1}^\infty$ is a Cauchy sequence, for every $\epsilon > 0$ there is an $N \in \mathbf{N}$ such that

$$j > k > N \Rightarrow \|T_j - T_k\| < \epsilon.$$

Consequently,

$$j > k > N \Rightarrow \|T_j(x) - T_k(x)\|_Y \le \epsilon\|x\|_X \quad \text{for all} \quad x \in X.$$

If $j \to \infty$, then

$$k > N \Rightarrow \|T(x) - T_k(x)\|_Y \le \epsilon\|x\|_X.$$

That is to say, $\|T_k - T\| \le \epsilon$ as $k > N$. Thus, $\|T_k - T\| \to 0$ as $k \to \infty$. □

Theorem 8.21 especially says that the dual space $X^* = B(X, \mathbf{F})$ of the normed linear space X over a given field $\mathbf{F}$ is always a Banach space no matter whether X is complete or not. To see this picture clearly, we will identify the dual spaces of three Banach spaces. Thanks to their importance, we will state them as three independent theorems.

The first one is about the sequence spaces.

Theorem 8.22. *Let $p \in [1,\infty)$. Then $\ell_p(\mathbf{N},\mathbf{F})^* = \ell_{\frac{p}{p-1}}(\mathbf{N},\mathbf{F})$ in the sense that $L \in \ell_p(\mathbf{N},\mathbf{F})^*$ if and only if there is a unique $y = (y_k)_{k=1}^\infty \in \ell_{\frac{p}{p-1}}(\mathbf{N},\mathbf{F})$ such that*

$$L(x) = \sum_{k=1}^\infty x_k\overline{y_k} \quad \textit{for all} \quad x = (x_k)_{k=1}^\infty \in \ell_p(\mathbf{N},\mathbf{F}).$$

Proof. Since

$$\sum_{k=1}^\infty |x_k y_k| \le \|x\|_p \|y\|_{\frac{p}{p-1}},$$

we have that the above-defined functional L is an element in $\ell_p(\mathbf{N},\mathbf{F})^*$. Conversely, assume $L \in \ell_p(\mathbf{N},\mathbf{F})^*$. To get the representation of L, we consider two cases.

Case 1: $p \in (1,\infty)$. Suppose $x = (x_k)_{k=1}^\infty \in \ell_p(\mathbf{N},\mathbf{F})$. For each $j \in \mathbf{N}$ let e_j be the vector in $\ell_p(\mathbf{N},\mathbf{F})$ having the jth entry equal to 1 and all other entries equal to 0. Set $z_n = \sum_{j=1}^n x_j e_j$. Then $z_n \in \ell_p(\mathbf{N},\mathbf{F})$ and

$$\lim_{n\to\infty} \|x - z_n\|_p = \lim_{n\to\infty} \Big(\sum_{j=n+1}^\infty |x_j|^p\Big)^{\frac{1}{p}} = 0.$$

Consequently, $L(z_n) = \sum_{j=1}^{n} x_j L(e_j)$ and

$$|L(x) - L(z_n)| = |L(x - z_n)| \le \|L\| \|x - z_n\|_p \to 0 \quad \text{as} \quad n \to \infty.$$

Hence $L(x) = \sum_{j=1}^{\infty} x_j L(e_j)$. Let $y_j = \overline{L(e_j)}$ and $y = (y_j)_{j=1}^{\infty}$. Then

$$L(x) = \sum_{j=1}^{\infty} x_j \overline{y_j},$$

and hence it remains to show $y \in \ell_{\frac{p}{p-1}}(\mathbf{N}, \mathbf{F})$. To this end, we choose

$$x_j = \begin{cases} |y_j|^{\frac{p}{p-1}-2} y_j \,, & y_j \neq 0, \\ 0 \,, & y_j = 0. \end{cases}$$

This choice gives

$$\|z_n\|_p^p = \sum_{j=1}^{n} |x_j|^p = \sum_{j=1}^{n} |y_j|^{\frac{p}{p-1}}.$$

Moreover

$$L(z_n) = \sum_{j=1}^{n} |y_j|^{\frac{p}{p-1}} \quad \text{and} \quad |L(z_n)| \le \|L\| \|z_n\|_p = \|L\| \Big(\sum_{j=1}^{n} |y_j|^{\frac{p}{p-1}} \Big)^{\frac{1}{p}}.$$

Hence

$$\Big(\sum_{j=1}^{n} |y_j|^{\frac{p}{p-1}} \Big)^{\frac{p-1}{p}} \le \|L\|.$$

This yields $\|y\|_{\frac{p}{p-1}} \le \|L\| < \infty$, and so that for any $x \in \ell_p(\mathbf{N}, \mathbf{F})$,

$$|L(x)| = \Big| \sum_{j=1}^{\infty} x_j \overline{y_j} \Big| \le \|x\|_p \|y\|_{\frac{p}{p-1}}.$$

Accordingly, $\|L\| = \|y\|_{\frac{p}{p-1}}$. The uniqueness of y is obvious.

Case 2: $p = 1$. To handle this case, we follow the foregoing argument until the definition of the vector y. To prove $y \in \ell_\infty(\mathbf{N}, \mathbf{F})$, we just observe that for each $j \in \mathbf{N}$,

$$|y_j| = |L(e_j)| \le \|L\| \|e_j\| = \|L\|.$$

Additionally, we obtain that for any $x \in \ell_1(\mathbf{N}, \mathbf{F})$,

$$|L(x)| = \Big| \sum_{j=1}^{\infty} x_j \overline{y_j} \Big| \le \|y\|_\infty \|x\|_1.$$

Thus, $\|L\| = \|y\|_\infty$. Of course, y is uniquely determined. □

Remark 8.23.

(i) From the argument for Theorem 8.22 it follows that $(\mathbf{F}^n)^* = \mathbf{F}^n$, i.e., $L \in (\mathbf{F}^n)^*$ if and only if there exists a unique $y = (y_1, \ldots, y_n) \in \mathbf{F}^n$ such that

$$L(x) = \sum_{k=1}^{n} x_k \overline{y_k} \quad \text{for all} \quad x = (x_1, \ldots, x_n) \in \mathbf{F}^n.$$

(ii) If $p \in (1, \infty)$, then $\ell_p(\mathbf{N}, \mathbf{F})$ is reflexive. However, if $c_0(\mathbf{N}, \mathbf{F})$ stands for the space of all vectors $(x_j)_{j=1}^{\infty}$ in ℓ_∞ with $\lim_{j\to\infty} x_j = 0$, then $c_0(\mathbf{N}, \mathbf{F})^* = \ell_1(\mathbf{N}, \mathbf{F})$ which can be argued in a similar way to proving Theorem 8.22, and hence $c_0(\mathbf{N}, \mathbf{F})$ is not reflexive thanks to $\ell_1(\mathbf{N}, \mathbf{F})^* = \ell_\infty(\mathbf{N}, \mathbf{F})$.

The second one characterizes the Banach dual of the space of all $\mathbf{F}$-valued continuous functions on a given finite closed interval in $\mathbf{R}$.

Theorem 8.24. *For $-\infty < a < b < \infty$ equip $C([a, b], \mathbf{F})$ with the sup-norm*

$$\|f\|_\infty = \sup_{x \in [a,b]} |f(x)|, \quad f \in C([a, b], \mathbf{F}),$$

and let $BV([a, b], \mathbf{F})$ be the class of all $\mathbf{F}$-valued functions having bounded variation on $[a, b]$. If

$$BV_0([a, b], \mathbf{F}) = \Big\{g \in BV([a, b], \mathbf{F}) : \int_a^b f(x) d\overline{g(x)} = 0 \text{ for all } f \in C([a, b], \mathbf{F})\Big\},$$

then

$$C([a, b], \mathbf{F})^* = BV([a, b], \mathbf{F})/BV_0([a, b], \mathbf{F})$$

in the sense that $L \in C([a, b], \mathbf{F})^*$ when and only when there is a unique equivalent class

$$g + BV_0([a, b], \mathbf{F}) \in BV([a, b], \mathbf{F})/BV_0([a, b], \mathbf{F}),$$

such that L can be written as the Riemann–Stieltjes integral

$$L(f) = \int_a^b f(x) d\overline{g(x)} \quad \text{for all } f \in C([a, b], \mathbf{F}).$$

Proof. On the one hand, suppose the statement after the when and only when is true. We may write $g = g_1 + ig_2$ where $g_1, g_2 \in BV[a, b]$, i.e., $V_a^b(g_k) < \infty$ for $k = 1, 2$, in the sense of Definition 3.1, and consequently,

$$\begin{aligned} |L(f)| &= \Big|\int_a^b f(x) d\big(g_1(x) - ig_2(x)\big)\Big| \\ &= \Big|\int_a^b f(x) dg_1(x) - i \int_a^b f(x) dg_2(x)\Big| \\ &\le \|f\|_\infty \big(V_a^b(g_1) + V_a^b(g_2)\big). \end{aligned}$$

Thus, this functional L belongs to $C([a, b], \mathbf{F})^*$.

Conversely, suppose $L \in C([a,b],\mathbf{F})^*$ and $\mathcal{E}$ is a Hahn–Banach extension of L to the space $BD([a,b],\mathbf{F})$ of all functions $f:[a,b]\to\mathbf{F}$ satisfying $\|f\|_\infty = \sup\{|f(x)| : x\in[a,b]\} < \infty$. For $t\in[a,b]$ let $g(t) = \overline{\mathcal{E}(1_{[a,t]})}$, but also for $\{t_0,t_1,\cdots,t_n\}$, a partition of $[a,b]$, and for each $k\in\{1,\cdots,n\}$ let λ_k be the sign of $g(t_k)-g(t_{k-1})$, i.e., the number in $\mathbf{F}$ obeying $|g(t_k)-g(t_{k-1})| = \lambda_k\big(g(t_k)-g(t_{k-1})\big)$. Then

$$\begin{aligned}\sum_{k=1}^n |g(t_k)-g(t_{k-1})| &= \sum_{k=1}^n \lambda_k\big(\mathcal{E}(1_{[a,t_k]}) - \mathcal{E}(1_{[a,t_{k-1}]})\big)\\ &\le \Big|\mathcal{E}\Big(\sum_{k=1}^n \lambda_k(1_{[a,t_k]} - 1_{[a,t_{k-1}]})\Big)\Big|\\ &\le \|\mathcal{E}\|\Big\|\sum_{k=1}^n \lambda_k(1_{[a,t_k]} - 1_{[a,t_{k-1}]})\Big\|_\infty \le \|\mathcal{E}\|.\end{aligned}$$

This means that g has bounded variation on $[a,b]$. Now let $f\in C([a,b],\mathbf{F})$ and $t_k = a+\frac{k}{n}(b-a)$ for $k=0,\ldots,n$, and define $f_n\in BD([a,b],\mathbf{F})$ via

$$f_n(x) = \sum_{k=1}^n f(t_{k-1})\big(1_{[a,t_k]}(x) - 1_{[a,t_{k-1}]}(x)\big), \quad x\in[a,b].$$

Because

$$1 = \sum_{k=1}^n \big(1_{[a,t_k]} - 1_{[a,t_{k-1}]}\big) \quad \text{on} \quad [a,b],$$

it follows from the uniform continuity of f on $[a,b]$ that

$$\|f_n - f\|_\infty \le \max_{1\le k\le n}\ \sup_{x\in[t_{k-1},t_k]} \big|f(x)-f(t_{k-1})\big| \to 0 \quad \text{as} \quad n\to\infty.$$

Note that $\mathcal{E}$ is continuous on $BD([a,b],\mathbf{F})$. So it follows from the definition of Riemann–Stieltjes integration that

$$\begin{aligned}L(f) &= \mathcal{E}(f)\\ &= \lim_{n\to\infty}\mathcal{E}(f_n)\\ &= \lim_{n\to\infty}\sum_{k=1}^n f(t_{k-1})\overline{(g(t_k)-g(t_{k-1})}\\ &= \int_a^b f(x)d\overline{g(x)},\end{aligned}$$

as required. Finally, if $h+BV_0([a,b],\mathbf{F})\in BV([a,b],\mathbf{F})/BV_0([a,b],\mathbf{F})$ also satisfies $L(f) = \int_a^b f(x)d\overline{h(x)}$ for all $f\in C([a,b],\mathbf{F})$, then

$$\int_a^b f(x)d\overline{\big(g(x)-h(x)\big)} = 0 \quad \text{for all} \quad f\in C([a,b],\mathbf{F}),$$

and hence $g-h\in BV_0([a,b],\mathbf{F})$, as desired. □

To reach the third dual Banach space, we need the following Olof Hanner's inequality which is viewed as a sort of improvement of Minkowski's inequality in Remark 4.36.

Theorem 8.25. *Let $g : \mathbf{R} \to \mathbf{R}$ be increasing, $E \subseteq \mathbf{R}$ m_g-measurable, $p \in [1, \infty)$, and $f_1, f_2 \in \mathcal{LRS}_g^p(E, \mathbf{F})$.*

(i) *If $p \in [1, 2]$, then*

$$\begin{aligned}&\|f_1 + f_2\|_{p,m_g,E}^p + \|f_1 - f_2\|_{p,m_g,E}^p \\ &\geq (\|f_1\|_{p,m_g,E} + \|f_2\|_{p,m_g,E})^p + \big|\|f_1\|_{p,m_g,E} - \|f_2\|_{p,m_g,E}\big|^p\end{aligned}$$

and

$$\begin{aligned}&(\|f_1 + f_2\|_{p,m_g,E} + \|f_1 - f_2\|_{p,m_g,E})^p + \big|\|f_1 + f_2\|_{p,m_g,E} - \|f_1 - f_2\|_{p,m_g,E}\big|^p \\ &\leq 2^p(\|f_1\|_{p,m_g,E}^p + \|f_2\|_{p,m_g,E}^p).\end{aligned}$$

(ii) *If $p \in [2, \infty)$, then*

$$\begin{aligned}&\|f_1 + f_2\|_{p,m_g,E}^p + \|f_1 - f_2\|_{p,m_g,E}^p \\ &\leq (\|f_1\|_{p,m_g,E} + \|f_2\|_{p,m_g,E})^p + \big|\|f_1\|_{p,m_g,E} - \|f_2\|_{p,m_g,E}\big|^p\end{aligned}$$

and

$$\begin{aligned}&(\|f_1 + f_2\|_{p,m_g,E} + \|f_1 - f_2\|_{p,m_g,E})^p + \big|\|f_1 + f_2\|_{p,m_g,E} - \|f_1 - f_2\|_{p,m_g,E}\big|^p \\ &\geq 2^p(\|f_1\|_{p,m_g,E}^p + \|f_2\|_{p,m_g,E}^p).\end{aligned}$$

Proof. It suffices to verify the first inequalities in (i) and (ii) since the second ones follow from the first ones via replacing f_1 and f_2 with f_1+f_2 and f_1-f_2. Note that the cases $p = 1$ and $p = 2$ are clear from Remark 4.36 and a direct computation. So, it remains to check the case $p \neq 2$. To this end, we may assume

$$R = \frac{\|f_2\|_{p,m_g,E}}{\|f_1\|_{p,m_g,E}} \leq 1 \quad \text{and} \quad \|f_1\|_{p,m_g,E} = 1.$$

With this assumption and $r \in [0, 1]$, we consider

$$\phi(r) = (1+r)^{p-1} + (1-r)^{p-1} \quad \text{and} \quad \psi(r) = \frac{(1+r)^{p-1} - (1-r)^{p-1}}{r^{p-1}}$$

and compute

$$\frac{d\phi(r)}{dr} + \frac{d\psi(r)}{dr}R^p = (p-1)\big((1+r)^{p-2} - (1-r)^{p-2}\big)\Big(1 - \big(\frac{R}{r}\big)^p\Big),$$

which vanishes only at $r = R$ and indicates that $\phi(r) + \psi(r)R^p$ has a maximum or minimum at $r = R$ when $p < 2$ or $p > 2$. Since

$$\psi(r)\begin{cases} \leq \phi(r), & p < 2, \\ \geq \phi(r), & p > 2, \end{cases}$$

for $R > 1$ one has

$$\phi(r) + \psi(r)R^p \begin{cases} \leq \psi(r) + \phi(r)R^p , & p < 2, \\ \geq \psi(r) + \phi(r)R^p , & p > 2. \end{cases}$$

Accordingly, for $a, b > 0$ one gets

$$\psi(r)a^p + \phi(r)b^p \begin{cases} \leq |a+b|^p + |a-b|^p , & p < 2, \\ \geq |a+b|^p + |a-b|^p , & p > 2, \end{cases}$$

with equality when $r = b/a \leq 1$. Of course, the last estimates, along with an integration with respect to dm_g, give the desired inequalities right away. □

An immediate example of the use of Theorem 8.25 is given by the following projection result which will be used later on.

Corollary 8.26. *Let $g : \mathbf{R} \to \mathbf{R}$ be increasing, $E \subseteq \mathbf{R}$ m_g-measurable, $p \in (1, \infty)$, and $\mathcal{K}$ a closed convex subset of $\mathcal{LRS}_g^p(E)$. If $f \in \mathcal{LRS}_g^p(E, \mathbf{F}) \setminus \mathcal{K}$, then there exists a function $h_0 \in \mathcal{K}$ such that*

$$\|f - h_0\|_{p,m_g,E} = \inf_{h \in \mathcal{K}} \|f - h\|_{p,m_g,E}.$$

Moreover, every function $h \in \mathcal{K}$ satisfies

$$\Re \int_E (h - h_0)(\overline{f - h_0})|f - h_0|^{p-2} dm_g \leq 0.$$

Proof. Without loss of generality, we may assume $f = 0$ and

$$\delta = \inf_{h \in \mathcal{K}} \|h\|_{p,m_g,E}.$$

For the first result, suppose $(h_j)_{j=1}^{\infty}$ is in $\mathcal{K}$ with $\lim_{j \to \infty} \|h_j\|_{p,m_g,E} = \delta$. Since $\mathcal{K}$ is convex, $(h_j + h_k)/2 \in \mathcal{K}$ and consequently,

$$\begin{aligned} 2\delta &\leq \|h_j + h_k\|_{p,m_g,E} \\ &\leq \|h_j\|_{p,m_g,E} + \|h_k\|_{p,m_g,E} \\ &\to 2\delta \quad \text{as} \quad k, j \to \infty. \end{aligned}$$

Suppose $(h_n)_{n=1}^{\infty}$ is not a Cauchy sequence in $\mathcal{LRS}_g^p(E, \mathbf{F})$. Then there is a constant $\kappa > 0$ such that $\|h_j - h_k\|_{p,m_g,E} \geq \kappa$ holds for infinitely many j's and k's.

Case 1: $p \in [2, \infty)$. According to the first inequality in Theorem 8.25 (ii), we have

$$\begin{aligned} &\|h_j + h_k\|_{p,m_g,E}^p + \|h_j - h_k\|_{p,m_g,E}^p \\ &\leq \left(\|h_j\|_{p,m_g,E} + \|h_k\|_{p,m_g,E}\right)^p + \left|\|h_j\|_{p,m_g,E} - \|h_k\|_{p,m_g,E}\right|^p, \end{aligned}$$

whence deriving a contradiction

$$(2\delta)^p < (2\delta)^p + \kappa^p \leq (2\delta)^p.$$

Case 2: $p \in (1,2]$. According to the second inequality in Theorem 8.25 (i), we have

$$\begin{aligned}&\big(\|h_j + h_k\|_{p,m_g,E} + \|h_j - h_k\|_{p,m_g,E}\big)^p\\&+\big|\|h_j + h_k\|_{p,m_g,E} + \|h_j - h_k\|_{p,m_g,E}\big|^p\\&\le 2^p\big(\|h_j\|^p_{p,m_g,E} + \|h_k\|^p_{p,m_g,E}\big)\\&\to 2^{p+1}\delta^p \quad \text{as} \quad j,k\to\infty,\end{aligned}$$

whence getting

$$|2\delta+\kappa|^p + |2\delta-\kappa|^p \le 2^{p+1}\delta^p.$$

Since $\phi(x) = |2\delta+x|^p$ is a strictly convex function with x; that is, $\phi(tx_1+(1-t)x_2) < t\phi(x_1)+(1-t)\phi(x_2)$ for any $t\in(0,1)$ and all $x_1,x_2\in\mathbf{R}$, we obtain the following contradiction:

$$2^{1+p}\delta^p < |2\delta+\kappa|^p + |2\delta-\kappa|^p \le 2^{p+1}\delta^p.$$

Thus, $(h_n)_{n=1}^\infty$ must be a Cauchy sequence in $\mathcal{LRS}^p_g(E,\mathbf{F})$. Note that $\mathcal{K}$ is closed. So $(h_n)_{n=1}^\infty$ is convergent to an element $h_0\in\mathcal{K}$ with $\delta = \|h_0\|_{p,m_g,E}$.

For the second result, let $h\in\mathcal{K}$. Since $\mathcal{K}$ is convex, $h_t = th+(1-t)h_0\in\mathcal{K}$ for all $t\in[0,1]$, and consequently, $\phi(t) = \|h_t\|^p_{p,m_g,E}\ge\delta^p$ while $\phi(0)=\delta^p$. Noticing both

$$\lim_{t\to0+}\frac{|h_t|^p-|h_0|^p}{t} = 2^{-1}p|h_0|^{p-2}\big(\overline{(h-h_0)}h_0 + (h-h_0)\overline{h_0}\big)$$

and

$$|h_0|^p - |2h_0-h|^p \le \frac{|h_t|^p-|h_0|^p}{t} \le |h|^p - |h_0|^p$$

which follows from the convexity $\big(tx_1+(1-t)x_2\big)^p \le tx_1^p+(1-t)x_2^p$ of the function x^p on $[0,\infty)$, we use the dominated convergence theorem to obtain that $\phi'(0)$ exists and equals

$$\Re\int_E (h-h_0)\overline{h_0}|h_0|^{p-2}dm_g \ge 0,$$

as desired. □

Now, we are ready to identify the dual space of each $\mathcal{LRS}^p_g(E,\mathbf{F})$ for $p\in[1,\infty)$ via the Frigyes Riesz representation theorem below.

Theorem 8.27. *Let $g:\mathbf{R}\to\mathbf{R}$ be increasing, $E\subseteq\mathbf{R}$ m_g-measurable and $p\in[1,\infty)$. Then $\mathcal{LRS}^p_g(E,\mathbf{F})^* = \mathcal{LRS}^{\frac{p}{p-1}}_g(E,\mathbf{F})$ in the sense that $L\in\mathcal{LRS}^p_g(E,\mathbf{F})^*$ if and only if there is a unique element $h\in\mathcal{LRS}^{\frac{p}{p-1}}_g(E,\mathbf{F})$ such that*

$$L(f) = \int_E f\bar{h}\,dm_g \quad \textit{for all} \quad f\in\mathcal{LRS}^p_g(E,\mathbf{F}).$$

Proof. The Hölder inequality (see also Theorem 4.33) implies the above-formulated functional is an element of $\mathcal{LRS}^p_g(E,\mathbf{F})^*$.

For the reversed conclusion, we may assume $0\ne L\in\mathcal{LRS}^p_g(E,\mathbf{F})^*$. Then we consider two cases as follows.

Case 1: $p \in (1, \infty)$. For the above-given L, define

$$\mathcal{K} = \{f \in \mathcal{LRS}_g^p(E, \mathbf{F}) : \ L(f) = 0\}.$$

Since L is continuous, the subset $\mathcal{K}$ of $\mathcal{LRS}_g^p(E, \mathbf{F})$ is closed and convex. Because of $L \neq 0$, there exists an element $f_0 \in \mathcal{LRS}_g^p(E, \mathbf{F})$ such that $L(f_0) \neq 0$, namely, $f_0 \notin \mathcal{K}$. According to Corollary 8.26 and the linearity of $\mathcal{K}$, we can find an $h_0 \in \mathcal{K}$ such that

$$\Re \int_E (\pm h)|f_0 - h_0|^{p-2}(\overline{f_0 - h_0}) dm_g \leq 0 \quad \text{for all} \quad h \in \mathcal{K}.$$

So the last integral equals 0 for all $h \in \mathcal{K}$.

If f is an arbitrary element of $\mathcal{LRS}_g^p(E, \mathbf{F})$ and

$$f = f_1 + f_2; \quad f_1 = \left(\frac{L(f)}{L(f_0 - h_0)}\right)(f_0 - h_0),$$

then $f_2 \in \mathcal{K}$ and hence

$$\begin{aligned}
&\int_E f|f_0 - h_0|^{p-2}(\overline{f_0 - h_0}) dm_g \\
&= \int_E f_1|f_0 - h_0|^{p-2}(\overline{f_0 - h_0}) dm_g + \int_E f_2|f_0 - h_0|^{p-2}(\overline{f_0 - h_0}) dm_g \\
&= \int_E f_1|f_0 - h_0|^{p-2}(\overline{f_0 - h_0}) dm_g \\
&= L(f)\left(\frac{\int_E |f_0 - h_0|^p dm_g}{L(f_0 - h_0)}\right).
\end{aligned}$$

Clearly, the desired element h determining the representation of L is

$$h = \frac{|f_0 - h_0|^{p-2}(f_0 - h_0)\overline{L(f_0 - h_0)}}{\int_E |f_0 - h_0|^p dm_g}.$$

In fact, such an element h is unique – if there is another element $\tilde{h}$ then

$$\int_E \overline{(h - \tilde{h})} f dm_g = 0 \quad \text{for} \quad f = (h - \tilde{h})|h - \tilde{h}|^{\frac{2-p}{p-1}} \in \mathcal{LRS}_g^p(E, \mathbf{F})$$

and hence $h = \tilde{h}$ m_g-a.e. on E.

Case 2: $p = 1$. We handle this case via two situations. The first one is $m_g(E) < \infty$. Under this condition, L is also in $\mathcal{LRS}_g^p(E, \mathbf{F})^*$ (for any $p \in (1, \infty)$) since the Hölder inequality yields that

$$|L(f)| \leq \|L\| \|f\|_{1,m_g,E} \leq \|L\| \big(m_g(E)\big)^{\frac{p-1}{p}} \|f\|_{p,m_g,E}$$

is valid for all $f \in \mathcal{LRS}_g^p(E, \mathbf{F})$. However, according to the previous *Case 1* there exists a unique $h \in \mathcal{LRS}_g^{\frac{p}{p-1}}(E, \mathbf{F})$ such that

$$L(f) = \int_E f\overline{h} dm_g \quad \text{for all} \quad f \in \mathcal{LRS}_g^p(E, \mathbf{F}).$$

So, by the inclusion $\mathcal{LRS}_g^{p_2}(E,\mathbf{F}) \subseteq \mathcal{LRS}_g^{p_1}(E,\mathbf{F})$, which holds for $1 < p_1 < p_2 < \infty$ and follows from Hölder's inequality, indicates that h does not depend on p. Now if $f = |h|^{\frac{p}{p-1}-2}\overline{h}$, then $f \in \mathcal{LRS}_g^p(E,\mathbf{F})$ and hence

$$\|h\|^{\frac{p}{p-1}}_{\frac{p}{p-1},m_g,E} = L(f) \le \|L\|\big(m_g(E)\big)^{\frac{p-1}{p}}\|h\|^{\frac{p}{p-1}-1}_{\frac{p}{p-1},m_g,E}.$$

Accordingly, for any $\epsilon > 0$ we have

$$\begin{aligned}&(\|L\|+\epsilon)\Big(m_g\big(\{x\in E : |h(x)| > \|L\|+\epsilon\}\big)\Big)^{\frac{p-1}{p}}\\ &\le \|h\|_{\frac{p}{p-1},m_g,E} \le \|L\|\big(m_g(E)\big)^{\frac{p-1}{p}},\end{aligned}$$

whence getting

$$m_g\big(\{x\in E : |h(x)| > \|L\|+\epsilon\}\big) \le \Big(\frac{\|L\|}{\|L\|+\epsilon}\Big)^{\frac{p}{p-1}} m_g(E).$$

Letting $p \to \infty$, we see that the last estimate forces

$$m_g\big(\{x\in E : |h(x)| > \|L\|+\epsilon\}\big) = 0,$$

namely, $h \in \mathcal{LRS}_g^\infty(E,\mathbf{F})$. This fact further implies that $\int_E |h||f|dm_g < \infty$ for all $f \in \mathcal{LRS}_g^1(E,\mathbf{F})$. With $f \in \mathcal{LRS}_g^1(E,\mathbf{F})$ and $j \in \mathbf{N}$, we consider

$$f_j(x) = \begin{cases} f(x), & |f(x)| \le j,\\ 0, & |f(x)| > j,\end{cases}$$

and find $|f_j| \in LRS_g^p(E)$, $f_j(x) \to f(x)$ and $|f_j(x)| \le |f(x)|$ for each $x \in E$. An application of the dominated convergence theorem yields

$$\lim_{j\to\infty}\|f_j - f\|_{1,m_g,E} = 0 \quad \text{and} \quad \lim_{j\to\infty}\|hf_j - hf\|_{1,m_g,E} = 0$$

and so that

$$L(f) = \lim_{j\to\infty} L(f_j) = \lim_{j\to\infty}\int_E f_j\overline{h}dm_g = \int_E f\overline{h}dm_g.$$

The second one is $m_g(E) = \infty$. Since $E = \cup_{j=-\infty}^{\infty} E\cap[j,j+1)$ and $m_g\big([j,j+1)\big) < \infty$, any function $f \in \mathcal{LRS}_g^1(E,\mathbf{F})$ can be written as

$$f(x) = f(x)1_E(x) = \sum_{j=-\infty}^{\infty} f(x)1_{E\cap[j,j+1)}(x) \quad \text{for} \quad x \in E.$$

Note that $f \in \mathcal{LRS}_g^1\big(E\cap[j,j+1),\mathbf{F}\big)$ if and only if $f1_{E\cap[j,j+1)} \in \mathcal{LRS}_g^1(E,\mathbf{F})$. So, $L_j(f) = L(f1_{E\cap[j,j+1)})$ defines an element in $\mathcal{LRS}_g^1\big(E\cap[j,j+1),\mathbf{F}\big)^*$, and consequently, there exists an element $h_j \in \mathcal{LRS}_g^\infty\big(E\cap[j,j+1),\mathbf{F}\big)$ such that

$$L(f1_{E\cap[j,j+1)}) = \int_{E\cap[j,j+1)} f\overline{h_j}dm_g$$

and

$$\|h_j\|_{\infty,m_g,E\cap[j,j+1)} \le \|L_j\| \le \|L\|.$$

Now, if the function h is defined on E by setting $h = h_j$ on $E\cap[j,j+1)$ for each $j\in\mathbf{Z}$, then $h\in\mathcal{LRS}_g^{\infty}(E,\mathbf{F})$ and

$$L(f) = L\Big(\sum_{j=-\infty}^{\infty} f1_{E\cap[j,j+1)}\Big) = \sum_{j=-\infty}^{\infty}\int_{E\cap[j,j+1)} f\bar{h}dm_g = \int_E f\bar{h}dm_g,$$

owing to the countable additivity of the measure m_g. Moreover, if there is another function $\tilde{h}$ satisfying the last representation, then $\int_E |h-\tilde{h}||f|dm_g = 0$ for all $f\in\mathcal{LRS}_g^1(E;\mathbf{F})$, and hence for $f = 1_{E\cap[j,j+1)}$ where $j\in\mathbf{Z}$. This deduces $h=\tilde{h}$ m_g-a.e. on E. Therefore, the function h is uniquely determined. □

Remark 8.28. From Corollary 8.26 to Theorem 8.27 we have used the following definition of Lebesgue-Radon-Stieltjes integration

$$\int_E fdm_g = \int_E(\Re f + i\Im f)dm_g = \int_E \Re f dm_g + i\int_E \Im f dm_g$$

(for any $|f|\in LRS_g(E)$) and its linearity

$$\int_E (c_1f_1 + c_2f_2)dm_g = c_1\int_E f_1dm_g + c_2\int_E f_2dm_g$$

(for any $|f_1|,|f_2|\in LRS_g(E)$ and $c_1,c_2\in\mathbf{F}$) as well as some elementary algebraic operations of complex numbers.

8.4 Weak and Weak-star Topologies

The purpose of this section is to discuss some special topologies on the Banach space X and on its dual X^*, which are weaker than the usual ones.

Definition 8.29. Let $(X,\|\cdot\|_X)$ be a normed linear space over $\mathbf{F}$. Then a sequence $(x_k)_{k=1}^{\infty}$ in X is said to converge weakly to $x\in X$, denoted $x_k\xrightarrow{w}x$, provided $\lim_{k\to\infty}|L(x_k)-L(x)| = 0$ for each $L\in X^*$.

Remark 8.30.

(i) Clearly, $x_k\to x$ in X implies $x_k\xrightarrow{w}x$ (see Theorems 4.39 (i) and 8.27 for a typical example), but not conversely – for example, consider $(\ell_2,\|\cdot\|_2)$ over $\mathbf{R}$: If $e_j = (\underbrace{0,\dots,0}_{j-1},1,0,\dots)$ for each $j\in\mathbf{N}$, then $\|e_j\|_2 = 1$ yields $e_j\not\to 0$; nevertheless according to Theorem 8.22, for any $L\in B(\ell_2,\mathbf{R})$ there exists a $y=(y_k)_{k=1}^{\infty}\in\ell_2$ (i.e., $\sum_{k=1}^{\infty}y_k^2<\infty$) such that $\lim_{j\to\infty}L(e_j) = \lim_{j\to\infty}y_j = 0$, namely, $e_j\xrightarrow{w}0$.

(ii) In addition, a sequence may have at most one weak limit for if $x\neq y$ then, as we saw in the proof of Corollary 7.34 (iv), there exists an element $L\in X^*$ such that

$L(x) - L(y) = L(x-y) = 1$. If $x_k \xrightarrow{w} x$ and $x_k \xrightarrow{w} y$, then there is an $N \in \mathbf{N}$ such that $k > N$ implies

$$|L(x_k) - L(x)| < \frac{1}{2} \quad \text{and} \quad |L(x_k) - L(y)| < \frac{1}{2},$$

and hence $|L(x) - L(y)| < 1$, a contradiction.

The following is a natural way to introduce the weak topology where the basis is formed by all weakly open sets.

Definition 8.31. Let $(X, \|\cdot\|_X)$ be a normed linear space over $\mathbf{F}$.

(i) Given $\epsilon > 0$ and a finite set $\{L_1, \cdots, L_n\}$ in X^*, the $(\epsilon, L_1, \cdots, L_n)$-neighborhood $N(x; \epsilon, L_1, \cdots, L_n)$ of a point $x \in X$ is defined by

$$\{y \in X : \ |L_k(x) - L_k(y)| < \epsilon, \ k = 1, \cdots, n\}.$$

(ii) A subset of X is called weakly open if it is a union of the neighborhoods $N(x; \epsilon, L_1, \cdots, L_n)$. The complement of a weakly open set is called a weakly closed set.

(iii) A subset E of X is called weakly compact provided every cover of E by weakly open sets has a finite subcover.

Remark 8.32. Note that $B_\epsilon^X(x) \subseteq N(x; \epsilon\|L\|, L)$ for each $L \in X^*$. So Definition 8.31 is a natural generalization of the idea of a ball in a metric space. From definition it turns out that $x_k \xrightarrow{w} x$ is equivalent to saying that to any such weak neighborhood of x there corresponds an $N \in \mathbf{N}$ such that x_k lies in this neighborhood for $k \geq N$.

Using the second dual we introduce the following concept.

Definition 8.33. Let $(X, \|\cdot\|_X)$ be a normed linear space over $\mathbf{F}$ and suppose $L, L_1, L_2, \cdots \in X^*$. Then we say that:

(i) $(L_n)_{n=1}^\infty$ is strongly convergent to L provided $\lim_{n\to\infty} \|L_n - L\| = 0$;

(ii) $(L_n)_{n=1}^\infty$ is weak* convergent to L provided $\lim_{n\to\infty} |L_n(x) - L(x)| = 0$ for all $x \in X$;

(iii) $(L_n)_{n=1}^\infty$ is weakly convergent to L provided $\lim_{n\to\infty} \|F(L_n) - F(L)\| = 0$ for all $F \in X^{**}$.

Remark 8.34.

(i) In general, (ii) and (iii) in Definition 8.33 are not equivalent. But, if there is an isometry between X and X^{**} then both concepts coincide.

(ii) From Theorem 8.15 (ii) we can see that if $(X, \|\cdot\|_X)$ is a Banach space over $\mathbf{F}$, then any weak* convergent sequence in X^* must be bounded and its converse is also true whenever this sequence is assumed to be convergent on a dense subset of X.

(iii) Motivated by Definition 8.33 (iii), we say that $(T_n)_{n=1}^{\infty}$ in $B(X,Y)$ is weakly convergent to $T \in B(X,Y)$ provided $\lim_{n\to\infty} |F(T_n(x)) - F(T(x))| = 0$ for all $x \in X$ and $F \in Y^*$. Here $(X, \|\cdot\|_X)$ and $(Y, \|\cdot\|_Y)$ are supposed to be normed linear spaces over $\mathbf{F}$. According to Definition 8.13, we can find out that the uniform convergence implies the strong convergence which implies the weak convergence, but not conversely. Since Example 8.14 has shown that the strong convergence does not yield the uniform convergence, it is enough to check that the weak convergence does not derive the strong convergence. To do so, consider $X = Y = \ell_2$ over $\mathbf{R}$, and $T_n(x) = (\underbrace{0, \ldots, 0}_{n}, x_1, x_2, \ldots)$ for $x = (x_1, x_2, \ldots) \in \ell_2$. Clearly, $\|T_n\| = 1$ and if $y = (y_1, y_2, \ldots) \in \ell_2$ then

$$\Big|\sum_{k=1}^{\infty} \big(T_n(x)\big)_k y_k\Big| = \Big|\sum_{k=n+1}^{\infty} x_{k-n} y_k\Big| \le \|x\|_2 \Big(\sum_{k=n+1}^{\infty} y_k^2\Big)^{\frac{1}{2}}$$

tends to 0 as $n \to \infty$, and hence by Example 8.22 it follows that $(T_n)_{n=1}^{\infty}$ is weakly convergent to 0. But, $(T_n)_{n=1}^{\infty}$ is not strongly convergent to 0 since

$$\|T_n(e_1) - T_m(e_1)\|_2 = \|e_{n+1} - e_{m+1}\|_2 = \sqrt{2}, \quad n > m.$$

Similarly, we can define the weak-star topology on X^* via all weak* open subsets of X^*.

Definition 8.35. Let $(X, \|\cdot\|_X)$ be a normed linear space over $\mathbf{F}$.

(i) Given $\epsilon > 0$ and a finite set $\{x_1, \cdots, x_n\}$ in X, the $(\epsilon, x_1, \cdots, x_n)$-neighborhood $N(F; \epsilon, x_1, \cdots, x_n)$ of a functional $F \in X^*$ is defined by

$$\{G \in X^* : \ |G(x_k) - F(x_k)| < \epsilon, \ k = 1, \cdots, n\}.$$

(ii) An arbitrary union of such neighborhoods is called a weak* open set. The complement of a weak* open set is called a weak* closed set.

(iii) A subset A of X^* is called weak* compact provided every cover of A by weak* open sets has a finite subcover.

Definition 8.35 yields immediately that a weak* closed subset of a weak* compact set is itself weak* compact. To grasp the essence of weak* compact sets, we extend Cartesian products from two sets to a family and work with their topological compactness.

Definition 8.36.

(i) A collection $\mathcal{T}$ of subsets of a set X is said to be a topology for X provided:

(a) $\emptyset, X \in \mathcal{T}$;

(b) $\cap_{j=1}^{n} E_j \in \mathcal{T}$ whenever $n \in \mathbf{N}$ and $E_1, E_2, \ldots, E_n \in \mathcal{T}$;

(c) $\cup_{j\in I} E_j \in \mathcal{T}$ whenever $\{E_j\}_{j\in I}$ is a family in $\mathcal{T}$.

In this case, $(X, \mathcal{T})$ is called a topological space. Meanwhile, members of $\mathcal{T}$ and their complements are called open and closed sets of $(X, \mathcal{T})$ respectively. Furthermore, the closed $\overline{E}$ of a subset E of X is defined to the set of all points $x \in X$ such that any open set $O \subseteq X$ containing x satisfies $O \cap E \neq \emptyset$. Finally, $(X, \mathcal{T})$ is called compact provided every cover of X by sets of $\mathcal{T}$ has a finite subcover.

(ii) Let $\{X_j\}_{j\in I}$ be a family of topological spaces indexed by the set I. Then the Cartesian product of the family is defined by

$$X = \prod_{j\in I} X_j = \{(x_j)_{j\in I} : \ x_j \in X_j\}$$

Furthermore, for each $j \in I$ the projection $p_j : X \to X_j$ is defined by

$$p_j\big((x_\alpha)_{\alpha\in I}\big) = x_j.$$

The product topology on X is defined to be the topology with the fewest open sets for which every projection p_j is continuous; that is, $p_j^{-1}(O)$ is open in X whenever O is open in X_j.

Lemma 8.37. *Let $\mathcal{F}$ be a family of subsets of a given set X. If $\mathcal{F}$ enjoys the finite intersection property (FIP) – each finite collection of subsets in the family has a nonempty intersection, then $\mathcal{F}$ can be extended to a family which is maximal with respect to having the FIP.*

Proof. Let $\mathcal{T}$ be the collection of all families of subsets of X that contain $\mathcal{F}$ and satisfy the FIP. Define an order on $\mathcal{T}$ via inclusion and let $\{\mathcal{T}_j : \ j \in J\}$ be any chain in $\mathcal{T}$ – a totally ordered subset of $\mathcal{T}$. If $\mathcal{S} = \cup_{j\in J}\mathcal{T}_j$, then $\mathcal{S}$ contains $\mathcal{F}$ and if $\{\mathcal{S}_1, \ldots, \mathcal{S}_n\}$ is any finite collection of members of $\mathcal{S}$ then $\{\mathcal{S}_1, \ldots, \mathcal{S}_n\} \subseteq \mathcal{T}_{j_0}$ for some j_0 since $\{\mathcal{T}_j\}_{j\in J}$ is ordered by inclusion. Now $\mathcal{T}_{j_0}$ enjoys the FIP. So $\cap_{j=1}^n \mathcal{S}_j \neq \emptyset$. In short, $\mathcal{S}$ has the FIP but also each chain in $\mathcal{S}$ has an upper bound. From Zorn's lemma we conclude that $\mathcal{S}$ has a maximal element, whence establishing the desired result. □

Using this lemma, we can derive the following Andrey Nikolayevich Tychonoff's theorem.

Theorem 8.38. *Let $\{X_j\}_{j\in I}$ be a family of compact topological spaces indexed by the set I. Then $X = \prod_{j\in I} X_j$ is compact.*

Proof. By forming the contrapositive statement and taking complements, we immediately see that X is compact if and only if any collection of closed subsets of X obeying the FIP has a nonempty intersection. For this reason, we make the following consideration.

Suppose $\mathcal{F}$ is a collection of closed subsets of X which enjoys the FIP. By Lemma 8.37 we can extend $\mathcal{F}$ to $\mathcal{G}$ which is maximal with respect to having the FIP. Moreover, for each $j \in I$ the family $\{p_j(B) : \ B \in \mathcal{G}\}$ of subsets of X_j has the FIP since for any finite collection $\{B_1, \ldots, B_n\}$ of elements in $\mathcal{G}$ one has

$$\emptyset \neq p_j\big(\cap_{k=1}^n B_k\big) \subseteq \cap_{k=1}^n p_j(B_k) \subseteq \cap_{k=1}^n \overline{p_j(B_k)}.$$

Note that each X_j is compact. By the equivalent statement on the compactness there exists an x_j in $\cap_{B\in\mathcal{G}}\overline{p_j(B)}$.

Define $f \in X$ by setting $f(j) = x_j$. Thanks to $\cap_{B\in\mathcal{G}}\overline{B} \subseteq \cap_{B\in\mathcal{F}}\overline{B}$, we can complete the argument through verifying $f \in \cap_{B\in\mathcal{G}}\overline{B}$. In so doing, let O be an arbitrary open subset of X containing f. Then for some finite set of indices $j_1, \ldots, j_n$ and open sets $O_{j_k} \subseteq X_{j_k}$, we have

$$f \in \cap_{k=1}^n p_{j_k}^{-1}(O_{j_k}) \subseteq O.$$

Accordingly, $x_{j_k} \in O_{j_k}$ and thus $O_{j_k} \cap \overline{p_{j_k}(B)} \neq \emptyset$ for all $B \in \mathcal{G}$. Using the fact that O_{j_k} is open and p_{j_k} is a projection, we can readily find $O_{j_k} \cap p_{j_k}(B) \neq \emptyset$ and hence $p_{j_k}^{-1}(O_{j_k}) \cap B \neq \emptyset$ for all $B \in \mathcal{G}$. Because $\mathcal{G}$ is maximal with respect to enjoying the FIP, we must then have $p_{j_k}^{-1}(O_{j_k}) \in \mathcal{G}$ and similarly $\cap_{k=1}^n p_{j_k}^{-1}(O_{j_k}) \in \mathcal{G}$, whence obtaining $O \in \mathcal{G}$. From this we see that O intersects every element of $\mathcal{G}$ and so that $f \in \overline{B}$ for all $B \in \mathcal{G}$ due to $f \in O$ and O being an arbitrary open set. □

Now, we are ready to discuss the well-known theorem of Leonidas Alaoglu (also known as the Banach–Alaoglu theorem).

Theorem 8.39. *Let $(X, \|\cdot\|_X)$ be a normed linear space over $\mathbf{F}$. Then the closed unit ball $\overline{B}_1^{X^*}(0) = \{F \in X^* : \|F\| \leq 1\}$ of X^* is weak* compact.*

Proof. For $x \in X$ let $D_x = \{\lambda \in \mathbf{F} : |\lambda| \leq \|x\|_X\}$. Note that $|F(x)| \leq \|x\|_X$ for all $F \in \overline{B}_1^{X^*}(0)$. So $\overline{B}_1^{X^*}(0)$ is a subset of the set of all functions $f : X \to D_x$, i.e., $\overline{B}_1^{X^*}(0) \subseteq \prod_{x \in X} D_x$. The product topology on $\prod_{x \in X} D_x$ has as open sets unions of neighborhoods of the form

$$\{f : |f(x_1) - f_0(x_1)| < \epsilon, \ldots, \ |f(x_n) - f_0(x_n)|\}$$

for given $f_0, \epsilon > 0$ and $x_1, \cdots, x_n \in X$. These open sets when restricted to $\overline{B}_1^{X^*}(0)$ are just the weak* open subsets of $\overline{B}_1^{X^*}(0)$. According to Theorem 8.38, the compactness of D_x implies the compactness of $\prod_{x \in X} D_x$. Thus to prove that $\overline{B}_1^{X^*}(0)$ is weak* compact it is enough to show that $\overline{B}_1^{X^*}(0)$ is weak* closed since $\prod_{x \in X} D_x$ is weak* compact and the argument for Theorem 5.37 (i) applicable. Suppose G is in the weak* closure of $\overline{B}_1^{X^*}(0)$; that is, each weak* neighborhood of G intersects $\overline{B}_1^{X^*}(0)$. Then we must check that G is linear and $\|G\| \leq 1$. Let $x, y \in X$ and $\epsilon > 0$. By the assumption on G we see that the neighborhood $N(G; \epsilon/3, x, y, x+y)$ contains some $F \in \overline{B}_1^{X^*}(0)$. Since $F(x+y) = F(x) + F(y)$, we have

$$\begin{aligned}
&|G(x) + G(y) - G(x+y)| \\
&\leq |G(x) - F(x)| + |G(y) - F(y)| + |G(x+y) - F(x+y)| \\
&< \epsilon/3 + \epsilon/3 + \epsilon/3 = \epsilon.
\end{aligned}$$

So, $G(x+y) = G(x) + G(y)$. In a similar manner, we can prove $G(\lambda x) = \lambda G(x)$ for $\lambda \in \mathbf{F}$. Furthermore, the inequality $|F(x)| \leq \|x\|_X$ implies

$$|G(x)| \leq |G(x) - F(x)| + |F(x)| \leq \epsilon/3 + \|x\|_X,$$

and hence $|G(x)| \leq \|x\|_X$ which means $\|G\| \leq 1$. In other words, $G \in \overline{B}_1^{X^*}(0)$. Therefore, $\overline{B}_1^{X^*}(0)$ is weak* closed and accordingly weak* compact. □

Interestingly, the above-established Banach-Alaoglu theorem can be used to derive the weak compactness of the closed unit ball of a reflexive normed linear space.

Corollary 8.40. *Let $(X, \|\cdot\|_X)$ be a normed linear space over* $\mathbf{F}$. *If X is reflexive, then the closed unit ball of X is weakly compact.*

Proof. Recall

$$\overline{B}_1^X(0) = \{x \in X : \|x\|_X \leq 1\}.$$

Since X is reflexive, we conclude

$$\widehat{\overline{B}_1^X(0)} = \{\widehat{x} \in X^{**} : \; x \in \overline{B}_1^X(0)\}$$

is exactly the closed unit ball of X^{**}. From Theorem 8.39 it follows that $\widehat{\overline{B}_1^X(0)}$ is weak* compact. But since X is reflexive, this says that $\overline{B}_1^X(0)$ is weakly compact. We are done. □

8.5 Compact and Dual Operators

Having had a careful look at the concept of a compact (or weakly compact, or weak* compact) set, we can find that this concept is a natural generalization of a finite set. In this section we discuss the so-called compact operators and their dual forms on Banach spaces which are important in many applications.

Let X and Y be two normed linear spaces over $\mathbf{F}$. If $T \in B(X,Y)$ has a finite dimensional range $T(X)$ then the image of any bounded set in X is bounded in $T(X)$ and hence has compact closure (in that $T(X)$ is isomorphic to a Euclidean space). This motivates the following definition of a compact operator.

Definition 8.41. Let $(X, \|\cdot\|_X)$ and $(Y, \|\cdot\|_Y)$ be normed linear spaces over $\mathbf{F}$. Then a linear operator $T : X \to Y$ is called compact provided the closure $\overline{T(B)}$ is a compact subset of Y for each bounded subset B of X.

Here we should note that Definition 8.41 does not require T to be continuous or bounded. Nevertheless, the following result tells us that the continuity or the boundedness of T is an immediate consequence of the definition.

Theorem 8.42. *Let $(X, \|\cdot\|_X)$ and $(Y, \|\cdot\|_Y)$ be normed linear spaces over* $\mathbf{F}$. *If a linear operator $T : \; X \to Y$ is compact, then it is bounded.*

Proof. In this case, $\overline{T(\overline{B}_1^X)}$ is compact for the closed unit ball

$$\overline{B}_1^X = \{x \in X : \|x\|_X \leq 1\},$$

so it is bounded in Y. Accordingly, there exists a constant $C > 0$ such that $\|y\|_Y \leq C$ for all $y \in \overline{T(\overline{B}_1^X)}$. In particular, $\|T(x)\|_Y \leq C$ for $x \in \overline{B}_1^X$, namely, $\|T\| \leq C$. □

Remark 8.43. Definition 8.41 actually produces three more facts.

(i) A linear combination of compact operators is also compact.

(ii) If $T \in B(X)$ is compact and $S \in B(X)$ then TS and ST are compact and hence the class of all compact operators in $B(X)$ form a two sided ideal in algebraic terms.

(iii) A linear operator $T \in B(X,Y)$ is compact if and only if for every bounded sequence $(x_j)_{j=1}^{\infty}$ in X, the sequence $\big(T(x_j)\big)_{j=1}^{\infty}$ has a convergent subsequence in Y – the necessity is obvious and to see the sufficiency, we assume the statement after the if and only if, and then get that for any bounded set $B \subseteq X$ and any point $y_k \in \overline{T(B)}$ there is a point $x_k \in B$ such that $\|y_k - T(x_k)\|_Y < k^{-1}$ and consequently each of $\big(T(x_k)\big)_{k=1}^{\infty}$ and $(y_k)_{k=1}^{\infty}$ has a convergent subsequence with limit in $\overline{T(B)}$, establishing the compactness of $\overline{T(B)}$.

Using the criterion in Remark 8.43 (iii), we obtain that the compactness is preserved under uniform limit in the Banach space setting.

Theorem 8.44. *Let $(X, \|\cdot\|_X)$ be a normed linear space and $(Y, \|\cdot\|_Y)$ a Banach space over $\mathbf{F}$. If each $T_j \in B(X,Y)$ is compact and $\lim_{j\to\infty} \|T_j - T\| = 0$, then $T : X \to Y$ is compact.*

Proof. Suppose $(x_j)_{j=1}^{\infty}$ is a bounded sequence in X. Since T_1 is compact, there is a subsequence $(x_{1,m})_{m=1}^{\infty}$ of $(x_j)_{j=1}^{\infty}$ such that $\big(T_1(x_{1,m})\big)_{m=1}^{\infty}$ is convergent. Also since T_2 is compact, there is a subsequence $(x_{2,m})_{m=1}^{\infty}$ of $(x_{1,m})_{m=1}^{\infty}$ such that $\big(T_2(x_{2,m})\big)_{m=1}^{\infty}$ is convergent. Continuing this process, we can obtain subsequence $(x_{n+1,m})_{m=1}^{\infty}$ of $(x_{n,m})_{m=1}^{\infty}$ such that $\big(T_{n+1}(x_{n+1,m})\big)_{m=1}^{\infty}$ is convergent. It follows that $\big(T_n(x_{m,m})\big)_{m=1}^{\infty}$ is convergent for any $n \in \mathbf{N}$.

Note that $(x_{m,m})_{m=1}^{\infty}$ is bounded in X. So $c = 1 + \sup_{m\in\mathbf{N}} \|x_{m,m}\|_X < \infty$. Given $\epsilon > 0$, $\lim_{j\to\infty} \|T_j - T\| = 0$ implies that there is an $N \in \mathbf{N}$ such that $\|T_N - T\| < \epsilon/(3c)$. Since $\big(T_N(x_{m,m})\big)_{m=1}^{\infty}$ is convergent in Y, there is an $N_1 \in \mathbf{N}$ such that

$$k, l > N_1 \Longrightarrow \|T_N(x_{k,k}) - T_N(x_{l,l})\|_Y < \epsilon/3.$$

With this, we achieve

$$\begin{aligned}
&\|T(x_{k,k}) - T(x_{l,l})\|_Y \\
&\le \|T(x_{k,k}) - T_N(x_{k,k})\|_Y + \|T_N(x_{k,k}) - T_N(x_{l,l})\|_Y + \|T_N(x_{l,l}) - T(x_{l,l})\|_Y \\
&\le \|T - T_N\|\|x_{k,k}\|_X + \epsilon/3 + \|T - T_N\|\|x_{l,l}\|_X < \epsilon,
\end{aligned}$$

and so $\big(T(x_{m,m})\big)_{m=1}^{\infty}$ is convergent in Y owing to the fact that Y is a Banach space under the norm $\|\cdot\|_X$. □

Example 8.45. For $1 \le p \le \infty$ let the linear operator T on $\ell_p(\mathbf{N}, \mathbf{F})$ be defined by $T\big((x_k)_{k=1}^{\infty}\big) = (x_k/k)_{k=1}^{\infty}$. Then T is a compact operator on $\ell_p(\mathbf{N}, \mathbf{F})$. To check the result, set

$$T_n\big((x_k)_{k=1}^{\infty}\big) = \big(x_1, x_2/2, \cdots, x_n/n, 0, \cdots\big), \quad n \in \mathbf{N}.$$

It is clear that each $T_n\big(\ell_p(\mathbf{N}, \mathbf{F})\big)$ is finite dimensional and so that T_n is compact. Note that for any $x = (x_k)_{k=1}^{\infty} \in \ell_p(\mathbf{N}, \mathbf{F})$,

$$\|(T - T_n)\big((x_k)_{k=1}^{\infty}\big)\|_p = \begin{cases} \left(\sum_{k=n+1}^{\infty} \frac{|x_k|^p}{k^p}\right)^{\frac{1}{p}} \le \frac{\|(x_k)\|_p}{n+1}, & p \in [1, \infty), \\ \sup_{k\ge n+1} \frac{|x_k|}{k} \le \frac{\|(x_k)\|_\infty}{n+1}, & p = \infty. \end{cases}$$

So, $\lim_{n\to\infty} \|T - T_n\| = 0$. By Theorem 8.44 we can now conclude that T is a compact operator.

Next, we consider the dual operator or the adjoint or the adjoint operator of a bounded operator and see how the compactness of the original operator is reflected in the behavior of its adjoint.

Theorem 8.46. *Let $(X, \|\cdot\|_X)$ and $(Y, \|\cdot\|_Y)$ be normed linear spaces over $\mathbf{F}$. For $T \in B(X,Y)$ set $T^*(f) = f \circ T$. Then $T^* \in B(Y^*, X^*)$ and $\|T^*\| = \|T\|$. Furthermore, if X and Y are Banach spaces, then T is compact when and only when T^* is compact.*

Proof. If $f \in Y^*$ and $x \in X$, it is easy to see that $T^*(f)(x) = f \circ T(x)$ defines an $\mathbf{F}$-valued linear function on X since f and T are linear. Consequently,

$$|T^*(f)(x)| \le \|f\|\|T(x)\|_Y \le \|f\|\|T\|\|x\|_X;$$

that is, $T^*(f) \in X^*$. Clearly, $T^* : Y^* \to X^*$ is linear and bounded. According to Corollary 7.34 (vi), we evaluate

$$\begin{aligned} \|T\| &= \sup_{\|x\|_X=1} \|T(x)\|_Y = \sup_{\|x\|_X=1} \sup_{\|f\|=1} |f \circ T(x)| \\ &= \sup_{\|f\|=1} \sup_{\|x\|_X=1} |T^*(f)(x)| = \sup_{\|f\|=1} \|T^*(f)\| = \|T^*\|. \end{aligned}$$

To argue the second part, it is enough to verify that if T is compact then so is T^* due to the symmetry between both operators. Suppose T is compact. Let $(f_j)_{j=1}^{\infty}$ be a sequence in the closed unit ball of Y^*, i.e., $\sup_{j\in\mathbf{N}} \|f_j\| \le 1$. Then

$$|f_j(y_1) - f_j(y_2)| \le \|y_1 - y_2\|_Y \quad \text{for} \quad y_1, y_2 \in Y,$$

and hence $(f_j)_{j=1}^{\infty}$ is equi-continuous. Since the closure $\overline{T(\overline{B})}$ of the image $T(\overline{B}) \subseteq Y$ of the closed unit ball $\overline{B} = \overline{B}_1^X(0) \subseteq X$ is compact, an application of Theorem 6.23 yields that $(f_j)_{j=1}^{\infty}$ has a subsequence $(f_{j_k})_{k=1}^{\infty}$ which converges uniformly on $T(B)$. Because of

$$\|T^*(f_{j_k}) - T^*(f_{j_l})\| = \sup_{\|x\|_X=1} |f_{j_k} \circ T(x) - f_{j_l} \circ T(x)|,$$

the completeness of X^* implies that $\big(T^*(f_{j_k})\big)_{k=1}^{\infty}$ converges in X^*. Accordingly, T^* is compact. □

Example 8.47. Let $[a,b]$ and $[c,d]$ be two finite closed intervals of $\mathbf{R}$. For $k(\cdot,\cdot) \in C([c,d] \times [a,b], \mathbf{F})$ let $T : C([a,b],\mathbf{F}) \to C([c,d],\mathbf{F})$ be given by

$$T(f)(x) = \int_a^b k(x,y) f(y) dy, \quad x \in [c,d].$$

Then T is a compact operator and so is its adjoint T^* which maps

$$C([c,d],\mathbf{F})^* = BV([c,d],\mathbf{F})/BV_0([c,d],\mathbf{F})$$

into

$$C([a,b],\mathbf{F})^* = BV([a,b],\mathbf{F})/BV_0([a,b],\mathbf{F})$$

by Theorem 8.46, where

$$T^*(g)(y) = \int_c^d \overline{k(x,y)}dg(x), \quad y \in [a,b],$$

which can be determined by Theorem 8.24. To verify the compactness of T, we notice that $k(\cdot,\cdot) \in C([c,d]\times[a,b],\mathbf{F})$ implies

$$M_1 = \|k(\cdot,\cdot)\|_\infty = \sup_{(x,y)\in[c,d]\times[a,b]} |k(x,y)| < \infty,$$

and thus get that if B is a bounded subset of $C([a,b],\mathbf{F})$; that is, there is a constant $M_2 > 0$ such that $\|f\|_\infty \le M_2$ for all $f \in B$, then

$$\|T(f)\|_\infty = \sup_{x\in[c,d]} \left| \int_a^b k(x,y)f(y)dy \right| \le M_1M_2(b-a).$$

This means that $T(B)$ is bounded in $C([c,d],\mathbf{F})$. Since $k(\cdot,\cdot)$ is indeed uniformly continuous on $[c,d]\times[a,b]$, we see that for any $\epsilon > 0$ there is a $\delta > 0$ such that

$$x_1, x_2 \in [c,d] \text{ and } |x_1 - x_2| < \delta \Rightarrow |k(x_1,y) - k(x_2,y)| < \frac{\epsilon}{M_2(b-a)}.$$

From this implication we further see that

$$x_1, x_2 \in [c,d] \text{ and } |x_1 - x_2| < \delta \Rightarrow |T(f)(x_1) - T(f)(x_2)| \le \epsilon$$

is valid for all $f \in C([a,b],\mathbf{F})$. By Theorem 6.23 we can now conclude that the closure $\overline{T(B)}$ is compact in $C([c,d],\mathbf{F})$ and so that T is a compact operator.

Problems

8.1. Prove that if $C^n([0,1],\mathbf{R})$ is the class of all functions $f:[0,1]\to\mathbf{R}$ for which the derivatives $f^{(0)}$, $f^{(1)}$,..., $f^{(n)}$ belong to $C([0,1],\mathbf{R})$ and satisfy

$$\|f\| = \sup_{0\le k\le n} \sup_{t\in[0,1]} |f^{(k)}(t)| < \infty,$$

then it is a Banach space under this norm $\|\cdot\|$.

8.2. Prove that if $(X,\|\cdot\|_X)$ and $(Y,\|\cdot\|_Y)$ are Banach spaces over $\mathbf{F}$ then so is $X\times Y$ under the norm $\|(x,y)\| = \max\{\|x\|_X, \|y\|_Y\}$ for $(x,y)\in X\times Y$.

8.3. Prove that $(C[0,1],\|\cdot\|_p)$, $p\in[1,\infty)$ is not complete.

8.4. Let $L^1(\mathbf{Z}, \mathbf{F})$ comprise all $\mathbf{F}$-valued functions f on $\mathbf{Z}$ satisfying

$$\|f\|_1 = \sum_{n=-\infty}^{\infty} |f(n)| < \infty.$$

Prove that this space is a Banach algebra under the following convolution:

$$f * g(n) = \sum_{m=-\infty}^{\infty} f(n-m)g(m), \quad f,\ g \in L^1(\mathbf{Z}, \mathbf{F}).$$

8.5. Show by an example that the uniform bounded principle does not hold once the completeness is dropped.

8.6. Prove that there is a continuous map $f : \mathbf{R} \to \mathbf{R}$ such that $f(U)$ is not open even if U is open.

8.7.

(i) Prove

$$\lim_{n\to\infty} \int_0^{2\pi} |\sin(n+\frac{1}{2})x||\sin\frac{x}{2}|^{-1} dx = \infty.$$

(ii) Given a Riemann–integrable function $f : [0, 2\pi] \to \mathbf{R}$, let its Fourier series be

$$s(x) = \sum_{m=-\infty}^{\infty} a_m e^{imx} \quad \text{where} \quad a_m = \frac{1}{2\pi}\int_0^{2\pi} f(y)e^{-imy} dy.$$

Extend the definition of f to make it 2π-periodic. Define the n-th partial sum of the Fourier series to be $s_n(x) = \sum_{m=-n}^{n} a_m e^{imx}$. Prove

$$s_n(x) = \frac{1}{2\pi}\int_0^{2\pi} f(x+y)\Big(\frac{\sin(n+\frac{1}{2})y}{\sin\frac{y}{2}}\Big) dy \quad \text{for all} \quad x \in (0, 2\pi).$$

(iii) Let X be the Banach space of continuous functions $f : [0, 2\pi] \to \mathbf{R}$ with $f(0) = f(2\pi)$ and $\|f\|_\infty = \sup_{x\in[0,2\pi]} |f(x)|$. Prove that the linear operator $T_n : X \to \mathbf{R}$ defined by

$$T_n(f) = \frac{1}{2\pi}\int_0^{2\pi} f(x)\frac{\sin(n+\frac{1}{2})x}{\sin\frac{x}{2}} dx$$

is bounded, and

$$\|T_n\| = \|T_n\|_{X\to\mathbf{R}} = \frac{1}{2\pi}\int_0^{2\pi} \left|\frac{\sin(n+\frac{1}{2})x}{\sin\frac{x}{2}}\right| dx.$$

(iv) Prove that there exists a continuous function $f : [0, 2\pi] \to \mathbf{R}$ with $f(0) = f(2\pi)$ such that its Fourier series diverges at $x = 0$.

8.8. Let $X = C^1([0,1],\mathbf{R})$ and $Y = C([0,1],\mathbf{R})$ be equipped with norms $\|f\|_X = \sup_{0\le k\le 1}\sup_{t\in[0,1]}|f^{(k)}(t)| < \infty$ and $\|f\|_Y = \sup_{t\in[0,1]}|f(t)| < \infty$ respectively. Prove the following results:

(i) X is not complete;

(ii) The map $(d/dx): X \to Y$ is closed but not bounded.

8.9. Suppose $(X,\|\cdot\|_X)$ and $(Y,\|\cdot\|_Y)$ are Banach spaces over $\mathbf{F}$ satisfying $\|T(x)\|_Y \ge c\|x\|_X$ for all $x \in X$ and for some constant $c > 0$. Verify the following facts:

(i) $N(T) = \{x \in X:\ T(x) = 0\} = \{0\}$;

(ii) $R(T) = \{y \in Y:\ y = T(x) \text{ for some } x \in X\}$ is closed;

(iii) $T^{-1} \in B\big(R(T), X\big)$ satisfies $\|T^{-1}\| \le c^{-1}$.

8.10. Prove the following two results:

(i) $(f_j)_{j=1}^\infty$ converges weakly to f in $C([0,1],\mathbf{R})$ if and only if $\sup_{j\in\mathbf{N}}\|f_j\|_\infty < \infty$ and $\lim_{j\to\infty} f_j(x) = f(x)$ for any $x \in [0,1]$;

(ii) $\big(x_j = (s_k^{(j)})_{k=1}^\infty\big)_{j=1}^\infty$ converges weakly to $x = (s_k)_{k=1}^\infty$ in the real sequence space ℓ_p where $p \in (1,\infty)$, if and only if, $\sup_{j\in\mathbf{N}}\|x_j\|_p < \infty$ and $\lim_{j\to\infty} s_k^{(j)} = s_k$ for any $k \in \mathbf{N}$.

8.11. Let $(X,\|\cdot\|_X)$ be a separable Banach space over $\mathbf{F}$ and M be a bounded subset of X^*. Prove that every sequence in M contains a weak* convergent subsequence.

8.12. Let $(X,\|\cdot\|_X)$ be a Banach space over $\mathbf{F}$. Show that X is reflexive if and only if X^* is reflexive.

8.13. Let $c_0 = c_0(\mathbf{N},\mathbf{R})$, the linear subspace of $\ell_\infty = \ell_\infty(\mathbf{N},\mathbf{R})$ consisting of all real-valued sequences that converge to 0. Prove the following two facts:

(i) c_0 is a separable, but non-reflexive Banach space over $\mathbf{R}$;

(ii) $L \in B(c_0,\mathbf{R})$ if and only if there is an element $y = (y_k)_{k=1}^\infty \in \ell_1$ such that $L(x) = \sum_{k=1}^\infty x_k y_k$ for all $x = (x_k)_{k=1}^\infty \in c_0$.

8.14. Let $(X,\|\cdot\|_X)$ be a normed linear space over $\mathbf{F}$ and K be a convex subset of X. Prove that the weak closure of K equals its norm closure.

8.15. Let $(X,\|\cdot\|_X)$ be a normed linear space over $\mathbf{F}$ and $A \subseteq X^*$ be weak* compact. Prove the two results:

(i) A is weak* closed;

(ii) Any weak* closed subset of A is weak* compact.

8.16. Let $(X,\|\cdot\|_X)$ and $(Y,\|\cdot\|_Y)$ be Banach spaces over $\mathbf{F}$. Prove that if $T: X \to Y$ is a linear mapping such that $f \circ T \in X^*$ for all $f \in Y^*$ then $T \in B(X,Y)$.

8.17. Prove that a topological space X is compact if and only if any collection of closed subsets of X obeying the FIP has a nonempty intersection.

8.18. Let $(X, \|\cdot\|_X)$ and $(Y, \|\cdot\|_Y)$ be normed linear and Banach spaces over $\mathbf{F}$ respectively. Prove that the set $B_c(X,Y)$ of all compact operators from X to Y is a Banach space under the usual operator norm for $B(X,Y)$.

8.19. Given a finite interval $[a,b] \subset \mathbf{R}$, let $k(\cdot,\cdot)$ be an $\mathbf{F}$-valued continuous function on $\{(x,y) \in \mathbf{R}^2 : \ x \in [a,b], \ y \in [a,x]\}$ and let $T : C([a,b],\mathbf{F}) \to C([a,b],\mathbf{F})$ be given by

$$T(f)(x) = \int_a^x k(x,y)f(y)dy.$$

Show that T is a compact operator.

8.20. Suppose that X is a Banach space over $\mathbf{F}$ and $T \in B(X)$ is a compact operator. Prove the following assertions:

(i) TS and ST are compact for any $S \in B(X)$;

(ii) $T(X)$ is separable.

8.21. Let $(X, \|\cdot\|_X)$ be a Banach space over $\mathbf{F}$. Prove the following three results:

(i) If $T : X \to X$ is the zero operator; that is, $T(x) = 0$ for all $x \in X$, then T is compact;

(ii) If $T \in B(X)$ is compact and X is infinite dimensional, then T is not invertible;

(iii) If $T \in B(X)$ ensures that $T(X)$ is closed and infinite dimensional, then T is not compact.

Chapter 9

Hilbert Spaces and Their Operators

Hilbert spaces, named after David Hilbert, are special Banach spaces which share most of the rich geometric structure of the finite-dimensional Euclidean spaces. The geometrical wealth of a Hilbert space is produced by a bilinear form on the space which allows the introduction of a notion of perpendicularity. This chapter is devoted to an introductory study of Hilbert spaces and their bounded and compact linear operators.

9.1 Definition, Examples and Basic Properties

Once again, $\mathbf{F}$ still denotes the field of real or complex numbers.

Definition 9.1. Let X be a linear space over $\mathbf{F}$. An inner product on X is a map $(x, y) \to \langle x, y\rangle$ from $X \times X$ to $\mathbf{F}$ such that:

(a) $\langle \alpha x + \beta y, z\rangle = \alpha\langle x, z\rangle + \beta\langle y, z\rangle$ for all $x, y, z \in X$ and for all $\alpha, \beta \in \mathbf{F}$;

(b) $\langle y, x\rangle = \overline{\langle x, y\rangle}$ for all $x, y \in X$;

(c) $\langle x, x\rangle \geq 0$ for all $x \in X$ and $\langle x, x\rangle = 0$ if and only if $x = 0$.

If X is equipped with $\langle x, y\rangle$, then it is called an inner product space or a pre-Hilbert space over $\mathbf{F}$.

Here it is perhaps appropriate to mention that the bar signifies complex conjugation – of course, if the scalar field is $\mathbf{R}$ then the axiom (b) is simply $\langle y, x\rangle = \langle x, y\rangle$.

Theorem 9.2. *Let X be a linear space over $\mathbf{F}$ under the inner product $\langle\cdot,\cdot\rangle$. If $\|x\| = \sqrt{\langle x, x\rangle}$ for all $x \in X$, then:*

(i) *Cauchy–Schwarz's inequality $|\langle x, y\rangle| \leq \|x\|\|y\|$ holds for all $x, y \in X$, with equality if and only if x and y are linearly dependent;*

(ii) *$\|\cdot\|$ defines a norm on X;*

(iii) *The parallelogram law*

$$\|x + y\|^2 + \|x - y\|^2 = 2(\|x\|^2 + \|y\|^2)$$

is valid for all $x, y \in X$.

Proof. (i) If $\langle x, y\rangle = 0$, then there is nothing to argue. Suppose now $\langle x, y\rangle \neq 0$. Then $x \neq 0$ and $y \neq 0$. Let $\alpha = \langle x, y\rangle$ and $z = \alpha y$. Then for $t \in \mathbf{R}$ we have

$$0 \leq \langle x - tz, x - tz\rangle = \|x\|^2 - 2t|\langle x, y\rangle|^2 + t^2|\langle x, y\rangle|^2\|y\|^2.$$

This ensures that the last quadratic function of t takes its absolute minimum at $t = \|y\|^{-2}$. Substituting this value for t, we get

$$0 \leq \|x - tz\|^2 = \|x\|^2 - \|y\|^{-2}|\langle x, y\rangle|^2$$

with equality if and only if $x - tz = x - \alpha t y = 0$, from which the desired result is immediate.

(ii) It is obvious that $\|x\| = 0 \Leftrightarrow x = 0$ and $\|\lambda x\| = |\lambda|\|x\|$. As for the triangle inequality, (i) is used to imply

$$\|x + y\|^2 = \|x\|^2 + 2\Re\langle x, y\rangle + \|y\|^2 \leq (\|x\| + \|y\|)^2.$$

(iii) This follows directly from expanding $\|x + y\|^2$ and $\|x - y\|^2$. □

The above definition and theorem actually induce the notion of a Hilbert space.

Definition 9.3. A Hilbert space X over $\mathbf{F}$ is a pre-Hilbert space which is complete with respect to the metric

$$d(x, y) = \|x - y\| = \sqrt{\langle x - y, x - y\rangle} \quad \text{for all} \quad x,\ y \in X.$$

Furthermore, we will refer to real or complex Hilbert space according to whether $\mathbf{F}$ is $\mathbf{R}$ or $\mathbf{C}$.

Example 9.4.

(i) For each $n \in \mathbf{N}$, $\mathbf{F}^n$ is a Hilbert space over $\mathbf{F}$ under the inner product $\langle x, y\rangle = \sum_{j=1}^n x_j\overline{y_j}$ for $x = (x_1, \ldots, x_n),\ y = (y_1, \ldots, y_n) \in \mathbf{F}^n$.

(ii) Regardless of the cardinality of an arbitrarily given set X, we can define the sequence space

$$\ell_2(X, \mathbf{F}) = \Big\{f : X \to \mathbf{F} : \sum_{x \in X} |f(x)|^2 < \infty\Big\},$$

where

$$\sum_{x \in X} |f(x)|^2 = \sup\Big\{\sum_{x \in Y} |f(x)|^2 : \ \text{all nonempty finite subsets Y of } X\Big\}.$$

This space becomes a Hilbert space over $\mathbf{F}$ with the inner product

$$\langle f_1, f_2\rangle = \sum_{x \in X} f_1(x)\overline{f_2(x)} \quad \text{for all} \quad f_1, f_2 \in \ell_2(X, \mathbf{F}).$$

Here the right-hand sum is said to converge provided there is a number s in $\mathbf{F}$ such that to each $\epsilon > 0$ there corresponds a finite subset Y of X with the property that if Z is any finite subset of X with $Y \subseteq Z$ then $|\sum_{x \in Z} f_1(x)\overline{f_2(x)} - s| < \epsilon$. Obviously, $\ell_2(\mathbf{N}, \mathbf{F})$ is just the square-summable $\mathbf{F}$-valued sequence space.

(iii) $\mathcal{LRS}^2_{id}([a,b],\mathbf{F})$, often denoted $\mathcal{L}^2([a,b],\mathbf{F})$, is a Hilbert space over $\mathbf{F}$ under the following inner product

$$\langle f_1, f_2\rangle = \int_{[a,b]} f_1\overline{f_2}dm_{id} \quad \text{for all} \quad f_1, f_2 \in \mathcal{LRS}^2_{id}([a,b],\mathbf{F}).$$

The following result tells us when a Banach space becomes a Hilbert space.

Theorem 9.5. *Let $(X, \|\cdot\|)$ be a normed linear space over $\mathbf{F}$ and satisfy the parallelogram law above.*

(i) *If $\mathbf{F} = \mathbf{C}$, then*

$$\langle x, y\rangle = 4^{-1}\sum_{n=1}^{4} i^n \|x + i^n y\|^2$$

defines an inner product on X.

(ii) *If $\mathbf{F} = \mathbf{R}$, then*

$$\langle x, y\rangle = 4^{-1}(\|x+y\|^2 - \|x-y\|^2)$$

defines an inner product on X.

Proof. It is enough to check (i). As a matter of fact, this $\langle\cdot,\cdot\rangle$ enjoys

$$\langle x, x\rangle = \|x\|^2 + \frac{i|1+i|^2}{4}\|x\|^2 - \frac{i|1-i|^2}{4}\|x\|^2 = \|x\|^2 \quad \text{for all} \quad x \in X.$$

To verify that $\langle\cdot,\cdot\rangle$ is actually an inner product, it suffices to prove that Definition 9.1 (a) holds for $\alpha = \beta = 1$ and $\langle\lambda\cdot,\cdot\rangle = \lambda\langle\cdot,\cdot\rangle$ for any $\lambda \in \mathbf{C}$.

For the former, we use the parallelogram law to achieve

$$\|u+v+w\|^2 + \|u+v-w\|^2 = 2\|u+v\|^2 + 2\|w\|^2$$

and

$$\|u-v+w\|^2 + \|u-v-w\|^2 = 2\|u-v\|^2 + 2\|w\|^2.$$

Hence

$$\begin{aligned} &2(\|u+v\|^2 - \|u-v\|^2) \\ &= (\|u+v+w\|^2 - \|u-v+w\|^2) + (\|u+v-w\|^2 - \|u-v-w\|^2). \end{aligned}$$

This infers

$$\Re\langle u+w, v\rangle + \Re\langle u-w, v\rangle = 2\Re\langle u, v\rangle.$$

In a similar fashion, we can establish the relation with the real part $\Re$ replaced by the imaginary part $\Im$:

$$\Im\langle u+w, v\rangle + \Im\langle u-w, v\rangle = 2\Im\langle u, v\rangle.$$

Accordingly,

$$\langle u+w, v\rangle + \langle u-w, v\rangle = 2\langle u, v\rangle.$$

When $u = w$, we have $\langle 2u, v\rangle = 2\langle u, v\rangle$. Taking $u + w = x, u - w = y, v = z$, we get

$$\langle x, z\rangle + \langle y, z\rangle = 2\Big\langle \frac{x+y}{2}, z\Big\rangle = \langle x + y, z\rangle.$$

To reach the latter, we observe that for any $m \in \mathbf{N}$,

$$\langle mx, y\rangle = \langle (m-1)x + x, y\rangle = \langle (m-1)x, y\rangle + \langle x, y\rangle = \cdots = m\langle x, y\rangle.$$

Thus for any $k \in \mathbf{N}$,

$$k\Big\langle \frac{x}{k}, y\Big\rangle = \langle x, y\rangle \quad \text{and} \quad \Big\langle \frac{x}{k}, y\Big\rangle = k^{-1}\langle x, y\rangle.$$

Consequently, for any $r = m/k$,

$$r\langle x, y\rangle = m\Big\langle \frac{x}{k}, y\Big\rangle = \Big\langle \frac{mx}{k}, y\Big\rangle = \langle rx, y\rangle.$$

Since $\lim_{\|x\|\to 0} \|x + i^n y\| = \|y\|$ holds for $n = 1, 2, 3, 4$, $\langle x, y\rangle$ is a continuous functional in x, and consequently $\lambda\langle x, y\rangle = \langle \lambda x, y\rangle$ for any $\lambda > 0$ thanks to the density of $\mathbf{Q}$ in $\mathbf{R}$. If $\lambda < 0$ then

$$\lambda\langle x, y\rangle - \langle \lambda x, y\rangle = \lambda\langle x, y\rangle - |\lambda|\langle -x, y\rangle = \lambda\langle 0, y\rangle = 0.$$

Also, it is easy to verify

$$i\langle x, y\rangle = 4^{-1}\sum_{n=1}^{4} \|x + i^{n-1}y\|^2 = \langle ix, y\rangle.$$

Therefore, for any $\lambda = \mu + i\nu \in \mathbf{C}$ we have

$$\lambda\langle x, y\rangle = \mu\langle x, y\rangle + i\langle \nu x, y\rangle = \langle (\mu + i\nu)x, y\rangle,$$

as desired. □

9.2 Orthogonality, Orthogonal Complement and Duality

First of all, let us consider orthogonality.

Definition 9.6. Let X be a Hilbert space over $\mathbf{F}$.

(i) The angle between two vectors $x, y \in X$ is defined by

$$\theta_{x,y} = \begin{cases} 0, & x \text{ or } y = 0, \\ \arccos \frac{\Re\langle x, y\rangle}{\|x\|\|y\|}, & \text{otherwise.} \end{cases}$$

(ii) Two vectors $x, y \in X$ are called orthogonal, denoted $x \perp y$, provided $\langle x, y\rangle = 0$.

(iii) For any subset S of X, $S^{\perp} = \{x \in X : \langle x, y\rangle = 0 \quad \text{for all} \quad y \in S\}$ is called the orthogonal complement of S.

The following result, which has a root in Corollary 8.26 and will be used later, has natural geometrical and finite-dimensional antecedents.

Theorem 9.7. *Let X be a Hilbert space over $\mathbf{F}$. If M is a closed convex subset of X, then there exists exactly one $x \in M$ such that $\|x\| = \inf_{y\in M}\|y\|$.*

Proof. Let $\delta = \inf_{y\in M}\|y\|$. Then by definition there is a sequence $(x_j)_{j=1}^{\infty}$ in M such that $\lim_{j\to\infty}\|x_j\| = \delta$. Since M is convex, we conclude $2^{-1}(x_j + x_k) \in M$ and consequently,

$$\|x_k + x_j\|^2 = 4\|2^{-1}(x_k + x_j)\|^2 \geq 4\delta^2.$$

Using the parallelogram law, we obtain

$$4\delta^2 + \|x_k - x_j\|^2 \leq \|x_k + x_j\|^2 + \|x_k - x_j\|^2 = 2(\|x_k\|^2 + \|x_j\|^2).$$

Letting $j, k \to \infty$ in the last inequality, we find that $\|x_j - x_k\| \to 0$ as $j, k \to \infty$; that is, $(x_j)_{j=1}^{\infty}$ is a Cauchy sequence and so there is a point $x \in M$ such that $x_j \to x$ in X since M is closed. The continuity of the norm leads to $\|x\| = \delta$. Finally, x is unique since if $y \in M$ satisfies $\|y\| = \delta$ then the foregoing argument can be used for the sequence $(x, y, x, y, x, y, ...)$ to show that this sequence is a Cauchy sequence, and hence $x = y$. □

Next, we introduce the concept of a direct sum which has implicitly appeared in Corollary 7.34.

Definition 9.8. Let X and Y be two linear subspaces of a given linear space Z over $\mathbf{F}$. Then Z is said to be the direct sum of X and Y, denoted $Z = X \oplus Y$, provided every $z \in Z$ can be expressed uniquely in the form $z = x + y$ where $x \in X$ and $y \in Y$ and $X \cap Y = \{0\}$.

We are about to prove a theorem on decomposing a Hilbert space into a direct sum of mutually orthogonal closed subspaces. Before doing so, we need the following result.

Lemma 9.9. *Let M be a proper closed linear subspace of a Hilbert space X over $\mathbf{F}$. Then there exists a nonzero $z \in X$ such that $\langle z, y\rangle = 0$ for all $y \in M$.*

Proof. Given any $x \in X$, the set $x + M$ is a closed convex set. Thus by Theorem 9.7 there exists a unique $z \in x + M$ such that $\|z\| = \inf_{y\in M}\|x + y\|$. Since $M \neq X$, we may assume $x \notin M$ which yields $z \neq 0$, and then prove that $\langle z, y\rangle = 0$ for all $y \in M$. Given any $y \in M$ and any $\alpha \in \mathbf{F}$, we have $z + \alpha y \in x + M$. By our choice of z we then have $\|z + \alpha y\|^2 \geq \|z\|^2$ and consequently,

$$|\alpha|^2\|y\|^2 + 2\Re(\bar{\alpha}\langle z, y\rangle) \geq 0 \quad \text{for all} \quad \alpha \in \mathbf{F}.$$

Choose $\theta \in [0, 2\pi)$ with

$$e^{-i\theta}\langle z, y\rangle = |\langle z, y\rangle|$$

and let $\alpha = -te^{i\theta}$, $t > 0$. The inequality obtained by substituting for this α is then $t\|y\|^2 \geq 2|\langle z, y\rangle|$. Letting $t \to 0$ we get $\langle z, y\rangle = 0$. Because $y \in M$ was arbitrary, we must have $\langle z, y\rangle = 0$ for all $y \in M$. □

Theorem 9.10. *If M is a closed linear subspace of a Hilbert space X over $\mathbf{F}$, then $X = M \oplus M^{\perp}$.*

Proof. Given $x \in X$, apply the procedure in the proof of Lemma 9.9 to obtain $z \in X$ such that $z \in x + M$ and $\langle z, y\rangle = 0$ for all $y \in M$. Then $z \in M^{\perp}$ and $z = x - y$ for some $y \in M$. Hence $x = y + z$, $y \in M$, and $z \in M^{\perp}$. Noting that $M \cap M^{\perp} = \{0\}$ since

$$x \in M \cap M^{\perp} \Rightarrow \langle x, x\rangle = 0 \Rightarrow x = 0,$$

we thus have $X = M \oplus M^{\perp}$. Observe that $M^{\perp}$ is closed. Indeed, if $x_j \in M^{\perp}$ and $x_j \to x$ in X, then for any $y \in M$ we have by the Cauchy–Schwarz inequality,

$$|\langle y, x\rangle| \leq |\langle y, x_j - x\rangle| + |\langle y, x_j\rangle| \leq \|y\|\|x_j - x\| \to 0 \quad \text{as} \quad j \to \infty,$$

whence deriving $x \in M^{\perp}$. □

Finally, we consider the dual space of a Hilbert space. Below is the classical Riesz representation theorem.

Theorem 9.11. *Given a Hilbert space X over $\mathbf{F}$ and $y \in X$, define $L_y : X \to \mathbf{F}$ by $L_y(x) = \langle x, y\rangle$. Then $L_y \in X^*$ and $\|L_y\| = \|y\|$. Conversely, for every $f \in X^*$ there exists a unique $y \in X$ such that $f = L_y$.*

Proof. Clearly, $L_y \in X^*$ with $\|L_y\| \leq \|y\|$. Note that

$$\|y\|^2 = L_y(y) \leq \|L_y\|\|y\|.$$

So $\|L_y\| = \|y\|$. Conversely, let $f \in X^*$ be given. If $f = 0$, then $f = L_y$ where $y = 0$. Suppose now $f \neq 0$. Then we may assume without loss of generality that $\|f\| = 1$ since

$$f/\|f\| = L_y \Rightarrow f = L_{\|f\|y}.$$

For such an f, let

$$M = \{x \in X : f(x) = 0\}.$$

Then M is closed linear subspace of X. Of course, $M \neq X$ otherwise $f = 0$ – a contradiction. By Lemma 9.9 we can obtain a nonzero $z \in M^{\perp}$ such that $f(z) \neq 0$. Now for any $x \in X$, we have

$$x - \frac{f(x)}{f(z)}z \in M \quad \text{and} \quad \Big\langle x - \frac{f(x)}{f(z)}z, z\Big\rangle = 0.$$

Accordingly,

$$\langle x, z\rangle = f(x)\Big\langle \frac{z}{f(z)}, z\Big\rangle.$$

Taking $y = \overline{f(z)}\|z\|^{-2}z$, we further get $f(x) = \langle x, y\rangle$, and then $f = L_y$. To see the uniqueness, we assume that there is another point $w \in X$ obeying $f = L_w$. Then $\langle x, w - y\rangle = 0$ for all $x \in X$, and hence

$$\|w - y\|^2 = \langle w - y, w - y\rangle = 0 \quad \text{and} \quad w = y.$$

We are done. □

Here is an easy consequence of Theorem 9.11 which says that any Hilbert space is self-reflexive.

Corollary 9.12. *Let X be a Hilbert space over $\mathbf{F}$. Then the mapping $L : X \to X^*$ given by $\big(L(x)\big)(\cdot) = \langle \cdot, x\rangle$ is an isometric embedding from X onto X^*. Moreover, X^* is also a Hilbert space over $\mathbf{F}$.*

Proof. The first part has just been proved in Theorem 9.11. Furthermore, it is easy to see that $L(x_1 + x_2) = L(x_1) + L(x_2)$ and the isometry is additive. Since

$$L(\alpha x)(y) = \langle y, \alpha x\rangle = \bar{\alpha}\langle y, x\rangle = \bar{\alpha}L(x)(y) \quad \text{for} \quad x, y \in X \quad \text{and} \quad \alpha \in \mathbf{F},$$

we conclude $L(\alpha x) = \bar{\alpha}L(x)$. If X^* is now equipped with the inner product $\langle L(x), L(y)\rangle = \langle y, x\rangle$, then X^* is a Hilbert space over $\mathbf{F}$. □

9.3 Orthonormal Sets and Bases

To better understand the structure of a Hilbert space, in this section we consider the concepts of orthonormal sets and bases.

Definition 9.13. Let X be a Hilbert space over $\mathbf{F}$. A set $S \subseteq X$ is called orthogonal provided any two different elements in S are orthogonal. An orthonormal set is an orthogonal set consisting entirely of elements of norm 1.

A constructive method of orthonormalizing a set of vectors in a Hilbert space is the Gram-Schmidt process, named for Jrgen Pedersen Gram and Erhard Schmidt, as follows.

Theorem 9.14. *Let $\{x_j\}_{j=1}^{\infty}$ be a countable linearly independent set of a Hilbert space X over $\mathbf{F}$. Then a countable orthonormal set $\{e_j\}_{j=1}^{\infty}$ can be constructed so that*

$$\mathit{span}\{e_j\}_{j=1}^{n} = \mathit{span}\{x_j\}_{j=1}^{n} \quad \text{for all} \quad n \in \mathbf{N}.$$

Proof. Define $e_1 = x_1/\|x_1\|$. Suppose $e_1, e_2, \ldots, e_n$ are successively defined for each $n \in \mathbf{N}$. Then e_{n+1} is determined by $y_{n+1}/\|y_{n+1}\|$, where

$$y_{n+1} = x_{n+1} - \sum_{j=1}^{n}\langle x_{n+1}, e_j\rangle e_j.$$

Thus $\|y_{n+1}\| \neq 0$ since otherwise we would have

$$x_{n+1} \in \text{span}\{e_j\}_{j=1}^{n} = \text{span}\{x_j\}_{j=1}^{n},$$

contradicting the linear independence of $\{x_j\}_{j=1}^{\infty}$. It is plain that

$$\operatorname{span}\{e_j\}_{j=1}^{n+1} = \operatorname{span}\{x_j\}_{j=1}^{n+1}$$

because this is true for $\{e_j\}_{j=1}^{n}$ and $\{x_j\}_{j=1}^{n}$. Finally, for $j \in \{1, 2, \ldots, n\}$ we have

$$\langle e_{n+1}, e_j \rangle = \frac{\langle x_{n+1}, e_j \rangle - \langle x_{n+1}, e_j \rangle \langle e_j, e_j \rangle}{\|y_{n+1}\|} = 0,$$

and consequently, the set $\{e_j\}_{j=1}^{\infty}$ obtained by this inductive construction is an orthonormal set with the desired property. $\square$

Example 9.15. Given $-\infty \le a < b \le \infty$ and a function $\omega : (a,b) \to (0,\infty)$ with the property that $\int_{(a,b)} t^n \omega(t) dm_{id}(t)$ converges for all $n \in \mathbf{N}$, define the Hilbert space $\mathcal{L}^{2,\omega}((a,b),\mathbf{F})$ as the linear space of all $\mathbf{F}$-valued functions f on (a,b) with $\int_{(a,b)} |f(t)|^2 \omega(t) dm_{id}(t) < \infty$ – of course, that two functions in the space coincide means $f_1(t) = f_2(t)$ for ωdm_{id}-almost all $t \in (a,b)$. It is not hard to prove that the linearly independent set $\{1, t, t^2, \ldots\}$ has a linear span which is dense in $\mathcal{L}^{2,\omega}((a,b),\mathbf{F})$. This set, together with the Gram-Schmidt process through the inner product

$$\langle f_1, f_2 \rangle_\omega = \int_{(a,b)} f_1(t) \overline{f_2(t)} \omega(t) dm_{id}(t),$$

derives various families of classical orthonormal functions below:

(i) If $\omega(t) = 1$ and $a = -1,\ b = 1$, then the process generates the Legendre polynomials, named after Adrien-Marie Legendre;

(ii) If $\omega(t) = (1-t^2)^{-\frac{1}{2}}$ and $a = -1,\ b = 1$, then the process produces the Chebychev polynomials, named after Pafnuty Chebyshev;

(iii) If $\omega(t) = t^{q-1}(1-t)^{p-q}$ with $q > 0,\ p - q > -1$ and $a = 0,\ b = 1$, then the process generates the Jacobi polynomials, named after Karl Gustav Jacob Jacobi;

(iv) If $\omega(t) = e^{-t^2}$ and $a = -\infty,\ b = \infty$, then the process produces the Hermite polynomials, named after Charles Hermite;

(v) If $\omega(t) = e^{-t}$ and $a = 0,\ b = \infty$, then the process gives the Laguerre polynomials, named after Edmond Laguerre.

Lemma 9.16. *For $n \in \mathbf{N}$, let $\{e_j\}_{j=1}^{n}$ be an orthonormal set of a Hilbert space X over $\mathbf{F}$. Then:*

(i) $\sum_{j=1}^{n} |\langle x, e_j \rangle|^2 \le \|x\|^2$ *holds for all $x \in X$;*

(ii) $\langle x - \sum_{j=1}^{n} \langle x, e_j \rangle e_j, e_k \rangle = 0$ *holds for all $x \in X$ and $k = 1, 2, \ldots, n$.*

Proof. (i) This follows from

$$0 \le \left\| x - \sum_{j=1}^{n} \langle x, e_j \rangle e_j \right\|^2 = \|x\|^2 - \sum_{j=1}^{n} |\langle x, e_j \rangle|^2,$$

where the last equality is obtained by expanding in the usual fashion and using the orthonormality of $\{e_j\}_{j=1}^n$.

(ii) This follows from

$$\left\langle x - \sum_{j=1}^{n} \langle x, e_j \rangle e_j, e_k \right\rangle = \langle x, e_k \rangle - \langle x, e_k \rangle \langle e_k, e_k \rangle = 0. \qquad \square$$

Corollary 9.17. *Let I be an index set such that $\{e_j\}_{j \in I}$ is an orthonormal set of a Hilbert space X over $\mathbf{F}$. Then $S = \{e_j : \langle x, e_j \rangle \neq 0\}$ is countable for any $x \in X$.*

Proof. For each $n \in \mathbf{N}$, define $S_n = \{e_j : |\langle x, e_j \rangle|^2 > \|x\|^2/n\}$. By Lemma 9.16 each S_n contains at most $n-1$ elements. Since $S = \cup_{n=1}^{\infty} S_n$, we conclude that S is countable. $\square$

Remark 9.18. Given an arbitrary orthonormal set $\{e_j\}_{j \in I}$ indexed by a set I, under Lemma 9.16 and Corollary 9.17, the sums $\sum_{j \in I} |\langle x, e_j \rangle|^2$ and $\sum_{j \in I} \langle x, e_j \rangle e_j$ can be written as the series $\sum_{k=1}^{\infty} |\langle x, e_{j_k} \rangle|^2$ and $\sum_{k=1}^{\infty} \langle x, e_{j_k} \rangle e_{j_k}$ respectively, where we restrict ourselves to the countable number of e_{j_k} for which $\langle x, e_{j_k} \rangle \neq 0$.

The following result assures that the two series in Remark 9.18 are well defined.

Theorem 9.19. *Let $\{x_k\}_{k=1}^{\infty}$ be a countable orthonormal set of a Hilbert space X over $\mathbf{F}$, and let $(c_k)_{k=1}^{\infty}$ be any sequence in $\mathbf{F}$. Then $\sum_{k=1}^{\infty} c_k x_k$ is convergent in X if and only if $\sum_{k=1}^{\infty} |c_k|^2 < \infty$, and if so then*

$$\left\| \sum_{k=1}^{\infty} c_k x_k \right\|^2 = \sum_{k=1}^{\infty} |c_k|^2.$$

Moreover, $\sum_{k=1}^{\infty} c_k x_k$ is independent of the order in which its terms are arranged.

Proof. From the orthonormality of $\{x_k\}_{k=1}^{\infty}$ it follows that for $m, n \in \mathbf{N}$ and $m > n$,

$$\left\| \sum_{k=n}^{m} c_k x_k \right\|^2 = \sum_{k=n}^{m} |c_k|^2.$$

This, together with the completeness of X, implies the if and only if part of the theorem. If $n = 1$ and $m \to \infty$, then the desired equality follows.

To complete the proof, assume $\sum_{k=1}^{\infty} |c_k|^2 < \infty$ and let $y = \sum_{l=1}^{\infty} c_{k_l} x_{k_l}$ be a rearrangement of $x = \sum_{k=1}^{\infty} c_k x_k$. Then

$$\|x - y\|^2 = \langle x, x \rangle + \langle y, y \rangle - \langle x, y \rangle - \langle y, x \rangle,$$

and

$$\langle x, x \rangle = \langle y, y \rangle = \sum_{k=1}^{\infty} |c_k|^2.$$

If

$$s_m = \sum_{k=1}^{m} c_k x_k \quad \text{and} \quad t_m = \sum_{l=1}^{m} c_{k_l} x_{k_l},$$

then

$$\langle x, y\rangle = \lim_{m\to\infty}\langle s_m, t_m\rangle = \sum_{k=1}^{\infty}|c_k|^2.$$

Note that $\langle y, x\rangle = \overline{\langle x, y\rangle} = \langle x, y\rangle$. So it follows that $\|x-y\| = 0$ and hence $x = y$. We are done. □

Here is a statement of Friedrich Wilhelm Bessel about the coefficients of an element in a Hilbert space with respect to an orthonormal set.

Theorem 9.20. *Let I be an index set such that $\{e_j\}_{j\in I}$ is an orthonormal set of a Hilbert space X over $\mathbf{F}$. Then:*

(i) *Bessel's inequality $\sum_{j\in I}|\langle x, e_j\rangle|^2 \le \|x\|^2$ holds for all $x\in X$;*

(ii) *$\langle x - \sum_{j\in I}\langle x, e_j\rangle e_j, e_k\rangle = 0$ holds for all $x\in X$ and $k\in I$.*

Proof. (i) This follows from

$$\sum_{j\in I}|\langle x, e_j\rangle|^2 = \lim_{n\to\infty}\sum_{k=1}^{n}|\langle x, e_{j_k}\rangle|^2 \le \|x\|^2.$$

(ii) Using the continuity of the inner product in its left-hand variable that follows from the Cauchy–Schwarz inequality, we obtain

$$\begin{aligned}\Big\langle x - \sum_{j\in I}\langle x, e_j\rangle e_j, e_k\Big\rangle &= \langle x, e_k\rangle - \Big\langle \sum_{j\in I}\langle x, e_j\rangle e_j, e_k\Big\rangle\\ &= \langle x, e_k\rangle - \Big\langle \lim_{n\to\infty}\sum_{m=1}^{n}\langle x, e_{j_m}\rangle e_{j_m}, e_k\Big\rangle\\ &= \langle x, e_k\rangle - \lim_{n\to\infty}\Big\langle \sum_{m=1}^{n}\langle x, e_{j_m}\rangle e_j, e_k\Big\rangle\\ &= \langle x, e_k\rangle - \langle x, e_k\rangle = 0.\end{aligned}$$

□

Theorem 9.20 induces the concept of an orthonormal basis for a Hilbert space.

Definition 9.21. Let I be an index set and X be a Hilbert space over $\mathbf{F}$. Then an orthonormal set $\{e_j\}_{j\in I}$ of X is called an orthonormal basis of X provided that $x = 0$ follows from $\langle x, e_j\rangle = 0$ for all $j\in I$.

This definition actually illustrates that an orthonormal set is an orthonormal basis when it is impossible to add one more nonzero element to the set while still preserving its orthonormality. An orthonormal basis is not generally a "basis", i.e., it is not generally possible to write every member of the space as a linear combination of finitely many members of an orthonormal basis. In the infinite-dimensional case the distinction really matters. More precisely, the definition given above requires only the span of an orthonormal basis to be dense in the normed linear space, but does not force it to equal to the entire space. A full description of the preceding statement is contained in the forthcoming Marc-Antoine Parseval's theorem.

Theorem 9.22. *Given an index set I, let $\{e_j\}_{j\in I}$ be an orthonormal set in a Hilbert space X over $\mathbf{F}$. Then the following statements are equivalent:*

(i) *$\{e_j\}_{j\in I}$ is an orthonormal basis of X;*

(ii) *The closure of the linear span of $\{e_j\}_{j\in I}$ is X;*

(iii) *Parseval's identity $\|x\|^2 = \sum_{j\in I} |\langle x, e_j\rangle|^2$ holds for all $x \in X$.*

Proof. First, we prove that (i) implies (ii) and (iii). If (i) is true, then Definition 9.21 and Theorem 9.20 (ii) yield that $x = \sum_{j\in I}\langle x, e_j\rangle e_j$ is valid for all $x \in X$. Clearly, (iii) follows from Theorem 9.19.

Next, we prove that each of (ii) and (iii) implies (i).

(ii)⇒(i) Suppose that $y \in X$ satisfies $\langle y, e_j\rangle = 0$ for all $j \in I$. To prove $y = 0$, consider $S = \{x \in X : \langle y, x\rangle = 0\}$. It is easy to see that S is a linear subspace of X. Since $e_j \in S$, it follows that S must contain the linear span of $\{e_j\}_{j\in I}$. On the other hand, S is closed in view of the continuity of the inner product, and so S must contain the closure of the linear span of $\{e_j\}_{j\in I}$. Hence $S = X$ by (ii). In particular, we have $y \in S$ and so $\langle y, y\rangle = 0$, whence $y = 0$ as required.

(iii)⇒(i) Suppose on the contrary that $\{e_j\}_{j\in I}$ does not form an orthonormal basis of X. Then there exists a nonzero $x \in X$ such that $\langle x, e_j\rangle = 0$ for all $j \in I$. As a result of this existence one gets

$$0 \neq \|x\|^2 = \sum_{j\in I} |\langle x, e_j\rangle|^2 = 0,$$

which is a contradiction. □

Example 9.23.

(i) The set $\{(1,0,0),(0,1,0),(0,0,1)\}$ forms an orthonormal basis of $\mathbf{R}^3$.

(ii) The set $\{e_j\}_{j\in\mathbf{N}}$ with the jth entry of $e_j \in \ell_2$ being 1 and others being 0 forms an orthonormal basis of the real sequence space ℓ_2.

(iii) The set $\{e^{int}\}_{n=-\infty}^{\infty}$ is an orthonormal basis for $\mathcal{LRS}^2_{id}([0,2\pi],\mathbf{C})$. Accordingly, $C([0,2\pi],\mathbf{C})$ is dense in $\mathcal{LRS}^2_{id}([0,2\pi],\mathbf{C})$. In fact, this basis is fundamental to the study of Fourier series, named in honor of Joseph Fourier.

Theorem 9.24.

(i) *Every Hilbert space over $\mathbf{F}$ has an orthonormal basis.*

(ii) *Any orthonormal basis in a separable Hilbert space over $\mathbf{F}$ is countable.*

Proof. (i) Let X be a Hilbert space over $\mathbf{F}$ with the inner product $\langle\cdot,\cdot\rangle$ and the norm $\|\cdot\|$, and consider the collection E of orthonormal subsets of X. It is clear that E is nonempty and can be partially ordered under inclusion. If F is any totally ordered subcollection of E, the set $U = \cup_{S\in F} S$ is member of E and an upper bound for F. By Zorn's lemma there is a maximal orthonormal set M. Since M is maximal, we conclude from Definition 9.21 that M is an orthonormal basis – otherwise, there would be a nonzero $x_0 \in X \setminus M$ such that $\langle x_0, e_j\rangle = 0$ holds for any $e_j \in M$.

Accordingly, $\{x_0/\|x_0\|\} \cup M$ forms an orthonormal set which properly contains M – this contradicts the maximality of M.

(ii) If X is separable, and if $\{e_j\}_{j\in I}$ is an uncountable orthonormal basis of X, then for $j, k \in I$ with $j \neq k$, we have

$$\|e_j - e_k\|^2 = \|e_j\|^2 + \|e_k\|^2 = 2,$$

and so the open balls $B^X_{1/2}(e_j)$ (with center e_j and radius 1/2) in X are mutually disjoint. If $\{x_j\}_{j=1}^{\infty}$ is a countable dense subset of X, because $\{e_j\}_{j\in I}$ is uncountable, there is an open ball $B^X_{1/2}(e_{j_0})$ which is disjoint from $\{x_j\}_{j=1}^{\infty}$. Hence e_{j_0} is not in the closure of $\{x_j\}_{j=1}^{\infty}$. This contradicts the density of $\{x_j\}_{j=1}^{\infty}$ in X. We are done. □

Example 9.25. There is a non-separable Hilbert space. As a matter of fact, let X be the linear space of all continuous functions $f : \mathbf{R} \to \mathbf{C}$ satisfying

$$|||f|||_2 = \Big(\lim_{N\to\infty} (2N)^{-1} \int_{-N}^{N} |f(x)|^2 dx\Big)^{\frac{1}{2}} < \infty.$$

Although $|||f|||_2 = 0$ does not ensure $f = 0$ on $\mathbf{R}$, if $Y = \{f \in X : \ |||f|||_2 = 0\}$ then X/Y is a normed linear space over $\mathbf{C}$. If H is the completion of this quotient space and is equipped with the following inner product

$$\langle f, g\rangle = \lim_{N\to\infty} (2N)^{-1} \int_{-N}^{N} f(x)\overline{g(x)}dx,$$

then H is a Hilbert space over $\mathbf{C}$. Note that $\{e^{it(\cdot)} + Y\}_{t\in\mathbf{R}}$ is an orthonormal set of H but also

$$\{f + Y \in H : \ |||f(\cdot) - e^{it(\cdot)}|||_2 < 1/2\} \text{ and } \{f + Y \in H : \ |||f(\cdot) - e^{is(\cdot)}|||_2 < 1/2\}$$

are disjoint for $t \neq s$. So H is not separable.

Corollary 9.26. *Any two infinite dimensional separable Hilbert spaces over* $\mathbf{F}$ *are isometrically isomorphic.*

Proof. Suppose X and Y are two such spaces equipped with the inner products $\langle\cdot,\cdot\rangle_X$ and $\langle\cdot,\cdot\rangle_Y$ as well as the norms $\|\cdot\|_X$ and $\|\cdot\|_Y$. Theorem 9.24 tells us that there are two orthonormal bases $\{x_j\}_{j=1}^{\infty}$ and $\{y_j\}_{j=1}^{\infty}$ of X and Y respectively. If $x \in X$ and $y \in Y$, then

$$x = \sum_{j=1}^{\infty} \langle x, x_j\rangle_X x_j \quad \text{and} \quad y = \sum_{j=1}^{\infty} \langle y, y_j\rangle_Y y_j.$$

Define a map $T : X \to Y$ by $T(x) = y$ if $\langle x, x_j\rangle_X = \langle y, y_j\rangle_Y$. It is clear that T is linear and one-to-one, and it maps X onto Y since $(\langle x, x_j\rangle_X)_{j=1}^{\infty}$ and $(\langle y, y_j\rangle_Y)_{j=1}^{\infty}$ run through all of elements in the $\mathbf{F}$-valued sequence space $\ell_2(\mathbf{N}, \mathbf{F})$. In addition,

$$\|T(x)\|_Y^2 = \sum_{j=1}^{\infty} |\langle y, y_j\rangle_Y|^2 = \sum_{j=1}^{\infty} |\langle x, x_j\rangle_X|^2 = \|x\|_X^2,$$

Thus, T is isometrically isomorphic. The proof is complete. □

9.4 Five Special Bounded Operators

For a Hilbert space X over $\mathbf{F}$, the elements in $B(X)$ are of particular interest. To see this, suppose $T \in B(X)$. For each fixed $y \in X$, the mapping that sends x to $\langle T(x), y\rangle$ is a continuous linear functional on X. Thus by the Riesz representation theorem there exists a unique $z \in X$ such that

$$\langle T(x), y\rangle = L_z(x) = \langle x, z\rangle.$$

This pairing actually produces a new operator on X – see also Theorem 8.46.

Definition 9.27. Let X be a Hilbert space over $\mathbf{F}$. If $T \in B(X)$ then its adjoint operator T^* is defined by

$$\langle T(x), y\rangle = \langle x, T^*(y)\rangle \quad \text{for all} \quad x, y \in X.$$

The three facts (i)-(ii)-(iii) in Theorem 9.28 below are the required conditions for $*$ to be an involution.

Theorem 9.28. *Let X be a Hilbert space over $\mathbf{F}$. Then the operation $*$ maps $B(X)$ into itself, and has the following properties for all $T, S \in B(X)$ and $\alpha, \beta \in \mathbf{F}$:*

(i) $(\alpha T + \beta S)^* = \bar{\alpha}T^* + \bar{\beta}S^*$;

(ii) $(TS)^* = S^*T^*$;

(iii) $T^{**} = T$;

(iv) $\|T^*\| = \|T\|$;

(v) $\|T^*T\| = \|T\|^2$.

Proof. First of all, we verify that $*$ maps $B(X)$ to $B(X)$. The linearity of T^* follows from the following calculation:

$$\begin{aligned}\langle x, T^*(\alpha y_1 + \beta y_2)\rangle &= \langle T(x), \alpha y_1 + \beta y_2\rangle \\ &= \bar{\alpha}\langle T(x), y_1\rangle + \bar{\beta}\langle T(x), y_2\rangle \\ &= \langle x, \alpha T^*(y_1) + \beta T^*(y_2)\rangle\end{aligned}$$

By the definition of the operator norm, we have

$$\begin{aligned}\|T^*\| &= \sup_{\|y\|=1} \|T^*(y)\| \\ &\le \sup_{\|x\|=1,\|y\|=1} |\langle x, T^*(y)\rangle| \\ &= \sup_{\|x\|=1,\|y\|=1} |\langle T(x), y\rangle| \\ &\le \sup_{\|x\|=1} \|T(x)\| = \|T\|.\end{aligned}$$

This implies that $*$ is bounded on $B(X)$.

Next, we check those five properties.

(i) For any $x, y \in X$, we have

$$\langle x, (\alpha T + \beta S)^*(y)\rangle = \alpha\langle T(x), y\rangle + \beta\langle S(x), y\rangle = \langle x, (\bar{\alpha}T^* + \bar{\beta}S^*)(y)\rangle.$$

(ii) This follows from

$$\langle x, (TS)^*(y)\rangle = \langle TS(x), y\rangle = \langle S(x), T^*(y)\rangle = \langle x, S^*T^*(y)\rangle.$$

(iii) This follows from

$$\langle x, T^{**}(y)\rangle = \langle T^*(x), y\rangle = \overline{\langle y, T^*(x)\rangle} = \overline{\langle T(y), x\rangle} = \langle x, T(y)\rangle.$$

(iv) It is known that $\|T^*\| \le \|T\|$ and $T^{**} = T$. So $\|T\| \le \|T^*\|$. This gives $\|T\| = \|T^*\|$.

(v) By (iv), we get

$$\|T^*T\| \le \|T^*\|\|T\| = \|T\|^2.$$

For the reverse inequality, we note that

$$\|T(x)\|^2 = \langle T^*T(x), x\rangle \le \|T^*T(x)\|\|x\| \le \|T^*T\|\|x\|^2.$$

So, $\|T\|^2 \le \|T^*T\|$, which completes the proof. □

Example 9.29. If T is the operator on $\ell_2(\mathbf{N}, \mathbf{C})$ defined by

$$T\big((x_1, x_2, \dots)\big) = (0, x_1, x_2, \dots),$$

then $T^*\big((x_1, x_2, \dots)\big) = (x_2, x_3, \dots)$. Clearly, $\|T\| = \|T^*\| = 1$.

In what follows, we deal with five special types of bounded linear operators on a given Hilbert space. They are self-adjoint, non-negative, unitary, normal and projection operators.

Definition 9.30. Let X be a Hilbert space over $\mathbf{F}$. An operator $T \in B(X)$ is said to be self-adjoint or symmetric provided $T = T^*$.

Example 9.31.

(i) On a finite-dimensional Hilbert space over $\mathbf{F}$, a self-adjoint operator is one that is its own adjoint, or, equivalently, one whose matrix is Hermitian, where a Hermitian matrix is one which is equal to its own conjugate transpose.

(ii) Given $n \in \mathbf{N}$, the operator T defined by $T(f)(x) = x^n f(x)$ is a self-adjoint operator on $\mathcal{LRS}^2_{id}([0,1], \mathbf{C})$.

The structure of self-adjoint operators on infinite dimensional Hilbert spaces is complicated somewhat by the following characterization and its immediate remark.

Theorem 9.32. *Let X be a Hilbert space over $\mathbf{F}$ and $T \in B(X)$.*

(i) *If T is self-adjoint, then $\|T\|$ equals $\sup_{\|x\|=1} |\langle T(x), x\rangle|$.*

(ii) *If $\mathbf{F} = \mathbf{C}$, then T is self-adjoint when and only when $\langle T(x), x\rangle$ is real for all $x \in X$. In particular, $T = 0$ when and only when $\langle T(x), x\rangle = 0$ for all $x \in X$.*

Proof. (i) The Cauchy–Schwartz inequality implies $\|T\| \geq \sup_{\|x\|=1} |\langle T(x), x\rangle|$. For the reverse estimate, we use the triangle inequality and the parallelogram law to obtain that for any $x \in X$ with $\|x\| = 1$,

$$\begin{aligned} &2|\langle T(x), y\rangle + \langle T(y), x\rangle| \\ &= |\langle T(x+y), x+y\rangle - \langle T(x-y), x-y\rangle| \\ &\leq 2 \sup_{\|z\|=1} |\langle T(z), z\rangle|(\|x+y\|^2 + \|x-y\|^2) \\ &= 4 \sup_{\|z\|=1} |\langle T(z), z\rangle|(1 + \|y\|^2). \end{aligned}$$

When $T(x) \neq 0$, taking $y = T(x)/\|T(x)\|$ in the above we get

$$\|T(x)\| \leq \sup_{\|z\|=1} |\langle T(z), z\rangle|.$$

Note that the last inequality is trivially valid for $T(x) = 0$. So, it follows that $\|T\| \leq \sup_{\|x\|=1} |\langle T(x), x\rangle|$, and the desired equality occurs.

(ii) If $T \in B(X)$ is self-adjoint, then $\langle T(x), x\rangle = \langle x, T(x)\rangle = \overline{\langle T(x), x\rangle}$ for any $x \in X$. Hence $\langle T(x), x\rangle$ is real for all $x \in X$. Conversely, If $f(x) = \langle T(x), x\rangle$, then

$$f(x+y) = f(x) + f(y) + \langle T(y), x\rangle + \langle T(x), y\rangle$$

and

$$f(x+iy) = f(x) + f(y) + i\langle T(y), x\rangle - i\langle T(x), y\rangle.$$

Since f is real-valued, we conclude from the last two identities that there are $r, s \in \mathbf{R}$ such that

$$\langle T(y), x\rangle + \langle T(x), y\rangle = r \quad \text{and} \quad \langle T(y), x\rangle - \langle T(x), y\rangle = is.$$

This yields

$$\langle T(y), x\rangle = \frac{r+is}{2} \quad \text{and} \quad \langle T(x), y\rangle = \frac{r-is}{2},$$

and thus

$$\langle T(y), x\rangle = \overline{\langle T(x), y\rangle} = \overline{\langle x, T^*(y)\rangle} = \langle T^*(y), x\rangle.$$

Consequently, for any $y \in X$ we have

$$\langle (T-T^*)(y), (T-T^*)(y)\rangle = 0, \quad \text{i.e.,} \quad T = T^*.$$

For the second half of (ii), it is enough to verify the sufficiency. Suppose $\langle T(x), x\rangle = 0$ for all $x \in X$. Then T is self-adjoint, and hence

$$4\langle T(x), y\rangle = \langle T(x+y), x+y\rangle - \langle T(x-y), x-y\rangle = 0$$

holds for all $y = T(x) \in X$. This gives $T(x) = 0$ for all $x \in X$, i.e., $T = 0$. $\square$

Remark 9.33. Unfortunately, Theorem 9.32 (ii) is not valid for any real Hilbert space. For instance, if $X = \mathbf{R}^2$ and $T(x) = T\big((x_1,x_2)\big) = (-x_2, x_1)$ for $x = (x_1, x_2) \in \mathbf{R}^2$ then $\langle T(x), x\rangle = 0$, $0 \neq T \in B(\mathbf{R}^2)$ and T is not self-adjoint since $T^*(x) = T^*\big((x_1,x_2)\big) = (x_2, -x_1)$ for $x = (x_1, x_2) \in \mathbf{R}^2$.

Definition 9.34. Let X be a Hilbert space over $\mathbf{C}$. An operator $T \in B(X)$ is said to be nonnegative, denoted $T \geq 0$, provided $\langle T(x), x\rangle \geq 0$ for all $x \in X$. Moreover, we say $T_1 \leq T_2$ provided that T_1 and T_2 are self-adjoint operators in $B(X)$ and $T_2 - T_1 \geq 0$.

Example 9.35.

(i) Any bounded operator T on a given Hilbert space over $\mathbf{C}$ always generates a nonnegative operator T^*T since $\langle T^*T(x), x\rangle = \|T(x)\|^2 \geq 0$.

(ii) The operator defined in Example 9.31 (ii) is nonnegative.

(iii) The operator T on $\mathbf{C}^2$ determined by $T\big((x_1,x_2)\big) = (x_1 + 2x_2, 2x_1 + x_2)$ is not nonnegative since $T\big((1,-1)\big) = (-1, 1)$ and the inner product between two vectors $(-1,1)$ and $(1,-1)$ is -2.

According to Theorem 9.32 (ii) and Example 9.35 (ii), any nonnegative operator is self-adjoint, but not conversely. Here is the basic structure of a nonnegative operator.

Theorem 9.36. *Given a Hilbert space X over $\mathbf{C}$, let $I \in B(X)$ be the identity operator.*

(i) *If $-I \leq T \leq I$ or $0 \leq T \leq 0$, then $\|T\| \leq 1$ or $T = 0$.*

(ii) *If $T \geq 0$, then $T+I$ is invertible, and the generalized Cauchy–Schwartz inequality holds:*

$$|\langle T(x), y\rangle| \leq \sqrt{\langle T(x), x\rangle\langle T(y), y\rangle} \quad x, y \in X.$$

(iii) *If $0 \leq T_1 \leq T_2 \leq \cdots \leq I$, then there exists a $T_\infty \in B(X)$ such that*

$$\lim_{j\to\infty} \|T_j(x) - T_\infty(x)\| = 0 \ \textit{for all } x \in X.$$

(iv) *$T \geq 0$ when and only when there exists a unique nonnegative operator $S \in B(X)$, denoted $S = \sqrt{T}$, such that $S^2 = T$.*

Proof. (i) Note that T is self-adjoint. So, $I \pm T \geq 0$ implies $\pm\langle T(x), x\rangle \leq \|x\|^2$ and $\|T\| \leq 1$ by Theorem 9.32 (i). Moreover, $\pm T \geq 0$ implies $\langle T(x), x\rangle = 0$ and $\|T\| = 0$ by Theorem 9.32 (i).

(ii) Since $T \geq 0$, we conclude

$$(T+I)(x) = 0 \Rightarrow \langle (T+I)(x), x\rangle = 0 \Rightarrow 0 \leq \langle T(x), x\rangle = -\|x\|^2 \Rightarrow x = 0,$$

and so the injectivity of $T + I$ follows. The surjectivity will follows if we can prove that $M = (T+I)(X)$, the image of $(T+I)$, is both dense and closed. The argument used for injectivity applies to $x \in M^\perp$ to infer that $\langle (T+I)x, x\rangle = 0$ is valid for all $x \in M^\perp$ and so $M^\perp = \{0\}$. On the other hand, for any $x \in X$ we have

$$\|(T+I)(x)\|^2 = \|T(x)\|^2 + 2\langle T(x), x\rangle + \|x\|^2$$

and hence $\|x\| \le \|(T+I)(x)\|$. Consequently, if $\big((T+I)(x_j)\big)_{j=1}^\infty$ is a Cauchy sequence in M, then $(x_j)_{j=1}^\infty$ is a Cauchy sequence in X and hence it is convergent. This shows that M is complete and thereby closed in X. From Theorem 9.10 it turns out that $X = M \oplus M^\perp = M$; that is, $T+I$ is surjective.

Regarding the generalized Cauchy–Schwartz inequality for any $x, y \in X$, for any $t \in \mathbf{R}$ let $\lambda = t\zeta \in \mathbf{F}$ obey $\zeta\langle y, T(x)\rangle = |\langle y, T(x)\rangle|$. Then we get

$$\begin{aligned} 0 &\le \langle x+\lambda y, T(x+\lambda y)\rangle \\ &= \langle x, T(x)\rangle + 2t|\langle y, T(x)\rangle| + t^2\langle y, T(y)\rangle, \end{aligned}$$

whence deriving

$$|\langle T(x), y\rangle|^2 - \langle x, T(x)\rangle\langle y, T(y)\rangle \le 0.$$

(iii) For $k > j$ and $x \in X$, we use the generalized Cauchy–Schwartz inequality in (ii) to get

$$\begin{aligned} \|T_k(x) - T_j(x)\|^2 &= \langle (T_k - T_j)(x), (T_k - T_j)(x)\rangle \\ &\le \sqrt{\langle (T_k - T_j)(x), x\rangle\langle (T_k - T_j)^2(x), (T_k - T_j)(x)\rangle} \\ &\le \sqrt{\langle (T_k - T_j)(x), x\rangle}\|x\| \\ &\le \sqrt{\langle T_k(x), x\rangle - \langle T_j(x), x\rangle}\|x\| \end{aligned}$$

since $0 \le T_k - T_j \le I$ implies $\|T_k - T_j\| \le 1$ and $\|(T_k - T_j)^2\| \le 1$. Note that $(\langle T_j(x), x\rangle)_{j=1}^\infty$ is convergent since it is increasing and bounded. So $\big(T_j(x)\big)_{j=1}^\infty$ is a Cauchy sequence in the Hilbert space X and consequently, this sequence is convergent to some point $T_\infty(x) \in X$. According to Theorem 8.15 (i), $T_\infty \in B(X)$.

(iv) The sufficiency is trivial. For the necessity, suppose $T \ge 0$. According to Theorem 9.32 (i) we have $\|T\| < \infty$ and equivalently $T \le \|T\|I$. Therefore, without loss of generality we may assume $T \le I$. To find a nonnegative operator S such that $S^2 = T$, let $U = I - T$, $T_1 = 0$ and $T_{j+1} = 2^{-1}(U + T_j^2)$ for $j \in \mathbf{N}$. By induction, we find three basic facts as follows:

(a) For $j \in \mathbf{N}$, $0 \le T_j$ is a polynomial of U with nonnegative coefficients;

(b) For $j \in \mathbf{N}$, $T_j \le I$. In fact, $T_j \le I$ implies

$$\langle T_j^2(x), x\rangle = \|T_j(x)\|^2 \le \|x\|^2$$

and so $T_j^2 \le I$ which, along with $U \le I$, yields $T_{j+1} \le I$;

(c) For $j \in \mathbf{N}$, $T_{j+2} - T_{j+1} \ge 0$. This is because the easy commutativity $T_{j+1}T_j = T_jT_{j+1}$ deduces

$$T_{j+2} - T_{j+1} = 2^{-1}(T_{j+1}^2 - T_j^2) = 2^{-1}(T_{j+1} + T_j)(T_{j+1} - T_j)$$

where $T_{j+1}+T_j$ is a polynomial of U with nonnegative coefficients, and so is $T_{j+1}-T_j$ by $T_2 - T_1 = 2^{-1}U$ and induction.

Now, (iii) is applied to produce a $T_\infty \in B(X)$ with $\lim_{j\to\infty} T_j(x) = T_\infty(x)$ for all $x \in X$. Then $T_\infty = 2^{-1}(U + T_\infty^2)$ and hence desired square root operator is $S = I - T_\infty$, i.e., $(I - T_\infty)^2 = T$.

It remains to check the uniqueness. Suppose $S_1 \geq 0$ satisfies $S_1^2 = T$. Then $S_1 T = S_1^3 = TS_1$ and hence $S_1 T^n = T^n S_1$ for any $n \in \mathbf{N}$. Now the previously-established limit process implies $SS_1 = S_1 S$. Consequently, if $y = (S-S_1)(x)$ for any $x \in X$ then $0 = \langle (S+S_1)(y), y\rangle = \langle S(y), y\rangle + \langle S_1(y), y\rangle$, and hence $S(y) = 0 = S_1(y)$ (here $S = \sqrt{S}^2$ and $S_1 = \sqrt{S_1}^2$) which ensures $(S^2 - SS_1)(x) = 0 = (S_1 S - S_1^2)(x)$. Accordingly, $\|(S - S_1)(x)\|^2 = \langle (S - S_1)^2(x), x\rangle = 0$, and so $S = S_1$. □

Definition 9.37. Given a Hilbert space X over $\mathbf{F}$ let $T \in B(X)$. Then T is called unitary provided T is an isometric isomorphism.

Example 9.38. For $f \in \mathcal{LRS}^2_{id}(\mathbf{R}, \mathbf{C})$ let

$$\mathcal{F}(f)(x) = \frac{1}{\sqrt{2\pi}} \int_{\mathbf{R}} f(t) \exp(itx) dm_{id}(t), \quad x \in \mathbf{R},$$

then $\mathcal{F}$ is a unitary operator on $\mathcal{LRS}^2_{id}(\mathbf{R}, \mathbf{C})$. This operator is called the Fourier transform and its adjoint operator is determined by

$$\mathcal{F}^*(f)(x) = \frac{1}{\sqrt{2\pi}} \int_{\mathbf{R}} f(t) \exp(-itx) dm_{id}(t), \quad x \in \mathbf{R}.$$

We can characterize unitary operators in terms of adjoints and inner products.

Theorem 9.39. *Given a Hilbert space X over $\mathbf{C}$ let $T \in B(X)$. If I is the identity operator in $B(X)$, then the following statements are equivalent:*

(i) *T is unitary;*

(ii) *$\langle T(x), T(y)\rangle = \langle x, y\rangle$ holds for all $x, y \in X$, and T is surjective;*

(iii) *$TT^* = T^*T = I$.*

Proof. (i)⇒(ii) If T is unitary, then $\|T(x)\| = \|x\|$ and hence

$$\begin{aligned} \langle T(x), T(y)\rangle &= 4^{-1}\sum_{n=1}^{4} i^n \|T(x) + i^n T(y)\|^2 \\ &= 4^{-1}\sum_{n=1}^{4} i^n \|T(x + i^n y)\|^2 \\ &= 4^{-1}\sum_{n=1}^{4} i^n \|x + i^n y\|^2 \\ &= \langle x, y\rangle. \end{aligned}$$

The surjectivity of T follows the definition of a unitary operator.

(ii)⇒(iii) Clearly, (ii) implies that T is injective. Moreover

$$\langle T^*T(x), x\rangle = \langle T(x), T(x)\rangle = \langle x, x\rangle.$$

This, along with Theorem 9.32 (ii), yields

$$\langle (T^*T - I)(x), x\rangle = 0 \Rightarrow T^*T = I \Rightarrow TT^* = I.$$

(iii)⇒(i) If (iii) is true, then T is surjective and

$$\|T(x)\|^2 = \langle T(x), T(x)\rangle = \langle x, T^*T(x)\rangle = \langle x, x\rangle = \|x\|^2.$$

This implies that T is injective, and thereby T is unitary. □

Theorem 9.39 leads to the following consideration.

Definition 9.40. Let X be a Hilbert space over $\mathbf{C}$. An operator $T \in B(X)$ is said to be normal if $TT^* = T^*T$.

Interestingly, the normal operators correspond to the complex numbers.

Theorem 9.41. *Let X be a Hilbert space over $\mathbf{C}$ and $T \in B(X)$. Then the following statements are equivalent:*

(i) *T is normal;*

(ii) *$T = T_1 + iT_2$ where T_1 and T_2 are self-adjoint and obey $T_1T_2 = T_2T_1$;*

(iii) *$\|T(x)\| = \|T^*(x)\|$ holds for all $x \in X$.*

Proof. (i)⇒(ii) Put

$$T_1 = \frac{T + T^*}{2} \quad \text{and} \quad T_2 = \frac{T - T^*}{2i}.$$

It is easy to see that $T = T_1 + iT_2$ holds with T_1 and T_2 being self-adjoint and commutative.

(ii)⇒(iii) Using the given decomposition of T plus $T_1T_2 = T_2T_1$, we obtain

$$\begin{aligned} \|T(x)\|^2 &= \langle x, T^*T(x)\rangle \\ &= \langle x, (T_1 - iT_2)(T_1 + iT_2)(x)\rangle \\ &= \langle x, (T_1T_1 + T_2T_2)(x)\rangle \\ &= \langle x, (T_1 + iT_2)(T_1 - iT_2)(x)\rangle \\ &= \langle x, TT^*(x)\rangle \\ &= \|T^*(x)\|^2. \end{aligned}$$

(iii)⇒(i) For any $x \in X$ we have

$$\langle (TT^* - T^*T)(x), x\rangle = \langle TT^*(x), x\rangle - \langle T^*T(x), x\rangle = \|T^*(x)\|^2 - \|T(x)\|^2 = 0.$$

So, Theorem 9.32 is employed to derive $TT^* - T^*T = 0$, as desired. □

Example 9.42. Let $T = 2iI$ on a given Hilbert space X over $\mathbf{C}$, where I is the identity operator in $B(X)$. Then $T^* = -2iI$ and $TT^* = T^*T = 4I$. Thus, T is normal operator, but it is neither unitary nor self-adjoint.

The fifth special operator that we take account of is the projection operator.

Definition 9.43. Let X be a Hilbert space over $\mathbf{F}$. Then an operator $T \in B(X)$ is called a projection provided $T^2 = T$.

Example 9.44. Let M be a closed subspace of a Hilbert space X over $\mathbf{F}$. Then $X = M \oplus M^\perp$; that is, for any $x \in X$ there are unique $y \in M$ and $z \in M^\perp$ such that $x = y + z$. If $P_M(x) = y$ then P_M is a projection. In fact,

$$P_M^2(x) = P_M(y) = y = P_M(x) \Rightarrow P_M^2 = P_M.$$

The fact that $P_M \in B(X)$ follows from

$$\|x\|^2 = \|y+z\|^2 = \|y\|^2 + \|z\|^2 \geq \|y\|^2 = \|P_M(x)\|^2 \Rightarrow \|P_M\| \leq 1.$$

Traditionally, P_M is called the orthogonal projection of X onto M. Moreover, if $M \neq \{0\}$ then $P_M \neq 0$ and hence for any $x \in M \setminus \{0\}$ we have $x = x + 0$ and $P_M(x) = x$, giving $\|P_M\| = 1$.

The following theorem shows that the above orthogonal projections exist as a very important subclass of the projection operators.

Theorem 9.45. *Let X be a Hilbert space over $\mathbf{C}$. If $T \in B(X)$ is a projection, then the following statements are equivalent:*

(i) *T is nonnegative;*

(ii) *T is self-adjoint;*

(iii) *T is normal;*

(iv) *T is the orthogonal projection on $T(X)$.*

Proof. Since (i)⇒(ii)⇒(iii) are straightforward, we only verify (iii)⇒(iv)⇒(i).

(iii)⇒(iv) Assume (iii) holds. To reach (iv), let $M = T(X)$. We first prove that M is closed. Given a sequence $(y_j)_{j=1}^\infty$ in M with $y_j \to y$, we have $y_j = T(x_j)$, $x_j \in X$. Since T is a projection, we can conclude from $y_j \to y$ that

$$y_j = T(x_j) = T^2(x_j) = T(y_j) \to T(y) \Rightarrow y = T(y) \in M$$

and hence M is closed.

Next, given $x \in X$ we write $x = y + z$, $y \in M$ and $z \in M^\perp$. We must verify $T(x) = y$. Because $T(x) = T(y) + T(z)$, it suffices to prove that $T(y) = y$ and $T(z) = 0$. Since $y \in M$, there is $w \in X$ such that $y = T(w)$ and so $T(y) = T^2(w) = T(w) = y$. By the definition of M we have $T(z) \in M$, and if we can also prove $T(z) \in M^\perp$, then we can conclude $T(z) = 0$. To do so, let $u \in M$ be given. Then there is $v \in X$ such that $u = T(v)$ and

$$\langle T(z), u\rangle = \langle T(z), T(v)\rangle = \langle z, T^*T(v)\rangle = \langle z, TT^*(v)\rangle = 0$$

due to $z \in M^{\perp}$ and $TT^*(v) \in M$. In other words, $T(z) \in M^{\perp}$.

(iv)⇒(i) For any $x \in X$, let

$$x = y + z, \quad y \in M = T(X) \quad \text{and} \quad z \in M^{\perp}.$$

Then

$$\langle T(x), x\rangle = \langle y, y + z\rangle = \langle y, y\rangle + \langle y, z\rangle = \langle y, y\rangle \geq 0.$$

Hence T is nonnegative and the proof is complete. □

Remark 9.46. Here it is worth remarking that there exists a natural one-to-one correspondence between projection operators T and direct sum decompositions $X = M \oplus N$ where M and N are closed. As a matter of fact, if T is a projection, then $X = M \oplus N$ where $M = T(X)$ and $N = (I - T)(X)$. Conversely, if $X = M \oplus N$, then we define T as was done for the orthogonal projection with $N = M^{\perp}$.

9.5 Compact Operators via the Spectrum

This section is devoted to a spectrum-based study of the structure of a compact operator acting on a Hilbert space.

Definition 9.47. Let $(X, \|\cdot\|_X)$ be a Banach space over $\mathbf{F}$. Then a linear operator T is said to be of finite rank provided it is of the following form:

$$T(x) = \sum_{k=1}^{n} L_k(x)x_k \quad \text{for} \quad x, x_k \in X \quad \text{and} \quad L_k \in X^*.$$

Clearly, an operator of finite rank is compact, for it takes a bounded sequence into a bounded sequence in a finite dimensional Banach space. Hence, the image of the sequence has a convergent subsequence. By Theorem 8.44 we know that in a Banach space the limit in norm of operators of finite rank is compact. So, it is very natural to wonder whether or not the converse is true; that is, for each compact operator, can we find a sequence of operators of finite rank that approximate this compact operator in norm? Although the answer is no in general for Banach spaces, we will show that the answer is yes for all complex Hilbert spaces.

Definition 9.48. Let X be a Banach space over $\mathbf{C}$ and $T \in B(X)$.

(i) The null space of T, denoted $N(T)$, is $\{x \in X : T(x) = 0\}$. The range of T, denoted $R(T)$, is $\{y \in X : y = T(x) \text{ for some } x \in X\}$.

(ii) A complex number λ is called an eigenvalue of T if there exists a nonzero $x \in X$ such that $T(x) = \lambda x$. In this case, x is called an eigenvector associated with λ.

(iii) The spectrum of T, denoted $\sigma(T)$, is the set of all complex numbers λ such that $T - \lambda I$ does not have a bounded inverse where I is the identity operator in $B(X)$. The resolvent of T, written $\rho(T)$, is $\mathbf{C} \setminus \sigma(T)$. The spectral radius of T, denoted $r_\sigma(T)$, is $\sup\{|\lambda| : \lambda \in \sigma(T)\}$. In addition, $\sigma(T)$ can be split into the following three classes:

(a) The point spectrum

$$\sigma_p(T) = \{\lambda \in \sigma(T) : \; N(T - \lambda I) \neq \{0\}\};$$

(b) The continuous spectrum

$$\sigma_c(T) = \{\lambda \in \sigma(T) : \; N(T - \lambda I) = \{0\}, \; \overline{R(T - \lambda I)} = X\};$$

(c) The residual spectrum

$$\sigma_r(T) = \{\lambda \in \sigma(T) : \; N(T - \lambda I) = \{0\}, \; \overline{R(T - \lambda I)} \neq X\}.$$

Example 9.49.

(i) For the closed interval $[0,1]$ of $\mathbf{R}$, consider $\mathcal{LRS}^2_{id}([0,1], \mathbf{C})$ and the differential operator $T = -d^2/dx^2$ defined on the linear subspace of all complex-valued functions f having derivatives of any order on $[0,1]$ and satisfying the boundary conditions: $f(0) = f(1) = 0$. Then a computation via integration-by-parts indicates that T is self-adjoint; its eigenfunctions are $f_j(x) = \sin(j\pi x)$, $j \in \mathbf{N}$ with the real eigenvalues $j^2\pi^2$; the well-known orthogonality of the sine functions follows as a consequence of the property of being self-adjoint.

(ii) As a subset of $\mathbf{C}$, $\sigma(T)$ is always compact. In fact, according to Theorem 8.10 (i), $|\lambda| > \|T\|$ implies

$$\lambda(T - \lambda I)^{-1} = (\lambda^{-1}T - I)^{-1} \in B(X)$$

and then $\lambda \notin \sigma(T)$. By contrapositive statement, if $\lambda \in \sigma(T)$ then $|\lambda| \leq \|T\|$. Thus, $r_\sigma(T) \leq \|T\|$. This implies that $\sigma(T)$ is bounded. To see that $\sigma(T)$ is closed, let $\Phi : \mathbf{C} \to B(X)$ be $\Phi(\lambda) = T - \lambda I$. This map is continuous on $\mathbf{C}$ since $\|\Phi(\lambda_1) - \Phi(\lambda_2)\|_X = \|I\||\lambda_1 - \lambda_2|$. Thus, $\sigma(T)$ is closed, as the set of all invertible elements of $B(X)$ is open. Of course, $\rho(T) = \mathbf{C} \setminus \sigma(T)$ is open.

(iii) Let T be defined by $T\big((x_1, x_2, \ldots)\big) = (x_2, x_3, \ldots)$ on $\ell_2(\mathbf{N}, \mathbf{C})$. It is easy to see $\sigma(T) \subseteq \{\lambda \in \mathbf{C} : \; |\lambda| \leq 1\}$. Since $|\lambda| < 1$ implies $x = (1, \lambda, \lambda^2, \ldots) \in \ell_2(\mathbf{N}, \mathbf{C})$ and $T(x) = \lambda x$, and consequently $\{\lambda \in \mathbf{C} : \; |\lambda| < 1\} \subseteq \sigma_p(T)$. Note that $\sigma(T)$ is closed. So $\{\lambda \in \mathbf{C} : \; |\lambda| = 1\} \subseteq \sigma(T)$. Also, $\lambda \in \mathbf{C}$ and $|\lambda| = 1$ and $T(x) = \lambda x$ imply $x = (x_1, x_2, \ldots) = x_1(1, \lambda, \lambda^2, \ldots) \notin \ell_2(\mathbf{N}, \mathbf{C})$. This means $\{\lambda \in \mathbf{C} : \; |\lambda| = 1\} \subseteq \sigma_c(T)$. Accordingly, $\sigma_r(T) = \emptyset$.

The following result, which will be used later, gives much more information on the spectrum of a self-adjoint operator.

Theorem 9.50. *Let X be a Hilbert space over $\mathbf{C}$ and $T \in B(X)$ be self-adjoint.*

(i) *If λ is an eigenvalue of T, then λ is real.*

(ii) *If x_1 and x_2 are eigenvectors associated with different eigenvalues λ_1 and λ_2 of T, then $\langle x_1, x_2\rangle = 0$.*

(iii) *If λ is not an eigenvalue of T, then $R(T - \lambda I)$ is dense in X.*

(iv) *$\lambda \in \rho(T)$ if and only if $\|(T - \lambda I)(x)\| \geq \kappa\|x\|$ for all $x \in X$ and some $\kappa > 0$.*

(v) *If*

$$m_T = \inf_{\|x\|=1} \langle T(x), x \rangle \quad \text{and} \quad M_T = \sup_{\|x\|=1} \langle T(x), x \rangle,$$

then $\|T\| = \max\{|m_T|, |M_T|\}$ *and* $\sigma(T)$ *is a nonempty subset of the closed interval* $[m_T, M_T]$. *In particular,* $m_T, M_T \in \sigma(T)$.

(vi) $r_\sigma(T) = \|T\|$.

Proof. (i) This follows from the fact that $T(x) = \lambda x$ for some $x \neq 0$ implies

$$\lambda \|x\|^2 = \langle T(x), x \rangle \in \mathbf{R}$$

due to Theorem 9.32.

(ii) In this case, by (i) we have

$$\lambda_1 \langle x_1, x_2 \rangle = \langle T(x_1), x_2 \rangle = \langle x_1, T(x_2) \rangle = \lambda_2 \langle x_1, x_2 \rangle$$

which yields $\langle x_1, x_2 \rangle = 0$.

(iii) Suppose λ is not an eigenvalue of T. If $z \in R(T - \lambda I)^\perp$ then

$$0 = \langle z, T(x) - \lambda x \rangle = \langle T(z), x \rangle - \langle \bar{\lambda} z, x \rangle = \langle (T - \bar{\lambda} I)(z), x \rangle$$

for all $x \in X$. If $z \neq 0$ then this says that $\bar{\lambda}$ is an eigenvalue of T. Since $T = T^*$, we must then have $\bar{\lambda} = \lambda$, which is a contradiction. Thus $z = 0$ and

$$\begin{aligned} X &= \overline{R(T - \lambda I)} \oplus \left(\overline{R(T - \lambda I)}\right)^\perp \\ &\subseteq \overline{R(T - \lambda I)} \oplus R(T - \lambda I)^\perp = \overline{R(T - \lambda I)} \subseteq X. \end{aligned}$$

(iv) If $\lambda \in \rho(T)$ then $(T - \lambda I)^{-1} \in B(X)$ and we may set $\kappa = \|(T - \lambda I)^{-1}\|^{-1}$. Conversely, if $\|(T - \lambda I)(x)\| \geq \kappa \|x\|$ for all $x \in X$ and some $\kappa > 0$, then $R(T - \lambda I)$ is closed. In fact, suppose $(T - \lambda I)(x_k) \to y$. Then $\left((T - \lambda I)(x_k)\right)_{k=1}^\infty$ is a Cauchy sequence and hence $(x_k)_{k=1}^\infty$ is a Cauchy sequence too. Since X is Hilbert space, there exists a $z \in X$ such that $x_k \to z$. By continuity we have $(T - \lambda I)(x_k) \to T(z)$ and therefore $y = T(z)$. Also, by (iii) above, we see that $R(T - \lambda I)$ is dense in X and so $R(T - \lambda I) = X$. The given inequality insures that $N(T - \lambda I) = \{0\}$. Hence $T - \lambda I$ is surjective and injective. Accordingly, $(T - \lambda I)^{-1} \in B(X)$, namely, $\lambda \in \rho(T)$.

(v) The formula for $\|T\|$ follows from Theorem 9.32 (i) and the trivial formula $\sup_{\|x\|=1} |\langle T(x), x \rangle| = \max\{|m_T|, |M_T|\}$.

We next prove that $\sigma(T)$ comprises only real numbers. In so doing, let $\lambda = \alpha + i\beta$ where $\beta \neq 0$. Then for any $x \in X$ we have

$$\|(T - \lambda I)(x)\|^2 = \|T(x) - \alpha x\|^2 + \beta^2 \|x\|^2 \geq \beta^2 \|x\|^2,$$

and so $\lambda \in \rho(T)$ by (iv). In other words, if $\lambda \in \sigma(T)$ then $\beta = 0$ and hence $\lambda \in \mathbf{R}$.

After that, if $\lambda \in (-\infty, m_T)$ then for any $x \in X$,

$$\|T(x) - \lambda x\| \|x\| \geq \langle T(x) - \lambda x, x \rangle = \langle T(x), x \rangle - \lambda \|x\|^2 \geq (m_T - \lambda) \|x\|^2$$

and hence $\lambda \in \rho(T)$ by (iv). Similarly, if $\lambda \in (M_T, \infty)$ then $\lambda \in \rho(T)$. Thus $\sigma(T) \subseteq [m_T, M_T]$.

Furthermore, to verify $M_T \in \sigma(T)$, we may assume $M_T \geq m_T \geq 0$ and $M_T = \|T\|$ via replacing T with $T - m_T I$ since $\|T\| = \max\{|m_T|, |M_T|\}$. The definition of M_T produces a sequence $(x_k)_{k=1}^{\infty}$ with $\|x_k\| = 1$ such that $\lim_{k\to\infty}\langle T(x_k), x_k\rangle = \|T\|$. Accordingly,

$$\|T(x_k) - M_T x_k\|^2 \leq \|T\|^2 - 2\|T\|\langle T(x_k), x_k\rangle + M_T^2 \to 0 \quad \text{as} \quad k \to \infty.$$

This, along with (iv), implies $M_T \in \sigma(T)$.

Finally, in order to check $m_T \in \sigma(T)$, we consider $S = -T$ and obtain $-m_T = M_S \in \sigma(S)$ by the previous argument. Thus

$$T - m_T I = -(S - M_S I)$$

does not have a bounded inverse, and hence $m_T \in \sigma(T)$.

(vi) By (v), we have $m_T, M_T \in \sigma(T)$ and so

$$r_\sigma(T) \geq \max\{|m_T|, |M_T|\} = \|T\|.$$

This and the general estimate $r_\sigma(T) \leq \|T\|$ yield the desired formula. □

When working with a compact self-adjoint operator, we find that the structure of its spectrum is particularly simple.

Theorem 9.51. *Let X be a Hilbert space over* $\mathbf{C}$. *Suppose $T \in B(X)$ is compact and self-adjoint.*

(i) *If $\lambda \in \sigma(T)$ is nonzero, then λ is an eigenvalue of T.*

(ii) *If $\{e_\alpha : \alpha \in A\}$ is an orthonormal set of eigenvectors corresponding to eigenvalues λ_α with $|\lambda_\alpha| > c > 0$, then A is a finite set.*

Proof. (i) By Theorem 9.50 (iv), we see that if $\lambda \in \sigma(T)$ is not equal to 0 then there is a sequence $(x_k)_{k=1}^{\infty}$ in X obeying $\|x_k\| = 1$ and $T(x_k) - \lambda x_k \to 0$. Since T is compact, there exists a subsequence $(x_{k_n})_{n=1}^{\infty}$ such that $T(x_{k_n}) \to y \in X$ as $n \to \infty$. Consequently,

$$x_{k_n} = \lambda^{-1}\Big(T(x_{k_n}) - \big(T(x_{k_n}) - \lambda x_{k_n}\big)\Big) \to \lambda^{-1} y \quad \text{as} \quad n \to \infty,$$

and therefore $\lambda y = \lim_{n\to\infty} \lambda T(x_{k_n}) = T(y)$ owing to the continuity of T; that is, λ is an eigenvalue of T and y is a corresponding eigenvector. Moreover, $y \neq 0$ since $\|x_k\| = 1$ and $\lambda \neq 0$.

(ii) Assume A is infinite. Then there exists an infinite sequence of orthonormal eigenvectors $(y_k)_{k=1}^{\infty}$ corresponding to eigenvalues $(\lambda_k)_{k=1}^{\infty}$ with $|\lambda_k| > c > 0$ for all $k \in \mathbf{N}$. Note that the orthonormality of $(y_k)_{k=1}^{\infty}$ gives

$$\|T(y_k) - T(y_l)\|^2 = \|\lambda_k y_k\|^2 + \|\lambda_l y_l\|^2 = |\lambda_k|^2 + |\lambda_l|^2 > 2c^2.$$

So, the compactness of T implies $0 \geq c$, a contradiction. □

To reach the main result of this section, we introduce the following terminology.

Definition 9.52. Let X be a Hilbert space over $\mathbf{C}$. If λ is an eigenvalue of $T \in B(X)$, then $N(T - \lambda I)$ is called the eigenspace associated with λ.

Remark 9.53.

(i) It is clear that $N(T - \lambda I)$ is invariant under T; that is, if $x \in N(T - \lambda I)$ then $T(x) \in N(T - \lambda I)$ since $T(T(x)) = T(\lambda x) = \lambda T(x)$.

(ii) If T is compact and self-adjoint, then the eigenspace corresponding to each nonzero eigenvalue must be finite dimensional, but also, there can be at most finitely many eigenvalues λ obeying $|\lambda| > c$ for a given constant $c > 0$. The former clearly follows from Theorem 9.51 (ii). To see the latter, we assume that there were an infinite sequence of different eigenvalues $(\lambda_k)_{k=1}^{\infty}$ obeying $|\lambda_k| > c > 0$. If $(y_k)_{k=1}^{\infty}$ is a corresponding sequence of norm one eigenvectors, then by Theorem 9.50 (ii) we see that $(y_k)_{k=1}^{\infty}$ are orthogonal and hence orthonormal. But, $(y_k)_{k=1}^{\infty}$ cannot be infinite by Theorem 9.51 (ii). Thus, there can be only finitely many eigenvalues obeying $|\lambda_k| > c > 0$. Consequently, the set of nonzero eigenvalues of the operator is at most countable. Moreover, if the operator has infinitely many eigenvalues, then they must converge to zero since at most finitely many eigenvalues can satisfy an inequality of the form $|\lambda| > c > 0$.

Below is the spectral representation of a compact and self-adjoint operator on a complex Hilbert space.

Theorem 9.54. *Let X be a Hilbert space over $\mathbf{C}$. Suppose $T \in B(X)$ is compact and self-adjoint. If $(\lambda_j)_{j=1}^{\infty}$ is an enumeration of the distinct nonzero eigenvalues of T, then for each $x \in X$ one has $T(x) = \sum_{k=1}^{\infty} \lambda_k P_k(x)$, where each P_k is the orthogonal projection of X onto the eigenspace $N(T - \lambda_k I)$.*

Proof. From the definition of each P_k and Theorem 9.7 it follows that for $x \in X$,

$$\|P_k(x) - x\| = \inf\{\|y - x\| : y \in N(T - \lambda_k I)\}.$$

If $\{y_{k,1}, \cdots, y_{k,n_k}\}$ is an orthonormal basis of $N(T - \lambda_k I)$, then by Remark 9.53 (ii), and Theorems 9.20 and 9.22, $P_k(x) = \sum_{j=1}^{n_k} \langle x, y_{k,j} \rangle y_{k,j}$. Because eigenvectors corresponding to different eigenvalues are orthogonal, the set $S = \cup_{k=1}^{\infty} \{y_{k,1}, \cdots, y_{k,n_k}\}$ is an orthonormal set. The vector

$$y = \sum_{k=1}^{\infty} P_k(x) = \sum_{k=1}^{\infty} \sum_{j=1}^{n_k} \langle x, y_{k,n_k} \rangle y_{k,n_k}$$

is then well-defined since

$$\sum_{k=1}^{\infty} \sum_{j=1}^{n_k} |\langle x, y_{k,n_k} \rangle|^2 \leq \|x\|^2$$

which follows from Bessel's inequality. Since $P_k(x) \in N(T - \lambda_k I)$, we have $T(y) = \sum_{k=1}^{\infty} \lambda_k P_k(x)$. Writing $x = y + (x - y)$, we find that the proof will be complete upon verifying $x - y \in N(T)$. To this end, let M be the smallest closed linear subspace of X containing S. Then S is an orthonormal basis of M and hence $y = P_M(x)$, the orthogonal projection onto M of x. From this it turns out that

$$x = (I - P_M)(x) + P_M(x) = P_{M^\perp}(x) + P_M(x).$$

Since M is invariant under T, $x \in M^\perp$ implies $\langle T(x), z\rangle = \langle x, T(z)\rangle = 0$ for $z \in M$, namely, $M^\perp$ is invariant under T. Therefore, if U stands for the restriction of T to $M^\perp$, then $U \in B(M^\perp)$ and it is obviously a compact self-adjoint operator on the Hilbert space $M^\perp$. Now, if $U \neq 0$, then it has a nonzero eigenvalue which would also be a nonzero eigenvalue of T. In other words, there is some nonzero $x \in M^\perp$ with $x \in N(T - \lambda I) \subseteq M$ for some nonzero $\lambda \in \sigma(T)$. Noticing $M \cap M^\perp = \{0\}$, we get $x = 0$, a contradiction. Therefore, U must be a zero operator and consequently,

$$T(x - y) = UP_{M^\perp}(x) = 0.$$

This completes the proof of the theorem. □

Remark 9.55. The argument for Theorem 9.54 produces a linear subspace $M^\perp$ of X comprising elements mapped to zero by T. So, we can choose an orthonormal basis of $M^\perp$, each element of which is an eigenvector of T with eigenvalue 0. If these new eigenvectors are included in the sequence of eigenvectors constructed in Theorem 9.54, we obtain an orthonormal basis $\{e_j\}_{j=1}^\infty$ for X. Note that the new eigenvalue is zero, their inclusion does not affect the convergence of the sequence $(\lambda_k)_{k=1}^\infty$. Consequently, if $x = \sum_{j=1}^\infty c_j e_j \in X$ and if $(\mu_j)_{j=1}^\infty$ is the sequence of eigenvalues corresponding to $\{e_j\}_{j=1}^\infty$, then

$$T(x) = \sum_{j=1}^\infty c_j \mu_j e_j = \sum_{k=1}^\infty c_k \lambda_k P_k(x) = \sum_{k=1}^\infty c_k \lambda_k \sum_{j=1}^{n_k} \langle x, y_{k,j}\rangle y_{k,j}.$$

In some ways, Theorem 9.54 tells us that the self-adjoint compact operators in a Hilbert space are similar to the symmetric matrices in $\mathbf{R}^n$. Moreover, as an interesting consequence of Theorem 9.54, we can approximate any compact operator on a Hilbert space by the operators of finite rank.

Theorem 9.56. *Let X be a Hilbert space over $\mathbf{C}$. Then for each compact operator $T \in B(X)$ there is a sequence of operators of finite rank converging to T in norm.*

Proof. First, assume X is separable. Then by Theorem 9.24 we see that X has a countable orthonormal basis $\{e_k\}_{k=1}^\infty$. For each $n \in \mathbf{N}$ define the operator P_n via

$$P_n(x) = \sum_{k=1}^n \langle x, e_k\rangle e_k, \quad x \in X.$$

From Theorem 9.19 or Remark 9.46 it follows that

$$\max\{\|P_n\|, \|I - P_n\|\} \le 1 \quad \text{for all} \quad n \in \mathbf{N}$$

and

$$\lim_{n\to\infty} \|P_n(x) - x\| = 0.$$

Now, if the assertion were false, then there would be a compact operator $T \in B(X)$ and a number $\delta > 0$ such that $\|T - F\| \geq \delta$ for all operators F of finite rank. Hence, for each $n \in \mathbf{N}$ there is an $x_n \in X$ such that $\|x_n\| = 1$ and $\|(T - F_n)(x_n)\| \geq \delta/2$, where the operator F_n defined by

$$F_n(x) = P_n\big(T(x)\big) = \sum_{k=1}^{n} \langle T(x), e_k\rangle e_k, \quad x \in X,$$

is an operator of finite rank. Since $(x_n)_{n=1}^{\infty}$ is bounded and T is compact, there is a subsequence $(x_{n_j})_{j=1}^{\infty}$ such that $\big(T(x_{n_j})\big)_{j=1}^{\infty}$ converges to some element $w \in X$. But

$$\begin{aligned} \|(T - F_{n_j})(x_{n_j})\| &\leq \|(I - P_{n_j})(T(x_{n_j}) - w)\| + \|(I - P_{n_j})(w)\| \\ &\leq \|T(x_{n_j}) - w\| + \|(I - P_{n_j})(w)\|. \end{aligned}$$

Now for n_j big enough, we have

$$\|(I - P_{n_j})(w)\| < \delta/4 \quad \text{and} \quad \|T(x_{n_j}) - w\| < \delta/4.$$

The foregoing estimates therefore produce a contradiction: $\delta/2 > \delta/2$, which naturally proves the assertion in the case when X is separable.

Next, assume X is any Hilbert space over $\mathbf{C}$. Set $S = T^*T$. Then S is self-adjoint and compact. By Remark 9.55, S can be written as the following form

$$S(x) = \sum_{k=1}^{\infty} \lambda_k \langle x, e_k\rangle e_k, \quad x \in X,$$

for some countable orthonormal set $\{e_k\}_{k=1}^{\infty}$. Suppose now that X_0 is the subspace of all linear combinations of elements of the form $T^n(e_k)$, $n + 1 \in \mathbf{N}; k \in \mathbf{N}$. Then $\overline{X_0}$ is a separable closed linear subspace of X, and T maps $\overline{X_0}$ into itself. By the first part, there exists a sequence $(F_n)_{n=1}^{\infty}$ of finite rank operators on $\overline{X_0}$ converging in norm to the restriction $\tilde{T}$ of T to $\overline{X_0}$. Now every element $x \in X$ can be decomposed into the form $x = y + z$ (where $y \in \overline{X_0}$, and $z \in \overline{X_0}^{\perp}$ is orthogonal to X_0). With this, we get that z is orthogonal to each e_k, and so $z \in N(S)$. Accordingly,

$$0 = \langle S(z), z\rangle = \langle T^*T(z), z\rangle = \|T(z)\|^2;$$

that is, $T(z) = 0$. Thus, if $G_n(x) = F_n(y)$ for $n \in \mathbf{N}$, then G_n is of finite rank and $\lim_{n\to\infty} \|G_n - T\| = 0$ thanks to

$$\|G_n(x) - T(x)\| = \|F_n(y) - T(y)\| = \|F_n(y) - \tilde{T}(y)\| \leq \|F_n - \tilde{T}\|\|x\|.$$

We are done. □

To close this section, we use Remark 9.55 to produce the forthcoming Fredholm's alternative which arises in the study of the following homogeneous and inhomogeneous Fredholm integral equations:

$$\int_{[a,b]} k(x,y)f(y)dm_{id}(y) - f(x) = 0; \quad \int_{[a,b]} k(x,y)f(y)dm_{id}(y) - f(x) = g(x)$$

for given $g \in \mathcal{LRS}^2_{id}([a,b], \mathbf{C})$ and $|k(\cdot,\cdot)|^2 \in LRS_{id}([a,b] \times [a,b])$.

Theorem 9.57. *Let X be a Hilbert space over $\mathbf{C}$. Suppose T is a compact self-adjoint linear operator on X.*

(i) *If the only solution to the homogeneous equation $T(f) - f = 0$ is $f = 0$, then the inhomogeneous equation $T(f) - f = g$ has a unique solution f for each $g \in X$.*

(ii) *If $T(f) - f = 0$ has nonzero solutions, then $T(f) - f = g$ has a solution for a given $g \in X$ only if $\langle g, f\rangle = 0$ for any solution f to $T(f) - f = 0$, in which case $T(f) - f = g$ has infinitely many solutions, the difference of any two of them being a solution of $T(f) - f = 0$.*

Proof. (i) From Remark 9.55 it follows that there exists a countable index set J such that $\{e_j\}_{j\in J}$ comprises eigenvectors of T and forms an orthonormal basis of X. Suppose $(\mu_j)_{j\in J}$ is the sequence of eigenvalues of T corresponding to $\{e_j\}_{j\in J}$. For $g = \sum_{j\in J} c_j e_j \in X$, we look for a solution $f = \sum_{j\in J} d_j e_j$ of the equation $T(f) - f = g$ through

$$\sum_{j\in J} d_j \mu_j e_j - \sum_{j\in J} d_j e_j = \sum_{j\in J} c_j e_j,$$

obtaining $d_j = c_j(\mu_j - 1)^{-1}$ provided $\mu_j \neq 1$. Note that if $T(f) - f = 0$ has no nonzero solution then 1 is not an eigenvalue of T and thus all d_j's exist. So the solution to $T(f) - f = g$ must be of the form $\sum_{j\in J} c_j(\mu_j - 1)^{-1} e_j$. Of course, this shows that if $T(f) - f = g$ has a solution then it must be unique. Now, it remains to check that the last series converges in X but also produces a solution to $T(f) - f = g$.

We claim that 1 is not a cluster point of the set $\{\mu_j\}_{j\in J}$ of eigenvalues of T. In fact, if J is finite, then our claim is valid. On the other hand, if J is infinite, then we can see from Remarks 9.53 (ii) that $\mu_j \to 0$ as $j \to \infty$, and so no subsequence of $(\mu_j)_{j\in J}$ can approach 1 – this means that 1 is not a cluster point of the set $\{\mu_j\}_{j\in J}$. Consequently, we get

$$\sup_{j\in J} |\mu_j - 1|^{-2} < \infty \quad \text{and} \quad \sum_{j\in J} |c_j(\mu_j - 1)^{-1}|^2 \le \big(\inf_{j\in J} |\mu_j - 1|\big)^{-2} \sum_{j\in J} |c_j|^2 < \infty.$$

This last finiteness, along with Theorem 9.22, implies that $\sum_{j\in J} c_j(\mu_j - 1)^{-1} e_j$ is absolutely convergent in X.

Next, let us verify that the last series is a solution to $T(f) - f = g$. Since $g \in X$ and $\{e_j\}_{j\in J}$ is an orthonormal basis of X, we conclude

$$g = \sum_{j\in J} \langle g, e_j\rangle e_j \quad \text{and} \quad \sum_{j\in J} |\langle g, e_j\rangle|^2 < \infty.$$

Also since T is self-adjoint and compact, it follows that $\inf_{j\in J}|\mu_j - 1| > 0$ and then

$$\sum_{j\in J} |\langle g, e_j\rangle|^2 |\mu_j - 1|^{-2} \le \big(\inf_{j\in J} |\mu_j - 1|\big)^{-2} \sum_{j\in J} |\langle g, e_j\rangle|^2 < \infty.$$

This yields that $f = \sum_{j\in J}\langle g, e_j\rangle(\mu_j - 1)^{-1}e_j$ is convergent in X thanks to Theorem 9.22. Accordingly,

$$\begin{aligned} T(f) &= \sum_{j\in J}\langle g, e_j\rangle(\mu_j - 1)^{-1}T(e_j) \\ &= \sum_{j\in J}\langle g, e_j\rangle(\mu_j - 1)^{-1}\mu_j e_j \\ &= \sum_{j\in J}\langle g, e_j\rangle(\mu_j - 1)^{-1}e_j + \sum_{j\in J}\langle g, e_j\rangle e_j \\ &= f + g. \end{aligned}$$

(ii) Given $g \in X$, assume now that f_1 satisfies $T(f) - f = g$ and f_2 is a nonzero solution to $T(f) - f = 0$. This assumption, plus $T^* = T$, gives

$$\langle f_1, f_2\rangle = \langle T(f_1), f_2\rangle - \langle g, f_2\rangle = \langle f_1, T(f_2)\rangle - \langle g, f_2\rangle = \langle f_1, f_2\rangle - \langle g, f_2\rangle,$$

whence deriving $\langle g, f_2\rangle = 0$. Here, since $T(f)-f = g$ implies $T(f+cf_2)-(f_1+cf_2) = g$ for any f_2 with $T(f_2) - f_2 = 0$ and $c \in \mathbf{C}$, there are infinitely many such solutions to $T(f) - f = g$. The final assertion follows simply from taking the difference between two solutions to $T(f) - f = g$. □

Clearly, the above Fredholm's alternative theorem is a simple generalization of facts on sets of linear algebraic equations: An inhomogeneous system has a unique solution when and only when the determinant of the coefficients is nonzero, i.e., the corresponding homogeneous system has no nonzero solution. In addition, we here want to say by an example that the compactness of the operator T in the Fredholm's alternative theorem is essential.

Example 9.58. On $\mathcal{LRS}^2_{id}([0,1],\mathbf{C})$ define $T(f)(x) = (1-x)f(x)$. Then T is self-adjoint but not compact. The homogeneous equation $T(f) - f = 0$ has no solution other than $f = 0$. Nevertheless, the inhomogeneous equation $T(f) - f = g$ has no solution in $\mathcal{LRS}^2_{id}([0,1],\mathbf{C})$ for any nonconstant function $g \in \mathcal{LRS}^2_{id}([0,1],\mathbf{C})$ – indeed, the solution to $T(f) - f = g$ is then proportional to $-1/x$, $x \in (0,1]$, which is certainly not in $\mathcal{LRS}^2_{id}([0,1],\mathbf{C})$.

Problems

9.1. Equip $C([-1,1],\mathbf{C})$ with the 2-norm and the inner product

$$\langle f, g\rangle = \int_{-1}^{1} f(x)\overline{g(x)}dx.$$

Prove that $C([-1,1],\mathbf{C})$ is an inner product space but not a Hilbert space.

9.2. Equip $\ell_p(\mathbf{N},\mathbf{C})$, $1 \le p < \infty$, with the p-norm. Prove that $\ell_2(\mathbf{N},\mathbf{C})$ is a Hilbert space under the inner product

$$\langle x, y\rangle = \sum_{j=1}^{\infty} x_j \overline{y_j} \quad \text{for all} \quad x = (x_j)_{j=1}^{\infty},\ y = (y_j)_{j=1}^{\infty} \in \ell_2(\mathbf{N},\mathbf{C}),$$

but $\ell_p(\mathbf{N},\mathbf{C})$ is not a Hilbert space under the p-norm whenever $p \ne 2$.

9.3. Let X be an inner product space over $\mathbf{F}$.

(i) If $\mathbf{F} = \mathbf{R}$, prove that $x \perp y$ is equivalent to $\|x+y\|^2 = \|x\|^2 + \|y\|^2$. Is this equivalence true for $\mathbf{F} = \mathbf{C}$?

(ii) $x \perp y$ if and only if $\|x + \beta y\| \ge \|x\|$ for all $\beta \in \mathbf{F}$.

9.4. Let X be a Hilbert space over $\mathbf{F}$. Prove that if M is a closed linear subspace of X then $(M^{\perp})^{\perp} = M$.

9.5. Equip $\mathcal{LRS}^2_{id}([-1,1],\mathbf{C})$ with the inner product $\langle f, g\rangle = \int_{[-1,1]} f\overline{g}\,dm_{id}$.

(i) Let

$$M = \big\{f \in \mathcal{LRS}^2_{id}([-1,1],\mathbf{C}) :\ f(x) = 0 \quad \text{for all} \quad x \in [-1,0]\big\}.$$

Find $M^{\perp}$.

(ii) Let

$$M_{odd} = \big\{f \in \mathcal{LRS}^2_{id}([-1,1],\mathbf{C}) :\ f(-x) = -f(x) \quad \text{for all} \quad x \in [-1,1]\big\}$$

and

$$M_{even} = \big\{f \in \mathcal{LRS}^2_{id}([-1,1],\mathbf{C}) :\ f(-x) = f(x) \quad \text{for all} \quad x \in [-1,1]\big\}.$$

Prove $\mathcal{LRS}^2_{id}([-1,1],\mathbf{C}) = M_{odd} \oplus M_{even}$.

9.6. Equip $\mathcal{LRS}^2_{id}([-\pi,\pi],\mathbf{C})$ with the inner product $\langle f, g\rangle = \int_{[-\pi,\pi]} f\overline{g}\,dm_{id}$. Prove that:

(i) $\big\{(2\pi)^{-\frac{1}{2}} e^{inx}\big\}_{n=-\infty}^{\infty}$ is an orthonormal set;

(ii)

$$\big\{(2\pi)^{-\frac{1}{2}}, \pi^{-\frac{1}{2}}\cos t, \pi^{-\frac{1}{2}}\sin t, \pi^{-\frac{1}{2}}\cos 2t, \pi^{-\frac{1}{2}}\sin 2t, \dots\big\}$$

is an orthonormal basis of $\mathcal{LRS}^2_{id}([-\pi,\pi],\mathbf{C})$.

9.7. Let $\mathcal{LRS}^2_{id}([-\pi,\pi],\mathbf{C})$ be as in Problem 9.6. For $\phi \in C([-\pi,\pi],\mathbf{C})$ let $T(f) = \phi f$ be defined on $\mathcal{LRS}^2_{id}([-\pi,\pi],\mathbf{C})$.

(i) Calculate T^* using the inner product defined above.

(ii) Prove that if ϕ is real-valued then T is self-adjoint.

(iii) Find a condition on ϕ such that T is respectively unitary, nonnegative, or a projection.

9.8. Let X be a Hilbert space over $\mathbf{C}$ and $T \in B(X)$. Prove:

(i) $R(T)^{\perp} = N(T^*)$, $N(T)^{\perp} = \overline{R(T^*)}$;

(ii) $R(T^*)^{\perp} = N(T)$, $N(T^*)^{\perp} = \overline{R(T)}$.

9.9. Equip $C([0, 2\pi], \mathbf{C})$ with the sup-norm: $\|f\|_{\infty} = \sup_{x \in [0,2\pi]} |f(x)| < \infty$.

(i) Define $T(f)(x) = xf(x)$ for $f \in C([0, 2\pi], \mathbf{C})$. Find $\sigma(T)$.

(ii) Define $T(f)(x) = e^{ix} f(x)$ for $f \in C([0, 2\pi], \mathbf{C})$. Prove $\sigma(T) = \{\lambda \in \mathbf{C} : |\lambda| = 1\}$.

9.10. Equip $\ell_2(\mathbf{N}, \mathbf{C})$ with the 2-norm.

(i) If $T(x) = T\big((x_1, x_2, \cdots)\big) = (x_2, x_3, \cdots)$, find $\sigma(T)$.

(ii) If $T(x) = T\big((x_1, x_2, \cdots)\big) = (0, -x_1, -x_2, -x_3, \cdots)$, prove that:

(a) T has no eigenvalue;

(b) $\rho(T) = \{\lambda \in \mathbf{C} : |\lambda| > 1\}$;

(c) $\|(T - \lambda I)^{-1}\| = (|\lambda| - 1)^{-1}$.

9.11. Suppose that X is a Hilbert space over $\mathbf{C}$, and that $T \in B(X)$. Prove $\sigma(T^*) = \{\overline{\lambda} : \lambda \in \sigma(T)\}$.

9.12. Let $(X, \|\cdot\|)$ be a Hilbert space over $\mathbf{C}$. If $T \in B(X)$ is compact and self-adjoint and $x \in X$ satisfies $\|x\| = 1$, prove the following two results:

(i) $\lambda \in \mathbf{R}$ obeys $\|T(x) - \lambda x\|^2 = \|T(x)\|^2 - \langle T(x), x\rangle^2$ when and only when $\lambda = \langle T(x), x\rangle$;

(ii) There exists a $\lambda \in \sigma(T)$ such that

$$|\lambda - \langle T(x), x\rangle| \leq \sqrt{\|T(x)\|^2 - \langle T(x), x\rangle^2}.$$

9.13. Let $T(f)(x) = \int_0^1 e^{x+y} f(y)dy$. Find the eigenvalues and eigenvectors of T.

9.14. Let X be a Hilbert space over $\mathbf{C}$. If $T = T_1 + iT_2$ is normal operator on X, prove $\|T\|^2 = \|T_1^2 + T_2^2\|$ and $\|T^2\| = \|T\|^2$.

9.15. Let X be a Hilbert space over $\mathbf{C}$, $\lambda \in \mathbf{C}$, and $T \in B(X)$ be normal. Prove the following results:

(i) $\|(T^* - \bar{\lambda} I)(x)\| = \|(T - \lambda I)(x)\|$ for $x \in X$;

(ii) If $T(x) = \lambda x$ then $T^*(x) = \bar{\lambda} x$;

(iii) $r_{\sigma}(T) = \|T\|$.

9.16. Let X be a Hilbert space over $\mathbf{C}$. Prove if $T \in B(X)$ and T^*T is compact then T is compact.

9.17. Suppose that $[a_{mn}]$ is an infinite matrix of real numbers obeying

$$\sum_{m,n=1}^{\infty} a_{mn}^2 < \infty.$$

Let the linear operator T on $\ell_2(\mathbf{N}, \mathbf{R})$ be defined by $T(x) = y$ where $x = (x_1, x_2, \cdots)$ and $y = \big(\sum_{n=1}^{\infty} a_{1n}x_n, \sum_{n=1}^{\infty} a_{2n}x_n, \cdots\big)$. Prove that T is a compact operator on $\ell_2(\mathbf{N}, \mathbf{R})$.

9.18. Consider $\mathcal{LRS}^2_{id}([0,1],\mathbf{C})$ on which the inner product is given by $\langle f,g\rangle = \int_{[0,1]} f\bar{g}dm_{id}$, and suppose $K(f)(x) = \int_{[0,1]} k(x,y)f(y)dy$ for $f \in \mathcal{LRS}^2_{id}([0,1],\mathbf{C})$.

(i) If

$$k(y,x) = \sum_{k=1}^{n} g_k(x)f_k(y) \quad \text{where} \quad f_k, g_k \in \mathcal{LRS}^2_{id}([0,1],\mathbf{C})$$

and $\{g_k\}_{k=1}^n$ are linearly independent, prove that T is compact.

(ii) If λ is nonzero eigenvalue, prove that its corresponding eigenvector has the following form:

$$f(x) = \sum_{k=1}^{n} c_k g_k(x) \quad \text{where} \quad c_k \quad \text{is constant;}$$

moreover, if $h_{k,j} = \int_{[0,1]} f_k g_j dm_{id}$ then $c_k = \lambda^{-1}\sum_{j=1}^n h_{j,k}c_j$, $k = 1,2,\dots,n$.

(iii) If $f_k = g_k$ and $\langle f_j, g_k\rangle = 0$ for $j \neq k$, evaluate eigenvalues and eigenvectors of K.

(iv) If $k(y,x) = \cos\frac{y+x}{\pi}$ for $x,y \in [0,1]$, evaluate eigenvalues and eigenvectors of K.

9.19. Suppose T is a compact operator on an infinite-dimensional Hilbert space $(X, \|\cdot\|)$ over $\mathbf{C}$. If $\{e_j\}_{j=1}^\infty$ is an orthonormal basis of X, prove $\lim_{j\to\infty}\|T(e_j)\| = 0$.

9.20. Let $(X, \|\cdot\|_X)$ and $(Y, \|\cdot\|_Y)$ be Hilbert spaces over $\mathbf{C}$. A bounded linear operator $T: X \to Y$ is called Hilbert-Schmidt (Erhard Schmidt) operator provided there exists an orthonormal basis $\{e_j\}_{j=1}^\infty$ in X such that $\sum_{j=1}^\infty \|T(e_j)\|_Y^2 < \infty$.

(i) If $T^*: Y \to X$ is defined by

$$\langle T(x), y\rangle_Y = \langle x, T^*(y)\rangle_X, \quad x \in X, \ y \in Y,$$

where $\langle\cdot,\cdot\rangle_X$ and $\langle\cdot,\cdot\rangle_Y$ stand for the inner products equipped with X and Y respectively, prove that T is Hilbert-Schmidt operator when and only when T^* is Hilbert-Schmidt operator.

(ii) Prove that any Hilbert-Schmidt operator is compact.

(iii) If $k(\cdot,\cdot): (a,b)\times(c,d) \to \mathbf{C}$ satisfies $\int_{(a,b)}\int_{(c,d)} |k(x,y)|^2 dm_{id}(x)dm_{id}(y) < \infty$ where $(a,b)\times(c,d) \subseteq \mathbf{R}^2$, prove that the integral operator

$$T(f)(x) = \int_{(c,d)} k(x,y)f(y)dm_{id}(y), \quad x \in (a,b)$$

is a Hilbert-Schmidt operator from $\mathcal{LRS}^2_{id}((c,d),\mathbf{C})$ to $\mathcal{LRS}^2_{id}((a,b),\mathbf{C})$ and thus compact.

9.21. Let X and Y be Hilbert spaces over $\mathbf{C}$. Suppose $\{e_j\}_{j=1}^\infty$ and $\{f_k\}_{k=1}^\infty$ are orthonormal bases of X and Y respectively. For a sequence $(c_k)_{k=1}^\infty$ in $\mathbf{C}$ define a linear operator $T: X \to Y$ by

$$T(x) = \sum_{k=1}^{\infty} c_k\langle x, e_k\rangle_X f_k, \quad x \in X,$$

where $\langle\cdot,\cdot\rangle_X$ and $\langle\cdot,\cdot\rangle_Y$ stand for the inner products equipped with X and Y respectively. Prove the following results:

(i) T is a bounded operator when and only when $\sup_{k\in\mathbf{N}} |c_k| < \infty$;

(ii) T is a compact operator when and only when $\lim_{k\to\infty} |c_k| = 0$;

(iii) T is a Hilbert-Schmidt operator when and only when $\sum_{k=1}^{\infty} |c_k|^2 < \infty$;

(iv) T is an operator of finite rank when and only when there is an $N \in \mathbf{N}$ such that $|c_k| = 0$ for $n > N$.

Hints and Solutions

This part comprises hints and solutions to those problems included at the end of each chapter in the text.

1 Preliminaries

1.1. If $x \in (X \cup Y) \setminus (X \cap Y)$ then $x \in X \cup Y$ but $x \notin X \cap Y$ and hence we must have: $x \in X$ but $x \notin Y$ or $x \in Y$ but $x \notin X$; that is, $x \in (X \setminus Y) \cup (Y \setminus X)$. Thus $(X \cup Y) \setminus (X \cap Y) \subseteq (X \setminus Y) \cup (Y \setminus X)$. The reverse inclusion can be proved similarly. Therefore, the desired equality follows.

1.2. $\cup_{j \in \mathbf{N}} X_j = [0,1]$ and $\cap_{j \in \mathbf{N}} X_j = \{0\}$.

1.3. If $x \in X \cap (\cup_{j \in I} X_j)$ then $x \in X$ and $x \in X_j$ for some $j \in I$ and hence $x \in \cup_{j \in I}(X \cap X_j)$. Consequently, $X \cap (\cup_{j \in I} X_j) \subseteq \cup_{j \in I}(X \cap X_j)$. The reverse inclusion can be proved similarly. So, the desired equality follows. The second equality can be checked in a similar manner.

1.4. This follows from the relevant definitions.

1.5. $f(x) = a + (b-a)x : (0,1) \to (a,b)$ and $g(x) = \tan \frac{\pi x}{2} : (0,1) \to (0,\infty)$ are bijective.

1.6. If $x \in (g \circ f)^{-1}(C)$ then $g \circ f(x) \in C$ and hence $f(x) \in g^{-1}(C)$ and $x \in f^{-1}\big(g^{-1}(C)\big)$. Accordingly, $(g \circ f)^{-1}(C) \subseteq f^{-1}\big(g^{-1}(C)\big)$. Similarly, we have $(g \circ f)^{-1}(C) \supseteq f^{-1}\big(g^{-1}(C)\big)$, thereby getting the desired equality.

1.7. Since X is infinite, $X \setminus \{x\}$ is infinite and hence there is an $x_1 \in X \setminus \{x\}$. Of course, $X \setminus \{x, x_1\}$ is infinite, and then there is an $x_2 \in X \setminus \{x, x_1\}$. This process produces a sequence of distinct points $(x_j)_{j=1}^{\infty}$ in $X \setminus \{x\}$. The map: $x \to x_1$, $x_j \to x_{j+1}$; $j \in \mathbf{N}$, $y \to y$ otherwise, is a bijection from X onto $X \setminus \{x\}$.

1.8. Since $f(X)$ is a subset of Y, $f(X)$ is countable. While f is one-to-one, X is countable too.

1.9. If there is a function ϕ from $[0,1]$ onto X, then for each $x \in [0,1]$ we have $\phi_x = \phi(x) \in X$ which is a function from $[0,1]$ to $\mathbf{R}$. For any $x \in [0,1]$ let

$$f(x) = \begin{cases} 0, & \phi_x(x) \neq 0, \\ 1, & \phi_x(x) = 0. \end{cases}$$

Since ϕ is surjective, there is an $x_0 \in [0,1]$ such that $f = \phi_{x_0}$. But $f(x_0) \neq \phi_{x_0}(x_0)$, a contradiction. Therefore, no such ϕ exists.

1.10. (i) $a^{-1}ax = a^{-1}b$ gives $x = a^{-1}b$ and conversely.
(ii) Use $a^{-1}(a^{-1})^{-1} = 1$.
(iii) Use $(ab)(ab)^{-1} = 1$ and $aba^{-1}b^{-1} = 1$.

1.11. Obviously, $|a_1| \le |a_1|$. Assuming the inequality for $n = k$, we get (by the triangle inequality) that

$$\begin{aligned} |a_1 + a_2 + \cdots + a_k + a_{k+1}| &\le |a_1 + a_2 + \cdots + a_k| + |a_{k+1}| \\ &\le |a_1| + |a_2| + \cdots + |a_k| + |a_{k+1}|, \end{aligned}$$

as desired.

1.12. Use $b^3 - a^3 = (b-a)(b^2 + ba + a^2)$ and $b^2 + ba + a^2 \ge 0$ (under $a, b \ge 0$).

1.13. Clearly, $\sup(X+Y) \le \sup X + \sup Y$. For any $\epsilon > 0$ there are $x \in X$ and $y \in Y$ such that $\sup X < x + \epsilon$ and $\sup Y < y + \epsilon$. So, $\sup X + \sup Y < \sup(X+Y) + 2\epsilon$. This gives $\sup X + \sup Y \le \sup(X+Y)$. Thus, $\sup(X+Y) = \sup X + \sup Y$. The proof of $\inf(X+Y) = \inf X + \inf Y$ is similar to the previous one.

1.14. (i) Since $(a_n)_{n=1}^{\infty}$ is increasing and bounded from above by any b_k, $a = \lim_{n\to\infty} a_n$ exists and belongs to $\cap_{n\in\mathbf{N}} I_n$. Similarly, $b = \lim_{n\to\infty} b_n$ exists and belongs to $\cap_{n\in\mathbf{N}} I_n$.
(ii) This follows from (i).
(iii) This follows from (i) and (ii).

1.15. Use Definition 1.20 and some simple estimates.

1.16. Use: If $M > 0$ then $s_n > M$ is equivalent to $s_n^{-1} < M^{-1}$.

1.17. Use $s_m - s_n = (n+1)^{-1} + \cdots m^{-1}$ for $m > n$.

1.18. (i) It suffices to prove the first equality. Since $(s_n)_{n\in\mathbf{N}}$ is bounded, $a = \limsup s_n \in \mathbf{R}$ and for any $\epsilon > 0$ there is an $N \in \mathbf{N}$ such that $n > N$ implies $s_n < a + \epsilon$. Thus for all $m > N$ we have $\sup\{s_n : n > m\} \le a + \epsilon$. Of course, this yields $\sup\{s_n : n > m\} \le a$ as $m > N$ and then $\lim_{m\to\infty} \sup\{s_n : n > m\} \le a$. For the reverse inequality, let $N \in \mathbf{N}$ be fixed. Then for any $\epsilon > 0$ there exists $n_0 > N$ such that $s_{n_0} > a - \epsilon$. Hence $\sup\{s_n : n > N\} \ge a$. This is valid for any $N \in \mathbf{N}$. So, $a \le \lim_{N\to\infty} \sup\{s_n : n > N\}$.
(ii) If $\lim_{n\to\infty} s_n = s \in \mathbf{R}$ exists, then all subsequences of $(s_n)_{n\in\mathbf{N}}$ have limit s. Thus $S = \{s\}$ and consequently $\limsup s_n = s = \liminf s_n$. Conversely, assume $\limsup s_n = s = \liminf s_n$. If $(s_n)_{n=1}^{\infty}$ has no limit, then there is an $\epsilon_0 > 0$ and a subsequence $(s_{n_k})_{k\in\mathbf{N}}$ of $(s_n)_{n=1}^{\infty}$ such that $|s_{n_k} - s| \ge \epsilon_0$. Since $(s_{n_k})_{k=1}^{\infty}$ is bounded, the Bolzano-Weierstrass property implies that this subsequence has a subsequence which converges to $t \in \mathbf{R}$. Of course, $|t - s| \ge \epsilon_0$. This indicates $t \in S$ and so $\sup S$ and $\inf S$ cannot both be s, contradicting the assumption.

2 Riemann Integrals

2.1. (i) Given $\epsilon > 0$, choose $\delta = \epsilon/2$. If P is any partition of $[0,1]$, then in $S(f,P,\xi)$ there are at most two nonzero terms (1/2 could be a partition point, say $x_j = 1/2$, and we could have $\xi_j = x_j = \xi_{j+1}$). Thus $\|P\| < \delta$ implies

$$0 \le S(f,P,\xi) \le 2\|P\| < \epsilon.$$

(ii) Given $\epsilon > 0$, there are at most $2/\epsilon$ of the numbers $1/k$ that satisfy $1/k > \epsilon/2$. Thus in any sum $P(f,\xi)$, those numbers contribute at most

$$(2/\epsilon)2(\sup_{x\in[0,1]} |f(x)|)\|P\| = 4\|P\|/\epsilon.$$

The remaining terms in $S(f,P,\xi)$ contribute at most $\sup_{x\in[0,1]} |f(x)|$ times the total length of those subintervals in $[0,\epsilon/2]$. Therefore $0 \le S(f,P,\xi) \le (4/\epsilon)\|P\| + (\epsilon/2)$. Define $\delta = \epsilon^2/8$ to get $|S(f,P,\xi)| < \epsilon$ whenever $\|P\| < \delta$.
(iii) Let P be a partition of $[0,2]$ and suppose $x_j \le 1 \le x_{j+1}$. In $S(f,P,\xi)$, if $k < j$ then $f(\xi_k) = 1$; and if $k > j+1$ then $f(\xi_k) = -2$. Thus, if $\Delta x_k = x_k - x_{k-1}$, then

$$\begin{aligned} S(f,P,\xi) &= \sum_{k=1}^{j-1} \Delta x_k + f(\xi_j)\Delta x_j + f(\xi_{j+1})\Delta x_{j+1} - 2\sum_{k=j+2}^{n} \Delta x_k \\ &= x_{j-1} + f(\xi_j)\Delta x_j + f(\xi_{j+1})\Delta x_{j+1} - 2(2 - x_{j+1}). \end{aligned}$$

Given $\epsilon > 0$, choose $\delta = \epsilon/4$. Then for $\|P\| < \delta$, one has

$$\begin{aligned} |S(f,P,\xi) + 1| &= \left|x_{j-1} - 1 + f(\xi_j)\Delta x_j + f(\xi_{j+1})\Delta x_{j+1} - 2(1 - x_{j+1})\right| \\ &\le \|P\| + \|P\| + 2\|P\| = 4\|P\| < \epsilon. \end{aligned}$$

(iv) Let P be a partition of $[0,2]$ and suppose $x_j \le 1 \le x_{j+1}$. In $S(f,P,\xi)$, if $k < j$ then $f(\xi_k) = 2$; and if $k > j+1$ then $f(\xi_k) = 1$. Thus, if $\Delta x_k = x_k - x_{k-1}$, then

$$\begin{aligned} S(f,P,\xi) &= 2\sum_{k=1}^{j-1} \Delta x_k + f(\xi_j)\Delta x_j + f(\xi_{j+1})\Delta x_{j+1} + \sum_{k=j+2}^{n} \Delta x_k \\ &= 2x_{j-1} + f(\xi_j)\Delta x_j + f(\xi_{j+1})\Delta x_{j+1} + (2 - x_{j+1}). \end{aligned}$$

Given $\epsilon > 0$, choose $\delta = \epsilon/(14)$. Then for $\|P\| < \delta$, one has

$$\begin{aligned} |S(f,P,\xi) - 3| &= \left|2x_{j-1} + f(\xi_j)\Delta x_j + f(\xi_{j+1})\Delta x_{j+1} + 2 - x_{j+1} - 3\right| \\ &\le |f(\xi_j)\Delta x_j| + |f(\xi_{j+1})\Delta x_{j+1}| + |x_{j-1} - 1| + |x_{j-1} - x_{j+1}| \\ &\le 5\|P\| + 5\|P\| + 2\|P\| + 2\|P\| = 14\|P\| < \epsilon. \end{aligned}$$

2.2. Let $P = \{0, \frac{1}{n}, \frac{2}{n}, \dots, \frac{n}{n}\}$ and $\mu_k = k/n$; then $S(f,P,\xi) = n^{-1}\sum_{k=1}^{n} f(\frac{k}{n})$. And by the geometric meaning of $\int_0^1 f(x)dx$, one has $\int_0^1 \sqrt{1-x^2}dx = \pi/4$.

2.3. f is integrable on $[-1,0]$; but f is unbounded on both $[0,1]$ and $[-1,1]$, so it is not integrable there.

2.4. This follows immediately from Corollary 2.12.

2.5. Since f is increasing, $m_k = f(x_{k-1}) = (k-1)/n$. Thus

$$L(f, P_n) = \sum_{k=1}^{n} \frac{k-1}{n}\left(\frac{k}{n} - \frac{k-1}{n}\right) = \frac{n-1}{2n}.$$

Similarly, $M_k = f(x_k) = k/n$, and

$$U(f, P_n) = \sum_{k=1}^{n} \frac{k}{n}\left(\frac{k}{n} - \frac{k-1}{n}\right) = \frac{n+1}{2n}.$$

Thus $U(f, P_n) - L(f, P_n) = 1/n$, and it is clear that for any $\epsilon > 0$ we can choose $n > 1/\epsilon$ and get $U(f, P_n) - L(f, P_n) < \epsilon$. Therefore f is integrable on $[0, 1]$. Also $\int_0^1 f dx = \lim_{n\to\infty} U(f, P_n) = 1/2$.

2.6. Define $f^+(x) = \max\{f(x), 0\}$ and $f^-(x) = -\min\{f(x), 0\}$. Then

$$f(x) = f^+(x) - f^-(x); \quad |f(x)| = f^+(x) + f^-(x).$$

So, $f \in R[a, b]$ implies $f^\pm \in R[a, b]$ and hence $|f| \in R[a, b]$ with

$$\left|\int_a^b f(x)dx\right| \leq \int_a^b f^+(x)dx + \int_a^b f^-(x)dx = \int_a^b |f(x)|dx.$$

For the converse assertion, taking $f(x) = 1$ when $x \in [a, b] \cap \mathbf{Q}$ and $f(x) = -1$ otherwise, one gets that $|f| = 1$ but $f \notin R[a, b]$.

2.7. Let $f \in R[a, b]$. Then for any partition P of $[c, d]$ then $P' = P \cup \{a, b\}$ is a partition of $[a, b]$, and $U(f, P) - L(f, P) \leq U(f, P') - L(f, P')$ and hence $f \in R[c, d]$. Conversely, let $f \in R[c, d]$ for any $[c, d] \subset (a, b)$. Then for any $\epsilon > 0$ we may take $[c, d]$ such that $a < c \leq a + \epsilon/(6K)$ and $b - \epsilon/(6K) \leq d < b$, where $K = \sup_{x\in[a,b]} |f(x)| + 1$. Because f is integrable on $[c, d]$, one can choose a partition P^* of $[c, d]$ such that $U(f, P^*) - L(f, P^*) < \epsilon/3$. Now let $P = \{a\} \cup P^* \cup \{b\}$. Then P is a partition of $[a, b]$, and

$$\begin{aligned}
&U(f, P) - L(f, P) \\
&= (M_1 - m_1)(c - a) + U(f, P^*) - L(f, P^*) + (M_n - m_n)(b - d) \\
&\leq 2K(c - a) + U(f, P^*) - L(f, P^*) + 2K(b - d) \\
&< 2K(\epsilon/(6K)) + (\epsilon/3) + 2K(\epsilon/(6K)) = \epsilon.
\end{aligned}$$

Hence $f \in R[a, b]$.

2.8. This follows the Cauchy–Schwarz inequality:

$$\int_0^\pi \sqrt{x \sin x} dx \leq \left(\int_0^\pi x dx\right)^{1/2} \left(\int_0^\pi \sin x dx\right)^{1/2} = \pi.$$

2.9. Since $(f+g)^2 = f^2 + 2fg + g^2$, by the Cauchy–Schwarz inequality

$$\begin{aligned}&\int_a^b (f(x)+g(x))^2 dx \\ &\le \int_a^b f^2(x)dx + 2\Big(\int_a^b f^2(x)dx\Big)^{1/2}\Big(\int_a^b g^2(x)dx\Big)^{1/2} + \int_a^b g^2(x)dx \\ &= \Bigg(\Big(\int_a^b f^2(x)dx\Big)^{1/2} + \Big(\int_a^b g^2(x)dx\Big)^{1/2}\Bigg)^2,\end{aligned}$$

as desired.

2.10. It is easy to see that if $f(x) \ge \delta > 0$ then $\inf(1/f) = 1/(\sup(f))$ and $\sup(1/f) = 1/(\inf(f))$ and hence

$$\begin{aligned} U(1/f,P) - L(1/f,P) &= \sum_{k=1}^{n} \frac{M_{f,k} - m_{f,k}}{M_{f,k} m_{f,k}}(x_k - x_{k-1}) \\ &\le \delta^{-2}\big(U(f,P) - L(f,P)\big). \end{aligned}$$

This implies $1/f \in R[a,b]$.

2.11. Given $\epsilon > 0$, choose $\delta = \epsilon^2/4$ and $x_1, x_2 \in [0,\infty)$. If both $x_1, x_2 < \epsilon^2/4$, then $|x_1 - x_2| < \delta$ and $|\sqrt{x_1} - \sqrt{x_2}| \le \sqrt{x_1} + \sqrt{x_2} < \epsilon$. If either $x_1 \ge \epsilon^2/4$ or $x_2 \ge \epsilon^2/4$, then $\sqrt{x_1} + \sqrt{x_2} \ge \epsilon/2$. Thus $|x_1 - x_2| < \delta$ implies

$$|\sqrt{x_1} - \sqrt{x_2}| = \frac{|x_1 - x_2|}{\sqrt{x_1} + \sqrt{x_2}} < \epsilon.$$

We note that an alternate proof is given via $\sqrt{|x_1 - x_2|} \le \sqrt{x_1} + \sqrt{x_2}$ and the choice of $\delta = \epsilon^2$.

2.12. Suppose f is unbounded on (a,b). For each $n \in \mathbf{N}$ choose $s_n \in (a,b)$ such that $|f(s_n)| \ge n$. Then $(s_n)_{n=1}^{\infty}$ has a convergent subsequence $(s_{n(k)})_{k=1}^{\infty}$, which means that $(s_{n(k)})_{k=1}^{\infty}$ is a Cauchy sequence in (a,b), while the unbounded sequence $\big(f(s_{n(k)})\big)_{k=1}^{\infty}$ is not a Cauchy sequence. Hence f is not uniformly continuous on (a,b).

2.13. Taking $x_{1,n} = \frac{1}{2n\pi}$ and $x_{2,n} = \frac{1}{2n\pi + \pi/2}$, we have that $|x_{1,n} - x_{2,n}| \to 0$ as $n \to \infty$ but $|f(x_{1,n}) - f(x_{2,n})| = 1 > \epsilon$ for any small enough number $\epsilon > 0$.

2.14. The function f is piecewise linear and is therefore continuous and bounded on $[0, k-1/2] \setminus \{j\}_{j=1}^{k-1}$. By defining a continuous function g on $[0, k-1/2]$ and $g = f$ on $[0, k-1/2] \setminus \{j\}_{j=1}^{k-1}$, we see that f is in $R[0, k-1/2]$.

2.15. Define $g(x) = x^{-1}\sin x$ respectively $g(x) = 1$ if $x \ne 0$ respectively $x = 0$. Then g is continuous on $[0,5]$ and so $g \in R[0,5]$. Consequently, $f \in R[0,5]$.

2.16. Since $f \in R[a,b]$, f is bounded and $F(x)$ exists for any $x \in [a,b]$. The continuity of F follows from

$$|F(x) - F(x_0)| = \Big|\int_{x_0}^{x} f(t)dt\Big| \le \sup_{x\in[a,b]} |f(x)||x - x_0|.$$

2.17. If $x_1 < x_2$, then there is a $\mu \in [a,b]$ such that

$$F(x_2) - F(x_1) = \int_{x_1}^{x_2} f(t)dt \geq \min_{x\in[a,b]} f(x)(x_2 - x_1) = f(\mu)(x_2 - x_1) > 0$$

since $f \in C[a,b]$ and $f > 0$.

2.18. Because $f\big(2/(\pi k)\big) = \sin(\pi k/2)$ has no limit as $k \to \infty$, f is not continuous at 0, and of course not continuous on $[0, 1/\pi]$. But f is bounded on $[0, 1/\pi]$ and continuous on $[\epsilon, 1/\pi]$ for every $\epsilon > 0$. So $f \in R[0, 1/\pi]$ by Problem 2.7.

2.19. $\int_1^\infty x^p dx$ is convergent if and only if $p < -1$ and $\int_0^1 x^p dx$ is convergent if and only if $p > -1$.

2.20. (i) Convergent. (ii) Convergent. (iii) Divergent. (iv) Divergent: $(\frac{1}{\ln x})' = -\frac{1}{x(\ln x)^2}$, and $\lim_{t\to 1+} \frac{-1}{\ln t} = -\infty$. This implies that $\int_{1+}^2 \frac{x}{(\ln x)^2} dx$ is divergent. Note that $\int_2^\infty \frac{x}{(\ln x)^2} dx$ is convergent, but this not sufficient to infer convergence over $[1, \infty)$.

2.21. Use $(\ln x)' = 1/x$ for $x > 0$.

2.22. Let $F(x) = \int_x^\infty e^{-a|x-y|-b|y|} dy$. Then $f * g(x) = F(x) + F(-x)$ and it suffices to evaluate $F(x)$. If $x \geq 0$ then $F(x) = \frac{1}{(a+b)e^{bx}}$ and if $x < 0$ then we have two subcases: Firstly, $a \neq b \Rightarrow F(x) = \frac{e^{ax}}{a+b} + \frac{e^{ax} - e^{bx}}{b-a}$; Secondly, $a = b \Rightarrow F(x) = -xe^{ax} + \frac{e^{ax}}{2a}$.

2.23. Since the polynomials are dense in $C[0,1]$, $\int_0^1 f(x)p(x)dx = 0$ for any polynomial p and consequently, for any $\epsilon > 0$ there is a polynomial p such that $\max_{x\in[0,1]} |f(x) - p(x)| < \epsilon$ and hence

$$\int_0^1 f^2(x)dx = \int_0^1 \big(f(x) - p(x)\big)f(x)dx \leq \epsilon \int_0^1 |f(x)|dx,$$

implying $\int_0^1 f^2(x)dx = 0$ and so $f = 0$.

2.24. Substitute $u = e^{-t}$ and $du = -e^{-t}dt$ which gives that $-\ln u = t$. Hence

$$\int_{0+}^{1-} \left(\ln \frac{1}{u}\right)^{-1/2} du = \int_{0+}^\infty e^{-t} t^{-1/2} dt = \Gamma(1/2) = \sqrt{\pi}.$$

2.25. If $n = 0$ then $\Gamma(1/2) = \sqrt{\pi}$ as obtained above. Suppose that the formula is valid for $n = k$. When $n = k+1$, we have

$$\begin{aligned}
\Gamma(k+1+1/2) &= (k+1/2)\Gamma(k+1/2) \\
&= \frac{2k+1}{2}(2k)!\sqrt{\pi}(4^k k!)^{-1} \\
&= (2(k+1))!\sqrt{\pi}\big(4^{k+1}(k+1)!\big)^{-1}.
\end{aligned}$$

as desired. The induction concludes the argument.

2.26. (i) This follows from some easy calculations.
(ii) $L\big(af(x)+bg(x)\big) = a\int_{0+}^{\infty} e^{-xt}f(t)dt + b\int_{0+}^{\infty} e^{-xt}g(t)dt = aL(f(x)) + bL(g(x))$.
(iii) $L(e^{ax}f(x)) = \int_{0+}^{\infty} e^{-(x-a)t}f(t)dt = L(f(x-a))$.
(iv) Integration by parts yields

$$\int_{0+}^{b} e^{-xt}f'(t)dt = e^{-xb}f(b) - f(0) + \int_{0+}^{b} xe^{-xt}f(t)dt.$$

Since $\lim_{b\to\infty} e^{-xb}f(b) = 0$, one has

$$\begin{aligned} L(f'(x)) &= \int_{0+}^{\infty} e^{-xt}f'(t)dt \\ &= -f(0) + \int_{0+}^{\infty} xe^{-xt}f(t)dt = -f(0) + xL(f(x)). \end{aligned}$$

(v) This follows from that $L(x^n e^{ax}) = L\big((x-a)^n\big) = \frac{n!}{(x-a)^{n+1}}$ for $n \in \mathbf{N}$, thanks to $L(x^n) = \frac{n!}{x^{n+1}}, \quad x > 0$.

3 Riemann–Stieltjes Integrals

3.1. Note that the total variation of a monotonic function is given by $V_x^y f = |f(y) - f(x)|$. So we can find $V_a^b f$ in general by partitioning $[a, b]$ into subintervals on which f is monotonic.
(i)

$$\begin{aligned} V_0^{3\pi} f &= |f(\pi/2) - f(0)| + |f(3\pi/2) - f(\pi/2)| \\ &+ |f(5\pi/2) - f(3\pi/2)| + |f(3\pi) - f(5\pi/2)| = 6. \end{aligned}$$

(ii) $f'(x) = 6x(x-1) = 0$ implies $x = 0$ and $x = 1$. Hence

$$V_{-1}^{2} f = |f(0) - f(-1)| + |f(1) - f(0)| + |f(2) - f(1)| = 11.$$

(iii) If $1/(n+1) < \delta < 1/n$, then on $[\delta, 1]$ the only contributions to $V_\delta^1 f$ occur at $x = 1/(k+1)$, $k = 1, \ldots, n-1$, where

$$\left|f\Big(\frac{1}{k+1}\Big) - f\Big(\frac{1}{k+1} - \epsilon_k\Big)\right| + \left|f\Big(\frac{1}{k+1} + \epsilon_k\Big) - f\Big(\frac{1}{k+1}\Big)\right| = 2|a_k|.$$

Here $\epsilon_k > 0$ is such that

$$1/(k+2) < 1/(k+1) - \epsilon_k < 1/(k+1) < 1/(k+1) + \epsilon_k < 1/k.$$

Therefore $V_\delta^1 f = \sum_{k=1}^{n-1} 2|a_k|$. Letting $\delta \to 0$, we get $V_0^1 f = \sum_{k=1}^{\infty} 2|a_k|$.

3.2. First of all, let us prove that if f is monotonic on $[a, b]$ then $v_f(x) = |f(x) - f(a)|$ for $x \in [a, b]$. It suffices to prove this for increasing f. When P is any partition of $[a, x]$, one has

$$\begin{aligned} S(f, P) &= \sum_{k=1}^{n} |f(x_k) - f(x_{k-1})| \\ &= \sum_{k=1}^{n} (f(x_k) - f(x_{k-1})) = f(x) - f(a). \end{aligned}$$

Hence

$$v_f(x) = \sup\{S(f, P) : \text{ partitions } P \text{ of } [a, x]\} = |f(x) - f(a)|.$$

Since $\sin x$ increases on $[0, \pi/2]$ and $[3\pi/2, 2\pi]$ and decreases on $[\pi/2, 3\pi/2]$, if $x \in [0, \pi/2]$ then $v_f(x) = \sin x$, if $x \in [\pi/2, 3\pi/2]$ then

$$v_f(x) = V_0^{\pi/2} f + V_{\pi/2}^{x} f = 2 - \sin x,$$

and if $x \in [3\pi/2, 2\pi]$ then

$$v_f(x) = V_0^{\pi/2} f + V_{\pi/2}^{3\pi/2} f + V_{3\pi/2}^{x} f = 4 + \sin x.$$

3.3. This follows from $L(P) = \sum_{k=1}^{n} \left((x(t_k)^2 + y(t_k)^2) \right)^{\frac{1}{2}}$.

3.4. Just use the relevant definitions.

3.5. Let $f = f_1$ and $g = f_2$. Within the kth term of the sum

$$S(gf, P) = \sum_{k=1}^{n} |g(x_k) f(x_k) - g(x_{k-1}) f(x_{k-1})|$$

add $-g(x_k) f(x_{k-1}) + g(x_k) f(x_{k-1})$, and factor by pairs. This leads to

$$S(gf, P) \leq \sum_{k=1}^{n} |g(x_k)| f(x_k) - f(x_{k-1})| + \sum_{k=1}^{n} |f(x_{k-1})| g(x_{k-1}) - g(x_{k-1})|,$$

and so $S(gf, P) \leq M_g S(f, P) + M_f S(g, P)$, where $M_g = \sup_{x\in[a,b]} |g(x)|$ and $M_f = \sup_{x\in[a,b]} |f(x)|$.

3.6. Refer to Example 3.4

3.7. Let $P = \{x_k\}_{k=0}^{n}$ be any partition of $[a, b]$. Then

$$\begin{aligned} \sum_{k=1}^{n} |f(x_k) - f(x_{k-1})| &= \sum_{k=1}^{n} \lim_{j\to\infty} |f_j(x_k) - f_j(x_{k-1})| \\ &= \lim_{j\to\infty} \sum_{k=1}^{n} |f_j(x_k) - f_j(x_{k-1})| \\ &\leq \sup_{j\in\mathbf{N}} V_a^b(f_j) < \infty, \end{aligned}$$

and hence f is of bounded variation on $[a, b]$.

3.8. (i) Since $[x]$ is a step function, each sum reduces to those terms consisting of x^2 evaluated near the jump points times the jump of $[x]$ at such an x. Thus

$$\int_0^4 x^2 d([x]) = 1^2(1-0) + 2^2(2-1) + 3^2(3-2) + 4^2(4-3) = 30.$$

(ii) $\int_0^1 x^3 d(x^2) = 2\int_0^1 x^4 dx = 2/5$.
(iii) $\int_a^c f dg = f(b)\big(g(b^+) - g(b)\big) = f(b)(1-0) = f(b)$.

3.9. It is enough to prove Theorem 3.12 (i).

$$\begin{aligned}
&\int_a^b \big(f_1(x) + f_2(x)\big) dg_1(x) \\
&= \lim_{\|P\|\to 0} \sum_{k=1}^{n} \big(f_1(\xi_k) + f_2(\xi_k)\big)\big(g_1(\xi_k) - g_1(\xi_{k-1})\big) \\
&= \lim_{\|P\|\to 0} \Big(\sum_{k=1}^{n} \big(f_1(\xi_k)\big(g_1(\xi_k) - g_1(\xi_{k-1})\big) + \sum_{k=1}^{n} \big(f_2(\xi_k)\big(g_1(\xi_k) - g_1(\xi_{k-1})\big)\big)\Big) \\
&= \int_a^b f_1 dg_1 + \int_a^b f_2 dg_1.
\end{aligned}$$

3.10.

$$\int_0^{\pi/2} x d(\sin x) = \pi/2 - \int_0^{\pi/2} \sin x dx = \pi/2 - 1.$$

3.11. If P is a partition of $[a, b]$ such that $c \notin P$, then the Riemann–Stieltjes sums are the same for $\int_a^b f dh$ as for $\int_a^b f dg$. Consider a partition P of $[a, b]$ such that $c = x_m \in P$. With the abbreviation $\Delta h_k = h(x_k) - h(x_{k-1})$, we have

$$\begin{aligned}
&\sum_{k=1}^{n} f(t_k)\Delta h_k - \sum_{k=1}^{n} f(t_k)\Delta g_k \\
&= f(t_m)\Delta h_m + f(t_{m+1})\Delta h_{m+1} - f(t_m)\Delta g_m - f(t_{m+1})\Delta g_{m+1} \\
&= f(t_m)\big(h(c) - g(c)\big) + f(t_{m+1})\big(g(c) - h(c)\big) \\
&= \big(f(t_m) - f(t_{m+1})\big)\big(h(c) - g(c)\big).
\end{aligned}$$

As $\|P\| \to 0$, t_m and t_{m+1} both tend to c, and the continuity of f yields a limit of 0. Hence, the Riemann–Stieltjes sums for $\int_a^b f dh$ approach the same limit as the Riemann–Stieltjes sums for $\int_a^b f dg$. Note that the assertion fails if c is allowed to be either endpoint. For example, if $f(x) = 1$ and $g(x) = 0$ for all $x \in [0, 1]$, and if

$$h(x) = \begin{cases} 0, & x \in [0, 1), \\ 1, & x = 1, \end{cases}$$

then $\int_0^1 f(x)dg(x) = 0 \neq 1 = \int_0^1 f(x)dh(x) = 1$.

3.12. If f has bounded variation on $[a,b]$, then it is Riemann integrable there. The converse is false, however, which can be seen by function

$$f(x) = \begin{cases} x \sin \frac{\pi}{2x}, & x \neq 0, \\ 0, & x = 0. \end{cases}$$

Clearly, this continuous (and therefore integrable) function f fails to have bounded variation.

3.13. Just choose $f = 1$ on $[0,1]$ and

$$g(x) = \begin{cases} 1, & x \in (0,1], \\ 0, & x = 0. \end{cases}$$

3.14. (i) Let $P = \{x_k\}_{k=0}^n$ be a partition of $[a,b]$ and $\xi_k \in [x_{k-1}, x_k]$ for $k \in \{1,2,\ldots,n\}$. Then

$$\begin{aligned} \left|\sum_{k=1}^n f(\xi_k)\big(g(x_k) - g(x_{k-1})\big)\right| &\leq \sum_{k=1}^n |f(\xi_k)||g(x_k) - g(x_{k-1})| \\ &\leq \sum_{k=1}^n |f(\xi_k)|\big(v_g(x_k) - v_g(x_{k-1})\big) \\ &\leq \sup_{x\in[a,b]} |f(x)| \sum_{k=1}^n \big(v_g(x_k) - v_g(x_{k-1})\big), \end{aligned}$$

thereby giving the required inequalities.
(ii) and (iii) These two limits follow from (i) above.

3.15. (i) This follows from Problem 3.14 (i).
(ii) For $x, x_0 \in [a,b]$, use

$$|F(x) - F(x_0)| = \left|\int_{x_0}^x f(t)dg(t)\right| \leq \sup_{t\in[a,b]} |f(t)||g(x) - g(x_0)|.$$

(iii) For $x, x_0 \in [a,b]$ with $x \neq x_0$, using Theorem 3.28 (i) we get a point ξ between x_0 and x such that

$$F(x) - F(x_0) = \int_{x_0}^x f(t)dg(t) = f(\xi)\big(g(x) - g(x_0)\big),$$

and consequently,

$$F'(x_0) = \lim_{x\to x_0} f(\xi)g'(x_0) = f(x_0)g'(x_0)$$

provided that f is continuous at x_0 and g is differential at x_0.
(iv) By (i) above it follows that $h \in RS_F[a,b]$ because of $h \in C[a,b]$. To get that formula, let $P = \{x_k\}_{k=0}^n$ be a partition of $[a,b]$ and $\xi_k \in [x_{k-1}, x_k]$ for $k = 1,2,\ldots,n$. Then

$$\sum_{k=1}^n h(\xi_k)\big(F(x_k) - F(x_{k-1})\big) = \sum_{k=1}^n h(\xi_k) \int_{x_{k-1}}^{x_k} f(x)dg(x)$$

and

$$\int_a^b h(x)f(x)dg(x) = \sum_{k=1}^n \int_{x_{k-1}}^{x_k} h(x)f(x)dg(x).$$

Suppose $M = 1 + \sup_{x\in[a,b]} |f(x)|$. Since h is uniformly continuous on $[a,b]$, for any $\epsilon > 0$ there is a $\delta > 0$ such that

$$x, y \in [a,b], |x-y| < \delta \Rightarrow |h(x) - h(y)| < \eta = \frac{\epsilon}{2M(1+V_a^b g)}.$$

Accordingly, $\|P\| < \delta$, Problem 3.14 and Lemma 3.4 (i) give

$$\begin{aligned}
&\Big|\int_a^b h(x)f(x)dg(x) - \sum_{k=1}^n h(\xi_k)\big(F(x_k) - F(x_{k-1})\big)\Big| \\
&\le \sum_{k=1}^n \Big|\int_{x_{k-1}}^{x_k} \big(h(x) - h(\xi_k)\big)f(x)dg(x)\Big| \\
&\le \sum_{k=1}^n \eta M V_{x_{k-1}}^{x_k} g = \eta M V_a^b g = \epsilon/2 < \epsilon,
\end{aligned}$$

and the desired formula.

3.16. If $g \in C[0,1]$ and $\int_0^1 f(x)dg(x) = 0$ for all increasing functions f on $[0,1]$, then g must be a constant. In fact: First, $f = 1$ implies $g(0) = g(1)$; Second, integrating by part, we have $\int_0^1 g(x)df(x) = \big(f(1) - f(0)\big)g(0)$ and so $\int_0^1 \big(g(x) - g(0)\big)df(x) = 0$. If $f(x) = x^n$, $n \in \mathbf{N}$, then $\int_0^1 \big(g(x) - g(0)\big)x^{n-1}dx = 0$. Since $f \in C[0,1]$, $g(x) - g(0) = 0$ follows from Problem 2.23.

3.17. Just integrate by part and use Remark 3.19.

3.18. (i) Modify the argument for Theorem 2.18 with $dg(x)$ replacing dx.
(ii) Expand the left-hand integral.
(iii) Write the inside integral of the left-hand side of the formula in (ii) as $\int_{y\ge x} + \int_{y<x}(\cdots)$. Using the monotone condition on f_1 and f_2, we find that the integral is always nonnegative, reaching the required inequality.
(iv) This is similar to (iii).

3.19. (i) Use $x^{3/2} \le x\sqrt{x+1} \le \sqrt{2}x^{3/2}$ for $x \ge 1$ and $x\sqrt{x+1} \le \sqrt{2}x$ for $0 \le x \le 1$.
(ii) Use $|\sin x^{-1}| \le 1$ for $x > 0$.
(iii) Use $t = 1/x$ and Example 3.39.

4 Lebesgue–Radon–Stieltjes Integrals

4.1. $m_g\big((0,1)\big) = 1 - e^{-1}$; $m_g\big([0,1]\big) = 3 - e^{-1}$; $m_g\big((-1,1)\big) = 4 - e^{-1}$; $m_g\big([0,0]\big) = 1 - e^{-1}$.

4.2. (i) Let $S_1 = \cup_{k=1}^{n_1} I_{1,k}$ and $S_2 = \cup_{k=1}^{n_2} I_{2,k}$ be disjoint simple subsets of $\mathbf{R}$, where $\{I_{1,k}\}_{k=1}^{n_1}$ and $\{I_{2,k}\}_{k=1}^{n_2}$ are two sets of disjoint intervals. Then $S_1 \cup S_2 = \cup_{k=1}^{n_1+n_2} I_k$ where $I_k = I_{1,k}$ for $k = 1, 2, \dots, n_1$ and $I_{k+n_1} = I_{2,k}$ for $k = 1, 2, \dots, n_2$. Hence

$$m_g(S_1 \cup S_2) = \sum_{k=1}^{n_1+n_2} m_g(I_k) = m_g(S_1) + m_g(S_2).$$

But, let $g(x) = x$. Then $S_1 = [-1, 1/2]$ and $S_2 = [-1/2, 1]$ yield $S_1 \cap S_2 \neq \emptyset$ and

$$m_g(S_1 \cup S_2) = 2 \neq 3 = m_g(S_1) + m_g(S_2).$$

Meanwhile, $S_1 = [-1, 0]$ and $S_2 = [0, 1]$ give $S_1 \cap S_2 = \{0\}$ and

$$m_g(S_1 \cup S_2) = 2 = m_g(S_1) + m_g(S_2).$$

(ii) In this case $S_2 \setminus S_1$ is a simple subset of $\mathbf{R}$ and $S_2 = S_1 \cup (S_2 \setminus S_1)$. Thus (i) is used to produce $m_g(S_2) = m_g(S_1) + m_g(S_2 \setminus S_1)$ and the required equality. But, under $g(x) = x$, $S_1 = (1, 3)$ and $S_2 = [2, 3]$ imply

$$m_g(S_2 \setminus S_1) = 0 \neq -1 = m_g(S_2) - m_g(S_1),$$

and $S_1 = \{0\}$ and $S_2 = (0, 2]$ imply

$$m_g(S_2 \setminus S_1) = 2 = m_g(S_2) - m_g(S_1).$$

4.3. (i) Yes, $A_g(s_1) = 1$. (ii) Yes, $A_g(s_2) = 0$. (iii) Yes, $A_g(s_3) = 3$. (iv) Yes, $A_g(s_4) = -3$. (v) No.

4.4. Write $(0, 1) \cap \mathbf{Q}$ as $\{r_j\}_{j=1}^{\infty}$ and define

$$s_j(x) = \begin{cases} 0\,, & x \in [0, r_j), \\ 1\,, & x \in [r_j, r_j], \\ 0\,, & x \in (r_j, 1], \\ 0\,, & x \in \mathbf{R} \setminus [0, 1]. \end{cases}$$

If $f_k = \sum_{j=1}^{k} s_j$, then it is a step function on $\mathbf{R}$, but $f = \lim_{k\to\infty} f_k$ is not a step function on $\mathbf{R}$ since it cannot be described via taking constant values on any finite set of subintervals of $[0, 1]$. Actually, if x is irrational in $(0, 1)$; equals 0 or 1; or belongs to $\mathbf{R} \setminus [0, 1]$, then $f_k(x) = 0 = f(x)$. If $x \in (0, 1)$ equals some r_N, then $f_k(r_N) = 1 = f(r_N)$ when $k \geq N$. Note that $A_{id}(s_j) = r_j - r_j = 0$. So $S_{id}(f) = 0$.

4.5. (i)

$$\int_0^b f(x)dx = \begin{cases} \frac{b-[b]}{1+[b]}\,, & [b] \leq b < [b] + \frac{1}{2}, \\ \frac{1+[b]-b}{1+[b]}\,, & [b] + \frac{1}{2} \leq b < [b] + 1. \end{cases}$$

(ii) Use (i) to verify $|\int_0^b f(x)dx| \leq \left(2(1 + [b])\right)^{-1}$.

(iii) Note that if $[b] > 1$ then

$$\int_0^b |f(x)|dx = \sum_{k=1}^{[b]} k^{-1} + \frac{b-[b]}{1+[b]}.$$

4.6. Use Theorem 4.13 (ii).

4.7. (i) Use Theorems 4.13 (ii) and 4.11.
(ii) Use $m_{g_1+g_2}(I) = m_{g_1}(I) + m_{g_2}(I)$ for any finite interval $I \subseteq \mathbf{R}$.

4.8. (i) Use $1_{E_1\cup E_2} \le 1_{E_1} + 1_{E_2}$ for $E_1, E_2 \subseteq \mathbf{R}$.
(ii) $E = \{0\}$ is not an m_g-null set where

$$g(x) = \begin{cases} 1, & x \in (-\infty, 0), \\ 0, & x \in [0,\infty). \end{cases}$$

(iii) Use Theorem 4.13 (ii) and the definition of m_g-a.e. on $\mathbf{R}$.

4.9. (i) Use Theorem 4.18 and 4.13 (ii) for $\sum_{k=1}^n f_k$.
(ii) Use Theorem 4.19.

4.10. (i) $f = 0$.
(ii) $\lim_{n\to\infty} \int_{\mathbf{R}} f_n(x)dm_{id}(x) = 1 \neq 0 = \int_{\mathbf{R}} f(x)dm_{id}(x)$.
(iii) $(f_n)_{n=1}^\infty$ is neither increasing nor decreasing.

4.11. (i) Since $1 - \frac{x}{n} \le e^{-\frac{x}{n}}$, the following sequence of functions

$$f_n(x) = \begin{cases} \left(1-\frac{x}{n}\right)^n, & x \in [0,n], \\ 0, & x \in (n,\infty) \cup (-\infty, 0), \end{cases}$$

is increasing and bounded from above by $1_{(0,\infty)}e^{-x}$. The monotone convergence theorem ensures the desired limit formula.
(ii) By the dominated convergence theorem we have

$$\begin{aligned} \int_{\mathbf{R}} 1_{(0,\infty)}(x)|x|^\alpha(e^x-1)^{-1}dm_{id}(x) &= \int_{\mathbf{R}} 1_{(0,\infty)}(x)|x|^\alpha \sum_{j=1}^\infty e^{-jx}dm_{id}(x) \\ &= \sum_{j=1}^\infty \int_{\mathbf{R}} 1_{(0,\infty)}(x)|x|^\alpha e^{-jx}dm_{id}(x) \\ &= \sum_{j=1}^\infty j^{-(1+\alpha)}\Gamma(1+\alpha). \end{aligned}$$

4.12. (i) For each $n \in \mathbf{N}$ let

$$f_n(x) = \begin{cases} 0, & x \in (-\infty, n^{-1/p}), \\ x^{-p}, & x \in [n^{-1/p}, 1]. \end{cases}$$

Then $(f_n)_{n=1}^{\infty}$ is increasing and $\lim_{n\to\infty} f_n(x) = f(x) = 1_{(0,1]}(x)|x|^{-p}$ for each $x \in \mathbf{R}$. By the monotone convergence theorem we have that $\int_{\mathbf{R}} \frac{1_{(0,1]}(x)}{|x|^p} dm_{id}(x)$ equals

$$\lim_{n\to\infty} \int_{\mathbf{R}} 1_{(0,1]}(x) f_n(x) dm_{id}(x) = \begin{cases} (1-p)^{-1}, & p \in (0,1), \\ \infty, & p \in [1,\infty). \end{cases}$$

(ii) For each $n-1 \in \mathbf{N}$ we have the following cases:
Case 1: $x \in (0,1)$ implies

$$x^{-1/n}\left(1+\frac{x}{n}\right)^{-n} \le x^{-1/n} \le x^{-1/2}.$$

Case 2: $x \in [1,\infty)$ implies

$$x^{-1/n}\left(1+\frac{x}{n}\right)^{-n} \le \left(1+x+\frac{n-1}{2n}x^2\right)^{-1} \le 4x^{-2}.$$

Now, if

$$h(x) = \begin{cases} 0, & x \in (-\infty,0], \\ x^{-1/2}, & x \in (0,1), \\ 4x^{-2}, & x \in [1,\infty), \end{cases}$$

then

$$\int_{\mathbf{R}} 1_{(0,\infty)}(x) h(x) dm_{id}(x) = \int_0^1 x^{-1/2} dx + 4\int_1^{\infty} x^{-2} dx = 6.$$

Using the dominated convergence theorem we obtain

$$\begin{aligned} &\lim_{n\to\infty} \int_{\mathbf{R}} \frac{1_{(0,\infty)}(x)}{|x|^{1/n}} \left(1+\frac{|x|}{n}\right)^{-n} dm_{id}(x) \\ &= \int_{\mathbf{R}} 1_{(0,\infty)}(x) \lim_{n\to\infty} |x|^{-1/n}\left(1+\frac{|x|}{n}\right)^{-n} dm_{id}(x) \\ &= \int_{\mathbf{R}} 1_{(0,\infty)}(x) e^{-x} dm_{id}(x) = 1. \end{aligned}$$

4.13. (i) If $x > 0$ then

$$f(x) = \sum_{n=1}^{\infty} e^{-nx} - 2\sum_{n=1}^{\infty} e^{-2nx} = \frac{e^{-x}-e^{-2x}}{1-e^{-2x}}.$$

(ii) Since $\int_0^\infty |f_n(x)|dx$ and $\int_0^\infty |f(x)|dx$ are convergent in the sense of improper Riemann integration, they are Lebesgue integrable on $(0,\infty)$.
(iii) $\int_{\mathbf{R}} 1_{(0,\infty)}(x) f(x) dm_{id}(x) \ne 0 = \sum_{n=1}^{\infty} \int_{\mathbf{R}} 1_{(0,\infty)}(x) f_n(x) dm_{id}(x)$.

4.14. (i) $N_1 = 1/4$; $N_2 = 0$; $N_3 = 3/4$; $N_4 = 1$.
(ii) We have $N_2 \le N_1 \le N_3 \le N_4$ which is a version of Fatou's lemma.

4.15. Assume $\lim_{x\to\infty} f(x) \ne 0$. Then there is an $\epsilon_0 > 0$ such that for each $n \in \mathbf{N}$ there is an $x_n \in [n,\infty)$ obeying $|f(x_n)| \ge \epsilon_0$. Since f is uniformly continuous on $(0,\infty)$, there exists a $\delta > 0$ such that $|f(t_1) - f(t_2)| < \epsilon_0/2$ whenever $t_1, t_2 \in (0,\infty)$

and $|t_1 - t_2| < \delta$. Accordingly, $|f(x) - f(x_n)| < \epsilon_0/2$ whenever $x \in (x_n - \delta, x_n + \delta)$. Consequently, $|f(x)| \geq |f(x_n)| - \epsilon_0/2 \geq \epsilon_0/2$. Note that $x_n \geq n$. So there is a subsequence $(x_{n_k})_{k=1}^{\infty}$ of $(x_n)_{n=1}^{\infty}$ such that $x_{n_k} \leq x_{n_{k+1}}$ and $|x_{n_{k+1}} - x_{n_k}| > 2\delta$ for all $k \in \mathbf{N}$. If $I_k = (x_{n_k} - \delta, x_{n_k} + \delta)$, then $f \in LRS_g(0, \infty)$ implies

$$\begin{aligned} \infty \quad > \quad & \int_{(0,\infty)} |f| dm_g \geq \int_{\cup_{k=1}^{\infty} I_k} |f| dm_g \\ = \quad & \sum_{k=1}^{\infty} \int_{I_k} |f| dm_g \geq \frac{\epsilon_0}{2} \sum_{k=1}^{\infty} m_g(I_k) = \infty, \end{aligned}$$

a contradiction.

4.16. (i) For any sequence $y_k \to y_0 \in [c, d]$, apply Theorem 4.18 to $f_k(\cdot) = f(\cdot, y_k)$.

(ii) Let $y_k \to y_0 \in [c, d]$, so for $x \in [a, b]$,

$$h_k(x) = \frac{f(x, y_k) - f(x, y_0)}{y_k - y_0} \to \frac{\partial f(x, y)}{\partial y}.$$

By the mean value theorem for derivatives, we obtain

$$|h_k(x)| \leq \sup_{y \in [c,d]} \left| \frac{\partial f(x, y)}{\partial y} \right| \leq h(x)$$

thereby deriving the required formula via Theorem 4.18.

4.17. It is enough to consider the case $\sum_{j=1}^{\infty} m_g(E_j) < \infty$. Apply the monotone convergence theorem with $f_n = \sum_{j=1}^{n} 1_{E_j}$ to obtain

$$\begin{aligned} m_g\big(\cup_{j=1}^{\infty} E_j\big) \quad &= \quad \int_{\mathbf{R}} 1_{\cup_{j=1}^{\infty} E_j} dm_g \\ &\leq \quad \int_{\mathbf{R}} \sum_{j=1}^{\infty} 1_{E_j} dm_g \\ &= \quad \lim_{n \to \infty} \int_{\mathbf{R}} \sum_{j=1}^{n} 1_{E_j} dm_g \\ &= \quad \sum_{j=1}^{\infty} m_g(E_j). \end{aligned}$$

4.18. If $\int_E |f| dm_g < \infty$ then

$$\begin{aligned} \infty &> \sum_{j=-\infty}^{0} \int_{E_j} |f| dm_g + \sum_{j=1}^{\infty} \int_{E_j} |f| dm_g \\ &\geq \sum_{j=-\infty}^{0} |j| m_g(E_j) + \sum_{j=1}^{\infty} (j-1) m_g(E_j) \\ &= \sum_{j=-\infty}^{\infty} |j| m_g(E_j) - \sum_{j=1}^{\infty} m_g(E_j) \\ &= \sum_{j=-\infty}^{\infty} |j| m_g(E_j) - m_g(\cup_{j=1}^{\infty} E_j), \end{aligned}$$

and hence

$$\sum_{j=-\infty}^{\infty} |j| m_g(E_j) \leq \int_E |f| dm_g + m_g(E) < \infty.$$

Conversely, if $\sum_{j=-\infty}^{\infty} |j| m_g(E_j) < \infty$ then

$$\begin{aligned} \int_E |f| dm_g &= \sum_{j=-\infty}^{0} \int_{E_j} |f| dm_g + \sum_{j=1}^{\infty} \int_{E_j} |f| dm_g \\ &\leq \sum_{j=-\infty}^{0} |j-1| m_g(E_j) + \sum_{j=1}^{\infty} j m_g(E_j) \\ &\leq \sum_{j=-\infty}^{\infty} |j| m_g(E_j) + \sum_{j=-\infty}^{0} m_g(E_j) \\ &\leq \sum_{j=-\infty}^{\infty} |j| m_g(E_j) + m_g(E) < \infty. \end{aligned}$$

4.19. If f is m_g-measurable, then for any $c \in \mathbf{R}$,

$$\{x \in \mathbf{R} : f(x) \geq c\} = \cap_{j=1}^{\infty} \{x \in \mathbf{R} : f(x) > c - j^{-1}\}$$

is m_g-measurable. Conversely, suppose $\{x \in \mathbf{R} : f(x) \geq c\}$ is m_g-measurable for any $c \in \mathbf{R}$. Then

$$\{x \in \mathbf{R} : f(x) > c\} = \cup_{j=1}^{\infty} \{x \in \mathbf{R} : f(x) \geq c + j^{-1}\}$$

is m_g-measurable and so is f.

4.20. (iii) For $n \in \mathbf{N}$ and $\epsilon > 0$ let $E_{n,\epsilon} = \{x \in \mathbf{R} : |f_n(x) - f(x)| \geq \epsilon\}$. Then

$$\epsilon m_g(\{x \in \mathbf{R} : |f_n(x) - f(x)| \geq \epsilon\}) \leq \int_{E_{n,\epsilon}} |f_n - f| dm_g \leq \int_{\mathbf{R}} |f_n - f| dm_g$$

gives the result.
(iv) For a Cauchy sequence $(f_n)_{n=1}^{\infty}$ in the m_g-measure, we choose a subsequence $(f_{n_k})_{k=1}^{\infty}$ such that if $E_k = \{x \in \mathbf{R} : |f_{k+1}(x) - f_k(x)| \geq 2^{-k}\}$ then $m_g(E_k) \leq 2^{-k}$ and hence

$$m_g(\cup_{j=k}^{\infty} E_j) \leq \sum_{j=k}^{\infty} m_g(E_j) \leq \sum_{j=k}^{\infty} 2^{-j} = 2^{1-k}$$

and for $x \in \mathbf{R} \setminus \cup_{j=k}^{\infty} E_j$ and $q > p > k$,

$$|f_{n_p}(x) - f_{n_q}(x)| \leq \sum_{l=p}^{q-1} |f_{n_{l+1}}(x) - f_{n_l}(x)| \leq \sum_{l=p}^{q-1} 2^{-l} \leq 2^{1-p}.$$

The last estimate indicates that $\big(f_{n_k}(x)\big)_{k=1}^{\infty}$ is a Cauchy sequence for $x \in \mathbf{R} \setminus \cup_{j=k}^{\infty} E_j$. Now if

$$f(x) = \begin{cases} \lim_{k\to\infty} f_{n_k}(x)\,, & x \in \mathbf{R} \setminus \cap_{k=1}^{\infty} \cup_{j=k} E_j, \\ 0\,, & x \in \cap_{k=1}^{\infty} \cup_{j=k} E_j, \end{cases}$$

then $f_{n_k} \to f$ m_g-a.e. since $m_g(\cap_{k=1}^{\infty} \cup_{j=k} E_j) = 0$; moreover $|f_{n_p}(x) - f(x)| \leq 2^{2-p}$ for $p \geq k$ and $x \notin \mathbf{R} \setminus \cap_{k=1}^{\infty} \cup_{j=k} E_j$. Consequently, $f_{n_k} \to f$ in the m_g-measure and then $f_n \to f$ in the m_g-measure since

$$\begin{aligned} &\{x \in \mathbf{R} :\ |f_n(x) - f(x)| \geq \epsilon\} \\ &\subseteq \{x \in \mathbf{R} :\ |f_n(x) - f_{n_k}(x)| \geq \epsilon/2\} \cup \{x \in \mathbf{R} :\ |f_{n_k}(x) - f(x)| \geq \epsilon/2\}. \end{aligned}$$

The uniqueness in the sense of m_g-a.e. follows from that if $f_n \to h$ in the m_g-measure then

$$\begin{aligned} &\{x \in \mathbf{R} :\ |h(x) - f(x)| \geq \epsilon\} \\ &\subseteq \{x \in \mathbf{R} :\ |f_n(x) - h(x)| \geq \epsilon/2\} \cup \{x \in \mathbf{R} :\ |f_n(x) - f(x)| \geq \epsilon/2\} \end{aligned}$$

and hence $m_g\big(\{x \in \mathbf{R} :\ |h(x) - f(x)| \geq \epsilon\}\big) = 0$ for any $\epsilon > 0$.
(v) By Fatou's lemma we have

$$0 \leq \int_{\mathbf{R}} f dm_g \leq \lim_{n\to\infty} \inf_{k\geq n} \int_{\mathbf{R}} f_k dm_g = 0$$

and thus $f = 0$ m_g-a.e. on X thanks to $f \geq 0$ m_g-a.e. on $\mathbf{R}$.
(vi) If $f_n = 1_{(n,n+1]}$ and m_g is the Lebesgue measure on $\mathbf{R}$, then $f_n \to 0$ m_{id}-a.e. on $\mathbf{R}$, but f_n does not tend to 0 in the Lebesgue measure.

4.21. (i)

$$\int_{\mathbf{R}} f_1 dm_{id} = \int_{-1}^{1} |x|^{-p} dx = 2\int_0^1 x^{-p} dx = 2/(1-p)$$

and (via integration by part)

$$\int_{\mathbf{R}} f_2 dm_{id} = -\int_{-1}^{1} \ln|x| dx = -2\int_{0+}^{1} \ln x dx = 2.$$

(ii)

$$\int_{\mathbf{R}} f_1 dm_{id} = \int_0^\infty m_{id}\big(\{x\in\mathbf{R}:\ |x|^{-p}1_{|x|<1} > t\}\big)dt = 2\int_0^\infty \min\{1, t^{-1/p}\}dt = 2\Big(1+\int_1^\infty t^{-1/p}dt\Big) = 2/(1-p)$$

and

$$\int_{\mathbf{R}} f_2 dm_{id} = \int_0^\infty m_{id}\big(\{x\in\mathbf{R}:\ (-\ln|x|)1_{|x|<1} > t\}\big)dt = 2\int_0^\infty e^{-t}dt = 2.$$

5 Metric Spaces

5.1. (i) Properties of Definition 5.1: (i), (ii), and (iii) hold.
(ii) Properties of Definition 5.1: (i), (ii), and (iii) hold.
(iii) Properties of Definition 5.1: (i) and (iii) hold, but (ii) does not hold since taking $x = (1,2)$ and $y = (0,4)$ yields $d(x,y) = 3 \neq \sqrt{5} = d(y,x)$. An effort on verifying (iii) is strongly needed. Below is the details: Given $x = (x_1, x_2), y = (y_1, y_2), z = (z_1, z_2)$. Let us consider the following cases.
Case 1. $x_2 \geq z_2$: This implies $d(x,z) = \big((x_1 - z_1)^2 + (x_2 - z_2)^2\big)^{1/2}$.
Subcase 1.1. $y_2 \geq z_2$: This gives $d(y,z) = \big((y_1 - z_1)^2 + (y_2 - z_2)^2\big)^{1/2}$. And $d(x,y)$ equals $\big((x_1 - y_1)^2 + (x_2 - y_2)^2\big)^{1/2}$ or $|x_1 - y_1| + |x_2 - y_2|$. Then by the triangle inequality for the Euclidean space $(\mathbf{R}^2, d_2)$ and

$$|x_1 - y_1| + |x_2 - y_2| \geq \big((x_1 - y_1)^2 + (x_2 - y_2)^2\big)^{1/2}$$

one has $d(x,y) + d(y,z) \geq d(x,z)$.
Subcase 1.2. $y_2 < z_2$: This yields $d(y,z) = |y_1 - z_1| + |y_2 - z_2|$. And $d(x,y)$ equals $\big((x_1 - y_1)^2 + (x_2 - y_2)^2\big)^{1/2}$ or $|x_1 - y_1| + |x_2 - y_2|$. Then by the triangle inequalities for both the Euclidean space distance d_2 and that one defined by Problem 5.1 (i), as well as

$$|y_1 - z_1| + |y_2 - z_2| \geq \big((y_1 - z_1)^2 + (y_2 - z_2)^2\big)^{1/2}$$

and

$$|x_1 - z_1| + |x_2 - z_2| \geq \big((x_1 - z_1)^2 + (x_2 - z_2)^2\big)^{1/2}$$

one has $d(x,y) + d(y,z) \geq d(x,z)$.
Case 2. $x_2 < z_2$: This infers $d(x,z) = |x_1 - z_1| + |x_2 - z_2|$.
Subcase 2.1. $y_2 \geq z_2$: This means $d(y,z) = \big((y_1 - z_1)^2 + (y_2 - z_2)^2\big)^{1/2}$. Note that $x_2 < z_2$ and $z_2 \leq y_2$ imply $x_2 < y_2$ and $|x_2 - y_2| > |z_2 - y_2|$. So $d(x,y) = |x_1 - y_1| + |x_2 - y_2|$. Hence by the triangle inequality of the distance for $\mathbf{R}$,

$$d(x,y) + d(y,z) \geq |x_1 - y_1| + |x_2 - y_2| + |y_1 - z_1| \geq |x_1 - z_1| + |x_2 - z_2| = d(x,z).$$

Subcase 2.2. $y_2 < z_2$: This tells us that $d(y,z) = |y_1 - z_1| + |y_2 - z_2|$ and thus $d(x,y)$ equals $\left((x_1-y_1)^2+(x_2-y_2)^2\right)^{1/2}$ or $|x_1-y_1|+|x_2-y_2|$. For the second case, one applies the triangle inequality of the distance for $\mathbf{R}$ to get

$$d(x,y) + d(y,z) \geq |x_1 - z_1| + |x_1 - z_2| = d(x,z).$$

Concerning the first case: $x_2 \geq y_2$, note that $d(x,y) + d(y,z) \geq d(x,z)$ is equivalent to

$$\left((x_1-y_1)^2+(x_2-y_2)^2\right)^{1/2} + |y_1 - z_1| + z_2 - y_2 \geq |x_1 - z_1| + z_2 - x_2$$

which is

$$|y_1 - z_1| + x_2 - y_2 \geq |x_1 - z_1| - \left((x_1-y_1)^2+(x_2-y_2)^2\right)^{1/2}.$$

Since

$$\left((x_1-y_1)^2+(x_2-y_2)^2\right)^{1/2} \geq |x_1 - y_1|,$$

one has

$$|x_1 - z_1| - \left((x_1-y_1)^2+(x_2-y_2)^2\right)^{1/2} \leq |x_1 - z_1| - |x_1 - y_1| \leq |y_1 - z_1|.$$

Note that $x_2 \geq y_2$, so the desired estimate follows.

5.2. Suppose S is the set of all positive integers $m \geq 2$ such that

$$d(x^{(1)}, x^{(m)}) \leq \sum_{j=2}^{m} d(x^{(j-1)}, x^{(j)})$$

for any set of m points in X. For $m = 2$ the result is trivial, and for $m = 3$ the assertion is the triangle inequality for (X,d). Assume $m \in S$ and let $\{x^{(j)}\}_{j=1}^{m+1}$ be any $m+1$ points in X. By the triangle inequality for (X,d), and the above assumption, one has

$$d(x^{(1)}, x^{(m+1)}) \leq d(x^{(1)}, x^{(m)}) + d(x^{(m)}, x^{(m+1)}) \leq \sum_{j=2}^{m+1} d(x^{(j-1)}, x^{(j)}).$$

Therefore $m+1 \in S$, and the mathematical induction ensures that $S = \mathbf{N} \setminus \{1\}$.

5.3. (i) It is enough to check the second result. Let $z^{(0)} = (x_1, x_2, \ldots, x_n) = x$, $z^{(1)} = (y_1, x_2, \ldots, x_n), \ldots$, and $z^{(n)} = (y_1, y_2, \ldots, y_n) = y$. Then for $j = 1, 2, \ldots, n$, one has

$$d_n^*(z^{(j-1)}, z^{(j)}) = |x_j - y_j| = d_n(z^{(j-1)}, z^{(j)}),$$

and by adding these equations, one gets

$$d_n^*(z^{(0)}, z^{(n)}) = \sum_{j=1}^{n} d_n^*(z^{(j-1)}, z^{(j)}) \geq d_n(z^{(0)}, z^{(n)}).$$

(ii) This is a routine argument. Clearly, $d_{*,n}(x,y) \le d_n(x,y) \le \sqrt{n} d_{*,n}(x,y)$.

5.4. First, let's prove that A° is the largest open subset of A. If $O \subseteq A$ is open, then any point of O is an interior point of A, and so this point belongs to A°. This gives $O \subseteq A^\circ$. Second, let $K \supseteq A$ be closed. If $x \in \overline{A}$ then it suffices to prove that $x \in K$ when x is a limit point of A. In this case, x is a limit point of K. But since K is closed, $x \in K$. We are done.

5.5. Let $x \in \overline{B}_1(0)$ and $\epsilon > 0$. We must show that $B_\epsilon(x) \cap B_1(0) \ne \emptyset$. Choose a number c such that $1-\epsilon < c < 1$, and consider the point $z = cx = (cx_1, cx_2)$; this gives $d_2(z,0) = cd_2(x,0) < 1$, so $x \in B_1(0)$. Also, $d_2(x,z) = (1-c)d_2(x,0) < \epsilon$, so $x \in B_\epsilon(x)$. Hence, every point of $\overline{B}_1(0)$ is in $\overline{B_1(0)}$, the closure of $B_1(0)$. Conversely, if $y \notin \overline{B}_1(0)$, then $d_2(y,0) > 1$, and if $\delta = d_2(y,0)-1$, then by the triangle inequality, $B_\delta(y) \cap B_1(0) = \emptyset$. Hence, only the points of $\overline{B}_1(0)$ are in $\overline{B_1(0)}$.

5.6. Let $p \in S$ and define $S_1 = \{p\}$ and $S_2 = S \setminus \{p\}$. Since finite sets have no limit points, it follows that the definition of disconnectness is satisfied.

5.7. This follows from the facts that $\overline{G_1} \cap G_2 = \emptyset$ and $\overline{G_2} \cap G_1 = \emptyset$.

5.8. (i) The sequence is convergent to $(1,1)$.
(ii) The sequence is convergent to $(0,0)$.
(iii) The sequence is divergent since $k \to \infty$.

5.9. For $k \in \mathbf{N}$ take $x_k = \frac{1}{2k}$. Since $x_k \to 0$ but $0 \notin (0,1)$.

5.10. (i) If $A = (x^{(k)})_{k=1}^\infty$ is bounded then there is an $M > 0$ such that $d_n(x,0) \le M$ for all $x = (x_1, \ldots, x_n) \in A$ and hence $\sup_{1\le j\le n} \sup_{k\in\mathbf{N}} |x_j^{(k)}| \le M$. The converse assertion is trivial.
(ii) This follows easily from the inclusion between cubes and balls in $\mathbf{R}^n$.

5.11. Assume that $(x^{(k)})_{k=1}^\infty$ is a Cauchy sequence and apply the definition of Cauchy sequence with $\epsilon \in (0,1)$. For this distance function, $d(x,y) < 1$ implies $d(x,y) = 0$ and hence $x = y$, so we have that $k > m > N$ implies $x^{(k)} = x^{(m)}$. Hence, $k > N$ implies $x^{(k)} = x^{(N+1)}$.

5.12. Let $B_r(p)$ be an arbitrary open ball in $\mathbf{R}^n$. Then $C_{r/\sqrt{n}}(p)$, the cube with side-length $r/\sqrt{n}$ and center p, is contained in $B_r(p)$. Since the irrational numbers $\mathbf{R} \setminus \mathbf{Q}$ are dense in $\mathbf{R}$, for each $j = 1, \ldots, n$, the interval $(p_j - r/\sqrt{n}, p_j + r/\sqrt{n})$ contains an $x_j \in \mathbf{R} \setminus \mathbf{Q}$. Thus $|x_j - p_j| < r/\sqrt{n}$, which defines a point $x \in C_{r/\sqrt{n}}(p)$.

5.13. This follows from the triangle inequality for d.

5.14. Let $(x_k)_{k=1}^\infty$ be a Cauchy sequence in X. Then there is $n_1 \in \mathbf{N}$ such that $d(x_n, x_{n_1}) < 1/2$ as $n \ge n_1$. Suppose $x_{n_1}, \ldots, x_{n_k}$ have been chosen such that $n_{j+1} > n_j$, $j = 1, \ldots, k-1$ and $d(x_n, x_{n_j}) < 2^{-j}$ as $n \ge n_j$. Take $n_{k+1} > n_k$ so that $d(x_n, x_{n_{k+1}}) < 2^{-(k+1)}$ for $n \ge n_{k+1}$. Consider $\overline{B}_{2^{-(k-1)}}(x_{n_k})$. We claim that this sequence of closed balls is nested. If $x \in \overline{B}_{2^{-k}}(x_{n_{k+1}})$, then $d(x, x_{n_{k+1}}) \le 2^{-k}$ and $d(x, x_{n_k}) \le d(x, x_{n_{k+1}}) + d(x_k, x_{n_{k+1}}) < 2^{-(k-1)}$. So $x \in \overline{B}_{2^{-(k-1)}}(x_{n_k})$. By hypothesis there is $x \in \cap_{k=1}^\infty \overline{B}_{2^{-(k-1)}}(x_{n_k})$. Obviously, $x_{n_k} \to x$ and so $x_n \to x$. That is, X is complete. Conversely, suppose X is complete. If $\overline{B}_{r_k}(x_k)$ with $r_k \to 0$

is nested, then $(x_k)_{k=1}^{\infty}$ is a Cauchy sequence in X. In fact, $k > m$ implies $\overline{B}_{r_k}(x_k) \subseteq \overline{B}_{r_m}(x_m)$, and so $x_k \in \overline{B}_{r_m}(x_m)$, i.e., $d(x_k, x_m) \leq r_m$. For any $\epsilon > 0$ there is an $N \in \mathbf{N}$ such that $m > N$ implies $r_m < \epsilon$. Consequently, $k > m > N$ yields $d(x_k, x_m) < \epsilon$. Accordingly, $(x_k)_{k=1}^{\infty}$ is convergent to a point $x \in X$. But, each $\overline{B}_{r_k}(x_k)$ contains all but possibly a finite number of the $\{x_k : k \in \mathbf{N}\}$ and since $\overline{B}_{r_k}(x_k)$ is closed, it follows that $x \in \overline{B}_{r_k}(x_k)$ and so that x is in all $\overline{B}_{r_k}(x_k)$.

5.15. Since S_j's are nonempty, there is a sequence $(x_j)_{j=1}^{\infty}$ such that $x_j \in S_j$ for any $j \in \mathbf{N}$. Given $\epsilon > 0$, there exists an $N \in \mathbf{N}$ depending only on ϵ such that $\operatorname{diam}(S_j) < \epsilon$ for $j > N$. Thus, $d(x_m, x_n) < \epsilon$ whenever $m, n \geq N$. This means that $(x_j)_{j=1}^{\infty}$ is a Cauchy sequence in the complete metric space (X, d), and so that it converges, to x, say. Since $S_{j+1} \subseteq S_j$ and S_j is closed, the fact $x_j \in S_j$ must give $x \in \cap_{j=1}^{\infty} S_j$.

5.16. If S is nowhere dense then $\overline{S}$ contains no sphere, i.e., $\overline{S}^{\circ} = \emptyset$. Suppose that O is any open ball in X. Then $\overline{S}^{\circ}$ does not contain O, and hence the open $O \setminus \overline{S}$ is not $\emptyset$. Consequently, there is an open ball O' with $O' \subseteq O \setminus \overline{S} \subseteq O$. This implies $O' \cap S = \emptyset$ since $S \subset \overline{S}$. Conversely, assume that every open ball O contains an open ball O' such that $O' \cap S = \emptyset$. If $\overline{S}^{\circ} \neq \emptyset$, then there would be a point x in the open set $\overline{S}^{\circ}$ and hence an open ball $B_r(x) \subseteq \overline{S}$ centered at x with a radius $r > 0$. As a by-product, any point p in $B_r(x)$ is a limit point of S, and then any open ball centered at p and contained in $B_r(x)$ has a non-void intersection with S. This is against the above assumption. Therefore $\overline{S}^{\circ} = \emptyset$.

5.17. Suppose $\{O_\beta\}$ is an open covering of $\cap_{\alpha \in I} E_\alpha$. Since E_α is compact, it is closed and $X \setminus \cap_{\alpha \in I} E_\alpha$ is open. Now $E_\alpha \subseteq \big(X \setminus \cap_{\alpha \in I} E_\alpha\big) \cup_\beta O_\beta$. By the compactness of E_α, there are finitely many elements of $\{O_\beta\}$, say $\{O_{\beta_j}\}_{j=1}^{N}$, such that

$$E_\alpha \subseteq \big(X \setminus \cap_{\alpha \in I} E_\alpha\big) \cup_{j=1}^{N} O_{\beta_j},$$

and consequently, $\cap_{\alpha \in I} E_\alpha \subseteq \cup_{j=1}^{N} O_{\beta_j}$. Therefore $\cap_{\alpha \in I} E_\alpha$ is compact.

5.18. Assume $\mathcal{O}$ is an open cover of $\{x_j\}_{j=0}^{\infty}$. Then there exists an open set $O \in \mathcal{O}$ such that $x_0 \in O$. Hence $\lim_{n \to \infty} d(x_n, x_0) = 0$ indicates that there is an $N \in \mathbf{N}$ such that $x_n \in O$ as $n > N$. For each $n \in \{1, \ldots, N\}$ there exists an open set $O_n \in \mathcal{O}$ such that $x_n \in O_n$. Now $\{O, O_1, \ldots, O_N\}$ forms a subcover of $\{x_j\}_{j=0}^{\infty}$. So, $\{x_j\}_{j=0}^{\infty}$ is compact.

6 Continuous Maps

6.1. Given $p = (p_1, p_2, p_3) \in \mathbf{R}^3$ and $\epsilon > 0$, choose $\delta = \epsilon$. Now $x = (x_1, x_2, x_3) \in \mathbf{R}^3$ and $d_3(x, p) < \delta$ imply

$$d_3\big(f(x), f(p)\big) = \big((x_1 - p_1)^2 + (x_2 - p_2)^2\big)^{1/2} \leq d_3(x, p) < \epsilon.$$

6.2. The natural choice is $f(0) = 0$ due to $d_2(0, 0) = 0$. We must now prove that f is continuous at 0. Given $\epsilon > 0$, choose $\delta = \epsilon$. Now $d_2(x, 0) < \delta$ implies $|f(x) - f(0)| = d_2(x, 0) < \epsilon$.

6.3. The range of f is $[0, \infty)$, so no point is mapped into $(-3, -2)$; hence $f^{-1}(S) = \emptyset$.

6.4. Since $0 \notin D$, $f(0) = 0$. For a fixed $x = (x_1, x_2, x_3) \in \mathbf{R}^3$, consider the points on the line segment $\{tx = (tx_1, tx_2, tx_3) \in \mathbf{R}^3 : t \in [0,1]\}$. We want to find $\lim_{t \to 0^+} f(tx)$. If $x_3 \leq 0$, then $tx \notin D$ and $f(tx) = 0$ for all $t \in [0,1]$. If $x_3 > 0$, then we claim that for t sufficiently small, $tx \notin D$ and therefore $f(tx) = 0$. This is seen by checking the coordinate inequality for $tx \in D$: $tx \in D$ if and only if $tx_3 < (tx_1)^2 + (tx_2)^2$, or $x_3 < t(x_1^2 + x_2^2)$. For any $x_3 > 0$, t can be chosen small enough to deny this. Therefore in either case, $f(tx) = 0$ for t sufficiently small. The discontinuity of f at 0 is shown by finding points of D that are in $B_\delta(0)$ for any $\delta > 0$.

6.5. $T\big((1,1)\big) = (3,-1)$ yields $a_{11} + a_{12} = 3$ and $a_{21} + a_{22} = -1$; $T\big((1,-1)\big) = (1,7)$ yields $a_{11} - a_{12} = 1$ and $a_{21} - a_{22} = 7$. Solving this system of equations, we get $a_{11} = 2$, $a_{12} = 1$, $a_{21} = 3$ and $a_{22} = -4$.

6.6. Since f is continuous on compact subset K, f assumes its minimum, i.e., $\min_{x \in K} f(x) = f(m)$ for some $m \in K$. Taking $\delta = f(m) > 0$ gives the desired result.

6.7. Let $y \in [0.1]$. If y is rational or irrational, then taking $x = y$ or $x = 1 - y$ gives $f(x) = y$. So f is onto. But f is continuous only at $x = 1/2$. In fact, $|f(x) - f(1/2)| = |f(x) - 1/2| = |x - 1/2|$ gives the continuity. Let $x \in [0,1] \setminus \{1/2\}$. If x is rational then $|f(x_k) - f(x)| = |f(x_k) - x|$. When x_k is rational resp. irrational, one then has $|f(x_k) - x| = |x_k - x|$ resp. $|1 - x_k - x|$. Thus, once choosing that x_k is rational but x_{k+1} irrational, we cannot get that $|f(x_k) - x| \to 0$ as $x_k \to x$.

6.8. (i) Taking $f_1 = 1$ and $f_2 = 0$ we have

$$d_{C[0,1]}\big(T(f_1), T(f_2)\big) = 1 = d_{C[0,1]}(f_1, f_2).$$

(ii) If $T(f) = f$, then $\int_0^x f(t)dt = f(x)$ and hence $f = 0$, giving the uniqueness.
(iii) Since

$$T \circ T\big(f(x)\big) = \int_0^x \Big(\int_0^y f(t)dt\Big)dy = \int_0^x (x-t)f(t)dt,$$

it follows that $d_{C[0,1]}\big(T \circ T(f_1), T \circ T(f_2)\big) \leq 2^{-1} d_{C[0,1]}(f_1, f_2)$.

6.9. The result follows from $|f(b) - f(a)| = |f'(c)(b-a)| \leq \alpha|b-a|$ for some $c \in [a,b]$.

6.10. Since the series is convergent, there is an $N \in \mathbf{N}$ such that $\alpha_N = \sup_{x_1 \neq x_2} d_X\big(T_{(N)}(x_1), T_{(N)}(x_2)\big)/d_X(x_1, x_2) < 1$. This means that $T_{(N)}$ is a contraction, and consequently, it has a unique fixed point thanks to Corollary 6.29, and so does T.

6.11. If $f(x) = d_X\big(x, T(x)\big)$, then $f : K \to \mathbf{R}$ is continuous. Since K is compact and nonempty, there is a point $x_0 \in K$ such that $f(x_0) = \min_{x \in K} f(x)$. Consequently, $T(x_0) = x_0$ – otherwise we would have $f\big(T(x_0)\big) < f(x_0)$ which shows that $f(x_0)$ is not the minimum of f over K, a contradiction. The uniqueness is trivial.

6.12. Consider the map $T : C[0,1] \to C[0,1]$ given by

$$T(f) = h(x) + \int_0^x f(x-t)\exp(-t^2)dt.$$

For $f_1, f_2 \in C[0,1]$, we have $d_{C[0,1]}\big(T(f_1), T(f_2)\big) \le \frac{\sqrt{\pi}}{2} d_{C[0,1]}(f_1, f_2)$. Since $C[0,1]$ is complete under $d_{C[0,1]}(f_1, f_2)$, T is a contraction and hence there exists an $f \in C[0,1]$ such that $T(f) = f$.

6.13. Show that the inverse map f^{-1} of f exists and apply the Banach contraction theorem to f^{-1}.

6.14. The equivalences can be readily checked via the relevant definitions.

6.15. Check that f is not injective.

6.16. Outline of the proof: For (X, d_X) define two Cauchy sequences $(x_k^{(1)})_{k=1}^{\infty}$ and $(x_k^{(2)})_{k=1}^{\infty}$ in X to be equivalent provided $\lim_{k\to\infty} d_X(x_k^{(1)}, x_k^{(2)}) = 0$. Let Y be the space of all equivalence classes of Cauchy sequences in X with metric

$$d_Y\big((x_k^{(1)})_{k=1}^{\infty}, (x_k^{(2)})_{k=1}^{\infty}\big) = \lim_{k\to\infty} d_X(x_k^{(1)}, x_k^{(2)}).$$

Then (Y, d_Y) is complete. Define a mapping f from X into Y by $f(x) = (x_k)_{k=1}^{\infty} \in Y$ where $x_k = x \in X$ for each $k \in \mathbf{N}$. Then f is an isometry and moreover $f(X)$ is dense in Y.

6.17. Use the triangle inequality: $d_X(x,y) \le d_X(x_0,y) + d_X(x,x_0)$.

7 Normed Linear Spaces

7.1. Let $\Phi(t) = t^{\frac{1}{p}}$ for $t \ge 0$. Since $p^{-1} \in (0,1)$, $\Phi''(s) < 0$ for all $s > 0$ and Φ is concave. Hence $\Phi(t) \le \Phi(1) + \Phi'(1)(t-1)$ or $t^{\frac{1}{p}} \le 1 + \frac{t-1}{p} = \frac{t}{p} + \frac{1}{q}$. Setting $t = u^p v^{-q}$ where $u \ge 0$ and $v > 0$, we find $uv \le \frac{u^p}{p} + \frac{v^q}{q}$ where $1 - q = -\frac{q}{p}$. Obviously, this inequality also holds when $v = 0$. The last inequality implies the desired Hölder inequalities which, plus $|a+b|^p \le |a+b|^{p-1}|a| + |a+b|^{p-1}|b|$ (for $a, b \in \mathbf{R}$), yield the desired Minkowski inequalities.

7.2. (i) $n-1$ since the following $n-1$ vectors

$$(1,-1,0,\ldots,0), (0,1,-1,0,\ldots,0), \ldots, (0,0,0,\ldots,1,-1)$$

are linearly independent.
(ii) ∞ since $1, t, t^2, \ldots, t^n$ are linearly independent for any $n \in \mathbf{N}$.
(iii) ∞ since $1, t, t^2, \ldots, t^n$ are linearly independent for any $n \in \mathbf{N}$.

7.3. (i) Obviously, $\|f\|_p \le \|f\|_\infty$ when $p \in [1,\infty)$ and $f \in C[0,1]$, but there is no such a constant $\kappa > 0$ that $\|f\|_\infty \le \kappa \|f\|_p$ for all $f \in C[0,1]$. For $n - 2 \in \mathbf{N}$ let

$$f_n(t) = \begin{cases} n^{\frac{2}{p}} t^{\frac{1}{p}}, & 0 \le t \le \frac{1}{n}, \\ n^{\frac{2}{p}} (\frac{2}{n} - t)^{\frac{1}{p}}, & \frac{1}{n} \le t \le \frac{2}{n}, \\ 0, & \frac{2}{n} \le t \le 1. \end{cases}$$

It is easy to see that $\|f_n\|_\infty = n^{\frac{1}{p}} \to \infty$ (as $n \to \infty$) and $\|f_n\|_p = 1$. This verifies the nonexistence of the above constant $\kappa > 0$.
(ii) For $n \in \mathbf{N}$ let $f_n(x) = x^n$. Then $\|f_n\|_\infty = 1$ and hence the unit sphere of $(C[0,1], \|\cdot\|_\infty)$ is not finite dimensional. Theorem 7.19 (ii) gives that the unit sphere is not compact.

7.4. Note that $|\|x\| - \|a\|| \le \|x - a\|$. So $\|\cdot\| : X \to \mathbf{R}$ is continuous. Also, regarding the continuity of the vector addition and the scalar multiplication, we naturally assume that the norms defined on $X \times X$ and $\mathbf{F} \times X$ are determined by $\|(x,y)\|_{X\times X} = \|x\| + \|y\|$ and $\|(\lambda, x)\|_{\mathbf{F}\times X} = |\lambda| + \|x\|$. Therefore the desired continuities follow from

$$\|(x+y) - (x_0 + y_0)\| \le \|x - x_0\| + \|y - y_0\| = \|(x,y) - (x_0, y_0)\|_{X\times X}$$

and

$$\|\lambda x - \lambda_0 x_0\| \le |\lambda - \lambda_0|\|x\| + |\lambda_0|\|x - x_0\| \le \|(\lambda, x) - (\lambda_0, x_0)\|_{\mathbf{F}\times X}(\|x\| + |\lambda_0|).$$

7.5. It is clear that ℓ_0 is a linear subspace of ℓ_∞. Note that $a = (1, \frac{1}{2}, \frac{1}{3}, \dots) \in \ell_\infty$. For every $n \in \mathbf{N}$, let $x_n = (1, \frac{1}{2}, \frac{1}{3}, \dots, \frac{1}{n}, 0, 0, \dots) \in \ell_0$. Then

$$\|x_n - a\|_\infty = \left\|\left(0, \dots, 0, \frac{1}{n+1}, \frac{1}{n+2}, \dots\right)\right\|_\infty = \frac{1}{n+1} \to 0.$$

It follows that $(x_n)_{n=1}^\infty$ converges in ℓ_∞, but the limit a does not belong to ℓ_0. Hence ℓ_0 is not closed in ℓ_∞.

7.6. (i) By Hölder's inequality it follows that for $1 < p < q < \infty$,

$$\int_{[0,1]} |f|^p dm_{id} \le \left(\int_{[0,1]} |f|^q dm_{id}\right)^{\frac{p}{q}},$$

and so that $\|f\|_{p,m_{id},[0,1]}$ increases with p. Since $\|f\|_{\infty,m_{id},[0,1]} < \infty$, the limit $a = \lim_{p\to\infty} \|f\|_{p,m_{id},[0,1]}$ is finite. It is clear that

$$t\big(m_{id}(\{x \in [0,1] : |f(x)| > t\})\big)^{\frac{1}{p}} \le \|f\|_{p,m_{id},[0,1]} \le a$$

for all $t > 0$. Accordingly, if $m_{id}(\{x \in [0,1] : |f(x)| > t\}) > 0$ then

$$\lim_{p\to\infty} \Big(m_{id}(\{x \in [0,1] : |f(x)| > t\})\Big)^{\frac{1}{p}} = 1$$

and

$$m_{id}\big(\{x \in [0,1] : |f(x)| > t\}\big) = 0 \quad \text{for} \quad t > a.$$

Thus, $a = \|f\|_{\infty,m_{id},[0,1]}$.
(ii) It suffices to prove the result under $0 < \|f_1\|_{1,m_{id},[0,1]} < \infty$ and

$$0 < \|f_2\|_{\infty,m_{id},[0,1]} < \infty.$$

For the inequality, one has

$$\int_{[0,1]} |f_1 f_2| dm_{id} = \int_{\{x\in[0,1]:\ |f_2(x)|\le \|f_2\|_{\infty,m_{id},[0,1]}\}} |f_1 f_2| dm_{id}$$
$$\le \|f_1\|_{1,m_{id},[0,1]} \|f_2\|_{\infty,m_{id},[0,1]}.$$

As for the equality, note that $|f_2| \le \|f_2\|_{\infty,m_{id},[0,1]}$ holds m_{id}-a.e. on $[0,1]$. So, if the equality is valid then

$$\int_{[0,1]} |f_1|\Big(1 - \frac{|f_2|}{\|f_2\|_{\infty,m_{id},[0,1]}}\Big) dm_{id} = 0$$

and hence $|f_2(x)| = \|f_2\|_{\infty,m_{id},[0,1]}$ for m_{id}-a.e. $x \in [0,1]$. The reverse assertion is trivial.

7.7. It is clear that T is linear. Furthermore, if $f \in C[0,1]$ then $|T(f)| = |f(0)| \le \|f\|_\infty$, giving the boundedness of T with $\|T\| \le 1$. If $f(x) = 1$ then $\|f\|_\infty = 1$ and $T(f) = 1$. This yields $\|T\| = 1$.

7.8. (i) Clearly,

$$\|T(x)\|_\infty \le \sup_{k\in\mathbf{N}} \sum_{j=1}^{\infty} |a_{kj}||x_j| \le \|x\|_\infty \sup_{k\in\mathbf{N}} \sum_{j=1}^{\infty} |a_{kj}|$$

and so $\|T\| \le \sup_{k\in\mathbf{N}} \sum_{j=1}^{\infty} |a_{kj}|$. To get the equality, we use $\sup_{k\in\mathbf{N}} \sum_{j=1}^{\infty} |a_{kj}| < \infty$ to find that for any $\epsilon > 0$ there exists $k_0 \in \mathbf{N}$ such that

$$\sup_{k\in\mathbf{N}} \sum_{j=1}^{\infty} |a_{kj}| < \sum_{j=1}^{\infty} |a_{k_0 j}| + \epsilon.$$

If $x_j = \text{sgn} a_{k_0 j}$, then $\|(x_j)_{j=1}^\infty\|_\infty = 1$, and hence $y = (y_k)_{k=1}^\infty = T(x) = T\big((x_j)_{j=1}^\infty\big)$ gives $y_{k_0} = \sum_{j=1}^{\infty} |a_{k_0 j}|$. So

$$\|T\| \ge \|T\big((x_j)_{j=1}^\infty\big)\|_\infty = \|(y_k)_{k=1}^\infty\|_\infty \ge y_{k_0} > \sup_{k\in\mathbf{N}} \sum_{j=1}^{\infty} |a_{kj}| - \epsilon.$$

Because ϵ is arbitrary, we have $\|T\| \ge \sup_{k\in\mathbf{N}} \sum_{j=1}^{\infty} |a_{kj}|$, deriving the equality.
(ii) It follows from the definition of $\|\cdot\|_2$.
(iii) It is clear that for $f \in R^1[a,b]$,

$$\|T(f)\|_1 = \int_a^b \Big|\int_a^x f(t)dt\Big| dx \le \int_a^b \Big(\int_a^x |f(t)|dt\Big) dx$$
$$\le \int_a^b \Big(\int_a^b |f(t)|dt\Big) dx = (b-a)\|f\|_1,$$

and so that T is bounded with $\|T\| \le b - a$. To see the equality, for any $n \in \mathbf{N}$ with $a + n^{-1} < b$ let

$$f_n(x) = \begin{cases} n, & t \in [a, a+n^{-1}], \\ 0, & t \in (a+n^{-1}, b]. \end{cases}$$

It is easy to check $\|f_n\|_1 = 1$ and

$$\|T(f_n)\|_1 = \int_a^{a+n^{-1}} n(x-a)dx + \int_{a+n^{-1}}^b dx = (b-a) - (2n)^{-1}.$$

So $\|T\| \ge \sup_{n\in\mathbf{N}} \|T(f_n)\|_1 = b-a$. Therefore $\|T\| = b-a$.

7.9. The boundedness is obvious. Since $T(f_1) = T(f_2)$ implies $f_1 = f_2$, we conclude that T is one-to-one. But, T is not onto. In fact, if $T(f) = 1$ on $(0,1)$ then the only possible candidate for f is $f(t) = t^{-1}$. It is clear that $f \in C(0,1)$ with $\|f\|_2 = \infty$. From this it turns out that T is not invertible.

7.10. Here, suppose that the norm on $\mathbf{R}^2$ is $(2,2)$-norm.
Linear: $T\big(\alpha(x_1,y_1) + \beta(x_2,y_2)\big) = (\alpha x_1 + \beta x_2, 0) = \alpha T\big((x_1,y_1)\big) + \beta T\big((x_2,y_2)\big)$.
Bounded: $\|T\big((x_1,x_2)\big)\|_{2,2} = |x_1| \le \|(x_1,x_2)\|_{2,2}$.
Not onto: $(x_1, 1)$ has no preimage under T.
An example: $S = (0,1)\times(0,1)$ is an open set of $\mathbf{R}^2$, but $TS = \{(x_1,0) : x_1 \in (0,1)\}$ is not open set of $\mathbf{R}^2$.

7.11. These results just follow from the relevant definitions.

7.12. (i) If $x \in X$ and $0 < \epsilon < \|x\|_X$, then $x \in B_{\|x\|_X+\epsilon}(0)$ and $x \notin B_{\|x\|_X-\epsilon}(0)$. This readily implies the desired result.
(ii) Clearly, we have

$$p(\kappa x) = \inf\{\lambda > 0 :\ \kappa x \in \lambda K\} = \kappa \inf\{\kappa^{-1}\lambda > 0 :\ x \in \kappa^{-1}\lambda K\} = \kappa p(x).$$

Moreover, if ϵ, λ, μ are positive and satisfy $x = \lambda x_1$, $y = \mu y_1$, $\lambda < p(x) + \epsilon/2$ and $\mu < p(y) + \epsilon/2$ for some $x_1, y_1 \in K$, then

$$x + y = (\lambda+\mu)\Big(\frac{\lambda}{\lambda+\mu}x_1 + \frac{\mu}{\lambda+\mu}y_1\Big) \in (\lambda+\mu)K.$$

So, $p(x+y) \le \lambda + \mu < p(x) + p(y) + \epsilon$ and hence $p(x+y) \le p(x) + p(y)$.
(iii) Consider $L_0(\lambda x_0) = \lambda$ for $\lambda \in \mathbf{R}$ which is a linear functional on the linear subspace $< x_0 >= \{\lambda x_0 : \lambda \in \mathbf{R}\}$. Since p is the Minkowski functional of K, we use the fact that $x_0 \notin K$ to obtain $\lambda x_0 \notin \lambda K$ for $\lambda \ne 0$ and thus $p(\lambda x_0) \ge \lambda = L_0(\lambda x_0)$. Consequently, by the Hahn-Banach extension theorem there exists a linear extension L of L_0 to X obeying $L(x) \le p(x)$ for any $x \in X$. When $x \in K$, we have $L(x) \le p(x) \le 1 = L_0(x_0) = L(x_0)$. Note that $0 \in K^\circ$. So $\pm\epsilon^{-1}y \in K$ for a given $\epsilon > 0$ and any y with $\|y\|_X$ being small enough. Accordingly, $|L(y)| < \epsilon$ for $\|y\|_X$ small enough, say $\|y\|_X < \delta$. Finally, the linearity of L gives that $|L(x_1) - L(x_2)| = |L(x_1 - x_2)| < \epsilon$ whenever $\|x_1 - x_2\|_X < \delta$, namely, L is continuous.

7.13. Note that $E_1 - E_2 = \{a - b :\ a \in E_1,\ b \in E_2\}$ is convex and $0 \notin E_1 - E_2$. So, by hypothesis, there is an $x_0 \in (E_1 - E_2)^\circ$. Consequently, $-x_0 + E_1 - E_2$ is convex and contains 0 in its interior. Of course, $-x_0 \notin -x_0 + E_1 - E_2$. Thus, an application of Problem 7.12 (iii) yields a continuous linear functional L such that $L(-x_0 + a - b) \le L(-x_0)$ for any $a \in E_1$ and $b \in E_2$. Consequently, $\sup_{a\in E_1} L(a) \le \inf_{b\in E_2} L(b)$. Now, any $\alpha \in [\sup_{a\in E_1} L(a), \inf_{b\in E_2} L(b)]$ gives the two inclusions.

7.14. Let $f \in B(X, \mathbf{F})$. If $(x_n)_{n=1}^{\infty}$ converges to $x \in X$ then $|f(x_n) - f(x)| \le \|f\|\|x_n - x\|_X \to 0$ and hence $f(x) = 0$, i.e., $x \in f^{-1}(\{0\})$. Thus $f^{-1}(\{0\})$ is closed. Conversely, assume that $f^{-1}(\{0\})$ is closed. If f is not in $B(X, \mathbf{F})$, then there is a sequence of points $(x_n)_{n=1}^{\infty}$ in X such that $\|x_n\|_X = 1$ but $c_n = f(x_n) \to \infty$. Since f is linear, $f(x_n/c_n) = 1$ and consequently $f(x_n/c_n - x_1/c_1) = 0$; that is, $x_n/c_n - x_1/c_1 \in f^{-1}(\{0\})$. Note that $x_n/c_n \to 0$ in X. So $x_n/c_n - x_1/c_1 \to -x_1/c_1$. Now, the assumption gives $x_1/c_1 \in f^{-1}(\{0\})$, contradicting $f(x_1/c_1) = 1$. Therefore, $f \in B(X, \mathbf{F})$.

7.15. Suppose $x_k = m_k + \lambda_k x \in \mathcal{M} + \mathbf{F}x$ is convergent to $y \in X$. Then $(\lambda_k)_{k=1}^{\infty}$ is bounded – otherwise, there exists a subsequence λ_{k_j} such that $0 < |\lambda_{k_j}| \to \infty$ and hence $x + m_{k_j}/\lambda_{k_j} = x_{k_j}/\lambda_{k_j} \to 0$ in X; but, $\mathcal{M}$ is closed, so we see that $x \in \mathcal{M}$, contradicting the assumption $x \in X \setminus \mathcal{M}$. Now the boundedness of $(\lambda_k)_{k=1}^{\infty}$ in $\mathbf{F}$ yields a subsequence, say $(\lambda_{k_j})_{j=1}^{\infty}$, which is convergent to a point $\lambda \in \mathbf{F}$. Consequently, $m_{k_j} = x_{k_j} - \lambda_{k_j} x \to y - \lambda x \in \mathcal{M}$; this implies, $y \in \mathcal{M} + \mathbf{F}x$. Therefore, $\mathcal{M} + \mathbf{F}x$ is closed.

7.16. If $\mathcal{M} = X$ then $\mathcal{N}$ is taken to be $\{0\}$. Now, suppose $\mathcal{M}$ is a closed proper subspace of X. For any $x \in X \setminus \mathcal{M}$, let $L(y + \lambda x) = \lambda d(x, \mathcal{M})$ for all $y \in \mathcal{M}$ and $\lambda \in \mathbf{F}$, then L is a linear functional defined on $\mathcal{M} + \mathbf{F}x$ over $\mathbf{F}$. Clearly, $L(x) = d(x, \mathcal{M})$, $L(y) = 0$ for all $y \in \mathcal{M}$, and $\|L\| = 1$. If L_x is the Hahn–Banach extension of L to X associated with x, then $L_x \in B(X, \mathbf{F})$ with $\|L_x\| = 1$, $L_x(x) = d(x, \mathcal{M})$ and $\mathcal{M} \subseteq \mathcal{N}_{L_x} = \{z \in X : \; L_x(z) = 0\}$. Next, if $\mathcal{M}$ is finite dimensional, then it is closed. Moreover, by Corollary 7.34 (vii) for every $x \in X \setminus \mathcal{M}$ there is a one-dimensional subspace Y_x of X such that $X = \mathcal{N}_{L_x} + Y_x$ and $\mathcal{N}_{L_x} \cap Y_x = \{0\}$. Accordingly, $\mathcal{M} = \bigcap_{x \in X \setminus \mathcal{M}} \mathcal{N}_{L_x}$. To see this equation, assume that it is not true. By the first part of the argument, there exists an $x_0 \in \bigcap_{x \in X \setminus \mathcal{M}} \mathcal{N}_{L_x} \setminus \mathcal{M}$ and hence an $L_{x_0} \in B(X, \mathbf{F})$ such that $L_{x_0}(x_0) = d(x_0, \mathcal{M})$ and $\mathcal{M} \subseteq \mathcal{N}_{L_{x_0}}$. Note that $L_{x_0}(x) = 0$ for all $x \in X \setminus \mathcal{M}$. So $L_{x_0}(x_0) = 0$, i.e., $x_0 \in \mathcal{M}$ thanks to the closedness of $\mathcal{M}$. This is a contradiction. Let $\mathcal{N} = \bigcap_{x \in X \setminus \mathcal{M}} Y_x$ which is closed. Since

$$X = \bigcap_{x \in X \setminus \mathcal{M}} (\mathcal{N}_{L_x} + Y_x) = \bigcap_{x \in X \setminus \mathcal{M}} \mathcal{N}_{L_x} + \bigcap_{x \in X \setminus \mathcal{M}} Y_x,$$

we conclude $X = \mathcal{M} + \mathcal{N}$ and $\mathcal{M} \cap \mathcal{N} = \{0\}$.

7.17. The result follows from considering

$$p(x) = \inf\{f(y) : \quad y \in \mathcal{M} \quad \text{and} \quad x \preceq y\}$$

and adapting the argument for Theorem 7.33.

8 Banach Spaces via Operators and Functionals

8.1. If $(f_j)_{j=1}^{\infty}$ is a Cauchy sequence in $C^n([0,1], \mathbf{R})$, then for any $\epsilon > 0$ there exists $N \in \mathbf{N}$ such that for all $x \in [0,1]$,

$$m, n \ge N \Rightarrow |f_m^{(k)}(x) - f_n^{(k)}(x)| \le \|f_m - f_n\|_\infty < \epsilon.$$

So for each integer $k \in [0,n]$, one has that $\big(f_j^{(k)}(x)\big)_{j=1}^{\infty}$ is a Cauchy sequence in $\mathbf{R}$. Therefore it converges to some real number $g_k(x)$ for every $x \in [0,1]$; this defines a new function g_k such that $(f_j^{(k)})_{j=1}^{\infty}$ converges to g_k pointwise on $[0,1]$. Moreover, $(f_j^{(k)})_{j=1}^{\infty}$ converges to g_k uniformly on $[0,1]$ and g_k belongs to $C([0,1],\mathbf{R})$ – this follows readily from the last estimate when letting $m \to \infty$. In particular, $k=0$ implies that $(f_j)_{j=1}^{\infty}$ converges uniformly on $[0,1]$ to $g_0 = f$, and f is differentiable with $f' = g_1$. Furthermore, the same reasoning yields $f^{(k)} = g_k$ on $[0,1]$. So, $f \in C^n([0,1],\mathbf{R})$.

8.2. The result follows from the estimate for $m,n \in \mathbf{N}$,

$$\|x_m - x_n\|_X,\ \|y_m - y_n\|_Y \le \|(x_m,y_m) - (x_n,y_n)\| \le \|x_m - x_n\|_X + \|y_m - y_n\|_Y.$$

8.3. Consider $f_n(x) = x^n$ for each $n \in \mathbf{N}$. It is clear that $f_n \in C[0,1]$ converges pointwise to the function

$$f(x) = \begin{cases} 1, & x = 1, \\ 0, & x \in [0,1) \end{cases}$$

which is not in $C[0,1]$. But

$$\|f_n - f\|_p^p = \int_0^1 |x^n - f(x)|^p dx = \int_0^1 x^{pn} dx = \frac{1}{1+pn} \to 0.$$

8.4. It suffices to check the inequality $\|f*g\|_1 \le \|f\|_1\|g\|_1$ for all $f,g \in L^1(\mathbf{Z},\mathbf{F})$. Since $f,g \in L^1(\mathbf{Z},\mathbf{F})$, it follows that

$$\sum_{m=-\infty}^{\infty} |f(n-m)||g(m)| \le \|f\|_1\|g\|_1 < \infty$$

and so that for any $k,l \in \mathbf{Z}$,

$$\begin{aligned} \|f*g\|_1 &= \lim_{k\to\infty, l\to-\infty} \sum_{n=l}^{k} |f*g(n)| \\ &\le \lim_{k\to\infty, l\to-\infty} \sum_{n=l}^{k} \Big(\lim_{j\to\infty} \sum_{m=-j}^{j} |f(n-m)||g(m)| \Big) \\ &= \lim_{k\to\infty, l\to-\infty} \lim_{j\to\infty} \sum_{m=-j}^{j} \sum_{n=l}^{k} |f(n-m)||g(m)| \\ &\le \|f\|_1 \lim_{j\to\infty} \sum_{m=-j}^{j} |g(m)| = \|f\|_1\|g\|_1. \end{aligned}$$

8.5. Take $X = Y = \ell_0$ and equip it with the 2-norm: $\|x\|_2 = \big(\sum_{j=1}^{\infty} |x_j|^2\big)^{\frac{1}{2}}\big)$. Here $x \in \ell_0$ if and only if $x \in \ell_\infty$ and it has only finitely many nonzero entries.

Then X and Y are not complete. Now define $T_n(x) = (0, \ldots, 0, nx_n, 0, \ldots)$ for $x = (x_1, x_2, \ldots)$. Then T_n is bounded with $\|T_n\| = n \to \infty$. On the other hand, if $x \in \ell_0$ then there is an $N \in \mathbf{N}$ such that $n > N$, $x_n = 0$ and hence $\|T_n(x)\|_2 = n|x_n| = 0$ and if $n \leq N$ then $\|T_n(x)\|_2 = n|x_n| \leq n\|x\|_2 \leq N\|x\|_2$. Hence for each $x \in X$ we have $\sup_{n \in \mathbf{N}} \|T_n(x)\|_2 < \infty$. Clearly, the uniform bounded principle fails.

8.6. If $f(x) = (1 + x^2)^{-1}$, then $f\big((-1,1)\big) = (1/2, 1]$ which is not open though $(-1, 1)$ is open.

8.7. (i) Since $|\sin x| \leq |x|$, we conclude that the integral is not less than

$$\int_0^{2\pi} \frac{2}{x}\Big|\sin(n + \frac{1}{2})x\Big|dx.$$

Note that

$$k\pi + \frac{\pi}{6} \leq (n + \frac{1}{2})x \leq k\pi + \frac{\pi}{3} \Rightarrow |\sin(n + \frac{1}{2})x| \geq \frac{1}{2}, \quad k \in \mathbf{N}.$$

So

$$\int_0^{2\pi} \frac{2}{x}\Big|\sin(n + \frac{1}{2})x\Big|dx \geq \sum_{k=0}^{2n} \Big(\frac{\pi(k + \frac{1}{3})}{n + \frac{1}{2}}\Big)^{-1} \to \infty \quad \text{as} \quad n \to \infty.$$

(ii) It follows from a change of variable that

$$s_n(x) = \frac{1}{2\pi} \int_{-x}^{2\pi - x} f(x + z)\Big(\sum_{m=-n}^{n} e^{-imz}\Big)dz.$$

This yields that $\overline{s_n(x)} = s_n(x)$ and hence $s_n(x)$ is real-valued. Note that $e^{ix} = \cos x + i \sin x$ and f is 2π-periodic. So

$$\begin{aligned} s_n(x) &= \frac{1}{2\pi} \int_{-x}^{2\pi - x} f(x + z)\Big(\sum_{m=-n}^{n} \cos mz\Big)dz \\ &= \frac{1}{2\pi} \int_{-x}^{2\pi - x} f(x + z)\Big(1 + 2\sum_{m=1}^{n} \cos mz\Big)dz \\ &= \frac{1}{2\pi} \int_{-x}^{2\pi - x} f(x + z)\Big(\frac{\sin(n + 2^{-1})z}{\sin 2^{-1}z}\Big)dz \\ &= \frac{1}{2\pi} \int_{0}^{2\pi} f(x + y)\Big(\frac{\sin(n + 2^{-1})y}{\sin 2^{-1}y}\Big)dy. \end{aligned}$$

(iii) For any $f \in X$, we have

$$|T_n(f)| \leq \frac{1}{2\pi}\|f\|_\infty \int_0^{2\pi} \Big|\frac{\sin(n + \frac{1}{2})x}{\sin \frac{x}{2}}\Big|dx,$$

and then

$$\|T_n\| \leq \frac{1}{2\pi} \int_0^{2\pi} \Big|\frac{\sin(n + \frac{1}{2})x}{\sin \frac{x}{2}}\Big|dx.$$

To prove that the equality actually holds, we take

$$q_n(x) = \frac{\sin(n+2^{-1})x}{\sin 2^{-1}x}$$

and $g_n(x) = \text{sgn} q_n(x)$; that is,

$$g_n(x) = \begin{cases} 1\,, & g_n(x) > 0, \\ 0\,, & g_n(x) = 0, \\ -1\,, & g_n(x) < 0. \end{cases}$$

Then $|g_n(x)| = g_n(x)q_n(x)$. Though g_n is not continuous, for any $\epsilon > 0$ there is a continuous function f_n such that

$$\frac{1}{2\pi}\Big|\int_0^{2\pi}(f_n(x) - g_n(x))q_n(x)dx\Big| < \epsilon.$$

This can be easily realized since q_n is continuous on $[0, 2\pi]$. In fact, it is enough to use piecewise-defined segments to connect the discontinuous points of g_n so that f_n is sufficiently close to g_n. Then $\|f_n\|_\infty = \max_{x\in[0,2\pi]}|f_n(x)| = 1$, but

$$\begin{aligned} |T_n(f_n)| &= \frac{1}{2\pi}\int_0^{2\pi} f_n(x)q_n(x)dx \\ &= \frac{1}{2\pi}\int_0^{2\pi}(f_n(x) - g_n(x))q_n(x)dx + \frac{1}{2\pi}\int_0^{2\pi} g_n(x)q_n(x)dx \\ &\geq \frac{1}{2\pi}\Big|\int_0^{2\pi} g_n(x)q_n(x)dx\Big| - \frac{1}{2\pi}\Big|\int_0^{2\pi}(f_n(x) - g_n(x))q_n(x)dx\Big| \\ &\geq \int_0^{2\pi}|q_n(x)|dx - \epsilon. \end{aligned}$$

Obviously, this implies

$$\|T_n\| \geq \frac{1}{2\pi}\int_0^{2\pi}\Big|\frac{\sin(n+\frac{1}{2})x}{\sin\frac{x}{2}}\Big|dx,$$

and so

$$\|T_n\| = \frac{1}{2\pi}\int_0^{2\pi}\Big|\frac{\sin(n+\frac{1}{2})x}{\sin\frac{x}{2}}\Big|dx.$$

(iv) It is clear that $T_n(f) = s_n(0)$ for all $f \in X$. Moreover, if the Fourier series of a function $f \in X$ converges at 0, then $\big(T_n(f)\big)_{n=1}^\infty$ is bounded since each element is just a partial sum of a convergent series. Thus if the Fourier series of f converges at 0 for all $f \in X$, then for each $f \in X$ the sequence $\big(T_n(f)\big)_{n=1}^\infty$ is bounded. By the uniform bounded principle, this implies that $(\|T_n\|)_{n=1}^\infty$ is bounded, contradicting (i) and (iii).

8.8. (i) Consider $f_n(x) = \sqrt{(x-2^{-1})^2 + n^{-2}}$. Then $(f_n)_{n=1}^\infty$ is convergent to the function $f(x) = |x - 2^{-1}|$ uniformly on $[0, 1]$ since

$$\big|f_n(x) - |x - 2^{-1}|\big| = \frac{n^{-2}}{\sqrt{(x-2^{-1})^2 + n^{-2}} + \sqrt{(x-2^{-1})^2}} \leq n^{-1}.$$

So

$$\lim_{n\to\infty} \|f_n - f\|_X = \lim_{n\to\infty} \|f_n - f\|_\infty = 0.$$

However, f is not in $C^1([0,1], \mathbf{R})$, namely, X is not complete under the norm $\|\cdot\|_X$.
(ii) To prove that $T = d/dx$ is closed, let $(x_n)_{n=1}^\infty$ be a sequence in $C^1([0,1], \mathbf{R})$ such that $x_n \to x, T(x_n) \to y$. Since the convergence in $C([0,1], \mathbf{R})$ means the uniform convergence, we conclude that $T(x_n)$ converges to y uniformly on $[0,1]$ and $y \in C([0,1], \mathbf{R})$. Of course, $x \in C([0,1], \mathbf{R})$ and $y(t) = x'(t)$; that is, T is closed. But, it is not bounded since if $x_n(t) = \sin n\pi t$ then

$$\|T(x_n)\|_Y \geq \|T(x_n)\|_X = \max_{t\in[0,1]} |\cos n\pi t| n\pi = n\pi \to \infty.$$

8.9. The result follows from the relevant definitions.

8.10. (i) Assume the statement after the if and only if. If $L \in B(C[0,1], \mathbf{R})$ then by Theorem 8.24 there is a function g of bounded variation on $[0,1]$ such that $L(f) = \int_0^1 f(x)dg(x)$ for all $f \in C[0,1]$. Note that $\sup_{j\in\mathbf{N}} \|f_j\|_\infty < \infty$. So the dominated convergence theorem yields

$$\lim_{j\to\infty} L(f_j) = \lim_{j\to\infty} \int_0^1 f_j(x)dg(x) = \int_0^1 f(x)dg(x) = L(f),$$

namely, $(f_j)_{j=1}^\infty$ converges weakly to f. Conversely, if $(f_j)_{j=1}^\infty$ converges weakly to f, then $\sup_{j\in\mathbf{N}} \|f_j\|_\infty < \infty$. For any $t \in [0,1]$ define $L_t(f) = f(t)$ for $f \in C[0,1]$. Clearly, $L_t \in B(C[0,1], \mathbf{R})$ and so

$$f_j(t) = L_t(f_j) \to L_t(f) = f(t) \quad \text{as} \quad j \to \infty.$$

(ii) Assume the statement after the if and only if. Let $L \in B(\ell_p, \mathbf{R})$. Then there exists a $y = (y_j)_{j=1}^\infty \in \ell_{\frac{p}{p-1}}$ such that

$$L(x) = \sum_{k=1}^\infty x_k y_k \quad \text{for all} \quad x = (x_k)_{k=1}^\infty \in \ell_p.$$

Moreover, for any $\epsilon > 0$ there exists an $N \in \mathbf{N}$ such that $n > N$ implies

$$\sum_{k=1}^N |s_k^{(n)} - s_k||y_k| < \frac{\epsilon}{2}$$

and

$$\sum_{k=N+1}^\infty |y_k|^{\frac{p}{p-1}} < \Big(\frac{\epsilon}{2(\|x\|_p + \sup_{j\in\mathbf{N}} \|x_j\|_p)}\Big)^{\frac{p}{p-1}}.$$

By Hölder's inequality,

$$
\begin{aligned}
&|L(x_j)-L(x)|\\
&=\Big|\sum_{k=1}^{\infty}(s_k^{(j)}-s_k)y_k\Big|\\
&\le \sum_{k=1}^{N}|s_k^{(j)}-s_k||y_k|+\sum_{k=N+1}^{\infty}|s_k^{(j)}y_k|+\sum_{k=N+1}^{\infty}|s_ky_k|\\
&\le \frac{\epsilon}{2}+\bigg(\Big(\sum_{k=N+1}^{\infty}|s_k^{(j)}|^p\Big)^{\frac{1}{p}}+\Big(\sum_{k=N+1}^{\infty}|s_k|^p\Big)^{\frac{1}{p}}\bigg)\Big(\sum_{k=N+1}^{\infty}|y_k|^{\frac{p}{p-1}}\Big)^{\frac{p-1}{p}}\\
&\le \frac{\epsilon}{2}+(\|x\|_p+\sup_{j\in\mathbf{N}}\|x_j\|_p)\Big(\sum_{k=N+1}^{\infty}|y_k|^{\frac{p}{p-1}}\Big)^{\frac{p-1}{p}}<\epsilon.
\end{aligned}
$$

That is to say, $x_j\to x$ weakly. Conversely, if $(x_j)_{j=1}^{\infty}$ converges weakly to x then the uniformly bounded principle gives $\sup_{j\in\mathbf{N}}\|x_j\|_p<\infty$. Let e_k be vector in ℓ_p for which the kth entry is 1 and others are 0. Then it produces an element $L_k\in B(\ell_p,\mathbf{R})$ such that

$$x_j^{(k)}=L_k(x_j)\to L_k(x)=x_k\quad\text{as}\quad j\to\infty.$$

This completes the argument.

8.11. Since X is separable, there is a countable dense subset $\{x_k\}_{k=1}^{\infty}$. Let $(L_j)_{j=1}^{\infty}$ be a sequence in M. Then $\sup_{j\in\mathbf{N}}\|L_j\|<\infty$ and so $\sup_{j\in\mathbf{N}}|L_j(x_k)|<\infty$ for each $k\in\mathbf{N}$. Using the Bolzano-Weierstrass property, we get a convergent subsequence $\big(L_{j,k}(x_k)\big)_{j=1}^{\infty}$ of $\big(L_j(x_k)\big)_{j=1}^{\infty}$. Now, $(L_{n,n})_{n=1}^{\infty}$ is a subsequence of $(L_j)_{j=1}^{\infty}$ which is convergent on $\{x_k\}_{k=1}^{\infty}$. Thus the desired follows from Theorem 8.15 (ii).

8.12. Denote by J_1 the map $\hat{(\cdot)}:X\to X^{**}$, and similarly, write J_2 for the map $\hat{(\cdot)}:X^*\to X^{***}$. Suppose $J_1(X)=X^{**}$. For any $L\in X^{***}$ and $x\in X$ let $f(x)=L\big(J_1(x)\big)$, then

$$\big(J_2(f)\big)\big(J_1(x)\big)=J_1(x)(f)=f(x)=L\big(J_1(x)\big),$$

and hence $J_2(f)=L$, giving $J_2(X^*)=X^{***}$. Conversely, assume $J_2(X^*)=X^{***}$. If $J_1(X)\neq X^{**}$ then there is an $L\in X^{***}$ such that $L=0$ on $J_1(X)$ but $\|L\|=1$. The assumption then yields an $f\in X^*$ such that $J_2(f)=L$, and consequently

$$f(x)=J_1(x)(f)=\big(J_2(f)\big)\big(J_1(x)\big)=L\big(J_1(x)\big)=0\quad\text{for}\quad x\in X,$$

whence giving a contradiction $0=\|J_2(f)\|=\|L\|=1$. So $J_1(X)=X^{**}$.

8.13. (i) To prove that c_0 is a Banach space, it is enough to prove that c_0 is a closed subspace of ℓ_∞. Suppose $\big(x^{(j)}=(x_k^{(j)})_{k=1}^{\infty}\big)_{j=1}^{\infty}$ is a sequence in c_0 and convergent to $x=(x_k)_{k=1}^{\infty}$ in ℓ_∞. Then for any $\epsilon>0$ there is a $J\in\mathbf{N}$ such that $j>J$ implies $\|x^{(j)}-x\|_\infty<\epsilon$. Note that $x^{(J+1)}\in c_0$. So there is a $K\in\mathbf{N}$ such that $m,n>K$ implies $|x_m^{(J+1)}-x_n^{(J+1)}|<\epsilon/3$. Accordingly,

$$|x_m-x_n|\le|x_m-x_m^{(J+1)}|+|x_m^{(J+1)}-x_n^{(J+1)}|+|x_n-x_n^{(J+1)}|<\epsilon.$$

Namely, $(x_k)_{k=1}^\infty$ is a Cauchy sequence in $\mathbf{R}$ and hence convergent to 0. Next, we prove that c_0 is separable. For $n \in \mathbf{N}$ let

$$A_n = \{x \in c_0 : \ x = (r_1, r_2, \ldots, r_n, 0, 0, \ldots), \ r_j \in \mathbf{Q}\}.$$

Then the countable set $\cup_{n=1}^\infty A_n$ is a subset of c_0. Now, given $x = (x_j)_{j=1}^\infty \in c_0$. Then for any $\epsilon > 0$ there is an $N \in \mathbf{N}$ such that $j > N$ implies $|x_j| < \epsilon/2$. Taking an $r_1, \ldots, r_N \in Q$ such that $\sup_{1\le j\le N} |x_j - r_j| < \epsilon/2$, we obtain $y = (r_1, \ldots, r_N, 0, 0, \ldots) \in \cup_{n=1}^\infty A_n$ and

$$\|x - y\|_\infty \le \sup_{1\le j\le N} |x_j - r_j| + \sup_{j>N} |x_j| < \epsilon.$$

Thus, $\cup_{n=1}^\infty A_n$ is a dense subset of c_0, deriving the separability of c_0. Finally, if c_0 is reflexive, then we reach $c_0 = \ell_\infty$ which is impossible.
(ii) It suffices to verify the necessity. For each $j \in \mathbf{N}$, let $e_j = (\underbrace{0, \ldots, 0}_{j-1}, 1, 0, \ldots)$.

Then $e_j \in c_0$. For any $L \in B(c_0, \mathbf{R})$ set $y_j = L(e_j)$, we have

$$\begin{aligned}
\sum_{j=1}^\infty |y_j| &= \sum_{j=1}^\infty L(e_j)\operatorname{sgn} L(e_j) \\
&= L\Big(\sum_{j=1}^\infty e_j \operatorname{sgn} L(e_j)\Big) \\
&\le \|L\| \Big\| \sum_{j=1}^\infty e_j \operatorname{sgn} L(e_j)\Big\|_\infty \\
&\le \|L\|
\end{aligned}$$

and

$$L(x) = L\Big(\sum_{j=1}^\infty x_j e_j\Big) = \sum_{j=1}^\infty x_j y_j \quad \text{for} \quad x = (x_k)_{k=1}^\infty \in c_0.$$

8.14. The weak closure clearly contains the norm closure. So it remains to check that if x is not in the norm closure of K then there exists a weak neighborhood of x which is disjoint from K. But, this follows right away from the convex separation theorem presented in Problem 7.13.

8.15. (i) It suffices to consider $A \ne X^*$. Note that for $f \in A$ and $g \in X^* \setminus A$ there is a point $x_0 \in X$ such that $f(x_0) \ne g(x_0)$ and hence for $0 < \epsilon < |f(x_0) - g(x_0)|$ there are two disjoint neighborhoods

$$O_f = \{F \in X^* : \ |F(x_0) - f(x_0)| < \epsilon/2\}$$

and

$$O_g = \{F \in X^* : \ |F(x_0) - g(x_0)| < \epsilon/2\}.$$

So, a combination of the compactness of $A = \cup_{f\in A} O_f$ and the last part of the argument for Example 5.31 (iii) completes the proof.

(ii) Just follow the argument for Theorem 5.37 (i).

8.16. For any $x \in X$, suppose $T(x) \neq 0$ otherwise there is nothing to argue. Then

$$\|T(x)\|_Y = \sup_{\|f\|=1} |f \circ T(x)| \leq \sup_{\|f\|=1} \|f \circ T\| \|x\|_X,$$

thereby obtaining $T \in B(X, Y)$.

8.17. Suppose X is compact. If $\{F_\alpha\}_{\alpha \in I}$ is a set of closed subsets of X and has the FIP, then any finite number of sets $\{F_j\}_{j=1}^n$ from $\{F_\alpha\}_{\alpha \in I}$ obeys $\cap_{j=1}^n F_j \neq \emptyset$, and hence $\cap_{\alpha \in I} F_\alpha \neq \emptyset$ – otherwise, $X = \cup_{\alpha \in I}(X \setminus F_\alpha)$. This yields a finite number of sets $\{X \setminus F_j\}_{j=1}^n$ such that $X = \cup_{j=1}^n X \setminus F_j$ thanks to X being compact. Consequently, $\cap_{j=1}^n F_j = \emptyset$ – a contradiction. Conversely, assume the statement after the if and only if. Suppose $X = \cup_{\alpha \in I} O_\alpha$ where $O_\alpha \subseteq X$ is open. Then $\cap_\alpha (X \setminus O_\alpha) = \emptyset$, and hence by the contrapositive statement of the assumption it follows that there is a finite number of sets $\{X \setminus O_j\}_{j=1}^n$ such that $\cap_{j=1}^n (X \setminus O_j) = \emptyset$ and consequently $X = \cup_{j=1}^n O_j$. Accordingly, X is compact.

8.18. Since $B_c(X, Y)$ is a closed linear subspace of the Banach space $B(X, Y)$, it is a Banach space, too.

8.19. The result follows from a modification of the argument for Example 8.47 – in fact, the proof does not employ the continuity of $k(\cdot, \cdot)$ on the region $\{(x, y) \in \mathbf{R}^2 : x < y,\ a \leq x, y \leq b\}$.

8.20. (i) Consider a bounded sequence $(x_j)_{j=1}^\infty$ in X. Since T is compact, the sequence $\big(T(x_j)\big)_{j=1}^\infty$ has a convergent subsequence, say, $\big(T(x_{j_k})\big)_{k=1}^\infty$ which is convergent to y in X. Then

$$\|ST(x_{j_k}) - S(y)\| \leq \|S\| \|T(x_{j_k}) - y\| \to 0 \quad \text{as} \quad k \to \infty.$$

This shows that ST is compact. Note that $\big(S(x_j)\big)_{j=1}^\infty$ is bounded. So $\big(TS(x_j)\big)_{j=1}^\infty$ has a convergent subsequence, showing that TS is compact. Similarly, ST is compact, too.

(ii) For any $n \in \mathbf{N}$, let $B_n^X \subseteq X$ be the open ball centered at 0 with radius n. Then $T(X) = \cup_{n=1}^\infty T(B_n^X)$. Since $\overline{T(B_n^X)}$ is compact, $\overline{T(B_n^X)}$ is separable by Theorem 5.42 and hence $T(X)$ is separable.

8.21. (i) For any bounded set $B \subseteq X$, we have $\overline{T(B)} = \{0\}$ and so T is compact.

(ii) Assume that T is invertible. Then the identity operator $I = T^{-1}T$ is compact on X. But since X is infinite dimensional, the unit sphere S of X is not compact and consequently $\overline{I(S)} = S$ is not compact, i.e., I is not compact on X, a contradiction. Thus, T is not invertible.

(iii) Note that $T(X)$ is a closed linear subspace of the Banach space X. If T is compact then the closed unit ball of $T(X)$ is compact and hence $T(X)$ must be finite dimensional thanks to Theorem 7.19 (ii), contradicting the assumption that $T(X)$ is infinite dimensional.

9 Hilbert Spaces and Their Operators

9.1. It is easy to check that the inner product $\langle f, g\rangle = \int_{-1}^{1} f(x)\overline{g(x)}dx$ satisfies (a), (b) and (c) of Definition 5.1.1, and so $C([-1,1],\mathbf{C})$ is an inner product space. Since the norm equipped with $C([-1,1],\mathbf{C})$ is the 2-norm: $\|f\|_2 = \sqrt{\int_{-1}^{1}|f(x)|^2dx}$, we can conclude that this space is not complete. In fact, for each $j \in \mathbf{N}$ let

$$f_j(x) = \begin{cases} -1\,, & x \in [-1,0), \\ jx\,, & x \in [-j^{-1}, j^{-1}], \\ 1\,, & x \in [j^{-1}, 1]. \end{cases}$$

then $f_j \in C([-1,1],\mathbf{C})$. Observe that for each $m, n \in \mathbf{N}$ satisfying $m > n$, one has

$$\begin{aligned} \|f_m - f_n\|_2^2 &= 2\Big(\int_0^{m^{-1}} (mx - nx)^2 dx + \int_{m^{-1}}^{n^{-1}} (1 - nx)^2 dx\Big) \\ &= 2\Big(\frac{(m-n)^2}{3m^3} + \frac{1}{3n} - \frac{1}{m} + \frac{n}{m^2} - \frac{n^2}{3m^3}\Big) \\ &< \frac{6}{m} + \frac{1}{n} < \frac{7}{n} \to 0 \quad \text{as} \quad n \to \infty. \end{aligned}$$

This means that $(f_j)_{j=1}^{\infty}$ is a Cauchy sequence in $C([-1,1],\mathbf{C})$. On the other hand, $(f_j)_{j=1}^{\infty}$ converges pointwise to

$$f(x) = \begin{cases} -1\,, & x \in [-1,0), \\ 0\,, & x = 0, \\ 1\,, & x \in (0,1]. \end{cases}$$

which does not belong to $C([-1,1],\mathbf{C})$. Therefore, $C([-1,1],\mathbf{C})$ is not a Hilbert space.

9.2. It is clear that $\langle x, y\rangle = \sum_{j=1}^{\infty} x_j\overline{y_j}$ is an inner product defined on $\ell_2(\mathbf{N},\mathbf{C})$. It is not hard to see that $\ell_2(\mathbf{N},\mathbf{C})$ is complete under the norm $\|x\|_2 = \sqrt{\langle x, x\rangle}$. So, $\ell_2(\mathbf{N},\mathbf{C})$ is a Hilbert space over $\mathbf{C}$. To obtain that $\ell_p(\mathbf{N},\mathbf{C})$ under $p \neq 2$ is not a Hilbert space, one takes $x = (1,1,0,0,\ldots)$ and $y = (1,-1,0,0,\ldots)$. Then $x, y \in \ell_p(\mathbf{N},\mathbf{C})$ and $\|x\|_p = \|y\|_p = 2^{\frac{1}{p}}$ but $\|x+y\|_p = \|x-y\|_p = 2$. Hence the parallelogram law fails at $p \neq 2$; that is to say, if $p \neq 2$ then $\|\cdot\|_p$ does not induce an inner product, and hence $\ell_p(\mathbf{N},\mathbf{C})$ is not a Hilbert space over $\mathbf{C}$.

9.3. (i) When X is a real inner product space, the equivalence follows from $\|x + y\|^2 = \|x\|^2 + \|y\|^2 + 2\langle x, y\rangle$. But, if X is an inner product space over $\mathbf{C}$, then the equivalence fails since $\|x\| = 1$ and $y = ix$ give $\|x+y\|^2 = \|x\|^2 + \|y\|^2$ and $\langle x, y\rangle = -i \neq 0$.
(ii) This follows from $\|x + \beta y\|^2 = \|x\|^2 + \|y\|^2 + \overline{\beta}\langle x, y\rangle + \beta\overline{\langle x, y\rangle} + |\beta|^2\|y\|^2$.

9.4. Obviously, $M \subseteq (M^{\perp})^{\perp}$. To get the reverse inclusion, let $x \in (M^{\perp})^{\perp}$. Then the projection theorem implies that there exist $y \in M \subseteq (M^{\perp})^{\perp}$ and $z \in M^{\perp}$ such that $x = y + z$. Because $x \in (M^{\perp})^{\perp}$ and $(M^{\perp})^{\perp}$ is a linear space, one has

$z = x - y \in (M^{\perp})^{\perp}$ and so $z \in M^{\perp} \cap (M^{\perp})^{\perp} = \{0\}$, i.e., $z = 0$ and $x = y$. This gives $(M^{\perp})^{\perp} \subseteq M$.

9.5. (i) Given $g \in M^{\perp}$. Then for any $f \in M$ one has

$$0 = \int_{[-1,1]} f(x)\overline{g(x)}dm_{id}(x) = \int_{[0,1]} f(x)\overline{g(x)}dm_{id}(x).$$

If f is taken to respectively be 0 m_{id}-a.e. on $[-1, 0]$ and g m_{id}-a.e. on $(0, 1]$, then

$$\int_{[0,1]} |g(x)|^2 dm_{id}(x) = 0$$

and hence $g = 0$ m_{id}-a.e. on $(0, 1]$. It follows that

$$M^{\perp} = \{g \in \mathcal{LRS}^2_{id}([-1,1], \mathbf{C}) : \ g(x) = 0 \quad m_{id} - \text{a.e on} \quad (0,1]\}.$$

(ii) Any function $f \in \mathcal{LRS}^2_{id}([-1,1], \mathbf{C})$ can be written as $f_{even} + f_{odd}$ where

$$f_{even}(x) = \frac{f(x) + f(-x)}{2} \quad \text{and} \quad f_{odd}(x) = \frac{f(x) - f(-x)}{2}.$$

Clearly, $f_{even} \in M_{even}$ and $f_{odd} \in M_{odd}$. Moreover, if $f \in M_{even} \cap M_{odd}$, then $f(x) = -f(x)$ and hence $f(x) = 0$. In other words, $M_{even} \cap M_{odd} = \{0\}$. This implies the desired direct sum decomposition.

9.6. (i) This assertion follows from

$$\frac{1}{2\pi}\int_{-\pi}^{\pi} e^{i(n-m)x}dx = \begin{cases} 1\,, & n = m, \\ 0\,, & n \neq m. \end{cases}$$

(ii) First of all, a calculation gives:

$$\int_{-\pi}^{\pi} 1dx = 2\pi, \quad \int_{-\pi}^{\pi} \cos^2 nxdx = \int_{-\pi}^{\pi} \sin^2 nxdx = \pi, \qquad n \in \mathbf{N};$$

$$\int_{-\pi}^{\pi} \cos nxdx = \int_{-\pi}^{\pi} \sin nxdx = 0, \quad n \in \mathbf{N};$$

$$\int_{-\pi}^{\pi} \cos mx \cos nxdx = \int_{-\pi}^{\pi} \sin mx \sin nxdx = 0, \quad m \neq n, \ m, n \in \mathbf{N};$$

and

$$\int_{-\pi}^{\pi} \sin mx \cos nxdx = 0, \quad m, n \in \mathbf{N}.$$

Now, let $\{e_j\}_{j=1}^{\infty}$ be this orthonormal set. According to the definition of orthonormal basis, we must prove that $\langle f, e_j\rangle = 0$ implies $f = 0$ m_{id}-a.e. on $[-\pi, \pi]$. To do so, let us first consider the case that f is continuous and real-valued. If $f \neq 0$ m_{id}-a.e. on $[-\pi, \pi]$, then there is an $x_0 \in [-\pi, \pi]$ at which $|f|$ achieves a maximum, and we may assume $f(x_0) > 0$. Thus, there is a $\delta > 0$ such that $f(x) > 2^{-1}f(x_0)$ for $x \in (x_0 - \delta, x_0 + \delta)$. If $g(x) = 1 + \cos(x_0 - x) - \cos\delta$, then $1 < g(x)$ for

$x \in (x_0 - \delta, x_0 + \delta)$ and $|g(x)| \leq 1$ for $x \in [-\pi, \pi] \setminus (x_0 - \delta, x_0 + \delta)$. Note that $\langle f, e_j \rangle = 0$. So for any $n \in \mathbf{N}$,

$$\begin{aligned} 0 &= \langle f, g^n \rangle = \int_{-\pi}^{\pi} f(x) g^n(x) dx \\ &= \int_{-\pi}^{x_0-\delta} f(x) g^n(x) dx + \int_{x_0-\delta}^{x_0+\delta} f(x) g^n(x) dx + \int_{x_0+\delta}^{\pi} f(x) g^n(x) dx. \end{aligned}$$

Using the properties of g above, we obtain

$$\Big|\int_{-\pi}^{x_0-\delta} f(x) g^n(x) dx\Big|, \quad \Big|\int_{x_0+\delta}^{\pi} f(x) g^n(x) dx\Big| \leq 2\pi f(x_0)$$

and

$$\int_{x_0-\delta}^{x_0+\delta} f(x) g^n(x) dx \geq \int_a^b f(x) g^n(x) dx$$

for all $[a, b] \subseteq (x_0 - \delta, x_0 + \delta)$. Since g is continuous on $[a, b]$, we can conclude that g achieves a minimum value, $\kappa > 1$, there. This implies

$$4\pi f(x_0) \geq \int_a^b f(x) g^n(x) dx \geq \frac{f(x_0)}{2} \kappa^n (b - a) \to \infty \quad \text{as} \quad n \to \infty.$$

This is a contradiction. Thus, $f = 0$ m_{id}-a.e. on $[-\pi, \pi]$. If f is continuous but not real-valued, then our hypothesis gives that for all $k = 0, \pm 1, \pm 2, \ldots$,

$$\int_{-\pi}^{\pi} f(x) e^{-ikx} dx = 0 \quad \text{and} \quad \int_{-\pi}^{\pi} \overline{f(x)} e^{-ikx} dx = 0.$$

Hence

$$\int_{-\pi}^{\pi} \Re f(x) e_j(x) dx = 0 \quad \text{and} \quad \int_{-\pi}^{\pi} \Im f(x) e_j(x) dx = 0.$$

By the first part, we get $\Re f(x) = 0 = \Im f(x)$ and thus $f = 0$ m_{id}-a.e. on $[-\pi, \pi]$. Last of all, we no longer assume that f is continuous. But, f generates a continuous function $F(x) = \int_{[-\pi,x]} f(t) dm_{id}(t)$. An integration by parts yields $\int_{-\pi}^{\pi} F(x) \sin(kx) dx = 0$. Similarly, $\int_{-\pi}^{\pi} F(x) \cos(kx) dx = 0$. This infers that F and $F - C$ for every constant C, is orthogonal to each of the non-constant members of $\{e_j\}_{j=1}^{\infty}$. For $(2\pi)^{-1/2}$, let $C_0 = \frac{1}{2\pi} \int_{-\pi}^{\pi} F(x) dx$. Then $\langle F - C_0, e_j \rangle = 0$ for all $j \in \mathbf{N}$. Since F is continuous, we conclude from the first two parts that $F - C_0 = 0$. Of course, $f = F' = 0$ m_{id}-a.e. on $[-\pi, \pi]$.

9.7. (i) From $\langle T(f), g \rangle = \langle f, T^*(g) \rangle$ we have

$$\int_{[-\pi,\pi]} \phi(x) f(x) \overline{g(x)} dm_{id}(x) = \int_{[-\pi,\pi]} f(x) \overline{\big(T^*(g)\big)(x)} dm_{id}(x)$$

and so $T^*(g) = \overline{\phi} g$ by the uniqueness of T^*.
(ii) It is clear that if ϕ is real-valued, then $\overline{\phi} = \phi$ and hence $T^* = T$.

(iii) If $|\phi| = 1$ m_{id}-a.e. on $[-\pi, \pi]$ then T is unitary; If $\phi \geq 0$ m_{id}-a.e. on $[-\pi, \pi]$ then $\langle T(f), f\rangle \geq 0$ and hence T is positive; If $\phi = \pm 1$ m_{id}-a.e. on $[-\pi, \pi]$ then $T^2(f) = \phi^2 f = f$ and hence T is projection.

9.8. If $x \in N(T)$ then $T(x) = 0$ and hence $\langle x, T^*(y)\rangle = \langle T(x), y\rangle = 0$ for all $y \in X$, $T^*y \in R(T^*)$. This gives $x \in R(T^*)^\perp$. Conversely, if $x \in R(T^*)^\perp$, then $\langle x, T^*(y)\rangle = \langle T(x), y\rangle = 0$ for any $y \in X$, and hence $T(x) = 0$, i.e., $x \in N(T)$. Therefore $N(T) = R(T^*)^\perp$. Replacing T by T^*, we get $N(T^*) = R(T)^\perp$ and $N(T^*)^\perp = \left(R(T)^\perp\right)^\perp$. Since $R(T) \subseteq \overline{R(T)}$, by the continuity of $\langle\cdot,\cdot\rangle$ and the closedness of $\overline{R(T)}$ we obtain $\overline{R(T)} = \left(\overline{R(T)}^\perp\right)^\perp = \left(R(T)^\perp\right)^\perp$. Thus $N(T^*)^\perp = \overline{R(T)}$. Replacing T^* by T, we also obtain $\overline{R(T^*)} = N(T)^\perp$.

9.9. (i) Consider $(T - \lambda I)(x) = y$. Thus $x(t) = y(t)/(t - \lambda)$ provided $t \neq \lambda$ for $t \in [0, 2\pi]$. So there is a unique solution $x \in C([0, 2\pi], \mathbf{C})$ except when $t = \lambda$ for $t \in [0, 2\pi]$ and so $\sigma(T) = [0, 2\pi]$.
(ii) The argument is similar to that for (i).

9.10. (i) For $\lambda \in \mathbf{C}$ with $|\lambda| < 1$ let $x_\lambda = (1, \lambda, \ldots, \lambda^n, \ldots)$. Then $x_\lambda \in \ell_2(\mathbf{N}, \mathbf{C})$ and $T(x_\lambda) = (\lambda, \lambda^2, \ldots, \lambda^n, \ldots) = \lambda x_\lambda$. This means $\{\lambda \in \mathbf{C} : |\lambda| \leq 1\} \subseteq \sigma(T)$. On the other hand, $\|T(x)\|_2 \leq \|x\|_2$ for any $x \in \ell_2(\mathbf{N}, \mathbf{C})$, and thus $\|T\| \leq 1$, giving $\sigma(T) \subseteq \{\lambda \in \mathbf{C} : |\lambda| \leq \|T\|\} \subseteq \{\lambda \in \mathbf{C} : |\lambda| \leq 1\}$. Therefore, $\sigma(T) = \{\lambda \in \mathbf{C} : |\lambda| \leq 1\}$.
(ii) Refer to the argument for (i).

9.11. The formula follows from $(\lambda I - T)^* = \overline{\lambda} I - T^*$.

9.12. (i) This follows from that fact that $\langle T(x), x\rangle, \lambda \in \mathbf{R}$ ensures

$$\|T(x) - \lambda x\|^2 = \left(\lambda - \langle T(x), x\rangle\right)^2 + \|T(x)\|^2 - \langle T(x), x\rangle^2.$$

(ii) By Theorem 9.54 we can write $x = x_0 + \sum_{k=1}^\infty P_k(x)$ and $T(x) = \sum_{k=1}^\infty \lambda_k P_k(x)$ where $x_0 \in N(T)$ and $(\lambda_k)_{k=1}^\infty$ are those nonzero eigenvalues of T. Then

$$T(x) - \langle T(x), x\rangle = \sum_{k=1}^\infty (\lambda_k - \langle T(x), x\rangle) P_k(x) - \langle T(x), x\rangle x_0.$$

Since $\sigma(T)$ is closed, we can choose a point $\lambda \in \sigma(T)$ such that it is nearest to $\langle T(x), x\rangle$, we use (i) to get

$$\begin{aligned} \|T(x) - \langle T(x), x\rangle x\|^2 &= \sum_{k=1}^\infty \left(\lambda_k - \langle T(x), x\rangle\right)^2 \|P_k(x)\|^2 + \langle T(x), x\rangle^2 \|x_0\|^2 \\ &\geq |\lambda - \langle T(x), x\rangle|^2 \Big(\sum_{k=1}^\infty \|P_k(x)\|^2 + \|x_0\|^2\Big) \\ &= |\lambda - \langle T(x), x\rangle|^2 \|x\|^2 = |\lambda - \langle T(x), x\rangle|^2. \end{aligned}$$

9.13. Let $c = \int_0^1 e^y f(y) dy$ and f obey $T(f) = \lambda f$. Then $ce^x = \lambda f(x)$. If $\lambda \neq 0$ then $f(x) = (c/\lambda)e^x$ and hence $c = \int_0^1 e^y (c/\lambda) e^y dy$, yielding $\lambda = (e^2 - 1)/2$ and

$f(x) = c_0 e^x$ where c_0 is any nonzero constant. If $\lambda = 0$ then $\int_0^1 e^x f(x)dx = 0$ and hence eigenvectors are all the nonzero elements in $\{e^x\}^\perp$.

9.14. Since $T_1 = (T+T^*)/2$ and $T_2 = (T-T^*)/(2i)$, we use $TT^* = T^*T$ to obtain

$$T_1^2 + T_2^2 = \frac{(T+T^*)(T+T^*)}{4} - \frac{(T-T^*)(T-T^*)}{4} = TT^*$$

thereby achieving $\|T_1^2+T_2^2\| = \|TT^*\| = \|T\|^2$ and $\|T^2\|^2 = \|(T^2)^*T^2\| = \|TT^*\|^2 = \|T\|^4$, as desired.

9.15. (i) This follows from $\|(T^* - \overline{\lambda}I)(x)\|^2 = \|(T - \lambda I)(x)\|^2$.
(ii) and (iii) These follow from a simple calculation via the definition.

9.16. Use $\|T(x_m) - T(x_n)\|^2 \leq \|T^*T(x_m) - T^*T(x_n)\|\|x_m - x_n\|$.

9.17. Given $j \in \mathbf{N}$, set $e_j = (\underbrace{0,\ldots,0}_{j-1},1,0,\ldots)$. For $x = (x_j)_{j=1}^\infty \in \ell_2(\mathbf{N},\mathbf{R})$ and $n \in \mathbf{N}$ let $T_n(x) = \sum_{j=1}^n \left(\sum_{k=1}^\infty x_k a_{jk}\right)e_j$. Then T_n has finite rank and hence it is compact. Note that

$$\|(T-T_n)(x)\|_2^2 = \sum_{j=n+1}^\infty \left|\sum_{k=1}^\infty x_k a_{jk}\right|^2 \leq \left(\sum_{j=n+1}^\infty \sum_{k=1}^\infty |a_{jk}|^2\right)\|x\|_2^2$$

thanks to the Cauchy–Schwarz inequality. So

$$\|T - T_n\| \leq \sqrt{\sum_{j=n+1}^\infty \sum_{k=1}^\infty |a_{jk}|^2} \to 0 \quad \text{as} \quad n \to \infty.$$

This implies the compactness of T.

9.18. (i) Note that

$$\begin{aligned} K(f)(x) &= \int_{[0,1]} \Big(\sum_{k=1}^n g_k(x)f_k(y)\Big)f(y)dm_{id}(y) \\ &= \sum_{k=1}^n \Big(\int_{[0,1]} f_k(y)f(y)dm_{id}(y)\Big)g_k(x). \end{aligned}$$

So, the range of K is finite-dimensional, and consequently, K is compact.
(ii) Just use the formula in (i).
(iii) In this case, we have

$$h_{j,k} = \begin{cases} 0\,, & j \neq k, \\ \int_{[0,1]} g_j^2(x)dm_{id}(x)\,, & j = k. \end{cases}$$

Moreover, $(h_{j,j} - \lambda)c_j = 0$ for $j = 1,2,\ldots,n$. This means that $\{h_{j,j}\}_{j=1}^n$ is the set of all nonzero eigenvalues, and g_j is the eigenvector corresponding to $h_{j,j}$ for each j. It is clear that if $M = \mathrm{span}\{g_j\}_{j=1}^n$ then any nonzero element in $M^\perp$ is an eigenvector corresponding to 0.

(iv) Since $\cos\pi(y+x) = \cos\pi y\cos\pi x + (i\sin\pi y)(i\sin\pi x)$, we can take $g_1(x) = f_1(x) = \cos(\pi x)$ and $g_2(x) = f_2(x) = i\sin(\pi x)$, obtaining $\langle g_1, g_2\rangle = 0$ and $h_{1,1} = 1/2$; $h_{2,2} = -1/2$. Accordingly, K has two nonzero eigenvalues $\lambda_1 = 1/2$ and $\lambda_2 = -1/2$ for which the corresponding nonzero eigenvectors are respectively $c\cos\pi x$ and $c\sin\pi x$ for all nonzero constants $c \in \mathbf{C}$. Of course, the eigenvectors corresponding to 0 are the nonzero functions in $\{\cos\pi x, \sin\pi x\}^\perp$.

9.19. Assuming that $\lim_{j\to\infty}\|T(e_j)\| \to 0$ is not true, we use the compactness of T to get a subsequence $(e_{j_k})_{k=1}^\infty$ and a nonzero $x \in X$ such that $\|T(e_{j_k}) - x\| < 1/k$ holds for any $k \in \mathbf{N}$. Letting $x_n = \sum_{k=1}^n e_{j_k}/k$, we find that $(x_n)_{n=1}^\infty$ is convergent in X and $\big(T(x_n)\big)_{n=1}^\infty$ is bounded since $\sum_{k=1} k^{-2} < \infty$ and $\{e_{j_k}/k\}_{k=1}^\infty$ is orthonormal, but also (by the triangle inequality)

$$\begin{aligned}
\|T(x_n)\| &= \Big\|\sum_{k=1}^n k^{-1}T(e_{j_k})\Big\| \\
&= \Big\|\sum_{k=1}^n k^{-1}(T(e_{j_k}) - x) + \big(\sum_{k=1}^n k^{-1}\big)x\Big\| \\
&\geq \|x\|\sum_{k=1}^n k^{-1} - \sum_{k=1}^n \|T(e_{j_k}) - x\| \\
&\geq \|x\|\sum_{k=1}^n k^{-1} - \sum_{k=1}^n k^{-2} \to \infty,
\end{aligned}$$

contradicting the boundedness of $\big(T(x_n)\big)_{n=1}^\infty$.

9.20. (i) Suppose $\{f_k\}_{k=1}^\infty$ is an orthonormal basis of Y. Then the result follows from

$$\begin{aligned}
\sum_{j=1}^\infty \|T(e_j)\|_Y^2 &= \sum_{j=1}^\infty\Big(\sum_{k=1}^\infty |\langle T(e_j), f_k\rangle_Y\Big) \\
&= \sum_{k=1}^\infty\Big(\sum_{j=1}^\infty |\langle e_j, T^*(f_k)\rangle_X\Big) \\
&= \sum_{k=1}^\infty \|T^*(f_k)\|_X^2.
\end{aligned}$$

(ii) For each $k \in \mathbf{N}$ and $x = \sum_{j=1}^\infty \langle x, e_j\rangle_X e_j \in X$ let

$$T_k(x) = T\Big(\sum_{j=1}^k \langle x, e_j\rangle_X e_j\Big) = \sum_{j=1}^k \langle x, e_j\rangle_X T(e_j).$$

Then T_k is a compact operator from X to Y. This fact, plus

$$\begin{aligned}\|(T_k - T)(x)\|_Y &\le \sum_{j=k+1}^{\infty} |\langle x, e_j\rangle_X| \|T(e_j)\|_Y \\ &\le \Big(\sum_{j=k+1}^{\infty} |\langle x, e_j\rangle_X|^2\Big)^{\frac{1}{2}} \Big(\sum_{j=k+1}^{\infty} \|T(e_j)\|_Y^2\Big)^{\frac{1}{2}} \\ &\le \|x\|_X \Big(\sum_{j=k+1}^{\infty} \|T(e_j)\|_Y^2\Big)^{\frac{1}{2}},\end{aligned}$$

derives

$$\|T_k - T\| \le \Big(\sum_{j=k+1}^{\infty} \|T(e_j)\|_Y^2\Big)^{\frac{1}{2}} \to 0 \quad \text{as} \quad k \to \infty,$$

whence the compactness of T follows.
(iii) Choosing any orthonormal basis $\{e_j\}_{j=1}^{\infty}$ in $\mathcal{LRS}^2_{id}((c,d), \mathbf{C})$, we get

$$T(e_j)(x) = \int_{(c,d)} k(x,y) e_j(y) dm_{id}(y) = \langle k(x,\cdot), \overline{e_j}\rangle_{(c,d)}$$

where the right-hand inner product is defined on $\mathcal{LRS}^2_{id}((c,d), \mathbf{C})$. Thus,

$$\begin{aligned}\sum_{j=1}^{\infty} \|T(e_j)\|^2 &= \lim_{k\to\infty} \sum_{j=1}^{k} \|T(e_j)\|^2 \\ &= \lim_{k\to\infty} \sum_{j=1}^{k} \int_{(a,b)} |\langle k(x,\cdot), \overline{e_j}\rangle_{(c,d)}|^2 dm_{id}(x) \\ &= \lim_{k\to\infty} \int_{(a,b)} \sum_{j=1}^{k} |\langle k(x,\cdot), \overline{e_j}\rangle_{(c,d)}|^2 dm_{id}(x) \\ &\le \lim_{k\to\infty} \int_{(a,b)} \int_{(c,d)} |k(x,y)|^2 dm_{id}(y) dm_{id}(x) < \infty.\end{aligned}$$

9.21. (i) Let $M = \sup_{k\in\mathbf{N}} |c_k|$. If $M < \infty$ then $\|T(x)\|_Y \le M\|x\|_X$ for any $x \in X$ and hence T is bounded. Conversely, if T is bounded but $M = \infty$, then for any $n \in \mathbf{N}$ there is c_n such that $|c_n| \ge n$, and hence $\|T(e_n)\|_Y = \|c_n f_n\|_Y = |c_n| \ge n$, contradicting the boundedness of T.
(ii) Let $\lim_{k\to\infty} |c_k| = 0$. For each $n \in \mathbf{N}$ and $x \in X$ define

$$T_n(x) = \sum_{j=1}^{n} c_k \langle x, e_k\rangle_X f_k.$$

Then this operator is compact. It is easy to see that $\lim_{n\to\infty} \|T_n - T\| = 0$. So T is compact. Conversely, if T is compact but $(|c_k|)_{k=1}^{\infty}$ does not approach 0, then there is an $\epsilon_0 > 0$ and a subsequence $(c_{k_j})_{j=1}^{\infty}$ such that $|c_{k_j}| \geq \epsilon_0$ for all $j \in \mathbf{N}$. Consequently, $j, l \in \mathbf{N}$ with $j \neq l$ implies

$$\|T(e_{k_j}) - T(e_{k_l})\|_Y^2 = \|c_{j_k} f_{j_k} - c_{j_l} f_{j_l}\|_Y^2 = |c_{j_k}|^2 + |c_{j_l}|^2 \geq 2\epsilon_0^2$$

and then no subsequence of $\big(T(e_{k_j})\big)_{j=1}^{\infty}$ is convergent, i.e., T is not compact, a contradiction.
(iii) This follows from $T(e_j) = c_j f_j$.
(iv) Since $f_k \in R(T)$ for any $k \in \mathbf{N}$ with $c_k \neq 0$, the desired equivalence follows from the linear independence of $\{f_k\}_{k=1}^{\infty}$.

Bibliography

[AmT] Ambrosio, L., Tilli, P.: *Topics on Analysis in Metric Spaces*, Oxford University Press, 2004.

[Apo] Apostol, T. M.: *Mathematical Analysis*, Addison-Wesley Publishing Company, Inc. 1964.

[Bol] Bollobás, B.: *Linear Analysis*, Combridge University Press, 1990.

[Bur] Burk, F.: *Lebesgue Measure and Integration*, John Wiley & Sons, Inc., 1998.

[Cain] Cain, G. L.: *Introduction to General Topology*, Addison-Wesley Publishing Company, 1993.

[CarB] Carter, M., Brunt, B.V.: *The Lebesgue–Stieltjes Integral*, UTM, Springer-Verlag New York, Inc., 2000.

[Con] Conway, J. B.: *A Course in Functional Analysis*, GTM, Springer-Verlag New York, Inc., 1985.

[CuP] Curtain, R. F., Pritchard, A. J.: Functional *Analysis in Modern Applied Mathematics*, Mathematics in Science and Engineering 132, Academic Press Inc. (London) Ltd., 1977.

[DaSe] Dangello, F., Seyfried, M.: *Introductory Real Analysis*, Houghton Mifflin Company, 2000.

[DeS] DePree J., Swartz, C.: *Introduction to Real Analysis*, New York, Toronto, Wiley, 1988.

[deS] de Souza, P. N., Silva, J. N.: *Berkeley Problems in Mathematics*, 2nd edition, Springer, 2001.

[EiMT] Eidelman, Y., Milman, V., Tsolomitis, A.: *Functional Analysis: An Introduction*, GSM 66, American Mathematical Society, Providence, Rhode Island, 2004.

[EvG] Evans, L. C.: *Measure Theory and Fine Properties of Functions*, CRC Press, 1992.

[Fla] Flattto, L.: *Advanced Calculus*, The Williams & Wilkins Company, 1976.

[Fol] Folland, G. B.: *Real Analysis, Modern Techniques and Their Applications, Pure & Applied Mathematics*, A Wiley-Interscience Series of Texts, Monographs, and Tracts, John Wiley & Sons, Inc., 1984.

[Frid] Fridy, J. A.: *Introductory Analysis, The Theory of Calculus* (2nd Edition), San Diego, Toronto, Harcourt Brace Jovanovich, Academic Press, 2000.

[Frie] Friedman A.: *Foundations of Modern Analysis*, Holt, Rinehart and Winston, Inc., 1970.

[GaN] Gaskill, H. S, Narayanaswami, P.P.: *Elements of Real Analysis*, Upper Saddle River, NJ, Prentice Hall, 1998.

[Geo] George, C.: *Exercises in Integration*, Springer-Verlag New York, Inc., 1984.

[Gro] Groetsch, C. W.: *Elements of Applicable Functional Analysis*, Marcel Dekker, Inc., New York and Basel, 1980.

[Hil] Hille, E.: *Methods in Classical and Functional Analysis*, Addison-Wesley Publishing Company, Inc., 1972.

[KolF] Kolmogorov, A. N., Fomin, S. V.: *Elements of the Theory of Functions and Functional Analysis*, Vol. 1 & 2, Graylock Press, 1957.

[KuS] Kurtz, D. S., Swartz, C. W.: *Theories of Integrations, The Integrals of Riemann, Lebesgue, Henstock-Kurzweil, and Mcshane*, Series in Real Analysis 9, World Scientific Publishing Co. Pte. Ltd., 2004.

[Nie] Nielsen, O. A.: *An Introduction to Integration and Measure Theory*, Canadian Mathematical Socity Series of Monographs and Advanced Texts, John Wiley & Sons, Inc. 1997.

[Pac] Packel, E. W.: *Functional Analysis*, A Short Course, Intext, Inc., 1974.

[Pit] Pitt, H. R.: *Measure and Integration for Use*, Clarendon Press, Oxford, 1985.

[Ros] Rosenlicht, M.: *Introduction to Analysis*, Scott, Foresman and Company, 1968

[Roy] Royden, H. L.: *Real Analysis*, Prentice-Hall, Inc., 1998.

[Rud] Rudin, W.: *Functional Analysis*, Second Edition, McGraw-Hill, Inc., 1991.

[RyY] Rynne, B. P., Youngson, M. A.: *Linear Functional Analysis*, SUMS, Springer-Verlag London Limited, 2000.

[Sax] Saxe, K.: *Beginning Functional Analysis*, UTM, Springer-Verlag New York, Inc., 2002.

[Sch] Schechter, M.: *Principles of Functional Analysis*, Academic Press, Inc., 1971.

[Tor] Torchinisky, A.: *Real Variables*, Addison-Wesley Publishing Company, 1988.

[Ves] Vestrup, E. W.: *The Theory of Measures and Integration*, Wiley Series in Probability and Statistics, John Wiley & Sons, Inc., 2003.

[War] Ward, T. B.: *Functional Analysis*, http://www.mth.uea.ac.uk/~h720/tea--ching/functionalanalysis/materials/FAnotes.pdf.

[You] Young, N.: *An Introduction to Hilbert Space*, Cambridge University Press, 1998.

[Zim] Zimmer, R. J.: *Essential Results of Functional Analysis*, The University of Chicago Press, 1990.

INDEX

G

H

I

K

L

M

N

O

P

R

S

T

U

V

W

Y